Wave Transmission and Fiber Optics

Wave Transmission and Fiber Optics

Paul Diament *Columbia University*

Macmillan Publishing Company
NEW YORK
Collier Macmillan Publishers
LONDON

Printed in the United States of America

Macmillan Publishing Company
866 Third Avenue, New York, New York 10022

Collier Macmillan Canada, Inc.

Library of Congress Cataloging-in-Publication Data

Diament, Paul.
Wave transmission and fiber optics / Paul Diament.
p. cm.
Includes index.
ISBN 0-02-328761-6
1. Electromagnetic waves—Transmission. 2. Waves. 3. Fiber optics. I. Title.
QC665.T7D53 1990
539.2—dc20 89-31737
CIP

Printing: 1 2 3 4 5 6 7 8 Year: 0 1 2 3 4 5 6 7 8 9

To my youngest son
Benjamin
who has no fear of modern technology

Preface

This work is intended to fill the need for an electrical engineering textbook to bridge the gap between the elementary texts on electromagnetic theory and the specialized ones on fiber optics. The latter area represents a rapidly expanding technology and an important field of application of electromagnetics, optics, telecommunications, and electrical engineering generally; the former is the theoretical basis for understanding the operation of optical fibers and integrated optics.

Students of electrical engineering, applied physics, and optics, as well as professionals who need to deal with optical fiber technology, may have used textbooks that expound the basics of electric and magnetic fields, from electrostatics to Maxwell's equations to the rudiments of wave propagation. They also may have access to a number of books that describe optical fibers as devices, as transmission media, and as communication channels and systems. The texts specifically devoted to optical fibers typically assume that the reader has a good grasp of electromagnetic theory and emphasize specialized descriptions of fiber optic systems and the fabrication and specification of practical fibers. There is, however, a gulf between the elementary texts on field theory and the advanced books on fibers. The gap is not easy to bridge for the student or worker who has learned elementary electromagnetics and is faced with the need to understand the capabilities and limitations of fiber optic systems.

This textbook is an outgrowth of a course for undergraduate seniors and first-year graduate students in electrical engineering at Columbia University's School of Engineering and Applied Science. The course has served as the second-semester elective in electromagnetics and introduces the vital new technologies of integrated optics and optical fibers.

In the present book, I assume familiarity with elementary concepts of electromagnetics and of the level of mathematics usually used in its development (vector analysis, differential equations, linear systems). However, the appendix reviews the necessary background. To achieve its purpose, the main part of the text begins with the fundamental concept of a wave and its description, then systematically builds through wave propagation in dielectrics and conductors, to optical reflection and refraction, to the key subject of total internal reflection, to waveguiding, and then to the dielectric slab and cylindrical waveguides. By the time optical fibers are to be covered, all the background required for understanding their operation has been thoroughly explained. I devote numerous sections to careful derivation and especially to physical interpretation of what would otherwise be esoteric, dry, hard-to-grasp mathematical results.

I address the book to two types of reader. The senior-level undergraduate or first-year graduate student in electrical engineering, particularly in electromagnetics or optics or applied physics or communications, is one type. The other is the professional engineer or applied physicist who is working in the field of integrated optics or optical fiber systems and must become conversant with the technicalities of describing, specifying, and utilizing the new technology to best advantage. These readers have had exposure to the fundamentals of Maxwell's equations and electromagnetic fields but may be daunted by the level of the specialized book on fiber optic systems, and of the vast technical literature they may have to peruse and absorb. My intention has been that the book enable these readers to raise their level of expertise and competency in wave transmission to the point at which these advanced texts and journal articles become fully accessible and understandable.

This textbook is replete with examples, some set off from the text, some integrated into the discussions. I have emphasized physical interpretations of results. I define fundamental concepts and explain them with care. I have tried to keep derivations simple but thorough. As I introduce new concepts, I try to have plausibility arguments (and, where useful, dimensional analysis) precede their formal derivation. I have listed necessary mathematical and physical background material in the appendix, to facilitate review. I have included answers to nearly all problems (excluding those that have the answers stated in the question itself) at the back of the book. Needless to say, judicious use of this answer key will be helpful, while injudicious abuse of it will be harmful.

From the outset, I have built the material from easy fundamentals, through increasingly complex cases and examples, to the point at which all the accumulated knowledge can be brought to bear to understand the properties of optical fibers. The book carefully defines the concepts of a field and of waves; it presents Maxwell's equations in their most fundamental, integral form, with the usual differential form as a less general alternative; it derives field energetics from basic mechanical definitions and verifies conservation of field energy in detail. The text examines signal distortion in real media and provides a full discussion of wave polarization; it explains group velocity in terms of narrow-band signals and wave packets; it discusses field energy and power in the time and frequency domains and distinguishes between the real and complex Poynting theorems, providing several interpretations and applications of the complex Poynting theorem. The book gives detailed interpretations of the exact and the two limiting cases of propagation in conducting media and of transitions between the limits. It derives field boundary conditions from the integral laws.

I present reflection and refraction at an interface in terms of impedance mismatch. I develop Snell's laws for obliquely-incident waves thoroughly, with the polarization properties included. I introduce the TE and TM wave designations early and use them consistently in different contexts (oblique waves, waveguides). The text includes detailed examples of optical concepts, such as Brewster's angle and antireflection coatings. It discusses total internal reflection thoroughly, including the dependence on polarization, as the basis for dielectric waveguiding.

The text explains VSWR and its significance for measurements; it generalizes transmission lines, in terms of electrostatics solutions, and generalizes waveguides, in terms of Helmholtz solutions. It introduces Bessel functions for the simpler case of a cylindrical pipe, before elaborating their use in analyzing fibers. It emphasizes the logical progression from two-conductor transmission lines, to single-conductor waveguides, to nonconducting dielectric guides.

For the more advanced topics, the book provides a compact, but full, derivation of the slab waveguide's characteristic equation, simplified by matrix methods. It presents graphical solution techniques and the calculation of cutoff frequencies for dielectric slab waveguides. It derives the exact modes for a step-index optical fiber with unbounded cladding and demonstrates that the modes are hybrid; it details, however, the conditions that justify the use of the simplified LP modes. Finally, it presents graded-index fiber results by analogy to those for the Schrödinger equation of quantum mechanics and introduces practical considerations of dispersion, wave launching, and mode coupling in optical fibers.

Wherever possible, I have preferred to keep the figures realistic, in the sense that mathematical curves are properly calculated and plotted, not merely sketched. I have also tried to keep the problems instructive and fresh.

Writing a textbook requires dedication, intensive application to the task, and meticulous attention to detail. The process—from the initial decision, through the mutual selection of a publisher, through the actual creation of the text, figures, and problems, to the proofreading and production stages—is an astonishing and instructive development. For me, the availability of an adequate tool for word and image processing (the Macintosh computer) was the indispensable condition for undertaking the project. The encouragement and help of many individuals has been vital and is deeply appreciated. Special thanks are due to John Griffin and Dora Rizzuto of Macmillan Publishing Company, as well as to many behind-the-scenes reviewers, editors, readers, and artists I met only through their work. The students who took my course over the many years of its development have also contributed to making this text what it is.

The fact that the book was produced at all is a monument to the cooperation of all the members of my family. Special appreciation is due my son Benjamin who, even while still in elementary school, evinced no fear of confronting, subduing, and mastering the intricacies of the computer, from manipulations of text, symbols, and figures down to font modification and the inner sanctum of the operating system itself. He got me through many a crisis and it is to him that I gratefully dedicate this book.

Paul Diament

Notations and Symbols

symbol	*meaning*	*units*
$\mathbf{a}$	acceleration vector	meter/sec^2
b	binding parameter (normalized eigenvalue)	1
$\mathbf{B}$	magnetic flux density vector	tesla
c	speed of light in vacuum	meter/sec
C	curve	
C	capacitance	farad
dA	differential area element	meter^2
dB	decibel	1
det	determinant (of a matrix)	
$d\boldsymbol{l}$	vector differential element of length	meter
$d\mathbf{S}$	vector differential element of area	meter^2
dV	differential volume element	meter^3
$\mathbf{D}$	displacement flux density vector	coulomb/meter^2
D	diffusion coefficient	meter^2/sec
$\hat{\mathbf{e}}$	unit vector (along direction of electric field)	1
$\mathbf{E}$	electric field vector	volt/meter
$\mathscr{E}$	real, physical electric field (in time domain)	volt/meter
EH	hybrid (mode)	

symbol	*meaning*	*units*
f	frequency	hertz
$\mathbf{f}$	force density vector	newton/meter^3
$\mathbf{F}$	force vector	newton
g	acceleration of gravity	meter/sec^2
G	conductance	siemens
GRIN	graded-index (fiber)	
h_{mn}	mode coupling coefficient	meter^{-1}
$\hat{\mathbf{h}}$	unit vector (along direction of magnetic field)	1
$\mathbf{H}$	magnetic field vector	ampere/meter
HE	hybrid (mode)	
I	current	ampere
$I_l(x)$	modified Bessel function of first kind	
Im	imaginary part of complex quantity	
j	imaginary unit ($\sqrt{-1}$)	
j_{lm}	mth zero of $J_l(x)$	
j'_{lm}	mth zero-slope point of $J_l(x)$	
$\mathbf{J}$	current density	ampere/meter^2
$J_l(x)$	Bessel function of first kind	
k	wavenumber or phase constant	meter^{-1}
$\mathbf{k}$	wave vector	meter^{-1}
$\mathbf{K}$	surface current density	ampere/meter
$K_l(x)$	modified Bessel function of second kind	
l	length	meter
L	length scale of waveshape	meter
L	inductance	henry
LED	light-emitting diode	
LHCP	left-hand circularly polarized	

symbol	*meaning*	*units*
LHEP	left-hand elliptically polarized	
LP	linearly polarized (mode)	
m	mass	kg
m	group index	1
n	index of refraction	1
$\hat{\mathbf{n}}$	unit vector, normal to a surface	1
NA	numerical aperture	1
p	power density	watt/meter^3
P	power	watt
q, Q	charge	coulomb
$\mathbf{r}$	position vector	meter
$\hat{\mathbf{r}}$, $\hat{\boldsymbol{\theta}}$, $\hat{\boldsymbol{\varphi}}$	unit vectors along spherical coordinate directions	1
R	resistance	ohm
Re	real part of complex quantity	
RHCP	right-hand circularly polarized	
RHEP	right-hand elliptically polarized	
S	surface	
t	time	second
T	time scale of waveform	second
T	transmission coefficient	1
T_e, T_h	electric (magnetic) field transmission coefficient	1
TE	transverse electric (wave)	
TEM	transverse electromagnetic (wave)	
TIR	total internal reflection	
TM	transverse magnetic (wave)	
U	magnetomotive force	ampere
$\mathbf{v}$	velocity vector	meter/sec
v_e	energy velocity	meter/sec

symbol	*meaning*	*units*
v_g	group velocity	meter/sec
v_p	phase velocity	meter/sec
V	electromotive force (voltage)	volt
V	volume	meter^3
V	normalized frequency (of fiber)	1
VSWR	voltage standing-wave ratio	1
W	energy or work	joule
W	energy density	joule/meter^3
w_e, W_e	electric energy density	joule/meter^3
w_m, W_m	magnetic energy density	joule/meter^3
x, y, z	coordinates of a point	meter
$\hat{\mathbf{x}}$, $\hat{\mathbf{y}}$, $\hat{\mathbf{z}}$	unit vectors along rectangular coordinate directions	1
X	reactance	ohm
Y	admittance	siemens
$Y_l(x)$	Bessel function of second kind	
Z	impedance	ohm
α	index profile parameter	1
α	attenuation constant	meter^{-1}
β	phase constant	meter^{-1}
γ	complex propagation constant	meter^{-1}
Γ	reflection coefficient	1
Γ_e, Γ_h	electric (magnetic) field reflection coefficient)	1
Γ_l	reflection coefficient at load	1
δ	skin depth	meter
Δ	relative index difference	1
ε, ε_0	permittivity, permittivity of free space	farad/meter
η, η_0	wave impedance, impedance of free space	ohm

symbol	*meaning*	*units*
θ	elevation (spherical coordinate)	radian
θ_B	Brewster's angle	radian, degree
θ_c	critical angle	radian, degree
κ		
λ	wavelength	meter
λ_g	guide wavelength	meter
Λ		
μ, μ_0	permeability, permeability of free space	henry/meter
ξ		
π		
ρ	charge density	coulomb/meter^3
ρ	radial cylindrical coordinate	meter
ρ_S	surface charge density	coulomb/meter^2
$\hat{\boldsymbol{\rho}}$, $\hat{\boldsymbol{\varphi}}$, $\hat{\mathbf{z}}$	unit vectors along cylindrical coordinate directions	1
σ	conductivity	siemens/meter
σ_S	surface conductivity	siemens
τ	time constant	second
τ_g	group delay	second
φ	azimuth (cylindrical or spherical coordinate)	1
Φ	magnetic flux	weber
Φ	phase	1
χ		
ψ		
Ψ	displacement flux	coulomb
ω	frequency	radian/sec
ω_c	cutoff frequency	radian/sec
Ω		
∂	partial derivative operator	

symbol	*meaning*	*units*
∇	gradient	meter^{-1}
$\nabla \cdot$	divergence	meter^{-1}
$\nabla \times$	curl	meter^{-1}
∇^2	Laplacian	meter^{-2}
$\cdot$	dot product	
$\times$	cross product	
$\propto$	proportionality (is proportional to)	
$*$	complex conjugate	
$\oint$	closed (line or surface) integral	
$\sum$	summation	
$\langle \ \rangle$	average (statistical or time)	
$\equiv$	identity or definition	
$\approx$	approximate equality	

Brief Contents

Detailed Contents

Wave Transmission and Fiber Optics

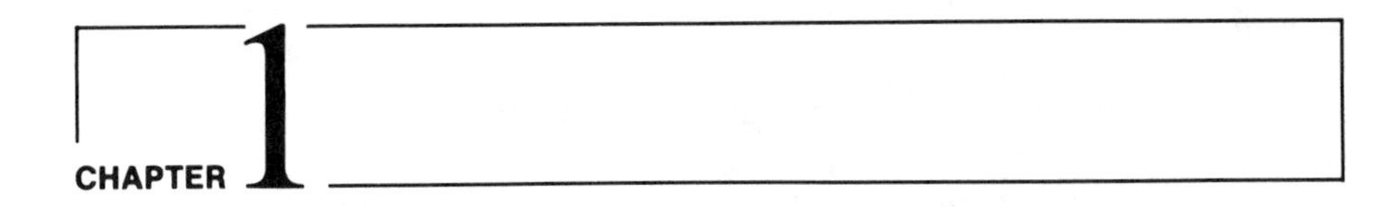

Introduction

We embark upon a study of the transmission of energy and information by electromagnetic waves. In one respect, this forms an extension of and presents a range of practical applications for the fundamentals of electromagnetic fields. It also has as its focus the introduction of an exciting new technology in electromagnetics, in communications, and in optics. We refer to a twofold innovation, comprised of:

Fiber optics: transmission of light along glass fibers;
Integrated optics: optical wave processing incorporated in integrated circuits (on electronic chips).

Together, these engineering achievements represent a revolution in the transmission and processing of signals.

To appreciate the technology and utilize it effectively, we must be capable of describing and understanding wave transmission generally, and particularly the similarities and differences in transmission in a vacuum, in dielectrics, in conductors, across interfaces between media, inside waveguides, on dielectric slabs (which can model integrated optics), and along dielectric cylinders (which model fiber optics).

We will need to combine a descriptive and an analytical exposition of the field, building from the fundamentals and simple cases to the intricacies of advanced field configurations and their analysis. We begin with a qualitative introduction.

Electromagnetics and Optics

Electric and magnetic fields are governed by Maxwell's equations, whose most fundamental consequence is that the fields tend to propagate, travel from one point to another, as a *wave motion.* This results in the phenomenon of *action at a distance*, but only *after a delay*. By "action" we mean the outcome of the fact that fields can exert forces, hence can do work, hence possess energy; it is a fundamental observation that whatever can carry energy can also convey information. Electromagnetic fields provide means for transmitting energy and information at a distance.

Electromagnetic energy tends to propagate: It "wants" to travel from its source to distant points. Literally nothing is needed to persuade fields to propagate; we can have waves in a vacuum. However, the propagation of waves is affected by the presence of matter and this affords us an opportunity to confine or direct the waves and make them work for us.

The electromagnetic engineering problem involves designing and utilizing configurations of materials that can process electromagnetic field energy. By "process" we mean variously to generate, transmit, guide, store, distribute, scatter, absorb, and detect electromagnetic fields, waves, and energy.

Wave Transmission

Besides a vacuum, wherein electromagnetic fields are free, we have available both dielectrics and conductors to confine and guide electromagnetic waves. For purposes of broadcasting, we can use an antenna to launch free waves, but for communication from one point to another, we need to guide the waves. How can this be accomplished?

At low frequencies (tens of hertz to kilohertz), we use simple bare or insulated wires. At higher frequencies (megahertz), shielding is needed, or else too much of the signal is shunted aside capacitively, or radiated, and we use coaxial lines. At microwave frequencies (gigahertz), it becomes practical to use waveguides; typically, these are hollow metal pipes. Figure 1–1 illustrates different means for guiding waves in various frequency regimes. The question arises: Can one go on to higher frequencies? A better question is: *Should* one go on to higher frequencies?

It is a fundamental result of communications theory that for the same fractional bandwidth, a higher carrier frequency allows utilization of more bandwidth, which permits more channels to be used and more information to be conveyed. A single telephone channel may allow a 4-kHz bandwidth; upon sampling at 8 kHz with 8 bits per sample, we achieve a signaling rate of 64 kbits/s per channel. A television channel occupies the bandwidth of nearly 1000 telephone channels. Communications engineers are hungry for more and more bandwidth and the possibility of using light waves, for which the carrier

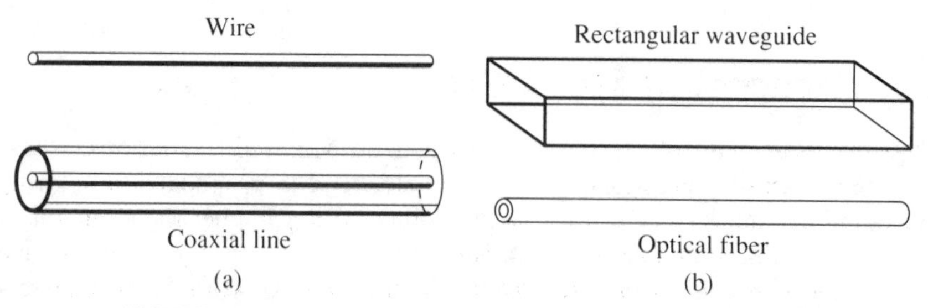

FIGURE 1–1 Transmission media for different frequencies.

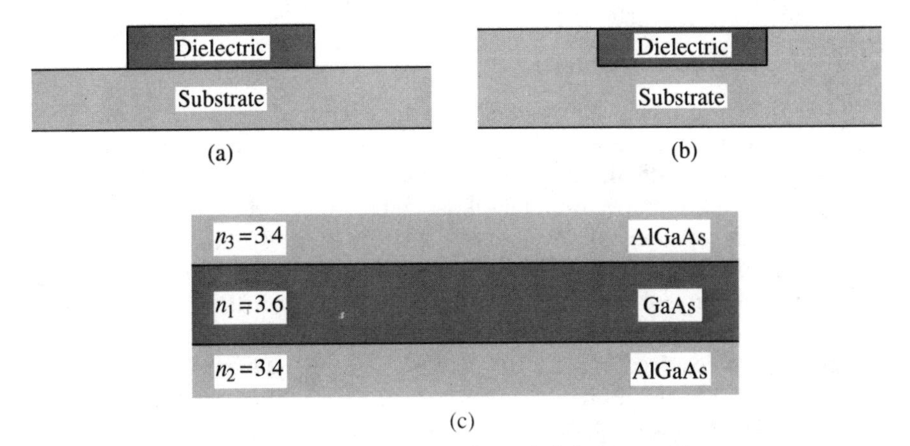

FIGURE 1–2 Dielectric strip and slab waveguides.

frequency can be about 10^{15} Hz (four to five orders of magnitude higher even than microwaves), makes their mouths water. But lightwave communications requires the availability of suitable sources, modulators, transmission media, and detectors.

Integrated Optics

There has been a convergence of advancing technology and of advancing need for it, making lightwave communication an inevitable, irresistible technology. The basic need has been for data transmission using many channels, multiplexed into a wideband signal and sent forth at Mbit/s to Gbit/s rates.

The need for sources was met by both the laser and the light-emitting diode (LED). These can operate at wavelengths of the order of 1 μm, some three orders of magnitude higher in frequency than even millimeter-wave technology. We refer not just to visible light (about 0.5 μm) but also to infrared radiation (particularly 0.8 to 1.6 μm) as "light."

The necessary light-transmitting and light-guiding medium was developed in the form of optical fibers, replacing the more usual optical components such as lenses and mirrors, which are awkward and expensive, and the atmosphere, which tends to scatter light. The advent of glass fibers—hair-thin glass threads that can guide light waves—has made lightwave communications not only a possibility but a reality; they represent the technology of choice in many systems.

The requisite signal processors have been developed vigorously as well, in the form of integrated optics: Unbelievably intricate combinations of optoelectronic devices, couplers, modulators, and detectors have been integrated with their electronic circuitry on solid-state chips. These microscopic optical circuits are fabricated by thin-film technology. Figure 1–2 shows typical layered configurations formed by such means, including dielectric strip waveguides and dielectric slab waveguides.

Fiber Optics

For practical use in a communications link, we need to be able to transmit the carrier signal over several, or even many, kilometers before the need for a repeater to regenerate the degraded signal can be considered tolerable. To compete with more conventional systems, fibers had to be developed and fabricated with losses of signal power kept below about 20 dB/km.

That this would be an astounding achievement becomes clear when we note that losses in pure water are equivalent to about 100 dB/km in the visible range and about 10^4 dB/km in the near infrared, while ordinary window glass has equivalent losses of about 10^5 dB/km. The necessary care in manufacturing and purity of the glass has been met, so that the goal of sufficiently low-loss fibers has been attained and surpassed, to the point that losses of only a fraction of 1 dB/km have been achieved.

An optical fiber is formed as a glass thread with suitably varying index of refraction, either changing abruptly but slightly in a step-index fiber or changing gradually but slightly in a graded-index fiber. Figure 1–3 shows these two configurations, with typical dimensions. The step-index fiber has a core of one refractive index and a surrounding cladding of slightly smaller index. The graded-index fiber may be formed of many layers of slightly different refractive indices.

A typical fiber optic communications link is described by the block diagram in Figure 1–4. The input data may be generated at Mbit/s to Gbit/s data rates and imposed on the light source by the modulator. The laser or LED source may operate at a power level of about 1 mW, at a wavelength of 0.82 to 0.9 μm, or 1.06 to 1.3 μm, or, more recently, 1.55 μm. The fiber itself may be some 10 km long and terminate into a silicon diode detector before the signal is regenerated and amplified in the repeater electronics for retransmission along the next link.

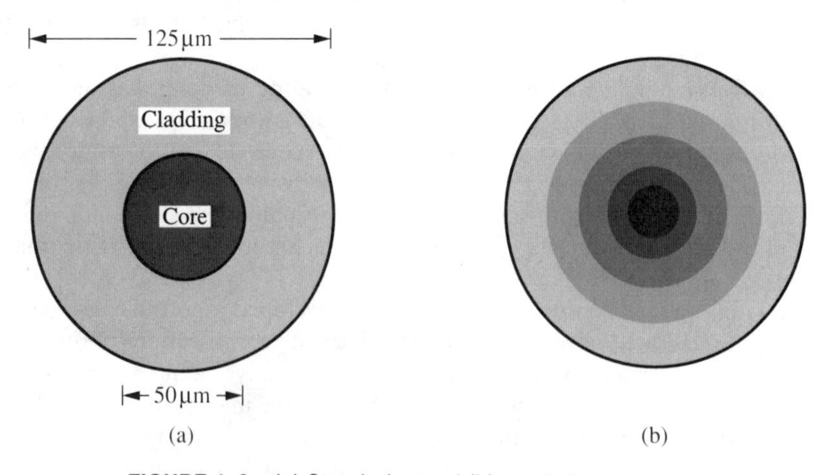

FIGURE 1–3 (a) Step-index and (b) graded-index fibers.

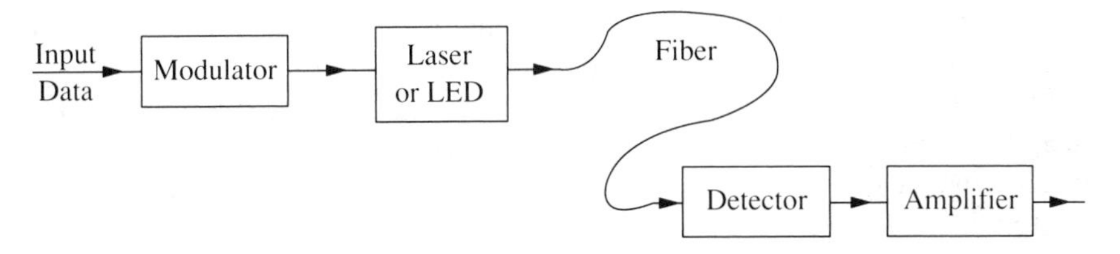

FIGURE 1–4 Typical elements of a fiber optic communications link.

Fibers are now the transmission medium of choice for ranges of 10 to 10,000 m and even hundreds of kilometers. They have the advantages of low cost and small size; they are not metallic, which implies low weight, no pickup through ground loops, no electromagnetic interference, and no need to protect against lightning (although the use of metallic members to strengthen fiber optic cables reintroduces some of these problems); they are more immune to crosstalk within a cable than are ordinary wires; they are more secure against wiretapping; they can extend over longer distances before a repeater is needed; above all, they have greater bandwidths. Their present use in telephone links will soon be augmented to convey television signals, video data, and facsimile to the home consumer, besides allowing many computer terminals to communicate with each other.

Fiber optic technology offers two versions of fibers for transmission. One is multimode fibers, wherein optical fields of many different types carry the signal. They may be excited by LEDs and their use amounts to optical energy transmission. The other type is the single-mode fiber, wherein the light fields take on a specific, well-defined pattern. These may be fed by lasers and allow for more sophisticated processing of the coherent light. With core sizes smaller than 10 μm, these are more difficult to fabricate, but they make a good match to integrated optics circuitry.

Signal Distortion

Signals transmitted along an optical fiber are not only attenuated as they travel, but also undergo some degree of distortion. Different frequency components in the spectrum of the signal are found to be transmitted at different speeds and therefore arrive at the receiver at various times and recombine into a new, distorted signal. We refer to the property of a wave-propagating system that makes different frequencies travel at different speeds as its *dispersion.*

For optical fibers, dispersion has two major sources. One is an inherent property of the glass; another reflects the variety of waves that can travel along the fiber, each with its own speed of propagation. The former source of distortion can be mitigated by choosing a special operating frequency at which the inherent dispersion of the glass material is eliminated or minimized. The other cause for dispersive signal distortion can be dealt with by suitable design of a graded-index fiber, with the aim of equalizing, as much as possible, the speeds of propagation of different types of waves within the fiber.

An understanding of the characteristics of waves traveling along optical fibers is essential for advantageous design of the fibers and for proper assessments of when special designs are needed to achieve the goals of signal transmission.

Organization of the Text

Signals on fibers get transmitted, but are also delayed, weakened, and distorted. The causes of, and remedies for, these effects can be quite subtle and require a thorough understanding of the fiber's wave types and their properties. We must first study waves and propagation in general, beginning with their definitions, provenance, and essential characteristics. We will need to understand how propagation differs in conductors and in dielectrics; we will have to discover how waveguiding occurs. We can then progress from this to the properties of flat and of round dielectric waveguides, before we can hope to analyze specifically the properties of optical fibers.

We intend to build methodically from fundamental definitions and interpretations to ever more complicated concepts relevant to the description and understanding of wave transmission and the properties of waveguiding systems, culminating in an exploration of the optical fiber. We first define and interpret waves and wave equations. We then define fields generally and electromagnetic fields in particular; we present Maxwell's equations in their general, integral form and show that they plausibly imply wave propagation. We can then confirm that electromagnetic fields possess and convey energy and interpret Poynting's theorem. Having dealt with these ideas in the time domain, we specialize to the sinusoidal steady state and interpret complex fields in the frequency domain, including their polarization properties. We then distinguish several wave velocities and discuss dispersive effects, and also develop and interpret the complex version of the Poynting theorem and its applications.

Having laid the foundations for describing waves generally, we can proceed to study how waves are affected by the presence of different types of materials. We first see the effects of conductivity in the medium and establish exact and approximate means for dealing with losses. We can then examine encounters between waves and interfaces between dissimilar media; for this, we first derive generalized boundary conditions directly from Maxwell's equations and apply them to the problem of waves normally incident on a planar interface between mismatched media.

To form a basis for interpretation of the mechanism of propagation in dielectric slab waveguides and optical fibers, we next examine oblique incidence and Snell's laws, including the polarizations of the scattered waves; a number of important optical applications follow. The process of total internal reflection, crucial to the operation of optical waveguides, is then examined, in terms of equivalent complex impedances of the two media involved.

The next step in building up to the ultimate discussion of propagation along fibers is to review the processes in effect along transmission lines and how these are described. The emphasis is on the similarities between propagation along terminated transmission lines and optical processes at interfaces; impedance calculations are illustrated. We can then present analyses of rectangular and cylindrical waveguides, above and below cutoff. The cylindrical case introduces the Bessel functions that are needed for the description of the operation of cylindrical fibers.

The payoff for the careful escalation from simple waves and media to the complexities of waveguiding comes first when the guiding of waves by a dielectric slab, as in integrated-optics configurations, is studied. The derivation of the characteristic equation for this case is simplified by matrix methods. Dispersion and the group index are discussed. We come then, at last, to the case of a dielectric cylinder, which models a fiber. We derive the properties of the step-index fiber and discuss the exact, hybrid modes of propagation. Finally, we are able to specialize the discussion of optical waveguides to the practical level that is appropriate for the standard types of fibers. The approximations commonly made in dealing with propagation along these structures are explained; in particular, the simplified LP modes are compared to the exact, hybrid ones. The dispersive processes in a fiber are accounted for and the advantages of graded-index fibers are explained.

For ready reference, a collection of mathematical formulas is presented in the Appendix, particularly those that are needed directly in the text.

PROBLEMS

For the questions below, use the following fundamental constants:

Speed of light: $c = (2.998)10^8$ m/s

Electron charge: $e = (1.602)10^{-19}$ C

Planck constant: $h = (6.626)10^{-34}$ J/Hz

Use of Engineering Parameters

1.1 Visible light has wavelengths that range roughly from 0.4 to 0.7 μm. What is the corresponding range of frequencies in hertz?

1.2 Photons of red light (0.62 μm) have an energy of about 2 eV. What is the range of photon energies of visible light?

1.3 What are the photon energies of radiation at the wavelengths 0.85 μm, 1.2 μm, and 1.55 μm commonly used in optical fibers?

1.4 If a bit corresponds to a single, square pulse that is present for a 1 and absent for a 0:

(a) What is the maximum duration of each pulse if the transmission rate is 1 Mbit/s? 1 Gbit/s?

(b) For each rate, how much energy is carried by a maximal pulse if its power level is 1 mW?

1.5 If window glass has losses equivalent to 10^5 dB/km, what fraction of the original light energy remains after it traverses 5 mm of such glass?

1.6 What is the speed of light in glass of refractive index $n = 1.5$?

CHAPTER 2

What Is a Wave?

We begin with the concept of a *wave*, which is qualitatively familiar but needs to be expressed mathematically. Roughly speaking, we recognize a wave as some pattern in space that appears to move in time.

Preliminaries

To make this more precise, let z be distance, t be time, and v be a fixed parameter. Consider the quantity $(z - vt)$ and let us try to set it equal to some constant:

$$z - vt = z_0 . \tag{2.1}$$

Where and when is this equation true? What the equation requires is that despite the fact that time elapses, the quantity on the left is to remain equal to the fixed value z_0. At any particular time, the equation is true at only one distance; for example, at $t = 0$ the equation holds at $z = z_0$ (which allows us to interpret the constant z_0 as the initial point of validity of the equation). At time $t = t_0$, it is true at distance $z = z_0 + vt_0$ instead. As time marches on, the point at which the equation is true changes: The distance to that point keeps increasing. At the general time t, the equation is true at the variable distance $z = z(t) = z_0 + vt$. Thus the point of validity of the equation *moves*. How fast does this point move? It moves at the rate $dz(t)/dt$, which is just v. [Of course, we knew when we constructed the quantity $(z - vt)$ that v had to have the dimensions of a speed, in order for both terms to represent distances that can be subtracted from each other.] The main conclusion is that the point of validity of the equation moves, at the speed v.

Consider now any function $f(x)$. At any fixed argument x_0, the function has some fixed value $f(x_0)$. An interesting fixed argument might be one at which the function peaks, or where it has an inflection point, or "starts" (from zero), or "ends" (returns to, and then remains, zero), or has any other feature of interest. For example, in Figure 2–1, to make the function $f(x)$ shown attain its peak value, just set its argument to the value x_2.

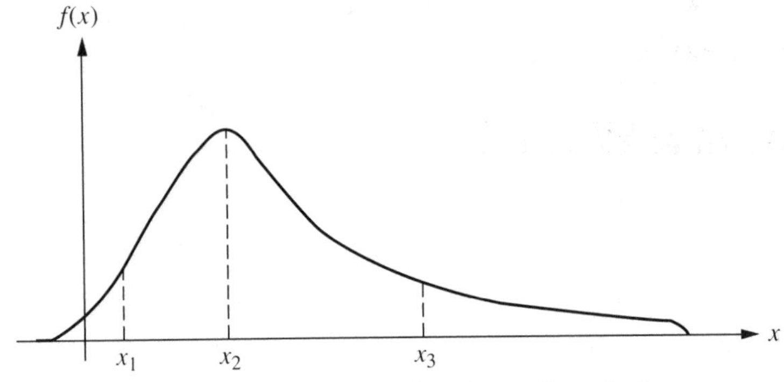

FIGURE 2–1 An arbitrary function, with peak at x_2.

Definition of a Wave

Now we are ready to form a new function, but this time it will be a function of both space and time, $F(z, t)$. We will construct this new function by using the old one $f(x)$, which had only one argument, but replacing that argument with the quantity $z - vt$:

$$F(z, t) = f(z - vt). \tag{2.2}$$

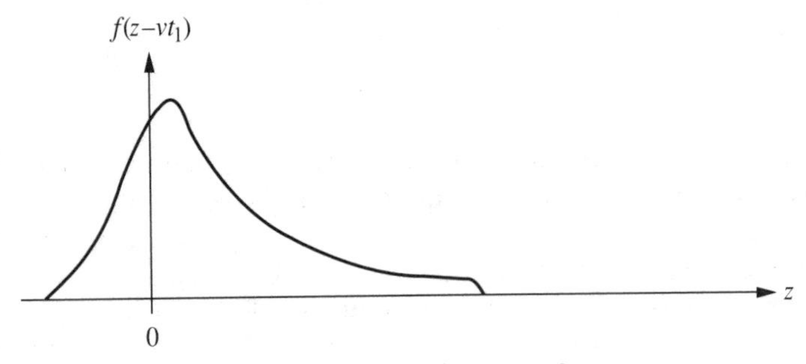

(a) Earlier (t_1): peak near $z = 0$

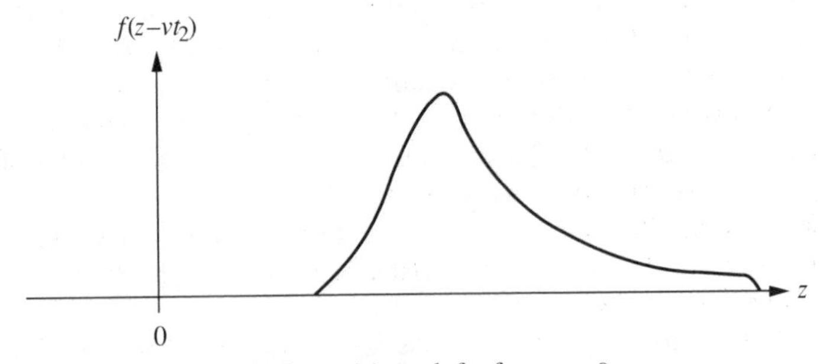

(b) Later (t_2): peak far from $z = 0$

FIGURE 2–2 The function $F(z, t)$ versus z, seen at two times, t_1 and t_2.

The peak value of the function $F(z, t)$ occurs wherever and whenever the argument of the $f(z - vt)$ function equals x_2. That happens wherever and whenever $z - vt = x_2$. As explained above, as time elapses, this occurs at increasing values of the distance z. This means that as time goes on, the peak value of the $F(z, t)$ function will be found at ever-larger distances. The peak of the $F(z, t)$ function *moves*, and it moves at speed v.

Other points of the curve, such as $f(x_1)$ or $f(x_3)$, also move, since the $F(z, t)$ function will attain either of these two values wherever and whenever the equation $z - vt = x_1$ or $z - vt = x_3$ is true. In all such cases, the point in question moves, at speed v. Therefore, the *entire* curve $f(x)$ that comprises the $F(z, t)$ function *moves* along the z-axis as time elapses, at speed v, as suggested in Figure 2–2.

Such motion is "wave motion." The quantity $f(z - vt)$ is a "wave." *Any* function of $z - vt$ is a wave, moving along the z-axis, at speed v.

For a quantity F to be a wave, it must depend on both position and time, but only in the combination $z - vt$ for some particular v, which specifies the speed of "propagation" (travel) along the direction of increasing distance z. The quantity F itself may be any physically observable entity; it may be a scalar, such as temperature, or it may be a vector, such as the velocity of a point within a fluid. If it is a vector, each of its components must be some function of the single quantity $z - vt$.

Waveshape

All waves that travel along the z-axis at speed v are expressible as functions of $z - vt$. They may differ in their "waveshape," the actual form of the function of one variable, $f(x)$, that defines the wave $F(z, t) = f(z - vt)$. There are hence two stages in the specification of a wave. First, we must tell the direction of travel, say z, and its speed, v. Then we need to specify the waveshape itself, by describing some function $f(x)$ of one variable, for all values of that variable x. The shape might be a pulse of some finite extent, or it might extend indefinitely along x; it might be periodic, such as $\sin kx$; it may be strong or weak in amplitude. In specifying the waveshape $f(x)$, we usually tell not only how it is shaped but also its scale height or amplitude or strength (along the ordinate), and its scale width, such as the pulse width or the period $2\pi/k$ of the sinusoid $\sin kx$ (along the abscissa). If the wave is a vector, we would specify each of the three components as functions of the single variable, or else give the vector's magnitude and direction as functions of the waveshape's single argument.

EXAMPLE 2.1

The quantity $F = 5 \exp[-(6t - 3y)^2]$ represents a wave that propagates along the y-axis, at speed $6/3 = 2$ m/s. Its waveshape is the bell-shaped curve

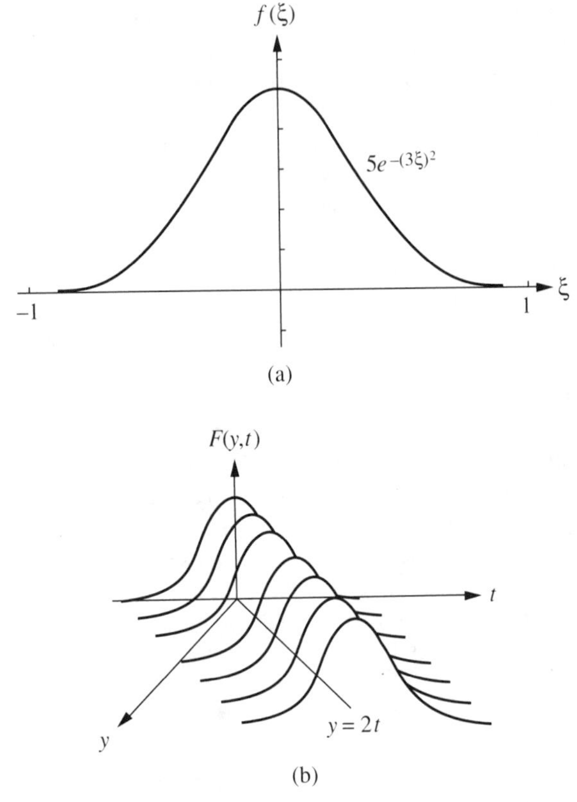

FIGURE 2–3 Bell-shaped wave propagating along the *y*-axis.

$f(\xi) = 5 \exp[-(3\xi)^2]$ of peak amplitude 5 and scale length $\frac{1}{3}$ m (the half-width of the "bell" at its $1/e$ points). The substitution $\xi = y - 2t$ converts this function $f(\xi)$ of one variable into the wave $F(y, t)$, as shown in Figure 2–3. ◆

Waveform

In this example, the functional dependence on $(y - 2t)$ was slightly disguised in the exponent's $(6t - 3y)$. Generally, a wave $F(z, t)$ may be thought of as formed from the shape $f(\xi)$ by the substitution $\xi = z - vt$, or else as built from the time signal $h(\tau)$ by the substitution $\tau = t - z/v$. The difference is in the point of view. The former version sees the quantity $F(z, t)$ primarily as a distribution in space $f(z)$ that evolves in time as the wave motion $f(z - vt)$; the other approach views $F(z, t)$ as a time signal $h(t)$ that spreads in space as the wave motion $h(t - z/v)$. In the first case, the $f(z)$ function is just $F(z, 0)$, the initial spatial variation of F; in the second case, the $h(t)$ signal is just $F(0, t)$, the time variation of F as seen at the spatial origin $z = 0$. Since $\xi = -v\tau$, the relation between the two describing functions, the "waveshape" $f(\xi)$ and the "waveform" $h(\tau)$, is just $h(\tau) = f(-v\tau)$ or $f(\xi) = h(-\xi/v)$, a simple rescaling of the arguments. In Example 2.1, the waveform is $h(\tau) = 5 \exp[-(6\tau)^2]$, which is a signal with a time scale of $\frac{1}{6}$ s; the waveshape is $f(\xi) = 5 \exp[-(3\xi)^2]$, which is a spatial distribution of length scale $\frac{1}{3}$ m.

Interpretation

We wish to construct a physical interpretation of the wave $F(z, t)$ without, however, being too specific at this stage about the character of the quantity F, which could be an acoustic wave, a thermal wave, an electromagnetic wave, an optical wave, or the like. We suppose only that there exist means for generating the wave and also for sensing its presence. At the origin of the z-axis, then, we place a generator capable of launching the wave and, at some distance $z = l$, we have a detector that senses or measures $F(z, t)$. The medium that separates the source and the sensor allows the quantity F to propagate along the z-axis, as a wave of speed v. What the source actually generates is a signal $h(t)$ in time, at its own location, $z = 0$, so that the generator is responsible for the existence of $F(0, t) = h(t)$. The medium makes a wave $F(z, t)$ out of this signal $F(0, t)$ and the detector at $z = l$ can sense $F(l, t)$ and follow its time variation.

In Figure 2–4(a), the generator signal $h(t)$ is shown as a pair of pulses, a strong one followed by a weaker one, of overall duration T seconds. This

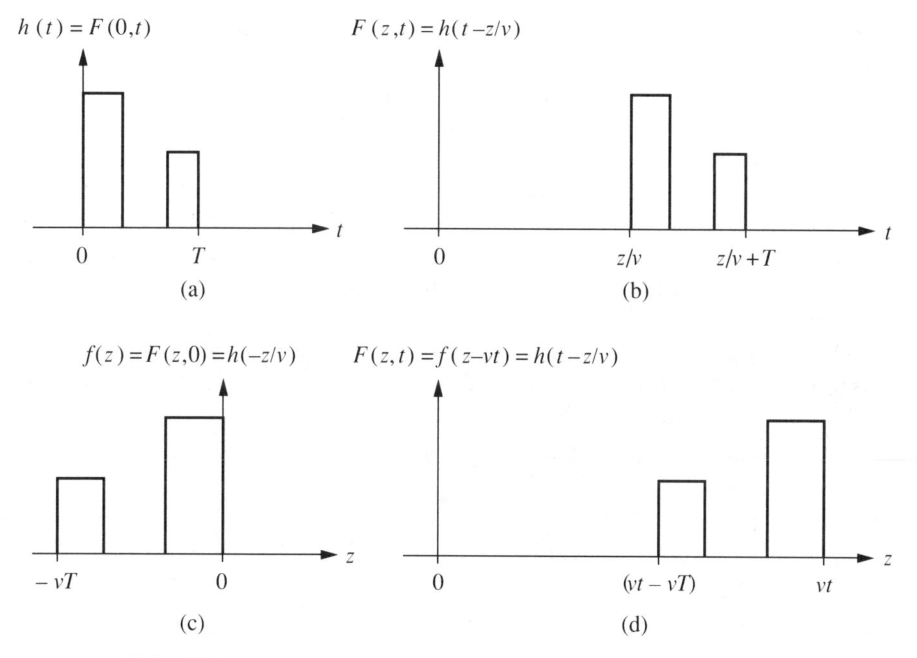

FIGURE 2–4 Four views of wave $F(z, t)$ versus time and space.

signal $F(0, t) = h(t)$ becomes $F(z, t) = h(t - z/v)$ elsewhere and is shown in part (b) of the figure, plotted against time t. Since the function $h(t)$ in (a) is zero until its argument becomes zero, then becomes the pulses and reverts to zero when the argument exceeds T, the function $h(t - z/v)$ in (b) is zero until its argument becomes zero, which occurs at time z/v, then becomes the pair of pulses and reverts to zero when the argument $(t - z/v)$ becomes T, which occurs at time $(z/v + T)$. Thus, at location z, an exact duplicate of the pair of pulses appears, but delayed in time by z/v seconds. The graph in (b) is the same as in (a) but shifted by z/v seconds along the t-axis. The detector at $z = l$ will receive the same signal that was produced by the pulse generator at $z = 0$, but delayed by l/v seconds. The generator signal has been transmitted to the detector, over a distance l, by the wave $F(z, t)$ in the intervening medium. The generator is the transmitter; the detector is the receiver.

Suppose that we were capable of visualizing the wave $F(z, t)$ at one instant of time but over a span of distance, rather than detecting it as a signal in time at one position $z = l$. That is, suppose that we could take an instantaneous snapshot of the wave's spatial distribution. The resulting picture would appear as in parts (c) and (d) of the figure, where we show F versus position z at fixed times, not versus t for fixed positions, as in (a) and (b). The waveshape $f(z)$ is $F(z, t) = h(t - z/v)$, evaluated at $t = 0$, so that $f(z) = h(-z/v)$. That is, the function f is the same as the waveform h, but with its argument rescaled by the $1/v$ factor and reversed by the minus sign. The waveshape is shown in (c); it extends along the negative z-axis, out to $-vT$, because that is where the $h(-z/v)$ function has positive argument, with nonzero values of h. $F(z, 0) = f(z)$ is the initial snapshot, at $t = 0$. [We are now imagining $F(z, t)$ to exist for all space and time, z, t, not just for $t > 0$ and $z > 0$, which would be appropriate if the wave were created at $t = 0$ by some generator at $z = 0$.]

We note the reversal of the graph in the snapshot (versus z) in (c), compared to the signal (versus t) in (a), corresponding to the minus sign in the rescaling of the argument from $h(t)$ to $f(z)$. In (d), the snapshot at time t is shown; this is $F(z, t) = f(z - vt)$, at the fixed time t. As compared to $f(z)$ in (c), this is shifted by distance vt along z. It is an exact, undistorted replica of the snapshot at $t = 0$, but displaced by distance vt. Since this displacement is proportional to the elapsed time, the waveshape *moves* along the z-axis as time goes on, at a constant rate.

On the time axis, the pair of pulses lasted T seconds; on the z-axis, they occupy vT meters of space, in accordance with the rescaling. The reversal of

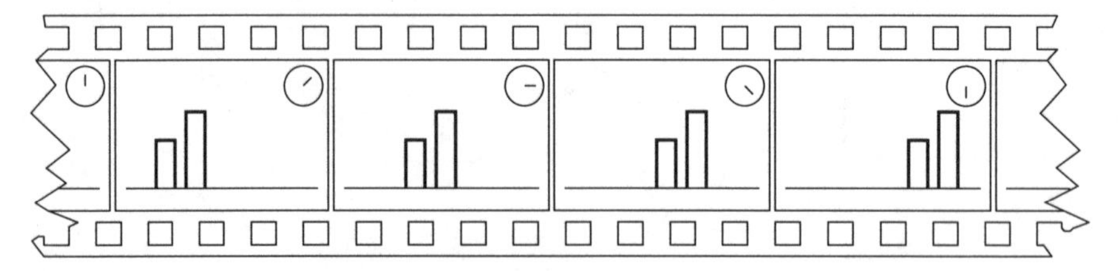

FIGURE 2–5 Filmstrip of traveling pulses.

the pair of pulses, due to the minus sign in the scaling, has a simple interpretation. The stronger pulse is the first to be generated in time, as in (a); it therefore has had more time to travel along z and thus leads the weaker pulse, which has not yet traveled so far, as in (d).

Successive snapshots of the pair of pulses, at equal time intervals, would correspond to the "filmstrip" in Figure 2–5, which is intended to illustrate that the pulses move along the z-axis, at a steady pace.

EXAMPLE 2.2

Figure 2–6 depicts how a triangular-pulse time signal $f(t)$ becomes a wave $F(z, t) = f(t - z/c)$ upon changing the argument t to $t - z/c$. The function of two variables, $F(z, t)$, is shown as a section of the shaded, prismatic surface over the zt-plane. The two interpretations of $F(z, t)$, either as a time signal that can be observed at a particular location z, or as a waveshape that might be seen at one instant t, are illustrated in the more detailed portion of the diagram. The cut made by the plane A–A perpendicular to the z-axis shows the waveform at a fixed position z; it has the same form as the original signal, a steep rise followed by a decline of more moderate slope, but the signal is delayed by z/c seconds. The cut along the plane B–B normal to the t-axis shows the waveshape as it would be seen in a snapshot at time t; it has the same triangular shape, but as viewed for increasing values of z, the display is reversed, showing the moderate ramp first, followed by the steep decline. ◆

Wave Equations

Not every function of z and t is expressible as a function of the single, combined argument $z - vt$. How might quantities that depend separately on space and time, such as $F(z, t)$, get to be a wave, such as $f(z - vt)$? To answer this question, it is useful to compare the rate of change of $F(z, t)$ in space with its rate of change in time, for the case that $F(z, t)$ is indeed a wave:

$$\frac{\partial F(z, t)}{\partial z} = f'(z - vt), \tag{2.3}$$

where $f'(x) = df(x)/dx$, while

$$\frac{\partial F(z, t)}{\partial t} = f'(z - vt)(-v), \tag{2.4}$$

by the chain rule of differentiation. Hence, regardless of the waveshape $f(x)$, if $F(z, t)$ is a wave that propagates along z at speed v, then

$$\frac{\partial F(z, t)}{\partial t} = -v \frac{\partial F(z, t)}{\partial z}. \tag{2.5}$$

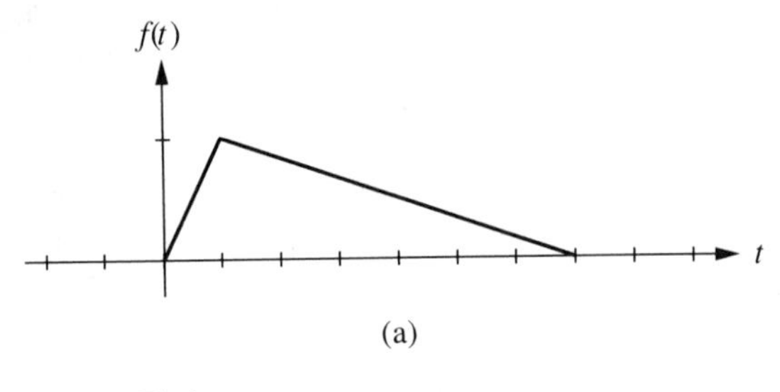

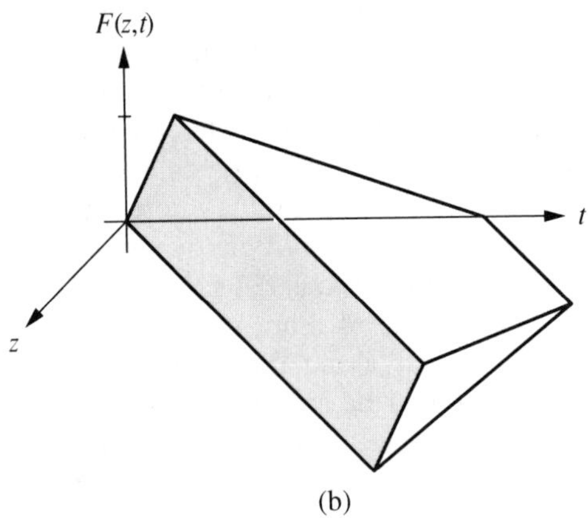

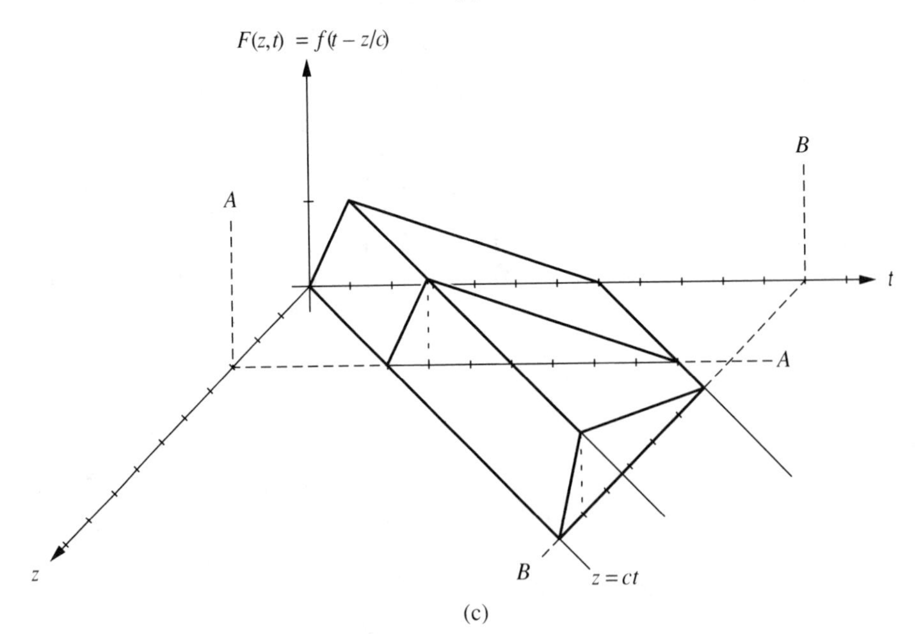

FIGURE 2–6 Waveform and waveshape as two cuts through the surface $F(z, t)$.

For any wave, the spatial rate of change is proportional to the temporal rate of change.

The converse is also true. If some physical law were to require the spatial and temporal rates of change of a quantity $F(z, t)$ to be proportional, this function's dependence on space and time would have to be that of a wave. Its wave speed would then be the negative of the proportionality constant in the physical law.

More commonly, physical laws (such as Newton's) involve second derivatives (signifying acceleration in time, or curvature in space) rather than first derivatives (velocity or slope). If the quantity $F(z, t)$ is in fact a wave $f(z - vt)$, its second derivatives are

$$\frac{\partial^2 F(z, t)}{\partial z^2} = f''(z - vt) \qquad \text{and} \qquad \frac{\partial^2 F(z, t)}{\partial t^2} = (-v)^2 f''(z - vt), \tag{2.6}$$

where $f''(x) = d^2 f(x)/dx^2$ is the second derivative of the waveshape, with respect to its argument. Hence, for any waveshape, the wave $F(z, t)$ satisfies the partial differential equation

$$\frac{\partial^2 F(z, t)}{\partial z^2} = \frac{1}{v^2} \frac{\partial^2 F(z, t)}{\partial t^2}. \tag{2.7}$$

This equation is called a "wave equation"; it implies that $F(z, t)$ is a wave, with wave speed v (the square root of the proportionality constant in the equation), because $F(z, t) = f(z - vt)$ is a solution, where the function of one variable $f(x)$ can be *any* function at all.

As we know from the theory of partial differential equations, this one is of second order and should therefore have two independent solutions. Our search for the second solution is an easy one, however, because the square root of the proportionality constant can be either $+v$ or $-v$, so that any function of $z + vt$ should serve as well as does an arbitrary function of $z - vt$. The general solution to this wave equation is therefore the sum of two arbitrary, independent functions of the two combinations of z and t, as in

$$F(z, t) = f(z - vt) + g(z + vt), \tag{2.8}$$

where $f(x)$ and $g(x)$ are *any* two, unrelated functions of one argument.

What is the interpretation of the second solution? As time elapses, the argument $(z + vt)$ remains fixed if z decreases, to compensate for the change in t, at the rate $dz/dt = -v$. The quantity $g(z + vt)$ is therefore a wave also, but one that travels along the negative z-axis, at the speed v. The general solution to the wave equation is a superposition of two waves, each of wave speed v, traveling in opposite directions along the z-axis. The two oppositely traveling waveshapes $f(x)$ and $g(x)$ are independent functions, to be determined from initial or boundary conditions associated with the differential equation. Note that the superposition of the two waves is itself not a wave; it cannot be expressed as some other function $h(z - ut)$, for any $h(x)$ or any parameter u.

EXAMPLE 2.3

Figure 2–7 shows two pulses $f(\xi)$ and $g(\xi)$ and several snapshots of superpositions of these pulses after each has become a wave, but traveling in opposed directions; the superposition is $F(z, t) = f(z - vt) + g(z + vt)$. Because we have arbitrarily chosen to make each pulse have the same width L, the initial superposition $F(z, 0)$ has a simple, trapezoidal shape. A short time later, at $t_1 \approx L/3v$, the two constituent pulses have moved, slightly, in opposite directions and the superposition is a more complex polygon. Still later, shown as $t_2 \approx 4L/3v$, the two pulses have completely separated and are easily identified individually as they continue to recede from each other. ◆

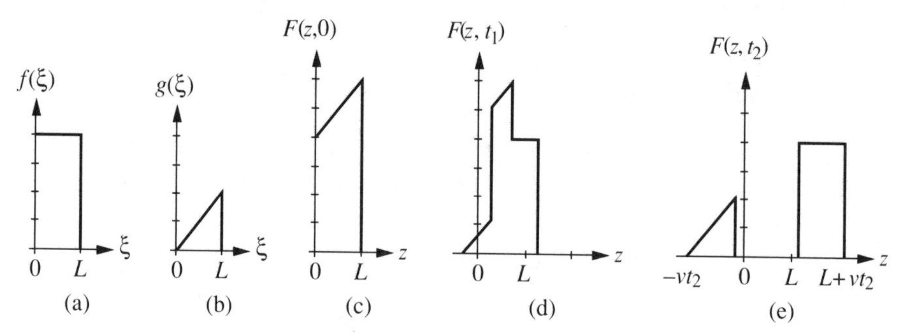

FIGURE 2–7 Two waveshapes superimposed as opposed waves.

Summary

A wave is a quantity that depends on both position and time, as any function of a single variable comprised of a linear combination of a distance and the time: $f(\alpha z + \beta t)$ is a wave that propagates along z at the speed $v = -\beta/\alpha$. A wave satisfies the wave equation, a second-order partial differential equation that has as its general solution a superposition of two arbitrary waves of equal and opposite speeds. A wave can transmit a signal waveform from one location to another, with no distortion other than a delay proportional to the separation between transmitter and receiver.

Waves can be of diverse nature and of types other than the simplest one defined in this chapter, which was one-dimensional and uniform. In what follows, we will find that electromagnetic fields can propagate as waves.

PROBLEMS

Wave in Arbitrary Direction

2.1 What is the speed v and direction $\hat{\mathbf{n}}$ of the wave $f(x, y, z, t) = \operatorname{sech}^2(x + y + z + t)$?

2.2 Convert the bell-shaped function $f(\xi) = 5 \exp [-(3\xi)^2]$ into a wave $f(x, y, z, t)$ of that waveshape that travels at speed 2 m/s in the direction of the vector $\mathbf{b} = 3\hat{\mathbf{x}} + 4\hat{\mathbf{y}} - 12\hat{\mathbf{z}}$.

Crest of a Wave

2.3 A transmitter located at $z = 0$ generates signal $f(t) = (t/T)^3 e^{-t/T}$, starting at $t = 0$, with $T = 4$ s. The signal propagates as a wave along the z-axis, at speed $v = 6$ m/s.

(a) Where is the peak of the wave at time $t = 20$ s?
(b) At what time should an observer stationed at $z = 20$ m expect to see the wave peak?

2.4 A transmitter located at $z = 0$ generates signal $f(t) = \alpha t$ for $0 < t < T$ and then $f(t) = \alpha T^2/t$ for $t > T$. It emits waves in both directions, $z > 0$ and $z < 0$, both at speed v. Where along the entire z-axis are the crests of these waves at time $t = 3T$?

Superposition of Waves

2.5 Two transmitters are located at $z = 0$ and $z = l$. The first generates signal $f(t) = (t/T)^2 e^{-t/T}$, the second produces $g(t) = (t/T)e^{-t/T}$. The first signal becomes a wave that travels toward $z = l$ at speed l/T; the second one travels toward $z = 0$ at the same speed.

(a) Where and when will an observer find the superposition of the two waves (their sum) to be the strongest?
(b) How strong will that peak value be?

General Wave Solutions

2.6 **(a)** Is $F_0(z, t) = f(z - vt) + g(z + vt) + C$ a more general solution to the wave equation $\partial^2 F/\partial z^2 = (1/v^2)\, \partial^2 F/\partial t^2$ than is $F(z, t) = f(z - vt) + g(z + vt)$ alone? If not, what functions $f_0(u)$ and $g_0(u)$ would make $F_0(z, t) = f_0(z - vt) + g_0(z + vt)$?

(b) Is $F_0(z, t) = f(z - vt) + g(z + vt) + Dz$ a more general solution to the wave equation than is $F(z, t) = f(z - vt) + g(z + vt)$ alone? If not, what functions $f_0(u)$ and $g_0(u)$ would make $F_0(z, t) = f_0(z - vt) + g_0(z + vt)$?

(c) Is $F_0(z, t) = f(z - vt) + g(z + vt) + Et$ a more general solution to the wave equation than is $F(z, t) = f(z - vt) + g(z + vt)$ alone? If not, what functions $f_0(u)$ and $g_0(u)$ would make $F_0(z, t) = f_0(z - vt) + g_0(z + vt)$?

2.7 Show that no function $h(x)$ and no parameter u can be found that can express the general superposition of waves $f(z - vt) + g(z + vt)$ as a wave $h(z - ut)$.

2.8 Let the pulsed signals $f(t)$ and $g(t)$ be given by

$$f(t) = 1 - \frac{t}{T} \quad \text{for } 0 < t < T \qquad \text{and} \qquad f(t) = 0 \quad \text{otherwise;}$$

$$g(t) = \frac{t}{T} \quad \text{for } 0 < t < T \qquad \text{and} \qquad g(t) = 0 \quad \text{otherwise.}$$

If the two pulses are emitted as oppositely traveling waves and added to form $F(z, t) = f(t - z/v) + g(t + z/v)$, sketch the superposition at:

(a) $z = 0$; **(b)** $z = \frac{vT}{3}$; **(c)** $z = \frac{vT}{2}$; **(d)** $z = \frac{2vT}{3}$.

CHAPTER 3

Maxwell's Equations

We will demonstrate that the physical laws that govern electromagnetic fields can require them to undergo wave motion. We must first define what we mean by fields in general and by electric and magnetic fields in particular.

Action at a Distance and with Delay

If charged particles are isolated, it can be observed that they interact at a distance: they can exert forces on other electrified matter, not merely on contact, but anywhere in their vicinity, across a gap between them. The action is even more subtle: it is found that a change in one charge affects another only after some time delay. The separation between cause and effect across space and over time greatly complicates the description of the interaction among charges.

Because the action occurs at a distance and after a delay, it is preferable not to attempt to describe the way one charge influences another in a direct way, but rather to ascribe the effect to an intermediary agent between the source and the recipient of the action. This agent is a "field."

Definition of Field

A *field* is a quantity associated with points in space. More generally, and most appropriately for our purpose, the quantities will also be associated with instants of time. Mathematically, then, a field is a function of position (x, y, z), or of the position vector $\mathbf{r} = (x, y, z)$. Thus $f = f(x, y, z) = f(\mathbf{r})$ is a field. Usually and more completely, we will deal with functions of time as well as of position: $f(x, y, z, t)$ or $f(\mathbf{r}, t)$. Any function of position (and also time) is a field.

The mathematics used to deal with fields involves calculations on functions of several variables, or functions of a vector argument, $\mathbf{r}$. For a quantity F to be a field, it must depend on position (and time). The quantity F itself may be any physically observable entity; it may be a scalar field, such as temperature, or it may be a vector field, such as the velocity of a point within a fluid. If it is a vector, each of its components must be some function of the position vector **r** (and of t). It is not the scalar or vector character of the quantity that determines whether it is a field; it is only the vector character of its argument, **r**, that is crucial.

Electric and Magnetic Fields

Returning to the interaction between charged particles, we prefer not to consider the cause of the action, which is some change in the state of the "source" charge, to act directly upon the recipient of the action, the remote "test" charge. A direct description would be too complicated. Instead, we conceive of the test charge as responding to *electric* and *magnetic fields*, which will be vector functions of position, to be evaluated at the location of the test charge. There will thus be no separation (and no delay) between the fields and the test charge; the action between these occurs "on contact." The intermediary agency, the fields, exists, however, because of the presence and behavior, elsewhere and earlier, of the source charge.

The contact force exerted by the fields on the test charge is given by

$$\mathbf{F} = q\mathbf{E} + q\mathbf{v} \times \mathbf{B}, \tag{3.1}$$

which is called the Lorentz force. The test charge q is at location $\mathbf{r}$ at time t with velocity $\mathbf{v}$; at that location and time, electric field $\mathbf{E}(\mathbf{r}, t)$ and magnetic field $\mathbf{B}(\mathbf{r}, t)$ exert the force $\mathbf{F}$ on this charge.

There are several ways to make use of the Lorentz force expression. It can serve to *define* the electric and magnetic fields. Note that the two fields are distinguishable, because the electric one is effective even when the test charge is not moving. The expression can serve to *measure* the electric and magnetic fields, if suitable test charges can be isolated. Most important, it can serve to relate electric and magnetic fields to their *mechanical* effects, by using this Lorentz force in Newton's law, $\mathbf{F} = m\mathbf{a}$, where m is the mass of the charge and $\mathbf{a}$ is its acceleration.

In practice, we almost never isolate charges. On the atomic level, however, all matter is electrified (but normally with no net charge), so that electric and magnetic fields can be utilized through their effects on conductors, dielectrics, or other forms of matter. Although we introduce fields as convenient agencies to mediate the interaction among charges, they are not mere figments of our imagination. They interact with each other; they will be seen to carry energy and to convey information. Their behavior is described by Maxwell's equations.

Maxwell's equations tell how electric and magnetic fields can interact with each other, as well as how they can be generated in the first place. However, it is found that the medium in which the fields are immersed can modify their interaction. Additional, "constitutive" relations describe the constitution of the medium and tell how it affects the fields.

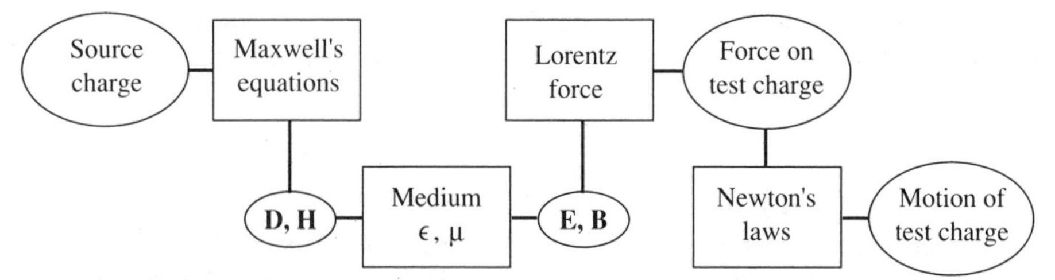

FIGURE 3–1 Fields as intermediaries between source and test charges.

To separate the field interactions from the effects of the medium and from the original sources of the fields, two additional electric and magnetic fields are introduced: **D** and **H**. These two fields are generated directly by the source charges; the **E** and **B** fields are the ones that act directly on the test charges. The medium determines how the two pairs of fields are related.

In a vacuum, **D** and **E** are the same and **B** and **H** are the same, but it is convenient to measure each type in both pairs with different units. The units conversion factors are ε_0 and μ_0:

$$\mathbf{D} = \varepsilon_0 \mathbf{E} \qquad \text{and} \qquad \mathbf{B} = \mu_0 \mathbf{H} \qquad \text{(vacuum)}. \tag{3.2}$$

In the presence of matter, the constitutive relations are less trivial.

The scheme whereby the electromagnetic fields act as intermediaries between source and test charges in the action of one on the other is illustrated in Figure 3–1. Starting with the source charge, fields **D** and **H** are deemed to be generated by its presence and its motion, in some way expressed by Maxwell's equations, not yet specified. The medium then converts these fields into the alternate versions **E** and **B**; these are then the fields that act on the test charge, by exerting a force on it, at its location. Newton's laws of motion then can yield the subsequent motion of the test charge.

Field Integrals

Maxwell's equations relate the fields **E**, **B**, **D**, and **H** to each other and to their ultimate sources, which are electric charges in motion. The fields are vectors, but their laws of interaction and generation involve scalars. These scalars are associated with the vector fields and with certain geometrical curves and surfaces in space. The relevant scalar quantities are five in number, as follows.

1. "Electromotive force," or *emf*, V along some specified curve C in space. This is the line integral of the **E** field along the given curve:

$$V = \int_C \mathbf{E} \cdot d\mathbf{l}. \tag{3.3}$$

It is measured in volts.

2. "Magnetomotive force," or *mmf*, U along some specified curve C in space. This is the line integral of the **H** field along the given curve:

$$U = \int_C \mathbf{H} \cdot d\mathbf{l}. \tag{3.4}$$

It is measured in amperes.

3. "Displacement (or electric) flux" Ψ over some specified surface S in space. This is the surface integral of the **D** field over the given surface:

$$\Psi = \int_S \mathbf{D} \cdot d\mathbf{S}. \tag{3.5}$$

It is measured in coulombs.

4. "Magnetic flux" Φ over some specified surface S in space. This is the surface integral of the **B** field over the given surface:

$$\Phi = \int_S \mathbf{B} \cdot d\mathbf{S}. \tag{3.6}$$

It is measured in webers.

5. Current I across some specified surface S. This is the rate of flow of charge across the given surface, or the net amount of charge that crosses the surface S per unit time. It is measured in amperes.

Properties of the Field Integrals

Each of the line and surface integrals depends both on the field pattern in the integrand and on the curve or surface of integration. Because of the dot products of the fields with the line or surface elements, these are scalars. Although the integrands depend on position, being fields, their spatial dependence gets integrated out and the resultant integrals are not functions of position. They are not fields themselves; they are higher-order creatures, being dependent on entire collections of points, forming the curve C or the surface S, while fields depend on the position vector, **r**, only. That is, to find the value of a field, the point **r** at which it is to be evaluated is to be specified; to determine the value of an emf, mmf, or flux, however, an entire curve or surface over which the quantity is to be evaluated must be specified. If either the field in the integrand, or the curve or surface of integration, or both, depend on time, however, then the resultant scalar quantity is a function of time.

Curves and surfaces of integration are oriented: there is a positive direction of traversal for a curve or of crossing for a surface. That direction is part of the specification of the curve or surface. The line element $d\mathbf{l}$ is an infinitesimal vector whose direction is tangential to the curve and agrees with the positive orientation of the curve. The surface element $d\mathbf{S}$ is an infinitesimal vector whose direction is normal to the surface and points toward the positive side of the surface. Two conventions are adhered to in selecting orientations of curves and surfaces:

1. If a surface is closed, its positive orientation is always outward.
2. If a surface is open, its edge forms a closed curve and then the surface and its boundary curve are always mutually oriented in accordance with the right-hand rule: the positive orientations of the surface and of the curve are to be in the same relation to each other as that of the thumb and fingers, respectively, of the right hand.

Maxwell's Equations

There are two laws governing the interaction and generation of electric and magnetic fields:

Faraday–Maxwell Law. For any (open) surface S and its (closed) boundary curve C, the emf V around the curve equals the rate of decrease of the magnetic flux Φ across the surface:

$$V(t) = -\frac{d\Phi(t)}{dt}. \tag{3.7}$$

Ampère–Maxwell Law. For any (open) surface S and its (closed) boundary curve C, the mmf U around the curve equals the sum of the current I and the rate of increase of the electric flux Ψ across the surface:

$$U(t) = I(t) + \frac{d\Psi(t)}{dt}. \tag{3.8}$$

The curves and surfaces must be mutually oriented by the right-hand rule; the signs in these laws are then appropriate. In the Ampère–Maxwell law, both I and Ψ refer to the same surface S, but this surface is unrelated to the one to be used in the Faraday–Maxwell law. Most important, each of the laws applies to *any* surface and its boundary curve. This necessarily puts rather stringent constraints on how the electric and magnetic fields can vary from point to point in space and from instant to instant in time. In fact, time variation of an electric field affects the magnetic field pattern, while a changing magnetic field alters the electric field pattern; the two types of field are so closely intertwined as to form a single "electromagnetic" field. We will see that one consequence of the interrelation among the fields is that they tend to propagate as waves.

Figure 3–2 shows schematically the relationship among the pointwise, or field, description of the electromagnetic interaction, the higher-level version in terms of scalars associated with any open surface and its edge, and the ultimate dynamic interaction among these scalars. On the lowest, local level, the description is in terms of fields, on a point-by-point basis, with the pairs of fields related pointwise by the medium. On a more global level, we deal with scalars obtainable from the fields by integration over any open surface and its oriented edge. Ultimately, it is these scalars that are related to each other, for any choice of surface, by the Maxwell laws in integral form.

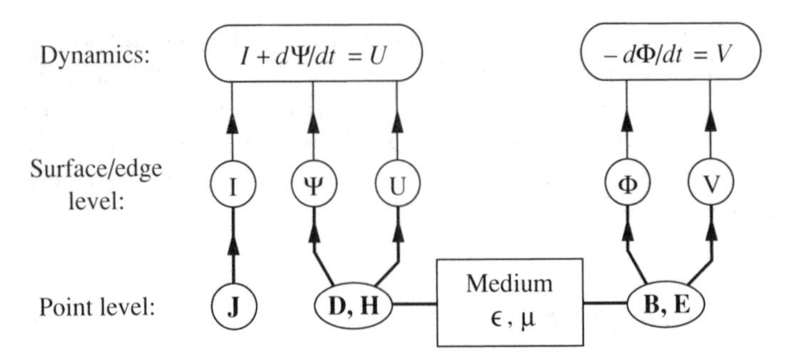

FIGURE 3–2 Maxwell's laws as dynamic relations among field integrals.

Plausibility of Waves

The fact that, in Maxwell's equations, the curves for the line integrals are the boundaries of the surfaces for the flux integrals is reflected geometrically in the *linking* of time-varying magnetic flux with electric field lines and of time-varying electric flux with magnetic field lines. Figure 3–3 suggests that a time-varying **D** field (or else a current) tends to get encircled by a magnetic field **H** and that a time-varying **B** field tends to get surrounded by an electric field **E**. Thus electric and magnetic fields tend to encircle each other and get intertwined or linked. This picture is only schematic, however, since the linking is three-dimensional, in all directions.

The time variation of one field sustains or generates the other. The interaction is dynamic: the existence of one field implies that the other changes in time, in a linked geometry. This intimates that wave motion may ensue, as suggested in Figure 3–4, which shows a time varying current in a loop. By Ampère's law, this generates a magnetic field that surrounds and links the loop. The diagram is only schematic; the field is generated in all directions. Since the current is time varying, so is the resultant **H** or **B** field, so that the rate of change of the magnetic flux builds up an electric field that is linked with the magnetic field lines. In turn, the **E** or **D** field, also being time varying, generates a further magnetic field, linked with it in its own vicinity. The

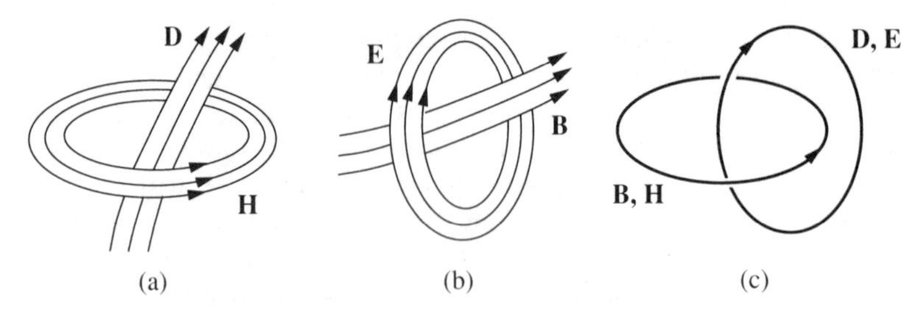

FIGURE 3–3 Linking of electric and magnetic fields.

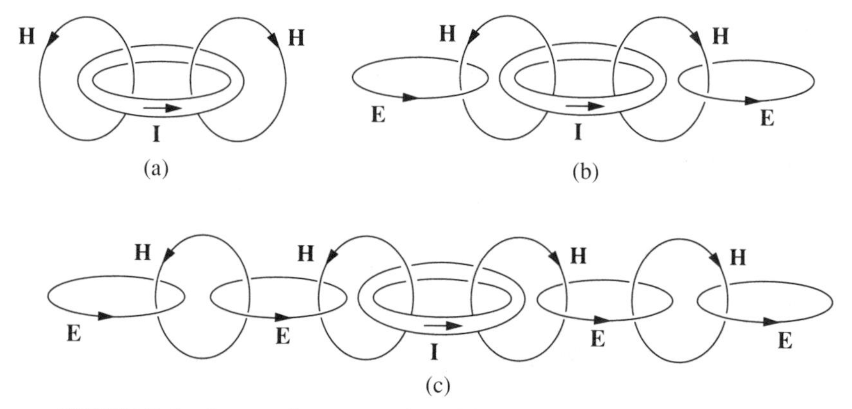

FIGURE 3–4 Successive generation of linked electromagnetic fluxes.

process continues, spreading outward in all directions as intertwined fluxes. The actual spatial configuration depends intimately on the time variation of the original source current in the loop.

This schematic diagram is not to be taken too literally, as the field lines are in reality not so neatly separated, but more closely intertwined and configured in all three dimensions. It does suggest the plausibility of wave motion, however, as the loop current creates a disturbance here (and now) and a replica of the signal can be observed elsewhere (and later), after the spreading of the mutually generated fields has had time to take place.

That a propagation delay must occur results from the fact that an emf or mmf is related to the time derivative of the corresponding flux, not instantaneously to the flux itself. We can stretch the plausibility argument one step further and gain some notion of the *rate* at which the fields may be expected to spread, by reducing the Maxwell equations to their simplest terms, through a dimensional analysis of their form.

We need to combine the two Maxwell's equations, which requires that the **B** and **D** fields be expressed in terms of **H** and **E**. This involves the properties of the medium in which the fields are immersed; it is the medium, then, that ultimately determines the rate of change of the fluxes, and hence the rate at which they can spread. For a vacuum, the two types of field are related through the units conversion factors ε_0 and μ_0 and we may consider a region devoid of any current sources (antennas). For a mere dimensional analysis, the emf V can be represented by the product of an average field strength E and an effective path length L_1 for the line integral, and similarly for the mmf and flux integrals:

$$V \sim EL_1 \qquad U \sim HL_2 \qquad \Phi \sim \mu_0 HA_1 \qquad \Psi \sim \varepsilon_0 EA_2. \tag{3.9}$$

If the time derivatives of the fluxes introduce effective time scales T_1 and T_2, the two Maxwell equations appear, on a dimensional basis only, as

$$EL_1 \sim \frac{\mu_0 HA_1}{T_1} \qquad HL_2 \sim \frac{\varepsilon_0 EA_2}{T_2} \tag{3.10}$$

and can be combined as

$$E \sim \frac{\mu_0 A_1}{L_1 T_1} \frac{\varepsilon_0 A_2}{L_2 T_2} E. \tag{3.11}$$

Overall effective length and time scales, L and T, can be defined as

$$L^2 \sim \frac{A_1 A_2}{L_1 L_2} \qquad T^2 \sim T_1 T_2, \tag{3.12}$$

so that

$$E \sim \frac{\mu_0 \varepsilon_0 L^2}{T^2} E \qquad \text{or} \qquad \frac{L}{T} \sim \frac{1}{\sqrt{\mu_0 \varepsilon_0}} \tag{3.13}$$

provides a measure of the effective speed of propagation to be expected in a vacuum. Similarly, dividing the two relations in Eq. (3.10) gives, dimensionally,

$$\frac{E}{H} \sim \frac{\mu_0 A_1/L_1 T_1}{\varepsilon_0 A_2/L_2 T_2} \frac{H}{E}, \tag{3.14}$$

so that, omitting the dimensionless factor $(A_1 L_2 T_2/A_2 L_1 T_1)$,

$$\frac{E}{H} \sim \sqrt{\frac{\mu_0}{\varepsilon_0}} \tag{3.15}$$

provides a measure of the ratio of the electric and magnetic field strengths to be expected in a vacuum.

In MKS units, one measures

$$D = \varepsilon_0 E \qquad \text{with} \quad \varepsilon_0 = (8.854)10^{-12}\ \text{F/m}, \tag{3.16}$$

$$B = \mu_0 H \qquad \text{with} \quad \mu_0 = (1.2566)10^{-6}\ \text{H/m}, \tag{3.17}$$

so that

$$\frac{1}{\sqrt{\mu_0 \varepsilon_0}} = (2.998)10^8\ \text{m/s} = c, \tag{3.18}$$

$$\sqrt{\frac{\mu_0}{\varepsilon_0}} = 376.7\ \Omega = \eta_0, \tag{3.19}$$

of which the former is the speed of light in vacuum and the latter is called the impedance of free space. Note that the speed of light and the impedance of free space are both implicitly built into the Maxwell equations. (In cgs units, c appears explicitly in them, while the impedance is hidden as unity.)

Of course, the plausibility argument for wave motion and the dimensional analysis that gave the wave speed and impedance can offer only suggestions of what may be expected from actually solving the equations. These suggestions need to be verified, detailed, and demonstrated.

EXAMPLE 3.1

We can illustrate an actual application of the Maxwell equations with what may well be the simplest of nontrivial electromagnetic field configurations, one in which the **E** and **H** fields are constants, but only in a half-space. We ask whether Maxwell's equations allow this sort of field, which is to be nonzero but constant in the half-space $z < s$, but zero for $z > s$. Figure 3–5 shows the field configuration, along with suitable curves and surfaces of integration that can yield nontrivial and informative emfs, mmfs, and fluxes for this case. With constant integrands, the integrals present no difficulties.

With $\mathbf{E} = E\hat{\mathbf{x}}$ for all points (x, y, z) such that $z < s$, we choose a rectangular area S_1 in the yz-plane, from y_1 to y_2 and z_1 to z_2, over which to calculate the displacement flux (since **E** is perpendicular to this area). The result Ψ_1 depends on where the point $z = s$ is, in relation to z_1 and z_2: if $z_1 > s$, there is no field over S_1 and $\Psi_1 = 0$; if $z_2 < s$, the entire area has the field E and the flux is $\Psi_1 = \varepsilon_0 E(y_2 - y_1)(z_2 - z_1)$, a fixed amount. If, however, $z_1 < s < z_2$, only part of the area has flux across it and

$$\Psi_1 = \varepsilon_0 E(y_2 - y_1)(s - z_1), \tag{3.20}$$

which depends on where s is between the ends of the rectangular area.

For the calculation of the emf, we can also use a rectangular path, but we need at least a segment along the x-direction, parallel to **E**. We choose the edge C_2 of the rectangular area S_2 in the xz-plane, from x_1 to x_2 and z_1 to z_2. The result V_2 depends on where the point $z = s$ is, in relation to z_1 and z_2: If $z_1 > s$, there is no field along C_2 and $V_2 = 0$; if $z_2 < s$, the entire path has the field E and the two segments parallel to **E** give equal and opposite contributions, so that $V_2 = 0$. If, however, $z_1 < s < z_2$, only that part of the path at z_1 has a field along it (actually, in the reverse direction if the path is oriented as shown) and

$$V_2 = -E(x_2 - x_1). \tag{3.21}$$

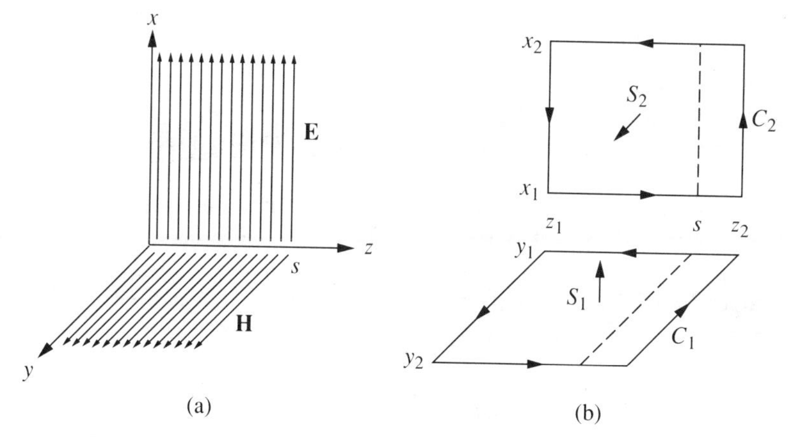

FIGURE 3–5 Uniform electromagnetic field in a half-space.

There is thus a nonzero (and fixed) emf, but only if s is between the ends of the rectangular area S_2. By the Faraday–Maxwell law, this emf equals the rate of decrease of a magnetic flux Φ over the surface S_2, which is (consistently with C_2) oriented to face along y. This implies that there is a magnetic field (or at least a component of it) along y; we ask for this also to be constant in the half-space $z < s$, $\mathbf{H} = H\hat{\mathbf{y}}$, and zero for $z > s$.

We calculate the magnetic flux Φ_2 over S_2; the result depends on where the point $z = s$ is, in relation to z_1 and z_2. If $z_1 > s$, there is no field over S_2 and $\Phi_2 = 0$; if $z_2 < s$, the entire area has the field H and the flux is $\Phi_2 = \mu_0 H(x_2 - x_1)(z_2 - z_1)$, a fixed amount. If, however, $z_1 < s < z_2$, only part of the area has flux across it and

$$\Phi_2 = \mu_0 H(x_2 - x_1)(s - z_1), \tag{3.22}$$

which depends on where s is between the ends of the rectangular area.

Finally, we calculate the mmf, using the rectangular path C_1, which has a segment along the y-direction, parallel to $\mathbf{H}$. This curve is the edge of the rectangular area S_1 in the xz-plane, from x_1 to x_2 and z_1 to z_2. The result U_1 depends on where the point $z = s$ is, in relation to z_1 and z_2: if $z_1 > s$, there is no field along C_1 and $U_1 = 0$; if $z_2 < s$, the entire path has the field H and the two segments parallel to $\mathbf{H}$ give equal and opposite contributions, so that $U_1 = 0$. If, however, $z_1 < s < z_2$, only that part of the path at z_1 has a field along it and

$$U_1 = H(y_2 - y_1). \tag{3.23}$$

There is thus a nonzero (and fixed) mmf, but only if s is between the ends of the rectangular area S_1. By the Ampère–Maxwell law, this mmf equals the rate of increase of the displacement flux Ψ over the surface S_1. This must be supplied by the electric field $\mathbf{E}$ with which we started.

Having calculated the four quantities Ψ_1, V_2, Φ_2, and U_1 we can assert that Maxwell's equations will accept this field configuration, provided that

$$V_2 = -\frac{d\Phi_2}{dt} \quad \text{or} \quad -E(x_2 - x_1) = -\frac{d}{dt}[\mu_0 H(x_2 - x_1)(s - z_1)] \tag{3.24}$$

and that

$$U_1 = \frac{d\Psi_1}{dt} \quad \text{or} \quad H(y_2 - y_1) = \frac{d}{dt}[\varepsilon_0 E(y_2 - y_1)(s - z_1)], \tag{3.25}$$

when s is between z_1 and z_2. We need nonzero time derivatives despite our stipulation that both E and H be constants. Since the limits of integration x_1, x_2, y_1, y_2, and z_1 are fixed by our choice of surfaces S_1 and S_2 and are not even properties of the field pattern, the only quantity that can vary in time in the last two equations is s, the location of the edge of the field space. The equations are consistent if

$$E = \mu_0 H \frac{ds}{dt} \quad \text{and} \quad H = \varepsilon_0 E \frac{ds}{dt} \tag{3.26}$$

and the product of these last equations, $EH = HE[\mu_0 \varepsilon_0 (ds/dt)^2]$, confirms that s must change at the constant rate

$$\frac{ds}{dt} = \frac{\pm 1}{\sqrt{\mu_0 \varepsilon_0}} = \pm c. \tag{3.27}$$

The edge of the field space must move, at the speed of light. By taking the ratio of the relations in Eq. (3.26), we also learn that

$$\frac{E}{H} = \pm \sqrt{\frac{\mu_0}{\varepsilon_0}} = \pm \eta_0, \tag{3.28}$$

the impedance of free space. We note that Maxwell's equations do allow the discontinuous field we postulated, provided that the edge of the half-space moves at the speed of light, either forward or backward along z. ◆

Integral and Differential Versions

Written out in detail, Maxwell's equations in integral form appear as

$$\oint_C \mathbf{E} \cdot dl = -\frac{d}{dt}\int_S \mathbf{B} \cdot d\mathbf{S} \qquad \oint_C \mathbf{H} \cdot dl = \frac{d}{dt}\int_S \mathbf{D} \cdot d\mathbf{S} + \int_S \mathbf{J} \cdot d\mathbf{S} \tag{3.29}$$

where $\mathbf{J}$ is the current density, a vector that gives both the magnitude and direction of the flow of charge, in A/m^2. Instead of determining the field configurations through these relations among the flux and line integrals over extended regions of space, it is most often convenient to specialize these equations to an infinitesimal region about some point in space. This yields differential relations among the field components at the point. Stokes's theorem converts closed line integrals into surface integrals of the curl of the vector integrand: $\oint_C \mathbf{F} \cdot dl = \int_S \nabla \times \mathbf{F} \cdot d\mathbf{S}$. This converts the equations into a set that involves only surface integrals:

$$\int_S \nabla \times \mathbf{E} \cdot d\mathbf{S} = -\frac{d}{dt}\int_S \mathbf{B} \cdot d\mathbf{S} \qquad \int_S \nabla \times \mathbf{H} \cdot d\mathbf{S} = \frac{d}{dt}\int_S \mathbf{D} \cdot d\mathbf{S} + \int_S \mathbf{J} \cdot d\mathbf{S} \tag{3.30}$$

and each of these equations applies to any surface S. Provided that this surface of integration is fixed in time, the dependence of the flux integrals on time is due only to that of the integrand, so that the time derivative outside the integral can be made a (partial) time derivative inside it, applied to the integrand only.

$$\int_S \nabla \times \mathbf{E} \cdot d\mathbf{S} = -\int_S \frac{\partial \mathbf{B}}{\partial t} \cdot d\mathbf{S} \qquad \int_S \nabla \times \mathbf{H} \cdot d\mathbf{S} = \int_S \frac{\partial \mathbf{D}}{\partial t} \cdot d\mathbf{S} + \int_S \mathbf{J} \cdot d\mathbf{S}. \tag{3.31}$$

These can hold for *all* fixed surfaces S only if the integrands are equal.

$$\nabla \times \mathbf{E} = -\frac{\partial \mathbf{B}}{\partial t} \qquad \nabla \times \mathbf{H} = \frac{\partial \mathbf{D}}{\partial t} + \mathbf{J}. \tag{3.32}$$

These are Maxwell's equations in differential form.

Note 1: For a moving medium, the differential equations are at best inconvenient, at worst incomplete, or at least must be reinterpreted. The integral equations are always correct. At discontinuities between different media, the differential equations involve infinities, while the integral equations apply without complications to yield boundary conditions.

Note 2: The current density $\mathbf{J}$ is normally zero almost everywhere, except where the source current is externally injected, as in an antenna. In a conducting medium, however, the mobile charges that are present are induced to flow as a current whenever an electric field is present. If such flow is balanced by the retarding effects of collisions with immobile atoms, the current may become proportional to the driving force, giving "Ohm's law" $\mathbf{J} = \sigma \mathbf{E}$. In a vacuum, $\sigma = 0$, since no mobile charges are available to respond to any electric field that may be present.

Note 3: Maxwell's two equations would be inconsistent ones if the fields were not to satisfy certain supplemental relations. Since $\nabla \cdot \nabla \times \mathbf{F} \equiv 0$ for any vector $\mathbf{F}$, it is necessary that $\partial(\nabla \cdot \mathbf{B})/\partial t = 0$ and that $\nabla \cdot \mathbf{J} + \partial(\nabla \cdot \mathbf{D})/\partial t = 0$ be true, in order for Eq. (3.32) to be consistent. In fact, *conservation of charge* demands that the outflow of charge at a point be exactly balanced by its rate of decrease there:

$$\nabla \cdot \mathbf{J} + \frac{\partial \rho}{\partial t} = 0, \tag{3.33}$$

where ρ is the charge density (C/m^3). Consequently, it is found that

$$\nabla \cdot \mathbf{D} = \rho \qquad \text{and} \qquad \nabla \cdot \mathbf{B} = 0 \tag{3.34}$$

hold as constraints on allowable spatial variations of the $\mathbf{D}$ and $\mathbf{B}$ fields; the first of these is Gauss's law. The integral version of these constraints is based on the fact that as an open surface S closes upon itself, its edge C vanishes, so that the emf or mmf must also vanish with it. Hence the dynamic integral laws are consistent in the limit of closed surfaces only because the constraints

$$\oint \mathbf{D} \cdot d\mathbf{S} = Q \qquad \text{and} \qquad \oint \mathbf{B} \cdot d\mathbf{S} = 0 \tag{3.35}$$

are found to hold; here Q is the total charge enclosed by the closed surface S.

Electromagnetic Waves

We are now ready to verify that Maxwell's equations do demand wave motion for time-varying electromagnetic fields. Because the three-dimensional, vector, partial differential equations are too formidable to deal with in all their glory, we content ourselves at this point with a simple version of what the equations require.

In a vacuum, away from the source antenna, electromagnetic fields may exist, provided that they satisfy

$$\nabla \times \mathbf{E} = -\mu_0 \frac{\partial \mathbf{H}}{\partial t}, \qquad \nabla \times \mathbf{H} = \varepsilon_0 \frac{\partial \mathbf{E}}{\partial t} \tag{3.36}$$

at each point and at each instant. These are a pair of three-dimensional, vector, partial differential equations.

To determine what these equations require in a simple way, consider the possibility that there might exist fields that satisfy them, but that vary along only one direction in space. Such fields would be one-dimensional, rather than the more general, three-dimensional sort. Call the special direction along which the fields vary the z direction. Then $\mathbf{E} = \mathbf{E}(z, t)$ and $\mathbf{H} = \mathbf{H}(z, t)$ only.

Further, to simplify the vectorial aspects of the general problem, we try to find solutions whose directions are unvarying: Only the magnitudes of the vectors, not their directions, are to be allowed to vary. Then $\mathbf{E} = \hat{\mathbf{e}}f(z, t)$ and $\mathbf{H} = \hat{\mathbf{h}}g(z, t)$, where the unit vectors $\hat{\mathbf{e}}$ and $\hat{\mathbf{h}}$ are constant, in both space and time, but not yet determined as to their directions.

It must be emphasized that the two constraints we have imposed—that the fields vary in only one direction and only in their magnitudes—are by no means required by Maxwell's equations. They merely simplify the task of solving the equations; they surely eliminate many other solutions.

To find the unknown magnitudes f and g of the electric and magnetic fields, the curls of their assumed forms must be equated to the appropriate time derivatives. Now the curl of a product of a scalar and a constant vector is known from a vector identity to equal the cross product of the gradient of the scalar with the vector; thus, for example, $\nabla \times (\hat{\mathbf{e}}f) = \nabla f \times \hat{\mathbf{e}}$. Also, the gradient of a function of only z has only a z-component: $\nabla f(z, t) = \hat{\mathbf{z}}(\partial f/\partial z)$. Since the unit vectors are constant in time as well as in space, Maxwell's equations reduce to

$$\frac{\partial f}{\partial z}\,\hat{\mathbf{z}} \times \hat{\mathbf{e}} = -\mu_0 \frac{\partial g}{\partial t}\,\hat{\mathbf{h}} \qquad \text{and} \qquad \frac{\partial g}{\partial z}\,\hat{\mathbf{z}} \times \hat{\mathbf{h}} = \varepsilon_0 \frac{\partial f}{\partial t}\,\hat{\mathbf{e}}. \tag{3.37}$$

Since the cross product of two vectors is perpendicular to both, it follows at once that $\hat{\mathbf{e}}$ and $\hat{\mathbf{h}}$ are both perpendicular to $\hat{\mathbf{z}}$ and to each other. Since the cross product of orthogonal unit vectors is also a unit vector, it also follows that $\hat{\mathbf{z}} \times \hat{\mathbf{e}} = \pm\hat{\mathbf{h}}$. For definiteness, we choose the upper sign; the choice is really immaterial, since the $g(z, t)$ function could absorb the sign. With this choice, however, there is no further leeway in selecting the direction of $\hat{\mathbf{z}} \times \hat{\mathbf{h}}$:

$$\hat{\mathbf{z}} \times \hat{\mathbf{e}} = \hat{\mathbf{h}} \qquad \text{and} \qquad \hat{\mathbf{z}} \times \hat{\mathbf{h}} = -\hat{\mathbf{e}}. \tag{3.38}$$

The three unit vectors $\hat{\mathbf{e}}$, $\hat{\mathbf{h}}$, and $\hat{\mathbf{z}}$ form a right-handed orthogonal triad. They are the directions, respectively, of the electric field, the magnetic field, and that

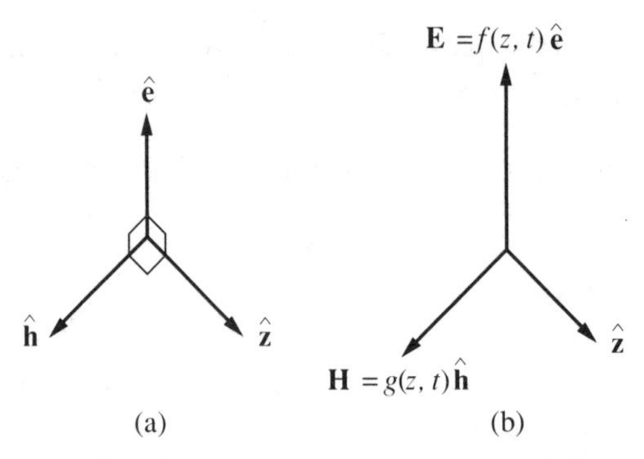

FIGURE 3-6 Right-handed orthogonal triad of vectors **E**, **H**, and ẑ.

single direction along which these fields have been permitted to vary. The field directions are illustrated in Figure 3–6.

Using Eq. (3.38) in Eq. (3.37) gives the following relations for the magnitudes of the vectors.

$$\frac{\partial f}{\partial z} = -\mu_0 \frac{\partial g}{\partial t}, \qquad \frac{\partial g}{\partial z} = -\varepsilon_0 \frac{\partial f}{\partial t}. \tag{3.39}$$

Thus the slope of each of the two unknown functions f and g is proportional to the rate of change in time of the other. These equations are still a pair of coupled partial differential equations, but now for scalar unknowns, f and g.

To uncouple the two equations, differentiate one of them and substitute the other: $\partial^2 f/\partial z^2 = -\mu_0\, \partial^2 g/\partial z \partial t = -\mu_0[-\varepsilon_0\, \partial^2 f/\partial t^2]$ eliminates g, while f can be similarly eliminated by starting with the second equation instead. The results are two separate partial differential equations for $f(z, t)$ and $g(z, t)$, but now of second order.

$$\frac{\partial^2 f}{\partial z^2} = \mu_0 \varepsilon_0 \frac{\partial^2 f}{\partial t^2}, \qquad \frac{\partial^2 g}{\partial z^2} = \mu_0 \varepsilon_0 \frac{\partial^2 g}{\partial t^2}. \tag{3.40}$$

These state that the curvature (in space) of each unknown function is proportional to the acceleration (in time) of that function.

But each of these equations has precisely the form of a scalar *wave equation* in one dimension. For each, the solution is already known to be a superposition of two arbitrary waves that travel at the same speed, in opposite directions. The wave speed is given by the square root of the coefficient in the wave equation, namely $1/\sqrt{\mu_0 \varepsilon_0} = c$, which is the speed of light in vacuum.

The general solutions to the two wave equations in Eq. (3.40) are

$$f(z, t) = f_1(z - ct) + f_2(z + ct), \tag{3.41}$$

$$g(z, t) = g_1(z - ct) + g_2(z + ct), \tag{3.42}$$

where f_1 and f_2 (or g_1 and g_2) are independent, arbitrary functions of one variable. However, g_1 and g_2 are *not* independent of f_1 and f_2, because of the relations in Eq. (3.39) that couple them to each other.

$$\frac{\partial f}{\partial z} = [f'_1 + f'_2] = -\mu_0 \frac{\partial g}{\partial t} = +\mu_0 c[g'_1 - g'_2], \qquad (3.43)$$

$$\frac{\partial g}{\partial z} = [g'_1 + g'_2] = -\varepsilon_0 \frac{\partial f}{\partial t} = +\varepsilon_0 c[f'_1 - f'_2]. \qquad (3.44)$$

But $\mu_0 c = 1/\varepsilon_0 c = \sqrt{\mu_0/\varepsilon_0} = \eta_0$, which is the impedance of free space, so that the last two equations combine into $f'_1 = \eta_0 g'_1$ and $f'_2 = -\eta_0 g'_2$. The derivatives of the f and g functions are proportional; since constants of integration can be incorporated into the arbitrary functions themselves, the f and g functions are themselves proportional in the same way. Hence the general solutions for the magnitudes of the electric and magnetic fields are

$$f(z, t) = f_1(z - ct) + f_2(z + ct), \qquad (3.45)$$

$$\eta_0 g(z, t) = f_1(z - ct) - f_2(z + ct). \qquad (3.46)$$

Each of the two independent solutions, f_1 and f_2, is a wave. The first propagates along $+z$, the second along $-z$; both travel at the same speed, c. Maxwell's equations allow these waveshapes to be any functions at all, of a single variable. The electric field magnitude is thus the sum of any two oppositely traveling waves; the magnetic field magnitude (scaled by the impedance η_0) is the difference of the same two waves. In Figure 3–7 the super-

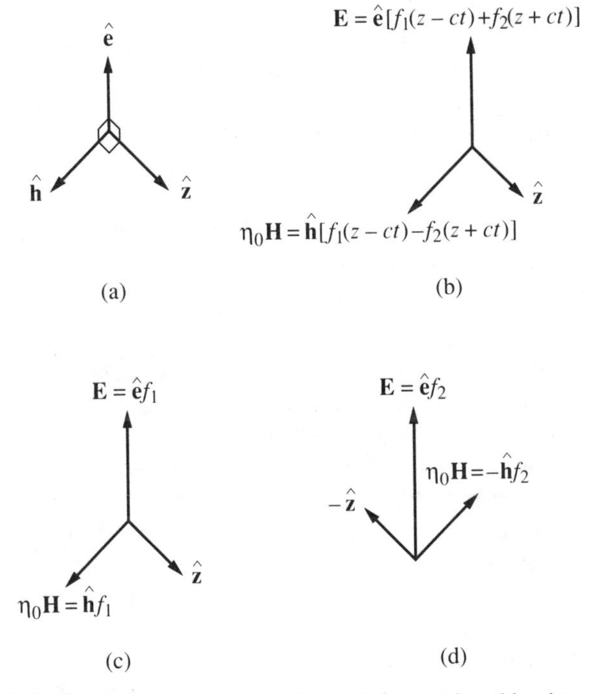

FIGURE 3–7 Superimposed, and individual, forward and backward waves.

position of forward- and backward-traveling waves is shown for the orthogonal triad of field and propagation directions; the two individual configurations when there is only one or the other of the two waves are also illustrated.

Wave Designators

The electromagnetic field configuration comprising one wave that propagates in a fixed direction (the $+z$ direction), that does not vary at all in the plane perpendicular to that direction, and whose field vectors have fixed directions in space can now be described in full detail. For any waveform $F(t)$, such fields are given by

$$\mathbf{E}(z, t) = \hat{\mathbf{e}}F\left(t - \frac{z}{c}\right) \qquad \mathbf{H}(z, t) = \hat{\mathbf{h}}\left(\frac{1}{\eta_0}\right)F\left(t - \frac{z}{c}\right) \qquad \hat{\mathbf{e}} \times \hat{\mathbf{h}} = \hat{\mathbf{z}}. \quad (3.47)$$

The electric and magnetic fields vary in space (along z) and in time as a wave motion. In time, the wave progresses along z, at the speed of light, c (light is itself an electromagnetic wave, but of more complex type, with certain coherence properties). The electric and magnetic field vectors are perpendicular to each other at each point in space. Both are also perpendicular to the direction of propagation. $\mathbf{E}$, $\mathbf{H}$, and $\hat{\mathbf{z}}$ form a right-handed orthogonal triad of vectors, at every point and instant.

At any point in space, the electric and magnetic fields vary in time in unison, or "in phase." At any instant, the waveshapes of the two fields correspond exactly. The waveshape (versus z) is in fact the same as the waveform (versus t), but displayed backward and rescaled by the factor c. At any point and instant, the magnitudes of the electric and magnetic field strengths are related by a constant factor, $\eta_0 = 376.7\ \Omega$, the "impedance of free space."

Because the simple wave we have described differs from a host of waves of other, more complicated types, a number of specific terms are in use to designate various features that may not be shared by more general forms.

- At any instant, the points in space at which the electric and the magnetic fields each have some fixed value are those locations where the quantity $(t - z/c)$ is some fixed constant. This collection of points forms a plane and this plane is perpendicular to the z-axis. As time elapses, any such plane of fixed field values moves along z, perpendicular to itself, at the speed of light. This type of wave is referred to as a *plane wave*.
- The field vectors $\mathbf{E}$ and $\mathbf{H}$ of this wave are everywhere and always perpendicular to the direction of propagation. Accordingly, this is called a *transverse electromagnetic wave*, or a TEM wave.
- The field vectors have here not been permitted to tilt; their directions have been required to remain constant, each along an unchanging line

directed along $\hat{\mathbf{e}}$ or $\hat{\mathbf{h}}$, at every point and for all time. The behavior of the field vectors is referred to as the wave's "polarization" and this wave is said to be *linearly polarized.*

- There has here also been imposed the constraint that no spatial variation of the fields, other than its propagation along z, be allowed. That is, the only variation in space has been along z, as a wave motion. The wave has the same appearance for all values of x and y. It is called a *uniform* wave. In particular, it is not a beam; a beam has only a finite transverse extent and hence is not independent of the transverse coordinates x and y.

The wave is a "uniform, linearly polarized, transverse electromagnetic plane wave," of arbitrary waveform, in a vacuum.

Although Maxwell's equations are satisfied by this TEM plane wave for *any* waveform whatsoever, the wave equation does prescribe an important relationship between the time scale T of the waveform that evolves at any one point and the distance scale L of the waveshape along the direction of propagation, as seen at any one instant: the scales are related by $L = cT$, where c is the vacuum speed of light.

Caution: The uniform plane wave is a permissible solution to the Maxwell equations alone, without any boundary conditions. It is physically quite unrealistic, in that the fields extend undiminished all the way out to infinity in any transverse plane. It is, however, feasible to set up a wave that is a close facsimile of this uniform one, varying along the z-direction and almost undiminished over vast distances perpendicular to z, vast on the scale L of variation along z. For example, radiation from the sun reaches the earth essentially as a plane wave and substantially uniform, by virtue of the immense distances involved.

Summary

We have verified both qualitatively and quantitatively that Maxwell's equations governing the behavior of electromagnetic fields can command them to propagate as a wave motion. The equations imply such motion of themselves, without extraneous influences such as a material medium or boundaries. An example we worked out showed that a waveshape in the form of a step function, from a constant to zero, could satisfy Maxwell's equations if it propagates at the speed of light. This example also illustrated the applicability of Maxwell's equations in integral form to a field with discontinuities, for which the differential form fails, or is at least awkward. It was also shown that a simple version of a wave, the uniform, linearly polarized, transverse electromagnetic plane wave, can exist and sustain itself in a vacuum, away from its original source, with any arbitrary waveform. There remains to verify that such waves can carry information and energy.

PROBLEMS

General Solution

3.1 Is $f(z, t) = f_1(z - ct) + f_2(z + ct) + C_1$, $\eta_0 g(z, t) = f_1(z - ct) - f_2(z + ct) + C_2$ a more general solution to the equations $\partial f/\partial z = -\mu_0\, \partial g/\partial t$, $\partial g/\partial z = -\varepsilon_0\, \partial f/\partial t$ than is $f_1(z - ct) \pm f_2(z + ct)$ alone? If not, what functions $f_{01}(u)$ and $f_{02}(u)$ could replace $f_1(u)$ and $f_2(u)$ to eliminate the constants C_1 and C_2?

Field Descriptions

3.2 Where in space is the field $f(\mathbf{r}) = (\mathbf{r} \cdot \mathbf{r})^3 \exp\,[-(\mathbf{r} \cdot \mathbf{r})/a^2]$ the strongest?

3.3 Where in space and time is the field $f(\mathbf{r}, t) = \operatorname{sech}^2\,[\gamma t - (\mathbf{r} \cdot \mathbf{r})/a^2]$ the strongest?

Discontinuous Fields

3.4 Constant, perpendicular electric and magnetic fields $\mathbf{E} = E\hat{\mathbf{x}}$ and $\mathbf{H} = H\hat{\mathbf{y}}$ in the half-space $z < s$ were found in Example 3.1 to satisfy Maxwell's equations if the edge of the half-space moves along $+z$ at the speed of light. Repeat the calculation for the case that these same fields are in the half-space $z > s$ and establish whether the edge of that space must move forward or backward along the z-axis.

Wave in Arbitrary Direction

3.5 **(a)** Write a TEM plane wave, $\mathbf{E}(x, y, z, t)$, $\mathbf{H}(x, y, z, t)$ with polarizations along $\hat{\mathbf{e}}$ and $\hat{\mathbf{h}}$, of waveform $F(t)$, but traveling along the direction of the vector $\mathbf{b} = 4\hat{\mathbf{x}} - 3\hat{\mathbf{y}} + 12\hat{\mathbf{z}}$ instead of along $\hat{\mathbf{z}}$.

(b) If the polarization $\hat{\mathbf{e}}$ is in the xy-plane (with positive x- and y-components), find $\hat{\mathbf{e}}$ and $\hat{\mathbf{h}}$.

Field of Moving Charge

3.6 Point charge Q moves along the z-axis, in air ($\mu = \mu_0$, $\varepsilon = \varepsilon_0$, $\sigma = 0$), at a steady speed v, passing through the origin at time $t = 0$.

(a) Assuming that its Coulomb field moves with it, obtain the mmf $U(t)$ along the circumference of a circle of radius ρ_0 in the plane $z = z_0$, centered on the z-axis and oriented azimuthally.

(b) What magnetic field $H(\rho, z, t)$ is generated by the moving charge?

3.7 A perfectly conducting ball (mass M, radius a) carries charge Q. Starting from rest at time $t = 0$ at the origin, the ball falls (acceleration of gravity $= g$) along the negative z-axis, in air ($\mu = \mu_0$, $\varepsilon = \varepsilon_0$, $\sigma = 0$).

(a) Obtain the mmf $U(t)$ along the circumference of a circle of radius ρ_0 in the plane $z = z_0$, centered on the z-axis and oriented azimuthally, where $\rho_0 > a$.

(b) What magnetic field $H(\rho, z, t)$ is generated by the falling ball?

CHAPTER 4

Field Energetics

We wish to confirm that electromagnetic waves can not only convey a waveform from one point to a distant one, but can carry energy in the process, and can hence do work as well as convey information. This confers upon fields the full status of a physically significant entity, not merely that of a mathematically convenient intermediary between cause and effect in electrical interactions.

Electric Power Density

As a preliminary to showing that energy resides in fields, we must show that the fundamental concepts of mechanical energy and power carry over to electrical phenomena.

We immerse ourselves in a region of space in which electric charges are streaming, in the presence of electric and magnetic fields. Consider an elementary area $d\mathbf{S}$ across which charges are flowing, forming an electric current, and follow the charges for an infinitesimal time dt.

The current crossing the area dS is $\mathbf{J} \cdot d\mathbf{S}$, by the definition of the current density $\mathbf{J}$. In time dt, an amount of charge $dq = \mathbf{J} \cdot d\mathbf{S}\, dt$ crosses the area dS and is conveyed along a displacement $d\mathbf{l}$, which is parallel to the vector $\mathbf{J}$.

The motion of this charge across dS and along dl defines a volume element dV that is swept out in the time dt. As shown in Figure 4–1, this volume is generally an oblique cylinder, since there is no need for the direction in which the base area faces (that of $d\mathbf{S}$) to be the same as the one along which the cylinder's height stretches (that of $d\mathbf{l}$); it is only necessary that $\mathbf{J}$ and $d\mathbf{l}$ be parallel, since both are along the direction of flow in this river of moving charge. The volume element swept out in time dt is given by $dV = d\mathbf{S} \cdot d\mathbf{l}$, since the dot product accounts for the obliqueness of the cylinder.

The charge that crosses dS in time dt is subjected to a force during its displacement; this is given by the Lorentz force as

$$d\mathbf{F} = dq\mathbf{E} + dq\mathbf{v} \times \mathbf{B} = dq\mathbf{E} + dq\left(\frac{d\mathbf{l}}{dt}\right) \times \mathbf{B}, \tag{4.1}$$

where $\mathbf{v} = d\mathbf{l}/dt$ is the velocity of streaming of the charge.

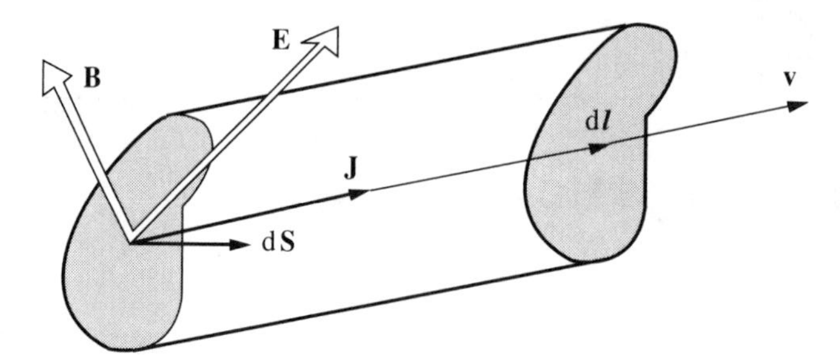

FIGURE 4–1 Volume element swept out along **J** or **v** or *dl* in time *dt*.

The work done on the charge by the fields during the time dt that the charge undergoes displacement $d\mathbf{l}$ is $dW = d\mathbf{F} \cdot d\mathbf{l}$ or

$$dW = d\mathbf{F} \cdot d\mathbf{l} = dq\mathbf{E} \cdot d\mathbf{l} + dq\left(\frac{d\mathbf{l}}{dt}\right) \times \mathbf{B} \cdot d\mathbf{l}$$

$$= \mathbf{J} \cdot d\mathbf{S}\ dt\mathbf{E} \cdot d\mathbf{l} + \mathbf{J} \cdot d\mathbf{S}\ d\mathbf{l} \times \mathbf{B} \cdot d\mathbf{l}$$

$$= \mathbf{J} \cdot d\mathbf{S}\ \mathbf{E} \cdot d\mathbf{l}\ dt + 0, \tag{4.2}$$

since $dq = \mathbf{J} \cdot d\mathbf{S}\ dt$ and the triple product $d\mathbf{l} \times \mathbf{B} \cdot d\mathbf{l}$ is identically zero. The magnetic field does not contribute to the work done, because the force it exerts is at right angles to the motion of the charge.

In the last expression, **J** and $d\mathbf{l}$ can be interchanged without changing the overall product, because **J** and $d\mathbf{l}$ are parallel to each other, so that

$$\mathbf{J} \cdot d\mathbf{S}\ \mathbf{E} \cdot d\mathbf{l} = d\mathbf{l} \cdot d\mathbf{S}\ \mathbf{E} \cdot \mathbf{J}, \tag{4.3}$$

by virtue of the fact that both expressions involve the same four vector magnitudes and the same cosines of the two angles between the pairs of vectors. Consequently, the work done in the process is

$$dW = \mathbf{E} \cdot \mathbf{J}\ d\mathbf{l} \cdot d\mathbf{S}\ dt = \mathbf{E} \cdot \mathbf{J}\ dV\ dt, \tag{4.4}$$

since the element of volume is $dV = d\mathbf{l} \cdot d\mathbf{S}$. The power, or rate of expenditure of energy, is dW/dt, so that the coefficient of the infinitesimals,

$$p = \mathbf{E} \cdot \mathbf{J}, \tag{4.5}$$

has the interpretation of power density: the power expended per unit volume, in W/m^3, at the point where **E** and **J** both exist.

At any point where **E** and **J** coexist (and are not perpendicular to each other), energy is being expended (by whatever agency is responsible for the presence of both **E** and **J**) at the rate of $p = \mathbf{E} \cdot \mathbf{J}$ joules per second per cubic meter. This power density is a (scalar) field, being a function of position.

Poynting's Theorem

The simultaneous presence of an electric field and a current density entails an expenditure of power. We wish to show now that the energy that is being expended is carried by the electromagnetic fields themselves. To this end, we use Maxwell's equations to re-express the power density entirely in terms of the electric and magnetic fields, instead of through the current density.

One of Maxwell's equations allows $\mathbf{J}$ to be expressed in terms of the fields, as $\mathbf{J} = \nabla \times \mathbf{H} - \partial\mathbf{D}/\partial t$, so that the power density can be rewritten as

$$p = \mathbf{E} \cdot \mathbf{J} = \mathbf{E} \cdot \nabla \times \mathbf{H} - \mathbf{E} \cdot \frac{\partial \mathbf{D}}{\partial t}. \tag{4.6}$$

This shows the power density as a mixture of fields and their derivatives, both spatial and temporal. We prefer to rewrite this in the form of derivatives of expressions involving the fields themselves. This can be achieved by invoking a vector identity for the divergence of a cross product:

$$\nabla \cdot (\mathbf{E} \times \mathbf{H}) \equiv \mathbf{H} \cdot \nabla \times \mathbf{E} - \mathbf{E} \cdot \nabla \times \mathbf{H}. \tag{4.7}$$

The last term is the one that appears in Eq. (4.6) and the middle one can be rewritten by using the other Maxwell equation, $\nabla \times \mathbf{E} = -\partial\mathbf{B}/\partial t$:

$$\begin{aligned} p = \mathbf{E} \cdot \mathbf{J} &= -\nabla \cdot (\mathbf{E} \times \mathbf{H}) + \mathbf{H} \cdot \nabla \times \mathbf{E} - \mathbf{E} \cdot \frac{\partial \mathbf{D}}{\partial t} \\ &= -\nabla \cdot (\mathbf{E} \times \mathbf{H}) - \mathbf{H} \cdot \frac{\partial \mathbf{B}}{\partial t} - \mathbf{E} \cdot \frac{\partial \mathbf{D}}{\partial t}. \end{aligned} \tag{4.8}$$

This expression still has a mixture of fields and their time derivatives, but that is easily remedied by recognizing that $\mathbf{H}$ and $\mathbf{B}$ are related, and $\mathbf{E}$ and $\mathbf{D}$ are related, by the properties of the medium. Thus

$$\frac{\partial(\mathbf{E} \cdot \mathbf{D})}{\partial t} = \frac{\partial \mathbf{E}}{\partial t} \cdot \mathbf{D} + \mathbf{E} \cdot \frac{\partial \mathbf{D}}{\partial t} \tag{4.9}$$

and if the medium is "linear," so that $\mathbf{E}$ and $\mathbf{D}$ are proportional to each other (e.g., in a vacuum, $\mathbf{D} = \varepsilon_0 \mathbf{E}$), then the last two terms are identical, as in

$$\mathbf{E} \cdot \frac{\partial \mathbf{D}}{\partial t} = \mathbf{E} \cdot \frac{\partial[\varepsilon_0 \mathbf{E}]}{\partial t} = \varepsilon_0 \mathbf{E} \cdot \frac{\partial \mathbf{E}}{\partial t} = \mathbf{D} \cdot \frac{\partial \mathbf{E}}{\partial t} \tag{4.10}$$

for a vacuum. Hence, for a linear medium,

$$\frac{\partial(\mathbf{E} \cdot \mathbf{D})}{\partial t} = 2\mathbf{E} \cdot \frac{\partial \mathbf{D}}{\partial t} \tag{4.11}$$

and similarly, if $\mathbf{H}$ and $\mathbf{B}$ are proportional (e.g., $\mathbf{B} = \mu_0 \mathbf{H}$), then

$$\frac{\partial(\mathbf{H} \cdot \mathbf{B})}{\partial t} = 2\mathbf{H} \cdot \frac{\partial \mathbf{B}}{\partial t}. \tag{4.12}$$

Finally, then, for a linear medium, the power density can be written as

$$-\mathbf{E} \cdot \mathbf{J} = \nabla \cdot (\mathbf{E} \times \mathbf{H}) + \frac{\partial}{\partial t}\left[\frac{1}{2}\mathbf{E} \cdot \mathbf{D} + \frac{1}{2}\mathbf{H} \cdot \mathbf{B}\right], \tag{4.13}$$

a sum of spatial and time derivatives of field quantities. This is the differential form of Poynting's theorem. To understand this theorem, the equation should be integrated over any fixed volume V:

$$-\int \mathbf{E} \cdot \mathbf{J} \, dV = \int \nabla \cdot (\mathbf{E} \times \mathbf{H}) \, dV + \frac{d}{dt} \int \left[\frac{1}{2} \mathbf{E} \cdot \mathbf{D} + \frac{1}{2} \mathbf{H} \cdot \mathbf{B} \right] dV. \tag{4.14}$$

By the divergence theorem, if S bounds the volume V and with $d\mathbf{S}$ outward, then upon rearranging the terms of the equation, we get finally

$$-\oint_S (\mathbf{E} \times \mathbf{H}) \cdot d\mathbf{S} = \int_V \mathbf{E} \cdot \mathbf{J} \, dV + \frac{d}{dt} \int_V \left[\frac{1}{2} \mathbf{E} \cdot \mathbf{D} + \frac{1}{2} \mathbf{H} \cdot \mathbf{B} \right] dV. \tag{4.15}$$

This is Poynting's theorem, valid for a linear medium; it is a direct consequence of Maxwell's equations. It requires interpretation.

Interpretation

On the right side of the equation, the meaning of the first term is already known: since $\mathbf{E} \cdot \mathbf{J}$ is power density, its integral must be the total power expended within the volume V; this term, in fact all the terms, are measured in watts.

Now power is defined as the *rate* at which energy is expended, or delivered, or transferred, or otherwise caused to change in time. In the equation, the last term is also a rate, the rate of increase in time of the integral of $[\frac{1}{2}\mathbf{E} \cdot \mathbf{D} + \frac{1}{2}\mathbf{H} \cdot \mathbf{B}]$ over the volume V. This power term must therefore represent the rate of increase of an amount of energy within the volume V. We are thus led to interpret the quantity $W = \int_V [\frac{1}{2}\mathbf{E} \cdot \mathbf{D} + \frac{1}{2}\mathbf{H} \cdot \mathbf{B}] \, dV$ as the energy that has been accumulated within the volume V.

The sum of the two terms on the right side of the equation describes two processes that can happen to the energy in the volume V: It can be *expended* within V, at the rate $P = \int_V \mathbf{E} \cdot \mathbf{J} \, dV$ (watts), or else it can be *stored*, or *accumulated*, at the rate dW/dt (J/s), so that W must be the energy *stored* within volume V, in joules.

We note that $W = \int_V [\frac{1}{2}\mathbf{E} \cdot \mathbf{D} + \frac{1}{2}\mathbf{H} \cdot \mathbf{B}] \, dV$ includes two contributions, one purely electric, the other purely magnetic. Since the expression is valid for any volume V, the integrand $\frac{1}{2}\mathbf{E} \cdot \mathbf{D}$ must represent the *density* of electric energy stored at a point, while the quantity $\frac{1}{2}\mathbf{H} \cdot \mathbf{B}$ must be the density of magnetic energy stored at a point, both measured in J/m^3.

We infer that the existence of a field $\mathbf{E}$ (proportional to $\mathbf{D}$) at a point entails the presence of $\frac{1}{2}\mathbf{E} \cdot \mathbf{D}$ joules of energy per unit volume at the point. The presence of $\mathbf{H}$ (proportional to $\mathbf{B}$) at a point similarly entails that of $\frac{1}{2}\mathbf{H} \cdot \mathbf{B}$ joules per cubic meter of energy there.

What the Poynting theorem requires is that the total of the rates at which energy is both *expended* and *stored* within a volume V (i.e., $P + dW/dt$) must be balanced by a certain surface integral, $-\oint_S (\mathbf{E} \times \mathbf{H}) \cdot d\mathbf{S}$, over the bounding surface S.

Conservation of energy requires that the energy expended or stored within a volume V must be supplied, instant by instant, from the exterior to the interior of the volume; that is, across the bounding surface.

Comparing these two requirements, of Poynting's theorem and of conservation of energy, we conclude that the surface integral $-\oint_S (\mathbf{E} \times \mathbf{H}) \cdot d\mathbf{S}$ must exactly equal the rate at which energy crosses the bounding surface S, from the exterior to the interior. It is therefore the rate at which energy is supplied to the volume, ultimately from some unspecified external sources.

Since the surface integral is a summation over all the infinitesimal elements of area of the closed surface, we can interpret the integrand as the power per unit area at a point on the bounding surface, to be summed over all such points to obtain the total power crossing the surface. The integrand is actually a vector, dotted with the surface element $d\mathbf{S}$; the magnitude of this vector is the power density (W/m^2) and its direction can indicate the orientation of the flow of this power. Since $-d\mathbf{S}$ points inward at every point of the closed surface and the power supplied to the interior must also be flowing inward from the outside, we can consider $\mathbf{E} \times \mathbf{H}$ to represent the power *flow* at a point, in the direction given by this vector, in the amount of $|\mathbf{E} \times \mathbf{H}|$ watts per square meter.

The vector $\mathbf{E} \times \mathbf{H}$ is the Poynting vector. It gives the power per unit area that flows at a point; it is a (vector) field, being a function of position.

Strictly speaking, only the closed surface integral of the Poynting vector can be unambiguously interpreted as total power crossing the surface. The point-by-point interpretation of $\mathbf{E} \times \mathbf{H}$ as power flow density is merely the simplest way of ascribing meaning to the integrand.

The relationship among electromagnetic power flow, energy storage, and power dissipation is illustrated schematically in Figure 4–2; the Poynting theorem expresses this power balance. For any volume, this theorem allows us to explore no deeper than the enclosing surface, by integrating the Poynting

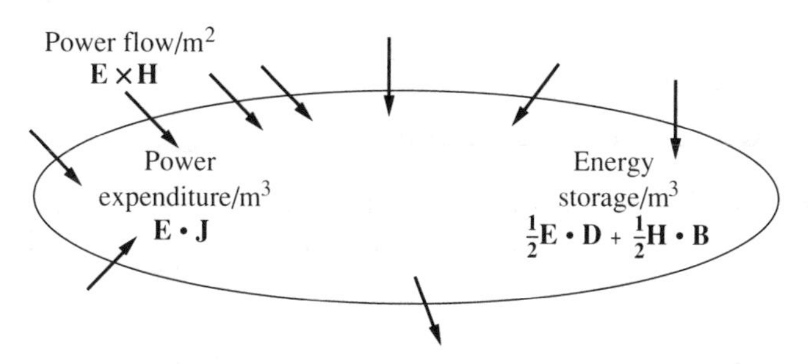

FIGURE 4–2 Net influx of power goes into dissipation and storage.

vector, in order to discover what is happening, energetically, inside the volume.

Synopsis of Field Energetics

At a point (and instant) where the electromagnetic fields are **E** and **H**, electromagnetic *power is flowing*, along the direction of $\mathbf{E} \times \mathbf{H}$, at the power density of $|\mathbf{E} \times \mathbf{H}|$ watts per square meter.

At a point (and instant) where the electric field is **E**, *electric energy is stored* in the vicinity of the point, with density $\frac{1}{2}\mathbf{E} \cdot \mathbf{D}$ joules per cubic meter (for a linear medium). In a vacuum, this is $\frac{1}{2}\varepsilon_0 E^2$; since there is no matter at all in a vacuum, the energy evidently resides in the electric field itself.

At a point (and instant) where the magnetic field is **H**, *magnetic energy is stored* in the vicinity of the point, with density $\frac{1}{2}\mathbf{H} \cdot \mathbf{B}$ joules per cubic meter (for a linear medium). In a vacuum, this is $\frac{1}{2}\mu_0 H^2$; since there is nothing else in a vacuum, the energy evidently resides in the magnetic field.

At a point (and instant) where an electric field **E** and a current density **J** coexist, *electric power is being expended* (converted from electric to some other form) in the vicinity of the point, at the rate $\mathbf{E} \cdot \mathbf{J}$ watts per cubic meter.

This last quantity is a signed scalar. If **E** causes the current density **J**, as it does in a conducting medium, then electric energy is *depleted* in the process. For a conductor of conductivity σ, so that $\mathbf{J} = \sigma\mathbf{E}$, the rate of energy expenditure per unit volume is σE^2 and the energy is converted to heat at exactly this rate; this process is Joule heating.

If **E** causes the motion of charged particles, thereby forming a current of density $\mathbf{J} = \rho\mathbf{v}$ (where ρ is charge density and $\mathbf{v}$ is charge velocity), then electric energy is being converted into mechanical energy of motion of the particles, at the rate $\mathbf{E} \cdot \mathbf{J} = \mathbf{E} \cdot \rho\mathbf{v} = \rho\mathbf{E} \cdot \mathbf{v} = \mathbf{f} \cdot \mathbf{v}$, which is the usual expression for mechanical power density, in watts per cubic meter.

If **E** and **J** are in opposite directions, the $\mathbf{E} \cdot \mathbf{J}$ rate of power "expenditure" is actually negative and power is being *supplied* to the vicinity of the point (by whatever agency is responsible for the current) for conversion *into* electric energy, at the rate $|\mathbf{E} \cdot \mathbf{J}|$. This happens, for example, within a chemical battery.

Energetics of a Plane Wave

We can now add to our description of the unidirectional, uniform, linearly polarized, transverse electromagnetic plane wave of arbitrary waveform $f(t)$, in a vacuum, by calculating its energetic properties. The fields are

$$\mathbf{E} = \hat{\mathbf{e}} f\left(t - \frac{z}{c}\right), \qquad \mathbf{H} = \hat{\mathbf{h}} \frac{1}{\eta_0} f\left(t - \frac{z}{c}\right), \qquad \text{with} \quad \hat{\mathbf{e}} \times \hat{\mathbf{h}} = \hat{\mathbf{z}}, \tag{4.16}$$

so that the Poynting vector is

$$\mathbf{E} \times \mathbf{H} = \hat{\mathbf{z}} \frac{1}{\eta_0} f^2\left(t - \frac{z}{c}\right), \tag{4.17}$$

the electric energy density is

$$W_e = \frac{1}{2} \varepsilon_0 E^2 = \frac{1}{2} \varepsilon_0 f^2\left(t - \frac{z}{c}\right), \tag{4.18}$$

the magnetic energy density is

$$\begin{aligned} W_m &= \frac{1}{2} \mu_0 H^2 = \frac{1}{2} \mu_0 \frac{1}{\eta_0^2} f^2\left(t - \frac{z}{c}\right) \\ &= \frac{1}{2} \mu_0 \frac{\varepsilon_0}{\mu_0} f^2\left(t - \frac{z}{c}\right) = \frac{1}{2} \varepsilon_0 f^2\left(t - \frac{z}{c}\right), \end{aligned} \tag{4.19}$$

and the total energy density is

$$W = W_e + W_m = \varepsilon_0 f^2\left(t - \frac{z}{c}\right). \tag{4.20}$$

We should note that the power flow and the energy densities are all proportional to the square of the waveform and that they all propagate as waves, at the speed of light. The total energy is here equally shared between electric and magnetic form. The power flow is along $\hat{\mathbf{z}}$, the direction of propagation of this unidirectional wave. Furthermore, since $c\varepsilon_0 = 1/\eta_0$, the following significant relation holds for this simple wave:

$$\mathbf{E} \times \mathbf{H} = \hat{\mathbf{z}} cW. \tag{4.21}$$

This indicates that the flow of power, per unit area, equals the total energy density W multiplied by the speed of wave propagation c, in the direction of propagation, as if an energy-carrying "fluid" were streaming at the speed c, conveying energy of density W at the speed of light.

As a hypothetical example of plane wave transmission from an emitter to a receiver, suppose that some "plane wave generator" produces a plane wave at the xy-plane ($z = 0$), with some specified waveform in time, such that the power emitted by an area A of the source plane at time t is $AS(t)$. Then the power per unit area $S(t)$ must be the magnitude of the Poynting vector of the emitted plane wave. In Figure 4–3, this power/area (P/A) is shown in part (a) as a strong pulse followed by a weaker one, of total duration T. The total energy emitted by a unit area of the infinitely extended source plane is the time integral of the pulses, which is just the area under the $S(t)$ curve.

Now the magnitude of the Poynting vector is related to the electric field generated by the source plane by $S(t) = E^2(t)/\eta_0$. Both the electric field and the Poynting vector propagate as plane waves, at the speed of light, so that anywhere in front of the source plane, the electric field magnitude is $E(t - z/c)$ and the magnitude of the Poynting vector is $S(t - z/c)$. In particular, at the absorbing plane at $z = l$, the power received (and absorbed) per unit area is the

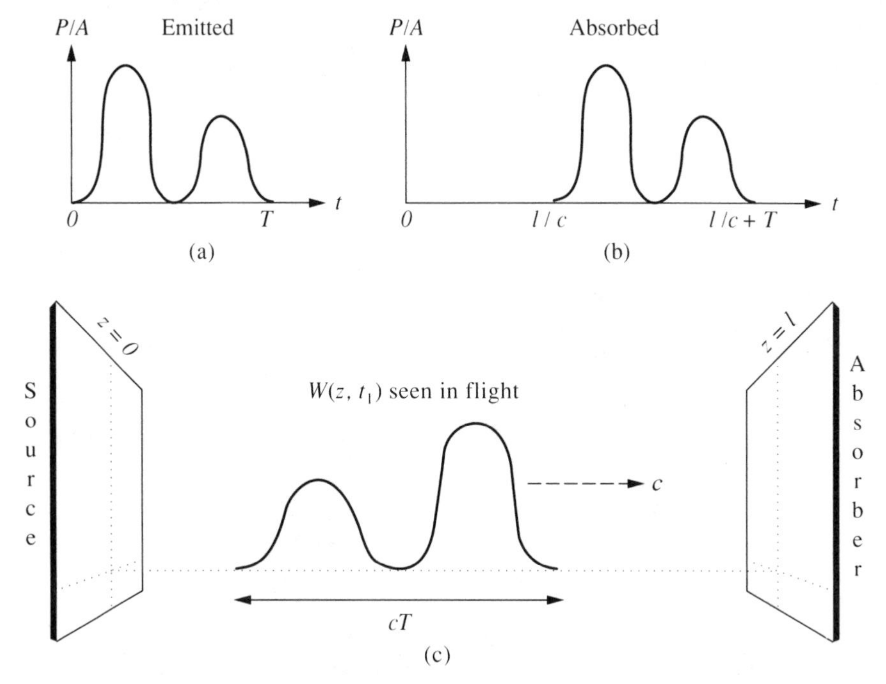

FIGURE 4–3 Power per unit area emitted, absorbed, and in flight.

magnitude of the Poynting vector at that location, $S(t - l/c)$, which is an exact replica of the same pair of pulses, but delayed by l/c seconds. The total energy absorbed by a unit area of the infinitely extended absorbing plane is the time integral of the pulses, which is just the area under the $S(t - l/c)$ curve shown as part (b) in the figure. Comparing the pulses emitted and those absorbed, it is evident that the areas under the two curves are identical; all of the energy transmitted by the source antenna is received intact by the absorber, after l/c seconds have elapsed.

Assuming that the source and receiving planes are sufficiently far apart for emission to be complete before absorption begins, the question to be addressed is: Where is the energy during the intervening time, after $t = T$ and before $t = l/c$? It is no longer in the generator, which has shut down after T seconds; it is not yet at the absorber, which is receiving nothing and is unaware of any activity until after time l/c.

The answer is that after emission but before absorption, the energy is distributed in the intervening space between the source plane and the absorbing one. We know that the sum of the electric and magnetic energy densities present between the planes is $W(z, t) = \varepsilon_0 E^2(t - z/c) = \varepsilon_0 \eta_0 S(t - z/c)$. We wish to verify that this energy in flight from source to receiver accounts for all the energy that was emitted and all that will be absorbed. At any intermediate instant $t = t_1$, where $T < t_1 < l/c$, the total energy in transit between the planes is the volume integral of the energy density; for a unit cross-sectional area, this total energy is

$$\int_0^l W\,dz = \int_0^l \varepsilon_0 \eta_0 S\left(t_1 - \frac{z}{c}\right) dz = \int_{t_1}^{t_1 - l/c} \varepsilon_0 \eta_0 S(\tau)(-c)\,d\tau$$

$$= \varepsilon_0 \eta_0 c \int_{t_1 - l/c}^{t_1} S(\tau)\,d\tau, \tag{4.22}$$

where we have made the change of integration variable $\tau = t_1 - z/c$, so that $dz = -c\,d\tau$, together with the corresponding change of limits. In the last expression, the coefficient is $\varepsilon_0 \eta_0 c = \varepsilon_0 \sqrt{\mu_0/\varepsilon_0}/\sqrt{\mu_0 \varepsilon_0} = 1$ and the lower limit of integration is less than zero while the upper one is greater than T. Consequently, this last form is the complete area under the pair of pulses that comprises the $S(\tau)$ curve, lasting only from $\tau = 0$ to $\tau = T$. Thus the total energy in flight, obtained as the volume integral (per unit area) of the energy density, exactly equals the total energy that was emitted earlier, and also the total energy to be absorbed later (per unit area), as obtained from the time integral of the Poynting vector magnitude at the two planes.

The energy is drained from the source during emission, disappearing from it thereafter. It subsists in transit, in the intervening space, undiminished and undistorted, as it progresses toward the absorber. Upon impinging onto the absorbing screen, it gets dissipated, into heat. The energy is conserved throughout the process, in its totality and instant by instant. Between emission and absorption, it resides only in the electromagnetic field distribution, equally divided between the electric and magnetic forms, and is localized, according to a waveshape that corresponds to the generated waveform, in a region that moves at the speed of light, perpendicular to the wavefront surface.

The process just analyzed is similar in most respects to what happens when a transmitting antenna emits a radio signal and a receiver picks it up, but it remains unrealistic in detail, especially in that infinitely extended source and receiver sheets are called for to maintain a uniform wave, independent of the transverse coordinates. We were forced to examine a unit area, since the total area, and also the total energy, was infinite. We have also left the constitution of both the emitter and the absorber vague; for the time being, let it suffice to point out that a suitable current distribution in the source plane could generate the desired plane wave, in accordance with the Ampère–Maxwell law. The details of this involve discontinuities in the field patterns; we will defer their study, to examine the engineering problems attendant to using electromagnetic waves to transmit signals—information—not merely energy.

Summary

From the fact that electromagnetic fields exert forces on charges in motion, we have deduced that power must be expended, generally, when they coexist. Combining Maxwell's equations led to Poynting's theorem, which was interpreted as a statement of conservation of energy and provided an expression for the flow of power, as $\mathbf{E} \times \mathbf{H}$, wherever the fields exist. A hypothetical application to an infinitely extended plane wave generator confirmed that the fields must carry and convey energy as they propagate. An arbitrary waveform was faithfully transmitted from a source plane to an absorbing screen; that fidelity is lost, however, when the medium is not a vacuum, as will be seen.

PROBLEMS

Strengths of Natural Fields

4.1 The sun irradiates the earth at the rate of 2.00 cal/cm^2 per minute (this rate is known as the solar constant).

(a) What is the magnitude of the Poynting vector (in W/m^2) in sunlight?

(b) What is the magnitude of the rms electric field (in V/m) in sunlight?

(c) What is the magnitude of the rms magnetic field (in A/m) in sunlight?

(d) What is the power output of the sun, in the form of sunlight alone, in watts? [*Note:* 1 cal = 4.186 J; distance to sun = $(1.50)10^{11}$ m.]

Energy of Decaying Fields

4.2 A point charge Q_0 finds itself in a conducting medium (parameters μ, ε, σ) at time $t = 0$.

(a) Combine Gauss's law and conservation of charge to show that $Q(t) = Q_0 e^{-t/T}$ afterward; what is T?

(b) Find the total energy expended (converted to heat) in the spherical shell $a < r < b$ around the point charge at the origin as the point charge decays away.

4.3 A conducting cylindrical shell (occupying the region $a < \rho < b$, $0 < z < h$ and with parameters μ, ε, σ) is in the presence of an externally imposed, uniform but time-varying magnetic field $B(t)\hat{\mathbf{z}}$ that occupies the cylindrical space $0 \leq \rho < R$ with $R < a$. The magnetic field was $B = B_0$ for $t < 0$ but then is caused to decay with time constant T as $B(t) = B_0 e^{-t/T}$ for $t > 0$.

(a) Obtain the emf $V(t)$ along the circumference of a circle centered on the z-axis, of radius ρ_0 at height z_0, within the shell, oriented azimuthally.

(b) Obtain the azimuthal electric field $E_\varphi(\rho, \varphi, z, t)$ and the current density $J_\varphi(\rho, \varphi, z, t)$ within the shell.

(c) Find the total current $I_0(t)$ that circulates around and within the shell [across the area $(b - a)h$ of a vertical cross section of the shell].

(d) Find the power density $p(\rho, \varphi, z, t)$ that heats the shell.

(e) Obtain the total energy expended within the shell as the magnetic field decays to zero.

Neglect fringing of the magnetic field and any corrections to that field that may arise from the circulating current $I_0(t)$.

4.4 Same as Problem 4.3, but with $R > b$.

4.5 Same as Problem 4.3, but with R within the shell: $a < R < b$.

Field Energy of Moving Charge

4.6 For the electromagnetic field that accompanies a point charge uniformly moving at speed v along the z-axis:

(a) Obtain the Poynting vector at any observation point and time.

(b) Find the total power that crosses the plane $z = z_0$ at time t.

CHAPTER 5

Waves in the Frequency Domain

Signal Distortion

In a vacuum, a signal of *any* waveform whatsoever is transmitted by electromagnetic plane waves absolutely undistorted in shape, duration, and amplitude, but merely delayed in time. In any other medium, some sort of distortion must occur in the process of transmission.

Many simple media appear to differ electrically from a vacuum only in that their permittivity and permeability differ from ε_0 and μ_0. With other values ε and μ for these parameters, the only differences from vacuum propagation would be that the speed of propagation would be slowed from $c = 1/\sqrt{\varepsilon_0 \mu_0}$ to $v = 1/\sqrt{\varepsilon\mu}$ and that the wave impedance E/H would change from $\eta_0 = \sqrt{\mu_0/\varepsilon_0}$ to $\eta = \sqrt{\mu/\varepsilon}$. Any signal in such media would also be transmitted entirely without distortion, but with longer delays.

Such behavior is only an idealization, however. Real media, at best, exhibit fixed values of ε and μ only for restricted classes of waveforms; more general waveforms must suffer some distortion in transmission. For example, in water, slowly changing waveforms (say, slower than on a time scale of a nanosecond) are transmitted at only $\frac{1}{9}c$, while rapidly varying signals [faster than a picosecond (e.g., optical)] travel at $\frac{3}{4}c$. A general signal emitted by the transmitter may have portions of gradual variation and others of rapid changes; these portions will arrive at the receiver after different delays. Clearly, then, the general type of signal transmitted through such real media must undergo some distortion. The severity of the distortion is an engineering concern.

Mere changes in amplitude of a signal, while retaining fidelity of shape and duration, are not of great concern as long as the signal remains strong enough to be detected and then amplified. Such loss of strength occurs even in a vacuum, when the wave is not a unidirectional plane wave but rather spreads in many directions; only a fraction of the available energy can then be picked up by the receiver and the detected signal is then weaker as well as delayed, compared to the emitted one. In real media, this benign weakening of the signal occurs but may be accompanied by a more serious attenuation, because some of the energy in the wave is abstracted by the medium and converted to heat. Once again, this would be inconsequential if signal strength remained adequate, but it also implies distortions if portions of the signal that vary at different rates contribute unequally to the power loss.

In simple, *linear* media, there is a class of waveforms that suffers no distortion in transmission, other than a change of amplitude. Since Maxwell's equations are linear, that class of waveforms, as for any linear system, comprises *exponentials*, generally complex, including pure exponentials, pure sinusoids, and growing or decaying sinusoids. For any member of this class of signals, the waveform is of identical shape at all times, differing from an early instant to a later one only in amplitude. For an exponential waveform, even a pure delay is indistinguishable from a change in amplitude. In a linear system, which includes electromagnetic transmission through a linear medium, the worst that can befall a signal of the exponential type is a change in amplitude.

Sinusoidal Steady State

Let the waveform $f(t)$ of a plane wave at $z = 0$ be an exponential; in particular, let it be a complex one that represents a pair of steady-state sinusoids at frequency ω: $f(t) = e^{j\omega t}$. Yes, this is complex; in fact, $f(t) = \cos \omega t + j \sin \omega t$. But the real and imaginary parts of this, or of any linear expression involving this complex signal, are readily recognized and separated from each other, and both parts qualify as *real* solutions to the equations of the linear system. It is a great convenience to retain *both* real solutions, combined into this complex form, throughout all the mathematical manipulations called for by the linear system. At the end of the calculation, or at any stage, we can examine what the real sinusoid has undergone by taking the real part, say, of the complex result. We thereby reap the benefit of dealing with a single exponential, which is guaranteed to survive all the linear operations unscathed, except for a change of amplitude. That amplitude will, however, also be a complex number, but the need to deal with complex arithmetic is a small price to pay for the ease of having the time signal remain undistorted by differentiations, integrations, or any linear operations.

Elsewhere than at the $z = 0$ plane, the general vacuum result says that the emitted signal $f(t)$ appears delayed, as $f(t - z/c)$. For the complex exponential, this is $e^{j\omega(t - z/c)}$ as a special case of the general result. This is rewritten as $e^{j(\omega t - kz)}$, where $k = \omega/c$. A number of designators are in common use to refer to the various features of such complex signals.

The plane wave is now complex and takes the form

$$\mathbf{E} = \hat{\mathbf{e}} E_0 e^{j(\omega t - kz)}, \qquad \mathbf{H} = \hat{\mathbf{h}} \frac{1}{\eta_0} E_0 e^{j(\omega t - kz)}, \qquad \hat{\mathbf{e}} \times \hat{\mathbf{h}} = \hat{\mathbf{z}}. \tag{5.1}$$

The various parts are identified as follows:

- The coefficient of the complex exponential, E_0, is a complex number, the *complex amplitude* of the electric field. As such, it has a real and an imaginary part, or else a magnitude and a phase: $E_0 = |E_0| e^{j\varphi_0}$. Consequently, combining the exponentials, the complex electric field can also be given as $\mathbf{E} = \hat{\mathbf{e}}|E_0|e^{j(\omega t - kz + \varphi_0)}$ and its real part is $\hat{\mathbf{e}}|E_0|\cos(\omega t - kz + \varphi_0)$, which is a physically meaningful plane wave's electric field. It is sinusoidal at frequency ω; the sinusoid has peak amplitude $|E_0|$ and initial phase φ_0 at $z = 0$. The electric field vector is directed along the real unit vector $\hat{\mathbf{e}}$.

- The real quantity $\Phi = \omega t - kz + \varphi_0$ is the *phase* of the wave.
- The time coefficient, ω, is the *angular frequency* of the sinusoidal signal, measured in radians per second.
- Since the function $e^{j\xi}$ is periodic in ξ, with period 2π, the signal $e^{j\omega t}$, or also $e^{j(\omega t - kz)}$, is periodic in time, with period $\tau = 2\pi/\omega$. The reciprocal of the period is the cyclical frequency, $f = \omega/2\pi$, the number of full cycles per second, measured in hertz.
- The distance coefficient, k, is the *phase constant* of the sinusoidal waveshape, measured in radians per meter. Since the function $e^{j\xi}$ is periodic in ξ, with period 2π, the waveshape e^{-jkz}, or also $e^{j(\omega t - kz)}$, is periodic in space, with period $\lambda = 2\pi/k$, called the *wavelength*.

As with the time and distance scales of any waveform propagating in a vacuum, the period and the wavelength are related by the speed of light. The expressions

$$\lambda = c\tau \quad \text{or} \quad \omega = kc \quad \text{or} \quad f\lambda = c \tag{5.2}$$

are equivalent statements of how the time scale of the waveform and the distance scale of the waveshape are related.

The fields maintain a fixed value wherever and whenever the phase $\Phi(z, t)$ remains fixed. As time elapses, $\Phi(z, t)$ stays fixed only if the z coordinate is allowed to increase at the appropriate rate dz/dt to keep Φ constant, or to make $d\Phi = 0$. Since $d\Phi = \omega\, dt - k\, dz$, the rate of progression along z that would be necessary to maintain a fixed phase (and hence fixed fields) is the *phase velocity* $v_p = dz/dt$ that achieves $d\Phi = 0$:

$$v_p = \frac{\omega}{k}. \tag{5.3}$$

The phase velocity is hence the *ratio of the coefficients of t and of z* in the phase. It is also the product of the cyclical frequency f and the wavelength λ. For the plane wave propagating in a vacuum, this phase velocity is the speed of light: $v_p = c$.

To this point, we have designated the single direction of propagation as the z direction. As soon as waves traveling in different directions are to be considered, it becomes appropriate to define a vector that points in the direction of propagation. This may be a unit vector $\hat{\mathbf{n}}$, whereupon the distance coordinate along the direction of wave motion is no longer just z but now becomes $\hat{\mathbf{n}} \cdot \mathbf{r}$, where $\mathbf{r} = (x, y, z)$ is the position vector from the origin to any point in space. The phase for a wave that propagates along the direction of $\hat{\mathbf{n}}$ is then $\Phi(\mathbf{r}, t) = \omega t - k\hat{\mathbf{n}} \cdot \mathbf{r}$. It is convenient to combine the phase constant k with the

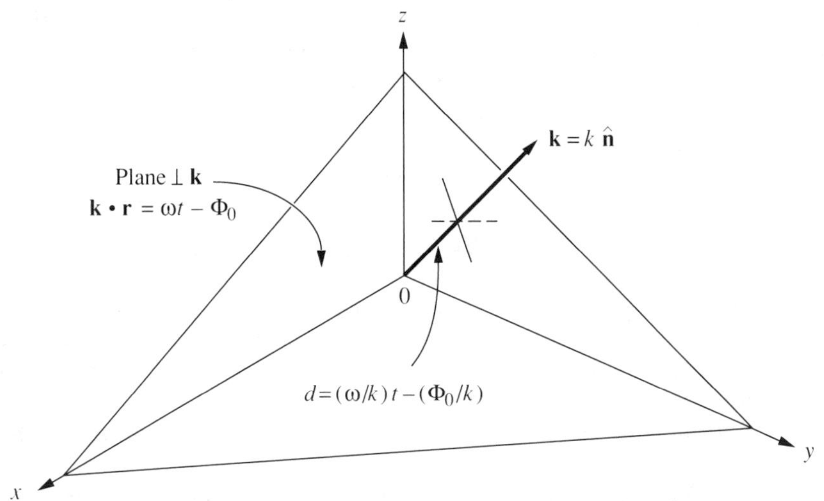

FIGURE 5–1 Planar wavefront propagating along **k**.

unit vector $\hat{\mathbf{n}}$ to form the *wave vector* $\mathbf{k} = k\hat{\mathbf{n}}$. This points in the direction of phase progression and has the magnitude $|\mathbf{k}| = k = \omega/v_p = 2\pi/\lambda$. The *wavefront* is the surface (in our case, planar) of fixed phase, identified analytically by the constraint $\omega t - \mathbf{k} \cdot \mathbf{r} = \Phi_0$. This is the equation of a *plane* perpendicular to the direction of **k** or $\hat{\mathbf{n}}$, whose distance d from the origin is given by $\hat{\mathbf{n}} \cdot \mathbf{r} = (\omega t - \Phi_0)/k$, which increases in time at the phase velocity ω/k. This wavefront is depicted in Figure 5–1, for one instant of time.

The complex plane wave $\mathbf{E}e^{j(\omega t - \mathbf{k} \cdot \mathbf{r})}$ is distinguished by its frequency ω, its wave vector **k**, and its complex amplitude **E**. Its real part (or also its imaginary part) is a sinusoidal plane wave that propagates along **k**.

Constitutive Relations

In media other than a vacuum, it is *not* true that the constitutive parameters ε and μ relate the fields as time functions. The relations $\mathbf{D} = \varepsilon\mathbf{E}$ and $\mathbf{B} = \mu\mathbf{H}$ do hold, however, for the *complex amplitudes* of the fields, with parameters that depend on the frequency of the sinusoidal signal: $\varepsilon = \varepsilon(\omega)$ and $\mu = \mu(\omega)$. Consequently, the phase velocity and wave impedance, among other properties, will depend on the frequency.

A single-frequency sinusoidal signal will be transmitted without distortion at the speed $v_p(\omega) = 1/\sqrt{\mu(\omega)\varepsilon(\omega)}$ and the complex field amplitudes will be related by the wave impedance $\eta(\omega) = \sqrt{\mu(\omega)/\varepsilon(\omega)}$. For a medium whose constitutive parameters are frequency dependent, individual sinusoidal signals at different frequencies propagate at different speeds; the different frequency components each get transmitted without distortion, but they arrive with different delays. When the constituent sinusoids are superimposed at the receiver, the resultant signal is a distorted version of the one that was emitted.

Spectral analysis, or Fourier decomposition of an arbitrary signal waveform into its sinusoidal components, allows each frequency in the spectrum of the signal to be treated separately, transmitted individually, and reconstituted ultimately as the received signal. There is thus no loss in generality in considering sinusoidal, or complex exponential, signals alone.

Interpretation of Complex Fields

We must distinguish carefully between the real, physical electromagnetic fields of sinusoidal time variation and the complex field amplitudes used as coefficients of the complex exponential signal $e^{j\omega t}$. The former are the real fields of ultimate interest; they are signals in the time domain. The latter are complex constants (independent of time) upon which we perform our mathematical operations; they are the frequency-domain counterparts of our sinusoidal signals. Whenever we shall need to distinguish the two entities, we shall denote the time-domain signal by $\mathscr{F}(t)$ and the corresponding complex constant Fourier amplitude by $\mathbf{F}$.

The interpretation of any complex expression is always made evident by appending the $e^{j\omega t}$ factor and then taking the real part of the resultant complex function of time. Thus a general sinusoidal steady-state (also called "harmonic") electric field at frequency ω may be given simply by its Fourier amplitude $\mathbf{E}(\mathbf{r})$ and interpreted in the time domain as

$$\mathscr{E}(\mathbf{r}, t) = \text{Re}\,\{\mathbf{E}(\mathbf{r})e^{j\omega t}\}. \tag{5.4}$$

Here $\mathscr{E}$ is the actual, real, physical field vector, a function of time as well as position, while $\mathbf{E}$ is a complex vector field, a function of position but *not* of time. That the complex quantity $\mathbf{E}$ is a vector means merely that both its real and its imaginary parts are ordinary vectors, each with a magnitude and a direction. Equivalently, it means that each of its three components, along the directions of the (real) unit vectors $\hat{\mathbf{x}}$, $\hat{\mathbf{y}}$, $\hat{\mathbf{z}}$, is a complex (scalar) number:

$$\mathbf{E} = \text{Re}\,\mathbf{E} + j\,\text{Im}\,\mathbf{E} \quad \text{or} \quad \mathbf{E} = E_1 e^{j\varphi_1}\hat{\mathbf{x}} + E_2 e^{j\varphi_2}\hat{\mathbf{y}} + E_3 e^{j\varphi_3}\hat{\mathbf{z}}. \tag{5.5}$$

Algebraic calculations with complex vectors are carried out by the usual rules, but using complex arithmetic. What is lost in the use of complex vectors is the interpretation of a vector as having a direction as well as a magnitude: a complex vector may not have an identifiable direction, unless both the real and imaginary parts share the same direction. For the same reason, dot or cross products of vectors may not have an interpretation that involves the cosine or sine of an "angle" between the vectors. However, the dot or cross product can still be evaluated from the components of the two complex vectors and orthogonality of two complex vectors $\mathbf{A}$ and $\mathbf{B}$ can still be defined by $\mathbf{A} \cdot \mathbf{B} = 0$, meaning that $A_1B_1 + A_2B_2 + A_3B_3 = 0 + j0$.

Linear operations on harmonic quantities expressed in terms of complex amplitudes may be carried out on the full complex expression $Ae^{j\omega t}$ rather than on the real part alone $\mathscr{A}(t)$, because the real part can be separated out at the end of the calculation. In particular, a time derivative of $\mathscr{A}(t)$ can be replaced by a factor $j\omega$ applied to A alone, because the $e^{j\omega t}$ factor survives intact after any linear operation. Since the exponential always appears on both sides of any linear equation, it may be canceled from the two sides, leaving operations to be applied to the complex amplitudes alone, with no time-dependent quantities at all. Thus Maxwell's equations applied to harmonic fields appear with the $\partial/\partial t$ operations replaced by $j\omega$:

$$\nabla \times \mathbf{E} = -j\omega\mathbf{B} \qquad \nabla \times \mathbf{H} = j\omega\mathbf{D} + \mathbf{J}, \tag{5.6}$$

where the complex fields depend on $\mathbf{r}$ only, not on t; time has been totally eliminated from the frequency-domain equations.

In a sourceless medium, for example, the complex Maxwell equations become $\nabla \times \mathbf{E} = -j\omega\mu\mathbf{H}$ and $\nabla \times \mathbf{H} = j\omega\varepsilon\mathbf{E}$. These partial differential equations will be satisfied by exponential trial functions $\mathbf{E} = \mathbf{E}_0 e^{\mathbf{q}\cdot\mathbf{r}}$ and $\mathbf{H} = \mathbf{H}_0 e^{\mathbf{q}\cdot\mathbf{r}}$ (with truly constant complex vector coefficients $\mathbf{E}_0$ and $\mathbf{H}_0$ and $\mathbf{q}$), provided that $\mathbf{q} \times \mathbf{E}_0 = -j\omega\mu\mathbf{H}_0$ and $\mathbf{q} \times \mathbf{H}_0 = j\omega\varepsilon\mathbf{E}_0$, since each spatial derivative in ∇ merely generates a factor of the corresponding component of $\mathbf{q}$ when applied to the exponential $e^{\mathbf{q}\cdot\mathbf{r}}$. These are algebraic equations, no longer differential equations, and they combine into

$$\mathbf{q} \times (\mathbf{q} \times \mathbf{E}_0) = -j\omega\mu\mathbf{q} \times \mathbf{H}_0 = -j\omega\mu j\omega\varepsilon\mathbf{E}_0 = \omega^2\mu\varepsilon\mathbf{E}_0. \tag{5.7}$$

The triple cross product on the left reduces to $\mathbf{q} \times (\mathbf{q} \times \mathbf{E}_0) = (\mathbf{q} \cdot \mathbf{E}_0)\mathbf{q} - (\mathbf{q} \cdot \mathbf{q})\mathbf{E}_0$ by an identity of vector algebra. Since the leftmost expression in Eq. (5.7) is orthogonal to $\mathbf{q}$ while the rightmost one is proportional to $\mathbf{E}_0$, it follows that $\mathbf{q} \cdot \mathbf{E}_0 = 0$ and the triple cross product becomes merely $-(\mathbf{q} \cdot \mathbf{q})\mathbf{E}_0$. Finally, then, Eq. (5.7) requires that $(\mathbf{q} \cdot \mathbf{q})\mathbf{E}_0 = -\omega^2\mu\varepsilon\mathbf{E}_0$, so that any vector $\mathbf{E}_0$ orthogonal to $\mathbf{q}$ will do, provided only that $\mathbf{q} \cdot \mathbf{q} = -\omega^2\mu\varepsilon$. This allows for the complex constant vector $\mathbf{q}$ to be purely imaginary: $\mathbf{q} = -j\mathbf{k}$, with $\mathbf{k}$ a real vector (the negative sign merely makes the interpretation of $\mathbf{k}$ easier; $\mathbf{q}$ could also be complex, with orthogonal real and imaginary parts, but we postpone consideration of such solutions). The solution to the complex Maxwell equations is thus

$$\mathbf{E} = \mathbf{E}_0 e^{-j\mathbf{k}\cdot\mathbf{r}} \qquad \text{and} \qquad \mathbf{H} = \mathbf{H}_0 e^{-j\mathbf{k}\cdot\mathbf{r}}, \tag{5.8}$$

subject to

$$k^2 = \mathbf{k} \cdot \mathbf{k} = \omega^2\mu\varepsilon \quad \text{and} \quad \mathbf{k} \cdot \mathbf{E}_0 = 0 \quad \text{and} \quad \mathbf{k} \times \mathbf{E}_0 = \omega\mu\mathbf{H}_0, \tag{5.9}$$

where vector $\mathbf{k}$ is real but $\mathbf{E}_0$ (and hence also $\mathbf{H}_0$) may be complex.

To interpret this solution, the time-dependent harmonic factor $e^{j\omega t}$ is restored and the real part taken, so as to revert to the time domain. This yields, if the real and imaginary parts of $\mathbf{E}_0$ are denoted $\mathbf{E}_1$ and $\mathbf{E}_2$,

$$\begin{aligned}\mathscr{E}(\mathbf{r}, t) &= \text{Re}\,\{\mathbf{E}e^{j\omega t}\} = \text{Re}\,\{\mathbf{E}_0 e^{-j\mathbf{k}\cdot\mathbf{r}} e^{j\omega t}\} = \text{Re}\,\{\mathbf{E}_0 e^{j(\omega t - \mathbf{k}\cdot\mathbf{r})}\} \\ &= \text{Re}\,\{[\mathbf{E}_1 + j\mathbf{E}_2][\cos(\omega t - \mathbf{k}\cdot\mathbf{r}) + j\sin(\omega t - \mathbf{k}\cdot\mathbf{r})]\} \\ &= \mathbf{E}_1 \cos(\omega t - \mathbf{k}\cdot\mathbf{r}) - \mathbf{E}_2 \sin(\omega t - \mathbf{k}\cdot\mathbf{r}).\end{aligned} \tag{5.10}$$

This last expression for the real $\mathscr{E}$ involves only ordinary, real, constant vectors $\mathbf{E}_1$, $\mathbf{E}_2$, and $\mathbf{k}$ and is recognized as a superposition of two sinusoidal plane waves, both oscillating at frequency ω and both propagating in the direction of $\mathbf{k}$, which is perpendicular to both $\mathbf{E}_1$ and $\mathbf{E}_2$. Both waves travel at the same speed, $v_p = \omega/k = \omega/|\mathbf{k}| = 1/\sqrt{\mu\varepsilon}$; the constitutive parameters μ and ε are those that describe the dielectric medium at frequency ω. Similarly, the real, physical magnetic field that accompanies the electric one is

$$\mathscr{H}(\mathbf{r}, t) = \mathbf{H}_1 \cos(\omega t - \mathbf{k} \cdot \mathbf{r}) - \mathbf{H}_2 \sin(\omega t - \mathbf{k} \cdot \mathbf{r}), \tag{5.11}$$

with $\mathbf{k} \times \mathbf{E}_1 = \omega\mu\mathbf{H}_1$ and $\mathbf{k} \times \mathbf{E}_2 = \omega\mu\mathbf{H}_2$, so that $E_1/H_1 = E_2/H_2 = \omega\mu/k = \sqrt{\mu/\varepsilon} = \eta$. Of course, if the complex $\mathbf{E}$ were to be purely real (just $\mathbf{E}_1$) or purely imaginary (just $j\mathbf{E}_2$), only one of the two sinusoidal waves would be present, but in general $\mathbf{E}$ is complex and its interpretation involves two superimposed harmonic plane waves with the same frequency and wave vector. The superposition is a vector sum of the two constituent fields, whose resultant at any point or instant is a vector in the plane formed by the real and imaginary parts of the complex vector $\mathbf{E} = \mathbf{E}_1 + j\mathbf{E}_2$.

The message to be gleaned from this calculation is that, if the fields are understood to vary harmonically in time, as $e^{j\omega t}$, then when the complex, frequency-domain Maxwell equations yield a solution of the form $\mathbf{E}e^{-j\mathbf{k}\cdot\mathbf{r}}$, this complex, time-independent vector field is to be interpreted in the time domain as a sinusoidal plane wave oscillating in time at frequency ω and propagating in space in the direction of the real vector $\mathbf{k}$, at the speed ω/k.

Polarization

Compared to the simple plane wave $\mathscr{E}(\mathbf{r}, t) = \hat{\mathbf{e}}E_0 f(t - z/c)$ that we studied first, the harmonic plane wave $\mathbf{E} = \mathbf{E}_0 e^{-j\mathbf{k}\cdot\mathbf{r}}$ in the frequency domain, which is $\mathscr{E}(\mathbf{r}, t) = \text{Re}\,[\mathbf{E}e^{j\omega t}]$ in the time domain, is more general in some respects but more specialized in others. The former could have any waveform $f(t)$ at all, but the latter is only sinusoidal at frequency ω. On the other hand, the former was allowed to vary only along z, but the latter varies along any direction, given by the vector $\mathbf{k}$. The former propagates at the vacuum speed of light, c, regardless of the waveform $f(t)$ but the latter's phase velocity is $v_p = 1/\sqrt{\mu(\omega)\varepsilon(\omega)}$, which varies with frequency for actual dielectric materials other than a vacuum. Most important, the former was required to have field vectors that remain fixed in direction, along $\hat{\mathbf{e}}$ and $\hat{\mathbf{h}}$, but this restriction was not imposed when we solved the Maxwell equations in the frequency domain. In fact, the wave vectors $\mathscr{E}$ and $\mathscr{H}$ can tilt in space as well as vary in strength, but in a particular manner consistent with their being harmonic in time.

The behavior of the field vectors at some fixed observation point as time elapses is termed the *polarization* of the wave. The wave fields previously considered were arbitrarily allowed to vary only in magnitude but not to tilt in their direction; that behavior was termed "linear polarization." For the sinus-

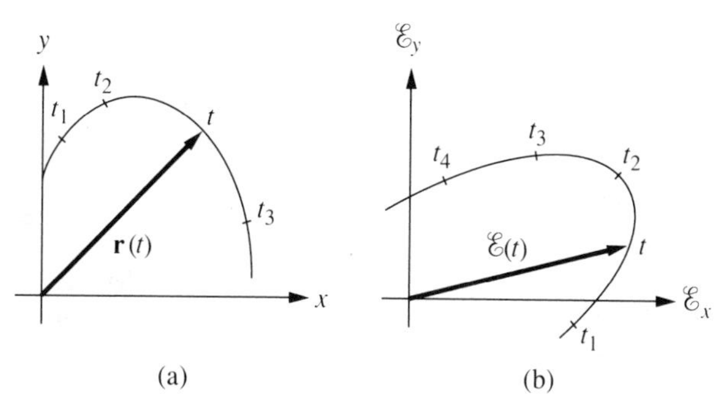

FIGURE 5–2 (a) Orbit $\mathbf{r}(t)$ of a particle; (b) curve traced by $\mathscr{E}(t)$ vector.

oidal plane waves, how the field vectors vary in strength and how they tilt or twist in direction are related.

Just as the time variation of the position vector $\mathbf{r} = \mathbf{r}(t)$ in a mechanics problem describes an orbit or trajectory of, say, a particle moving through space, so does any vector function of time, like $\mathscr{E}(t)$, describe some curve in the space in which that vector may be "plotted," as in Figure 5–2. Thus *any vector function of one scalar variable plots as a curve* in the space of that vector, parametrized by the scalar. If we could visualize the vector $\mathscr{E}(\mathbf{r}_0, t) = \mathscr{E}(t)$ at a fixed observation point $\mathbf{r}_0$ as it twists and turns and waxes and wanes in time, what curve would the tip of the $\mathscr{E}$ vector trace out?

Analytically, the answer is already known to us from Eq. (5.10): If $\mathbf{E} = \mathbf{E}_1 + j\mathbf{E}_2$ is the given complex constant vector, the time variation of the actual field is given by

$$\mathscr{E}(t) = \text{Re}\,\{\mathbf{E}e^{j\omega t}\} = \mathbf{E}_1 \cos \omega t - \mathbf{E}_2 \sin \omega t, \tag{5.12}$$

where $\mathbf{E}_1$ and $\mathbf{E}_2$ are the real and imaginary parts of $\mathbf{E}$, hence real vectors. This gives the curve traced by $\mathscr{E}(t)$ in parametric form and can readily be plotted, by evaluating $\mathscr{E}$ at many instants of time. The curve lies entirely in the plane formed by the real and imaginary parts of $\mathbf{E}$, and this plane is perpendicular to the wave vector $\mathbf{k}$. The parametric form of the equation for this curve may not be so familiar, however, as compared to an alternative form that relates the components of the $\mathscr{E}$ vector to each other, without reference to the time parameter. Conversion of the parametric form to a nonparametric equation requires elimination of the time t.

This elimination is easily achieved by solving for the trigonometric functions of time in Eq. (5.12), in terms of the field components. When the cosine and sine are squared and added, the sum is unity and time has been eliminated from the equation. Since the real and imaginary parts of $\mathbf{E}$ lie in the plane perpendicular to $\mathbf{k}$, they have only two orthogonal components in that plane; let these be called the x- and y-components. It follows that Eq. (5.12) can be expressed as the matrix equation

$$\begin{bmatrix} \mathscr{E}_x(t) \\ \mathscr{E}_y(t) \end{bmatrix} = \begin{bmatrix} E_{1x} & E_{2x} \\ E_{1y} & E_{2y} \end{bmatrix} \begin{bmatrix} \cos \omega t \\ -\sin \omega t \end{bmatrix} \tag{5.13}$$

or, more simply, as

$$F = \mathbf{M}\Omega, \tag{5.14}$$

where F comprises the components of the variable $\mathscr{E}$, $\mathbf{M}$ the components of the real vectors $\mathbf{E}_1$ and $\mathbf{E}_2$ as its columns, and Ω the trigonometric functions. Solving for the latter yields

$$\Omega = \mathbf{M}^{-1}F, \tag{5.15}$$

where the two entries in Ω are $\cos \omega t$ and $-\sin \omega t$, so that multiplication by the transpose of the matrix yields the sum of their squares, which is unity:

$$\Omega'\Omega = 1 = F'(\mathbf{M}^{-1})'(\mathbf{M}^{-1})F = F'(\mathbf{M}\mathbf{M}')^{-1}F, \tag{5.16}$$

where primes indicate transposes of the matrices and we have used the fact that the inverse of a product of matrices is the product of their inverses, in reverse order.

The relation $F'\mathbf{G}F = 1$ is a quadratic form in the components of F, or of the vector variable $\mathscr{E}$, or in $X = \mathscr{E}_x$ and $Y = \mathscr{E}_y$, its rectangular components in the plane. Fully expanded, this is a quadratic form like $AX^2 + 2BXY + CY^2 = 1$, where A, B, B, and C are the four entries in the symmetric real matrix $\mathbf{G} = (\mathbf{M}\mathbf{M}')^{-1}$. This quadratic form represents a conic section in the XY-plane; it can be a hyperbola, parabola, or ellipse, depending primarily on the sign of the discriminant $AC - B^2$. But this discriminant is just the determinant of the matrix $\mathbf{G}$, which is the reciprocal of the determinant of the product $\mathbf{M}\mathbf{M}'$; this, in turn, equals the product of the determinants of the two factors and these, being transposes of each other, have equal determinants. Hence the discriminant is here $1/(\det \mathbf{M})^2$, which is positive, so that the curve must be an ellipse, or a degenerate form of an ellipse (a circle or a straight line) in special cases. The general harmonic plane wave is *elliptically polarized.*

This designation is descriptive of the behavior of the field vector as time goes on. Giving the field in the frequency domain by specifying a complex constant vector $\mathbf{E}$ implies that the time-domain variation of the actual field $\mathscr{E}$ must be sinusoidal in time, but this requires only that each vector component oscillate sinusoidally; the entire vector is able to change its direction as well as vary in strength, but these two variations are constrained to make the tip of the $\mathscr{E}$ vector trace out an ellipse in the plane perpendicular to the direction $\mathbf{k}$ of propagation. Figure 5–3 shows the ellipse formed by the motion of the tip of the $\mathscr{E}$ vector in time, as a resultant of the summation of the two vectors $\mathbf{E}_1 \cos \omega t$ and $-\mathbf{E}_2 \sin \omega t$, where $\mathbf{E}_1$ and $\mathbf{E}_2$, which are fixed and which are also shown in the figure, are the real and imaginary parts of the complex constant vector $\mathbf{E}$. The figure also shows that the same ellipse can be traced

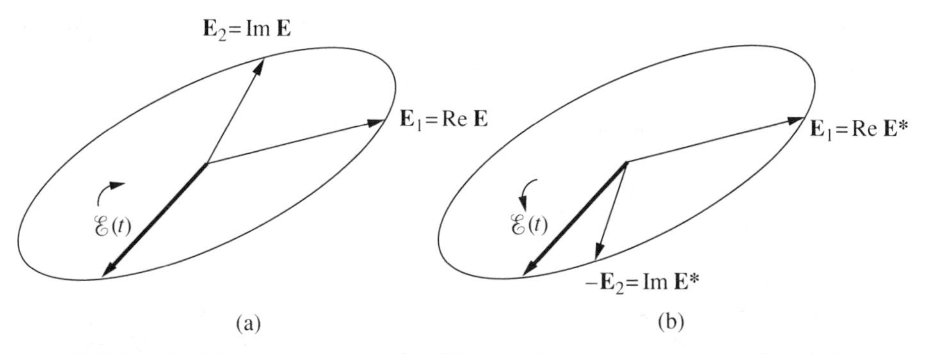

FIGURE 5–3 Ellipses traced out by $\mathscr{E}(t)$, based on complex vectors **E** and **E***.

out, but in the opposite direction, by the $\mathscr{E}$ vector that corresponds to the complex conjugate $\mathbf{E}^*$ of the vector **E** used for the first ellipse.

Which way the field vector rotates around the ellipse is a matter about which there is much confusion, but no mystery. Since $\mathscr{E}(t) = \mathbf{E}_1 \cos \omega t - \mathbf{E}_2 \sin \omega t$, the rotating $\mathscr{E}$ vector is along $\mathbf{E}_1$ when $\omega t = 0$ (and then not again until $\omega t = 2\pi$), but it lies along $\mathbf{E}_2$ when $\omega t = -\pi/2$, earlier than when it reaches $\mathbf{E}_1$. Thus the sense of the rotation is always from Im **E** toward Re **E**. Whether this is clockwise or counterclockwise rotation depends on the configuration of the $\mathbf{E}_1$ and $\mathbf{E}_2$ vectors, that is, on which way the imaginary part would have to turn to reach the real part, through the smallest angle. The confusion arises in the designations used to distinguish the two senses of rotation.

Since clockwise as seen from the front becomes counterclockwise when viewed from the rear, an unambiguous designation requires specification of whether the rotating vector is being visualized from the direction in which the wave is either approaching or receding from the observer; the sense is reported in terms of the "handedness" of the rotation. By the engineer's standards, with the thumb pointing in the direction of advance of the wave, the polarization is either right-handed or left-handed, according to the hand whose fingers conform to the direction of rotation. In Figure 5–3, if the waves are approaching the reader, then the one on the left is termed "left-handed elliptically polarized, wave approaching" while the other is "right-handed. . . ."

Unfortunately and incredibly, there is disagreement about this designation. Physicists, including optics workers, refer to the two cases with the opposite designations (but without specifying "wave approaching"; they prefer to have the thumb point to where the wave is coming from!). There is a further source of confusion in the physicists' preference for the complex exponential to be written $e^{-i\omega t}$, compared to the engineers' $e^{j\omega t}$, which of course reverses the role of the real and imaginary parts of **E** in determining the sense of rotation. Still another ambiguity lies in the two signs in the full expression for the phase, $\omega t \pm kz$, which pertains to the direction of advance of the wave. The combination of all these ambiguities effectively frustrates attempts to memorize a rule as to which sense of rotation is designated right or left. It seems safest to compare the orientation of the $\mathscr{E}$ field at two easily distinguished times, say at $\omega t = 0$ and $\omega t = \pi/2$, when the complex exponential is purely real and purely imaginary, respectively, making it especially simple to get $\mathscr{E}$ from $\mathbf{E}$. One should also be specific about the direction of advance of the wave.

Linear and Circular Polarization

There are two important special cases of the behavior of the field in time, one in which the ellipse collapses to a straight line, the other in which it opens out to a circle.

The case of linear polarization occurs when the real and imaginary parts of the $\mathbf{E}$ vector are parallel, so that $\mathbf{E} = (E_1 + jE_2)\hat{\mathbf{e}}$. The derivation of the equation for the curve traced by $\mathscr{E}$ then fails, because the matrix $\mathbf{M}$ in Eq. (5.14) is singular when $\mathbf{E}_1$ and $\mathbf{E}_2$ are parallel, so that there is no inverse matrix. The behavior in time is then given by $\mathscr{E} = (E_1 \cos \omega t - E_2 \sin \omega t)\hat{\mathbf{e}}$, which remains aligned with the fixed, real, unit vector $\hat{\mathbf{e}}$ and does not rotate or tilt in any way; this is linear polarization.

The other special case is that in which the ellipse reduces to a circle. This happens when the quadratic form $AX^2 + 2BXY + CY^2 = 1$ satisfies two conditions: it has no cross term, so that $B = 0$, and the ellipse's semiaxes are equal, so that $A = C$. In terms of the equivalent quadratic form $F'\mathbf{G}F = 1$, the matrix $\mathbf{G} = (\mathbf{MM}')^{-1}$ is required to be proportional to the unit matrix (the constant of proportionality is then interpreted as the inverse square of the radius of the resultant circle). This condition is satisfied when $\mathbf{M}'$ (the transpose of matrix $\mathbf{M}$) is proportional to $\mathbf{M}^{-1}$ (the inverse of matrix $\mathbf{M}$). In that case, the product $\mathbf{MM}'$ is the same as $\mathbf{M}'\mathbf{M}$ and writing out the condition that $\mathbf{M}'\mathbf{M} \propto \mathbf{I}$ shows that the real and imaginary parts of $\mathbf{E}$ are orthogonal vectors ($\mathbf{E}_1 \cdot \mathbf{E}_2 = 0$) and are of equal magnitude ($E_1^2 = E_2^2$). The complex vector $\mathbf{E}$ then has the form $\mathbf{E} = (\hat{\mathbf{e}}_1 + j\hat{\mathbf{e}}_2)E$, where E is real and the real unit vectors $\hat{\mathbf{e}}_1$ and $\hat{\mathbf{e}}_2$ are perpendicular to each other and to the direction of propagation of the wave. The time-domain field is then the vector $\mathscr{E} = \hat{\mathbf{e}}_1 E \cos \omega t - \hat{\mathbf{e}}_2 E \sin \omega t$, whose magnitude is just E and is constant in time and whose direction is at an angle ωt to that of vector $\hat{\mathbf{e}}_1$; this angle increases uniformly in time, so that the real physical electric field vector turns, its tip tracing out a circle as it sweeps around in the direction from $\hat{\mathbf{e}}_2$ toward $\hat{\mathbf{e}}_1$. This is circular polarization.

For example, the complex constant $\mathbf{E} = (\hat{\mathbf{x}} - j\hat{\mathbf{y}})E$ represents a right-hand circularly polarized (RHCP) plane wave if the wave travels along $\hat{\mathbf{z}}$ and the engineers' standards are adopted; the complex exponential is then $e^{j(\omega t - kz)}$. That the sense of rotation is right-handed is clear from the fact that it runs from the imaginary part, here $-\hat{\mathbf{y}}$, to the real part, here $\hat{\mathbf{x}}$, as time elapses.

Note that although all polarizations involve periodic motion of the real field vector $\mathscr{E}$, with period $2\pi/\omega$, circular polarization entails a uniform rotation of the field, while elliptic polarization exhibits a nonuniform rotation: it takes as long to sweep around the ellipse from $\mathbf{E}_2$ to $\mathbf{E}_1$ as it then takes to sweep from $\mathbf{E}_1$ to $-\mathbf{E}_2$; both partial sweeps take a quarter period.

An elliptically polarized field changes both its magnitude and direction, periodically in time. A linearly polarized one changes only in magnitude while maintaining a fixed direction; a circularly polarized one changes only in direction while retaining a constant magnitude.

The importance of the special cases of linear and circular polarization is enhanced by the fact that a wave of any polarization, generally elliptic, can be expressed as a superposition of two simpler partial waves. The two partial waves can be linearly polarized, at right angles to each other; alternatively, they can be circularly polarized, with opposite senses.

The first assertion is confirmed simply by recognizing that an arbitrary complex vector $\mathbf{E}$ is always expressible as $\mathbf{E} = \hat{\mathbf{x}}E_x + \hat{\mathbf{y}}E_y$, where the first term is evidently linearly polarized along $\hat{\mathbf{x}}$ and the second is linearly polarized along $\hat{\mathbf{y}}$. Note that E_x and E_y are complex numbers, however.

The second assertion, that a superposition of oppositely sensed circularly polarized waves can comprise any elliptically polarized wave, is verified by noting that any complex vector $\mathbf{E}$ can be expressed as a combination of the circularly polarized vectors $\hat{\mathbf{x}} \pm j\hat{\mathbf{y}}$. It is in fact an identity that $\mathbf{E} = R(\hat{\mathbf{x}} - j\hat{\mathbf{y}}) + L(\hat{\mathbf{x}} + j\hat{\mathbf{y}})$, where $R = (E_x + jE_y)/2$ and $L = (E_x - jE_y)/2$. Note again that E_x and E_y are complex numbers, so that, despite appearances, R and L are not necessarily complex conjugate numbers. The magnitudes of the complex numbers R and L give the radii of the circles traced by the two circularly polarized field vectors.

EXAMPLE 5.1

There are media in which the speed of wave propagation depends on the wave's polarization. In particular, left and right circularly polarized waves may travel at different speeds in certain media, notably in a magnetized plasma such as the ionosphere, or in certain "optically active" crystals, or even in a sugar solution. Without pausing to consider the underlying mechanism responsible for the difference in wave speeds, let the two speeds for the two senses of rotation be such that the phase constant $k = \omega/v$ is $k_L = k_0 + \kappa$ for the LHCP wave and $k_R = k_0 - \kappa$ for the RHCP wave. Suppose that, at $z = 0$, a wave is linearly polarized, along x, and propagates along z in the active medium. What will its polarization be at some distance z?

If κ were zero, so that all polarizations propagated at the same speed, making $k = k_0$, the original linearly polarized field $\mathbf{E}(0) = E_0\hat{\mathbf{x}}$ at $z = 0$ would become $\mathbf{E}(z) = E_0 e^{-jk_0 z}\hat{\mathbf{x}}$ at distance z, which is still linearly polarized, still along $\hat{\mathbf{x}}$ (since the real and imaginary parts of $\mathbf{E}$ are both along $\hat{\mathbf{x}}$). Instead, we know that *circularly* polarized waves have different phase constants in this medium and we need to determine what happens to a *linearly* polarized field. But any polarization, including a linear one, can be expressed as a superposition of two oppositely sensed circular polarizations, for each of which we know the phase constant. We rewrite the original field at $z = 0$ as

$$\mathbf{E}(0) = E_0\hat{\mathbf{x}} = \tfrac{1}{2}E_0(\hat{\mathbf{x}} + j\hat{\mathbf{y}}) + \tfrac{1}{2}E_0(\hat{\mathbf{x}} - j\hat{\mathbf{y}}) \qquad (5.17)$$

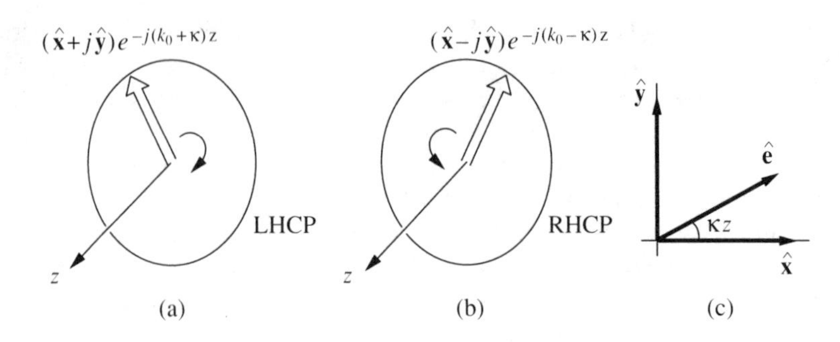

FIGURE 5–4 Rotation of polarization in optically active medium.

and assign each circularly polarized partial wave its own propagation factor:

$$\mathbf{E}(z) = \tfrac{1}{2}E_0(\hat{\mathbf{x}} + j\hat{\mathbf{y}})e^{-j(k_0+\kappa)z} + \tfrac{1}{2}E_0(\hat{\mathbf{x}} - j\hat{\mathbf{y}})e^{-j(k_0-\kappa)z}. \tag{5.18}$$

Now, to identify the polarization at distance z, we may collect terms so as to compare the real and imaginary parts more easily.

$$\begin{aligned}\mathbf{E}(z) &= \tfrac{1}{2}E_0 e^{-jk_0z}[(\hat{\mathbf{x}} + j\hat{\mathbf{y}})e^{-j\kappa z} + (\hat{\mathbf{x}} - j\hat{\mathbf{y}})e^{+j\kappa z}] \\ &= E_0 e^{-jk_0z}\left[\hat{\mathbf{x}}\,\frac{(e^{j\kappa z} + e^{-j\kappa z})}{2} + \hat{\mathbf{y}}\,\frac{(e^{j\kappa z} - e^{-j\kappa z})}{2j}\right] \\ &= E_0 e^{-jk_0z}[\hat{\mathbf{x}}\cos\kappa z + \hat{\mathbf{y}}\sin\kappa z] = E_0 e^{-jk_0z}\hat{\mathbf{e}},\end{aligned} \tag{5.19}$$

instead of $E_0 e^{-jk_0z}\hat{\mathbf{x}}$ at $z = 0$. The real and imaginary parts are both along the real vector $\hat{\mathbf{e}}$, so that this $\mathbf{E}(z)$ is still linearly polarized, but now along the unit vector $\hat{\mathbf{e}} = (\hat{\mathbf{x}}\cos\kappa z + \hat{\mathbf{y}}\sin\kappa z)$ instead of along $\hat{\mathbf{x}}$. The new direction of linear polarization makes angle κz with the original direction. Figure 5–4 shows the superposition of the two circularly polarized waves and the resultant rotated linear polarization.

The result is that the wave in this medium remains linearly polarized everywhere, but the orientation of its polarization tilts through an angle κz over an interval of z meters, where κ is half the difference between the phase constants of the two constituent circularly polarized partial waves. The orientation of the field vector tilts progressively from point to point along the direction of propagation, at the rate of κ radians per meter. An instantaneous "snapshot" of the electric field would show a twist in its orientation, as suggested in Figure 5–5. This, however, is only its spatial behavior; at any fixed point, the temporal behavior is merely a sinusoidal oscillation along a fixed direction in space, which defines a linear polarization.

Certain sugars in solution are chemically equivalent but distinguishable from each other by the sense of rotation they impart to the polarization of a light wave that traverses them (dextrose versus levulose). Faraday rotation refers to a similar progressive tilt of the optical wave polarization in a crystal in which the phase velocities of the circularly polarized components of the

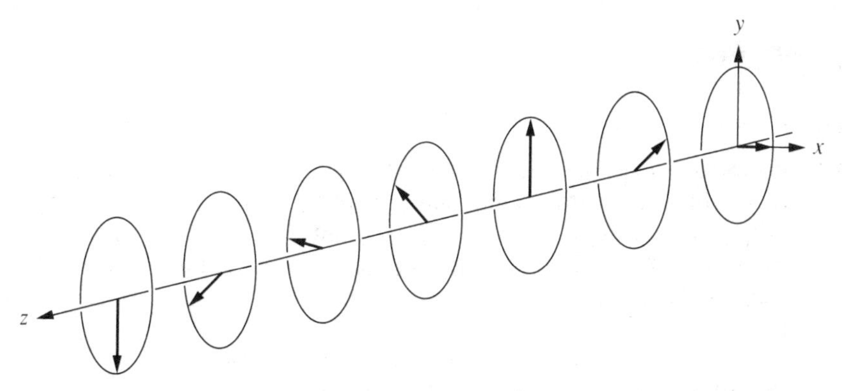

FIGURE 5–5 Twist in orientation of linear polarization, at one instant.

light are different and dependent on an applied magnetic field. In the latter case, there is a preferred direction in space (that of the applied field) and, upon reflection from a mirror, the wave polarization twists even more; in the case of sugar solutions, there is no such global asymmetry and a reflected wave's polarization unwinds back to its original orientation upon its return. Optical fibers can also exhibit wave rotary effects when their phase velocities differ for different polarizations, either by design or by imperfect fabrication that affects the cylindrical symmetry. Such effects can be used to impart modulation on a carrier. ◆

The polarization of light from natural or artificial sources exhibits randomness and requires a statistical description. "Unpolarized" light refers to a superposition of many waves, of all possible polarizations, equally distributed so that no particular polarization predominates. Sunlight or thermal radiation emanating from many independent sources has this character. If, however, the statistical distribution of all the possible polarizations is not uniform in the superposition of waves from many sources, the light is termed "partially polarized."

Summary

Linear systems distort signals, except for exponentials; the latter include complex ones that designate steady-state sinusoids. For such harmonic signals, the description is made in terms of complex constant amplitudes. The nomenclature for harmonic plane waves was reviewed; this includes amplitude and phase, frequency and wave vector, phase velocity and polarization. The latter is generally elliptic, with linear and circular polarizations as special cases.

We examine next superpositions of waves, particularly waves of a range of frequencies, as well as nonlinear properties of harmonic waves, such as their power.

PROBLEMS

Distortion of Pulse

5.1 Consider a hypothetical medium in which the permittivity $\varepsilon(\omega)$ has just two values, a low-frequency and a high-frequency value, such that the propagation delay of a wave from transmitter to receiver is T_1 for $|\omega| < \omega_0$ and T_2 for $|\omega| > \omega_0$. Suppose that the pulse $E(t) = 1/[1 + t^2/T^2]$, which is known to have spectrum $E(\omega) = \pi T \exp(-|\omega T|)$, is transmitted.

(a) What is the spectrum $E'(\omega)$ of the received pulse?
(b) What is the distorted shape $E'(t)$ of the received pulse?

Identifying Properties of Plane Waves

5.2 The sinusoidal plane wave $\mathscr{E}(\mathbf{r}, t)$ is linearly polarized along the x-axis and travels along the y-axis, in vacuum. At time $t = 0$, the field is zero at the point (3, 0, 2) (coordinates in meters) and attains its peak value of 3 V/m at the point (5, 8, -3).

(a) Express this wave as a real field, $\mathscr{E}$.
(b) Express this wave as a complex field, $\mathbf{E}$.
(c) What is the lowest possible frequency, f, for this wave?

Doppler Shifts

5.3 A transmitter generates a signal $U(t) = \sin \omega t$ in the direction of the z-axis; the medium (say, vacuum) propagates this signal at the speed c.

(a) If the receiver is moving, so that it is at $z = z(t) = l + ut$ at time t, what signal is received? What is the frequency of this received signal?
(b) If the transmitter is moving as it emits its signal, so that it is at $z = z(t) = vt$ at time t, what signal is received at a stationary receiver at $z = l$? What is the frequency of this received signal?
(c) If both the receiver and the transmitter are moving, both along the z-axis, with the transmitter at $z = vt$ and the receiver at $z = l + ut$ at time t, what signal is received? What is the frequency of this received signal?
(d) If a "snapshot" of the propagating signal could be made at some instant $t = t_0$, between the source at $z = vt$ and the receiver at $z = l + ut$, what wavelength would be observed?

Superposition of Polarizations

5.4 Two waves, both at frequency ω and both propagating in air along the positive z-axis, have identical electromagnetic fields at $z = 0$, $t = 0$, but one is linearly polarized along the x-axis while the other is right-hand circularly polarized, wave approaching. Express the electric field of the superposition of these two waves at any z, t:

(a) In complex form;
(b) As a real, physical field.

Conditions for Elliptical Polarization

5.5 For the quadratic form $AX^2 + 2BXY + CY^2 = 1$ to represent an ellipse, it is not sufficient that the discriminant $AC - B^2$ be positive; either A or C must also be positive. Is the latter condition necessarily satisfied when A, B, B, and C are the components of the matrix $\mathbf{G} = (\mathbf{MM}')^{-1}$ we used to establish that the polarization is elliptic?

Sense of Rotation Around Ellipse

5.6 Identify the sense of rotation of the following elliptically polarized plane waves, using the engineering standard (RHEP or LHEP handedness, with wave approaching and $e^{j\omega t}$ time dependence). E_0 is a real scale factor.

(a) Given orthogonal components:

$$\mathbf{E} = E_0\{\hat{\mathbf{x}}[5 - j3] + \hat{\mathbf{y}}[-2 + j]\}e^{-jkz}.$$

(b) Given real and imaginary parts:

$$\mathbf{E} = E_0\{[2\hat{\mathbf{x}} + 3\hat{\mathbf{y}}] + j[5\hat{\mathbf{x}} - 6\hat{\mathbf{y}}]\}e^{-jkz}.$$

(c) Given components as magnitude and phase:

$$\mathbf{E} = E_0\{\hat{\mathbf{x}}5e^{j\pi/8} - \hat{\mathbf{y}}3e^{-j\pi/6}\}e^{-jkz}.$$

(d) Given as combinations of circularly polarized waves:

$$\mathbf{E} = E_0\{(3 + j2)[\hat{\mathbf{x}} + j\hat{\mathbf{y}}] + (1 - j3)[\hat{\mathbf{x}} - j\hat{\mathbf{y}}]\}e^{-jkz}.$$

Identifying Polarization Properties

5.7 Find X (and Y) in each case if:
(a) $\mathbf{E} = E_0\{[3\hat{\mathbf{x}} + 4\hat{\mathbf{y}}] + j[-5\hat{\mathbf{x}} + X\hat{\mathbf{y}}]\}e^{-jkz}$ is a linearly polarized wave.
(b) $\mathbf{E} = E_0\{\hat{\mathbf{x}}[3 + j4] + \hat{\mathbf{y}}[-5 + jX]\}e^{-jkz}$ is a linearly polarized wave.
(c) $\mathbf{E} = E_0\{[3\hat{\mathbf{x}} + X\hat{\mathbf{y}}] + j[4\hat{\mathbf{x}} + Y\hat{\mathbf{y}}]\}e^{-jkz}$ is a circularly polarized wave (RHCP).

Properties of the Polarization Ellipse

5.8 Let dA be the infinitesimal area swept out by the $\mathscr{E}(t)$ vector in time dt as it traces out the polarization ellipse, as in Fig. P5–8.
(a) Express dA/dt in terms of $\mathscr{E}$ and $d\mathscr{E}/dt$.
(b) Express dA/dt in terms of $\mathbf{E}_1$ and $\mathbf{E}_2$, the real and imaginary parts of the complex amplitude $\mathbf{E}$. Confirm that this is constant, so that equal

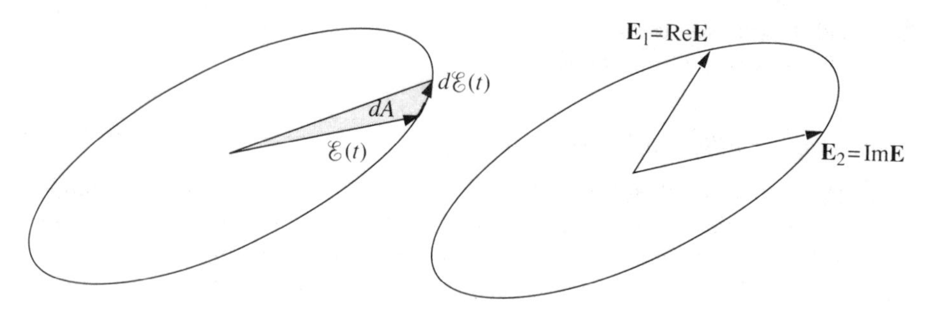

FIGURE P5–8 Area swept out by elliptically polarized field vector.

areas are swept out in equal times. The rate of rotation is therefore slower at the apogee and faster at the perigee, as for planetary orbits.

Another Description of Polarization

5.9 An alternative to specifying the wave polarization through the real and imaginary parts of the complex amplitude **E** is furnished by the single complex number $m = E_y/E_x$ (for a wave propagating along z).

(a) If m is real, the wave is linearly polarized. What is the angle from the x-axis to the direction of polarization?

(b) If $m = \pm j$, the wave is circularly polarized. Which sign corresponds to RHCP?

(c) If $m = Me^{j\varphi}$, what range of φ corresponds to each of RHEP and LHEP?

Poincaré Sphere

5.10 Still another description of waves and their polarization is provided by the Stokes parameters, which are quadratically related to the field amplitudes, and by expressing these parameters in spherical coordinates, thereby mapping them onto the Poincaré sphere. The Stokes parameters are defined (for a wave propagating along z) in terms of $E_x = E_1 e^{j\delta_1}$ and $E_y = E_2 e^{j\delta_2}$ by the four quantities s_0, s_1, s_2, and s_3 (not all independent) in

$$s_0 = E_1^2 + E_2^2 \qquad s_1 = E_1^2 - E_2^2 \qquad s_2 = 2E_1E_2 \cos\delta \qquad s_3 = 2E_1E_2 \sin\delta$$

where $\delta = \delta_2 - \delta_1$. Noting that $s_0^2 = s_1^2 + s_2^2 + s_3^2$, the polarization can then be specified by the two angular spherical coordinates χ and ψ in

$$s_1 = s_0 \cos 2\chi \cos 2\psi \qquad s_2 = s_0 \cos 2\chi \sin 2\psi \qquad s_3 = s_0 \sin 2\chi .$$

Note that the radius of the sphere is proportional to the wave energy; the equator of the sphere corresponds to $\chi = 0$ and the north and south poles to $2\chi = \pm\pi/2$. The angles 2χ and 2ψ correspond to latitude and longitude.

(a) What point on the sphere corresponds to linear polarization along a direction at angle θ to the x-axis?
(b) What point on the sphere corresponds to RHCP? to LHCP?
(c) What portions of the sphere correspond to RHEP and LHEP?
(d) If two waves map to diametrically opposed points on the sphere, how are their polarizations related?

Relation of Polarization Ellipse to Complex Amplitude

5.11 If an elliptically polarized plane wave is represented by the complex amplitude $\mathbf{E} = E_x \hat{\mathbf{x}} + E_y \hat{\mathbf{y}}$ with $E_x = E_1 e^{j\delta_1}$ and $E_y = E_2 e^{j\delta_2}$, relate the indicated points A, B, C, D, E, and F on the polarization ellipse and the angle θ and semiaxes a and b shown in Fig. P5–11 to the parameters E_1, δ_1, E_2, and δ_2.

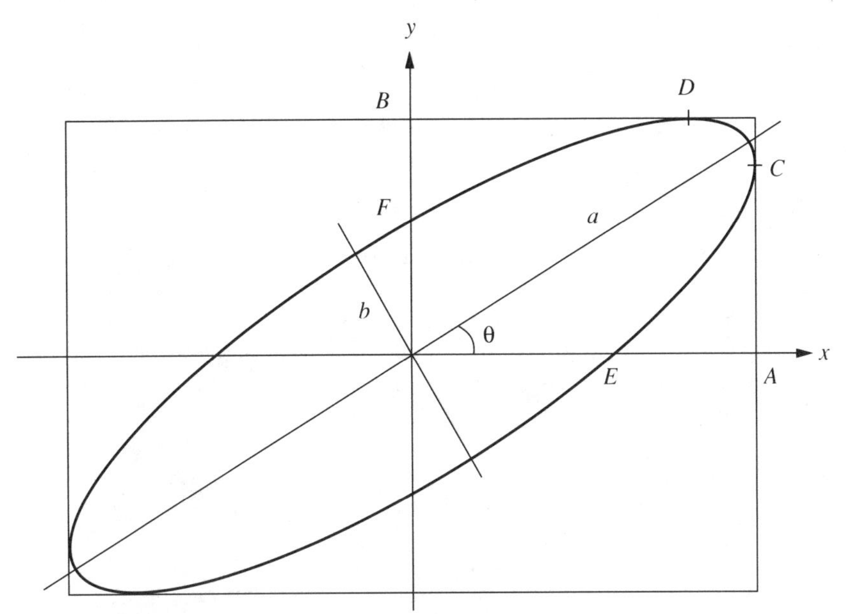

FIGURE P5–11 Salient points of the polarization ellipse.

Measurement of Polarization

5.12 Suppose an antenna is available that responds in proportion to the peak component of the electric field along the direction of the antenna and that the antenna is rotated in the plane perpendicular to the direction of propagation of an incident elliptically polarized plane wave. If the response is plotted, in polar coordinates, as a function of the direction of the antenna, a figure like Fig. P5–12 results. Relate this pattern to the polarization ellipse and show how the parameters of the wave can be deduced from measurements of the dimensions of the figure.

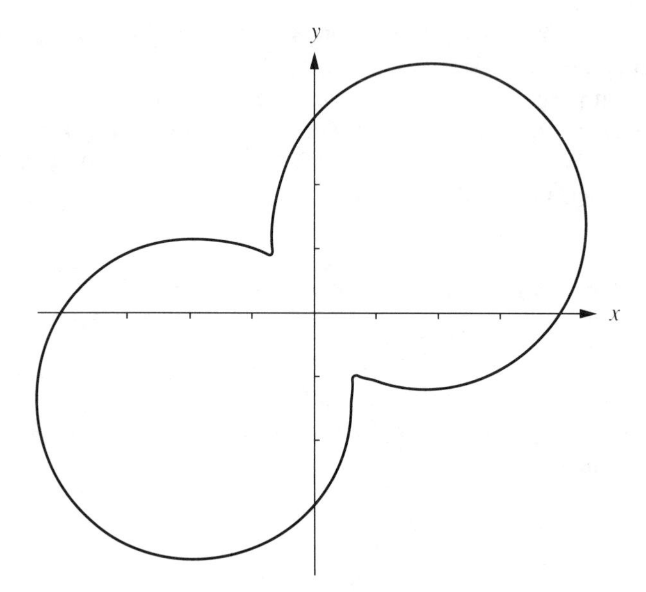

FIGURE P5–12 Polarization pattern for elliptical polarization.

Quarter-Wave Plate

5.13 A birefringent material is one that propagates waves with two different, orthogonal polarizations at different speeds, say c/n_1 and c/n_2 for waves polarized along the x- and y-axes, respectively. A quarter-wave plate made of such material has a thickness l such that the phase difference between waves initially polarized along x and along y is $\pi/2$ after traversing the distance l.

(a) How thick (in terms of free-space wavelength) is a quarter-wave plate?

(b) If a wave is initially linearly polarized along a direction at 45° to the x-axis, what will its polarization be at the other end of the plate?

CHAPTER 6

Wave Dispersion and Complex Power

Expressing fields and waves in the frequency domain means dealing with signals one frequency at a time. The great convenience that results stems from the fact that complex exponentials (single-frequency sinusoids) survive any linear operation with only their amplitude affected; these signals are otherwise undistorted by the linear process. Such Fourier analysis is useful because any signal in time can be expressed as a superposition of complex exponentials. The effect of the linear system on an arbitrary signal can be found by reverting to the time domain after the effect on the amplitude of each frequency component has been found. We therefore lose no generality but gain simplicity by dealing with single-frequency exponentials.

The frequency-domain approach becomes even more useful when we learn how to interpret and manipulate single-frequency results in a way that allows us to extract certain hidden information without actually reverting to the time domain. Such concealed information is of two types. One is the sort that involves a small range of frequencies; the other would normally be found only after nonlinear operations, which do not preserve exponentials. The former involves a special class of information-bearing, narrow-band signals; they are dealt with by studying wave dispersion. The other type involves the nonlinear operations that yield energy and power; they entail quadratic operations on the fields and can be dealt with in terms of complex power expressions.

Narrow-Band Signals

Of itself, a single-frequency sinusoid, forever oscillating with fixed amplitude, phase, and frequency, conveys almost no information at all. It carries no message other than its own existence and the duration of its period. An information-bearing signal is comprised of an entire spectrum of frequencies. How the spectrum is affected when the signal is conveyed from a transmitter to a receiver is an important engineering concern.

In a vacuum, the single-frequency exponential $e^{j\omega t}$ is transmitted as $e^{j(\omega t - kz)}$ and the phase constant k is proportional to the frequency ω: $k = k(\omega) = \omega/c$

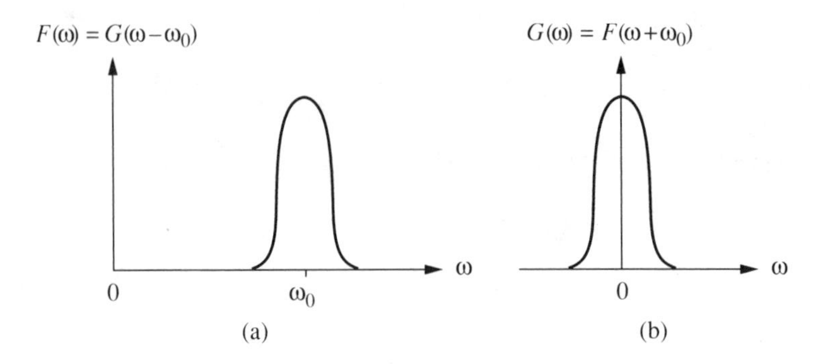

FIGURE 6–1 Spectra $F(\omega)$ and $G(\omega)$ of a narrow-band signal and its envelope.

so that the phase velocity $\omega/k = c$ is the same for all frequency components. All the frequencies in the spectrum are transmitted at the same speed and the entire signal arrives undistorted.

For a medium in which the constitutive parameters μ and ε are dependent on frequency, the phase constant is a more complicated function of frequency: $k = k(\omega) = \omega\sqrt{\mu(\omega)\varepsilon(\omega)}$, so that the phase velocity $\omega/k = 1/\sqrt{\mu(\omega)\varepsilon(\omega)} = v_p(\omega)$ is no longer the same for all frequencies. Different frequencies in the spectrum of the signal are transmitted at different speeds and arrive at different times. The reconstructed signal at the receiver therefore appears distorted. We say that the medium is *dispersive* when the phase velocity depends on the frequency.

For an important class of information-bearing signals, the distortion is benign. The full signal does get distorted in a dispersive medium, but the information in the signal can remain undistorted, being merely transmitted at a speed different from that of any frequency component. This class comprises narrow-band signals, meaning that the spectrum is confined to a relatively narrow range of frequencies.

First, we verify that narrow-band signals represent slow modulations of a high-frequency sinusoidal "carrier" oscillation. If the spectrum $F(\omega)$ of the signal is significantly different from zero only in a narrow band of frequencies near $\omega = \omega_0$, as shown in Figure 6–1, it can be expressed as a shifted version $F(\omega) = G(\omega - \omega_0)$ of a spectrum $G(\omega)$ that is confined to the vicinity of zero frequency. The nature of the time-domain signal is revealed by the change of variable $\omega = \omega_0 + \Omega$, $d\omega = d\Omega$ in the inverse Fourier transform:

$$\begin{aligned} f(t) &= \int F(\omega) e^{j\omega t} \frac{d\omega}{2\pi} && (\omega \text{ near } \omega_0) \\ &= \int F(\omega_0 + \Omega) \exp\left[j(\omega_0 + \Omega)t\right] \frac{d\Omega}{2\pi} && (\Omega \text{ near } 0) \\ &= e^{j\omega_0 t} \int G(\Omega) e^{j\Omega t} \frac{d\Omega}{2\pi} && (\Omega \text{ near } 0) \\ &= e^{j\omega_0 t} g(t), && (6.1) \end{aligned}$$

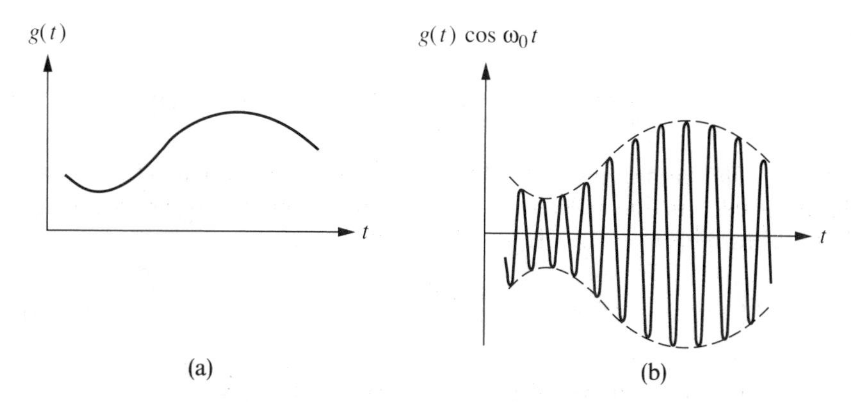

FIGURE 6–2 (a) Envelope signal and (b) modulated carrier.

where $g(t)$ is the inverse Fourier transform of the spectrum $G(\omega)$ that has the same shape as the $F(\omega)$ spectrum, but centered about zero frequency, not about the central frequency ω_0. The last form of the narrow-band signal $f(t)$ shows it to be a complex exponential $e^{j\omega_0 t}$ multiplied by an amplitude factor $g(t)$ that is a function of time. The product is a sinusoidal oscillation whose amplitude varies in time. Since the spectrum of $g(t)$, which is $G(\omega)$, contains only low frequencies (low compared to ω_0), the time signal $g(t)$ is slowly varying (slow compared to the period $2\pi/\omega_0$). The underlying oscillation of the carrier is therefore still recognizable as a sinusoidal swing over short time intervals, but the amplitude of this oscillation changes slowly, over longer time spans. The slowly varying amplitude is called the envelope of the modulated carrier signal, as suggested schematically in Figure 6–2. Thus, a narrow-band signal is equivalent to a slowly modulated sinusoid. We can now ask how the narrow-band signal $f(t)$ gets transmitted in a given medium.

Group Velocity

In a vacuum, the signal $f(t) = g(t)e^{j\omega t}$ emitted by the transmitter is received at distance z as $f(t - z/c) = g(t - z/c)e^{j\omega(t - z/c)}$, where $c = (\mu_0 \varepsilon_0)^{-1/2}$. In a dielectric, however, with μ and ε functions of ω, there is no single value of $(\mu\varepsilon)^{-1/2}$ that will be valid for all frequencies. We do know that each individual frequency will propagate with its own phase constant $k = k(\omega)$, however. This means that $e^{j\omega t}$ at $z = 0$ becomes $\exp\{j[\omega t - k(\omega)z]\}$ at $z \neq 0$, where $k(\omega) = \omega\sqrt{\mu(\omega)\varepsilon(\omega)}$. Hence the effect of the linear medium is obtainable by superimposing all the frequency components, each individually affected by its own propagation factor. That is, we know what happens to each component of the spectrum of the emitted signal and we can reconstruct what the receiver sees by reverting to the time domain, through the inverse Fourier transform:

$$f(t) = \int F(\omega)e^{j\omega t}\,\frac{d\omega}{2\pi} \qquad \text{(at } z = 0\text{)} \tag{6.2}$$

becomes

$$f(z, t) = \int F(\omega) \exp\{j[\omega t - k(\omega)z]\} \frac{d\omega}{2\pi} \qquad (\text{at } z \neq 0). \tag{6.3}$$

This is valid for any signal in a linear medium, even a wideband one, but we can go further for the special case of a narrow-band signal, using the same change of variable $\omega = \omega_0 + \Omega$ as applied earlier.

$$\begin{aligned} f(z, t) &= \int F(\omega) \exp\{j[\omega t - k(\omega)z]\} \frac{d\omega}{2\pi} && (\omega \text{ near } \omega_0) \\ &= \int F(\omega_0 + \Omega) \exp\{j[(\omega_0 + \Omega)t - k(\omega_0 + \Omega)z]\} \frac{d\Omega}{2\pi} && (\Omega \text{ near } 0) \\ &= e^{j\omega_0 t} \int G(\Omega) \exp\{j[\Omega t - k(\omega_0 + \Omega)z]\} \frac{d\Omega}{2\pi} && (\Omega \text{ near } 0). \end{aligned} \tag{6.4}$$

Since $\omega = \omega_0 + \Omega$ is near ω_0 and assuming that the function $k(\omega)$ is well behaved in the vicinity of the carrier frequency ω_0, we can express $k(\omega)$ as a Taylor series about ω_0:

$$\begin{aligned} k(\omega) = k(\omega_0 + \Omega) &= k(\omega_0) + \left[\frac{dk}{d\omega}\right]_0 \Omega + \frac{1}{2}\left[\frac{d^2k}{d\omega^2}\right]_0 \Omega^2 + \cdots \\ &\approx k_0 + \left[\frac{dk}{d\omega}\right]_0 \Omega. \end{aligned} \tag{6.5}$$

The approximation that retains only the first two terms of the series is valid if terms quadratic, and of higher order, in the small quantity Ω are negligible, compared to the linear terms retained. The quantity k_0 is just the phase constant $k(\omega_0)$, at the central frequency ω_0; the derivatives of $k(\omega)$ are all evaluated at this carrier frequency.

Provided that the approximation is valid in the narrow band near ω_0, substitution of $k(\omega_0 + \Omega) = k_0 + [dk/d\omega]_0 \Omega$ into the last of the inverse transform expressions for $f(z, t)$ yields

$$\begin{aligned} f(z, t) &= e^{j\omega_0 t} \int G(\Omega) \exp\left\{j\left[\Omega t - \left(k_0 + \left[\frac{dk}{d\omega}\right]_0 \Omega\right)z\right]\right\} \frac{d\Omega}{2\pi} \\ &= e^{j\omega_0 t} e^{-jk_0 z} \int G(\Omega) \exp\left\{j\left[\Omega t - \left[\frac{dk}{d\omega}\right]_0 \Omega z\right]\right\} \frac{d\Omega}{2\pi} \\ &= e^{j(\omega_0 t - k_0 z)} \int G(\Omega) \exp\left\{j\left[\Omega\left(t - \left[\frac{dk}{d\omega}\right]_0 z\right)\right]\right\} \frac{d\Omega}{2\pi}. \end{aligned} \tag{6.6}$$

The integral in the last expression is already known, however, since the envelope signal $g(t)$ was defined in terms of its spectrum $G(\Omega)$ by the inverse transform in Eq. (6.1): Since $\int G(\Omega)\exp(j\Omega t)\,d\Omega/2\pi = g(t)$,

$$\int G(\Omega)\exp\{j[\Omega(t-[dk/d\omega]_0 z)]\}\,d\Omega/2\pi = g(t-[dk/d\omega]_0 z), \quad (6.7)$$

so that, finally,

$$\begin{aligned} f(z, t) &= e^{j(\omega_0 t - k_0 z)} g\left(t - \left[\frac{dk}{d\omega}\right]_0 z\right) \\ &= \exp\left\{j\omega_0\left(t - \left[\frac{k_0}{\omega_0}\right] z\right)\right\} g\left(t - \left[\frac{dk}{d\omega}\right]_0 z\right) \end{aligned} \quad (6.8)$$

is the signal received at $z \neq 0$ when the narrow-band signal

$$f(0, t) = f(t) = e^{j\omega_0 t} g(t) \quad (6.9)$$

is emitted at $z = 0$.

To interpret this result, we note first that the emitted narrow-band signal is a product of the carrier oscillation $e^{j\omega_0 t}$ and the envelope signal $g(t)$. We note next that the received signal is also a narrow-band signal, the product of a delayed carrier oscillation $\exp j\omega_0(t - z/u_0)$ and a delayed envelope signal $g(t - z/v_0)$. But the delays that affect the carrier and the envelope in their transmission from the emitter at $z = 0$ to the receiver at z are not the same! Both delays are proportional to the distance z, but with different coefficients and different speeds of propagation:

$$u_0 = \frac{\omega_0}{k_0} \qquad v_0 = \frac{1}{[dk/d\omega]_0} = \left[\frac{d\omega}{dk}\right]_0. \quad (6.10)$$

The former is just the phase velocity, evaluated at the carrier frequency; the latter is called the *group velocity*, also evaluated at the carrier frequency.

$$v_p = \frac{\omega}{k} \qquad v_g = \frac{d\omega}{dk}. \quad (6.11)$$

Mathematically, the distinction is that the phase velocity is the *ratio* of the frequency ω to the phase constant k, while the group velocity is the *derivative* of the frequency with respect to the phase constant; since k is a function of ω, ω is also a function of k and its derivative $d\omega/dk$ can be obtained from either $\omega = \omega(k)$ or the inverse relation $k = k(\omega)$.

Physically, the distinction is that the carrier oscillation propagates as a wave at the phase velocity $v_p(\omega_0)$, while the information-bearing envelope or modulation propagates as a wave at another speed, the group velocity $v_g(\omega_0)$. There is hence progressive slippage between the timing of the underlying carrier and of its envelope. Each factor of the overall signal, the carrier and the envelope, arrives undistorted, but each with its own delay. The product signal is therefore not precisely identical in shape to the emitted signal, but it does preserve the information that was imposed on the carrier by the modulation. For a narrow-band signal, then, the distortion caused by dispersion does not affect the information or message carried by the envelope or modulating signal, and in this sense, this distortion is benign.

The term *group velocity* refers to the group of frequencies, in the vicinity of the carrier frequency, that comprise the narrow-band signal. Another term used to designate a narrow-band signal wave, particularly when the modulation takes the form of a pulse, is *wave packet*. If the envelope is a pulse of finite duration (but much longer than a carrier period), the resultant wave is localized in space as it travels, at the group velocity, forming a wave packet with a recognizable identity. Generally, since the information carried by a modulated carrier wave resides in its envelope, the group velocity represents the velocity of transmission of information.

Dispersion Relation

The functional relation between frequency ω and phase constant k in a medium, or in any wave-propagating structure or system, is the *dispersion relation* for that medium or system.

If ω and k are proportional, as they are in a vacuum, then $d\omega/dk = \omega/k$ and the phase and group velocities are actually the same (in a vacuum, both are c). In that special case, the medium is nondispersive. For any other variation of ω with k, the medium is dispersive. When the wave-propagating features of a medium are being considered, its dispersion relation is one of the most important properties to establish about that medium.

EXAMPLE 6.1

There are many waveguiding media or systems for which the vacuum relationship between frequency and phase constant, $\omega^2 = k^2c^2$, is found to be modified by a constant shift, say ω_c^2, so that the dispersion relation turns out to be

$$\omega^2 = \omega_c^2 + k^2c^2, \tag{6.12}$$

where ω_c is a fixed frequency characteristic of the system or medium. Note that, in such cases, ω_c is the minimum frequency for which waves that satisfy this dispersion relation can propagate: Below that frequency, no real value of the phase constant k could be found.

Examples of such waveguiding systems include metallic waveguides, in the form of hollow pipes of any shape, and also a cold, tenuous plasma (electrified gas). For waveguides, the fixed quantity ω_c is called the cutoff frequency, because waves are unable to propagate below that frequency; this cutoff frequency depends on the size and geometry of the waveguide. For a plasma, typically a gas of ions and unbound electrons, the quantity ω_c is called the plasma frequency; the square of that frequency measures the number of electrons or ions per unit volume.

We will examine waveguides in detail later; at this point, we wish merely to illustrate the distinction between phase and group velocities for any system with this form of dispersion relation. A plot of the dispersion relation, ω versus k, is called the dispersion curve. For this example, the curve is a hyperbola,

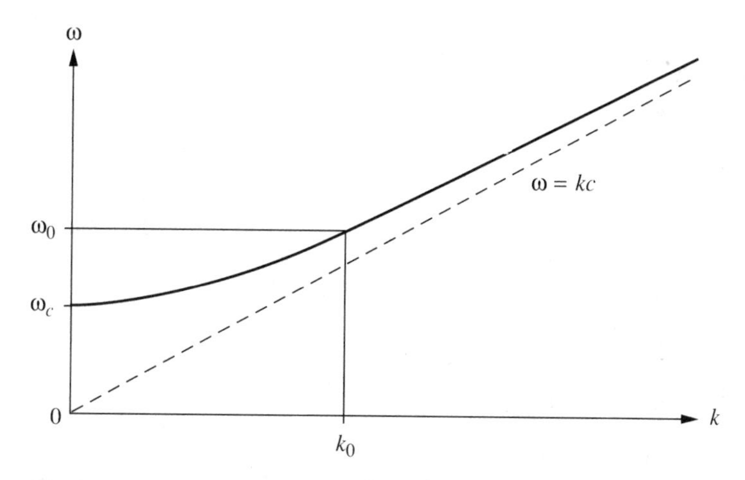

FIGURE 6–3 Dispersion curve $\omega^2 = \omega_c^2 + k^2c^2$ and asymptote $\omega = kc$.

with vertex at ω_c and asymptotic to the line $\omega = kc$; this is shown in Figure 6–3. The phase velocity at frequency ω is

$$v_p = v_p(\omega) = \frac{\omega}{k} = \frac{c\omega}{\sqrt{\omega^2 - \omega_c^2}}. \tag{6.13}$$

Note that the phase velocity exceeds the vacuum speed of light ($v_p > c$) for all frequencies ($\omega > \omega_c$) at which the wave can propagate. In fact, the phase velocity becomes infinitely high as the operating frequency ω drops closer to and approaches the cutoff frequency ω_c. Asymptotically, far above the cutoff frequency, the phase velocity approaches c, from above.

To obtain the group velocity, we need the derivative $d\omega/dk$ at any frequency. It is sufficient simply to differentiate the complete dispersion relation, Eq. (6.12), with respect to k, recalling that ω_c is constant, and to solve for the required derivative: $\omega^2 = \omega_c^2 + k^2c^2$ yields $2\omega(d\omega/dk) = 2kc^2$, so that $d\omega/dk = kc^2/\omega$ or

$$v_g = v_g(\omega) = c\,\frac{\sqrt{\omega^2 - \omega_c^2}}{\omega}. \tag{6.14}$$

Note that the group velocity is less than the vacuum speed of light ($v_g < c$) for all frequencies ($\omega > \omega_c$) at which the wave can propagate. In fact, the group velocity approaches zero as the operating frequency ω drops closer to and approaches the cutoff frequency ω_c. Asymptotically, far above the cutoff frequency, the group velocity approaches c, from below.

Note also that for this case of a hyperbolic type of dispersion relation, the phase and group velocities are related by

$$\frac{d\omega}{dk} = \frac{c^2}{\omega/k} \qquad \text{or} \qquad v_p v_g = c^2, \tag{6.15}$$

so that the product of the phase and group velocities is the same for all frequencies. This is not a general law, however; it is a consequence of the particular form (i.e., hyperbolic) of the dispersion relation in this example. Although it is valid for waveguides of any shape, and also for a plasma, it is by no means universal.

The fact that for these systems, the phase velocity exceeds the speed of light is no cause for alarm, despite the strictures of relativistic mechanics. This is because no object, mass, energy, or even information actually travels at the phase velocity in these systems; only a geometrically defined point does. The phase velocity denotes merely the speed at which an observer would have to travel to keep up with some fixed phase, say a crest, of the wave. That the phase velocity for a waveguide is greater than the vacuum speed of light does not violate relativistic principles. It merely warns us that no observer could ever, in fact, keep up with a fixed phase of this wave. On the other hand, the group velocity represents the speed at which information is conveyed by a narrow-band propagating wave, and information cannot travel faster than light. We did find that the group velocity for the waveguide is less than the speed of light, so that the results are consistent with the requirements of relativity. ◆

It is important to remember that our conclusion that the envelope of a narrow-band signal propagates undistorted in a dispersive medium was dependent on an approximation. In expanding the function $k(\omega)$ in a Taylor series prior to using it in the exponential factor of the Fourier transform, we truncated that series after the linear term. Neglecting the higher-order terms in that series implies that near the carrier frequency, we feel justified in approximating the dispersion curve by a straight line tangent to the curve at the carrier frequency. This is valid only if the neglected terms are sufficiently small, not merely in relation to the terms retained, but small enough to allow their exponential factor in the integrand to be approximated by unity. For the leading neglected term, $\frac{1}{2}[d^2k/d\omega^2](\omega - \omega_0)^2 z$, to be small, the transmission distance must not be too large, the curvature of the dispersion curve, $d^2k/d\omega^2$, must be sufficiently small, and the range of frequencies for which there is significant spectral strength must be narrow enough. The results therefore apply to sufficiently narrow-band signals. The carrier must be at a frequency at which the dispersion curve is well behaved, exhibiting no resonance or discontinuity nearby. At sufficiently great distances z, the neglected terms no longer remain small enough and the envelope signal does suffer distortion in the dispersive medium. In particular, a wave packet will eventually lose its original shape and, typically, stretch out as it travels.

EXAMPLE 6.2

If a waveguide with the hyperbolic dispersion curve considered above is operated with a carrier frequency 10% above the cutoff frequency, how fast will a pulse, or other modulating signal, propagate and how far can it travel before dispersive distortion becomes worrisome? From Eq. (6.14), the group velocity is $c[(\omega_0^2 - \omega_c^2)^{1/2}]/\omega_0$, or $c[1 - (\omega_c/\omega_0)^2]^{1/2}$ with $\omega_0 = 1.1\omega_c$, so that the pulse travels at $(0.4166)c$, or 12.5 cm/ns.

To determine how far the pulse can travel before dispersion affects its shape significantly, examine the highest-order neglected term in the Taylor series for $k(\omega)$ about ω_0. The quadratic term in the series introduces the phase factor $\exp\{-j\frac{1}{2}[d^2k/d\omega^2]_0(\omega - \omega_0)^2 z\}$ into the inverse Fourier transform $f(z, t) = \int F(\omega) \exp\{j[\omega t - k(\omega)z]\}\, d\omega/2\pi$. That factor can safely be replaced by unity, leaving the undistorted pulse $f(z, t) = \exp\{j[\omega_0 t - k_0 z]\}g(t - [dk/d\omega]_0 z)$ as in Eq. (6.8), if $[d^2k/d\omega^2]_0(\omega - \omega_0)^2 z$ remains less than, say, 0.1 in magnitude, over the range of frequencies of significant spectral strength $F(\omega) = G(\omega - \omega_0)$. If the highest frequency in the baseband signal $G(\Omega)$ is Ω_m, then dispersive distortion of the pulse will be negligible for $z < 0.1/|[d^2k/d\omega^2]_0 \Omega_m^2|$. To obtain the curvature $[d^2k/d\omega^2]_0$ of the dispersion relation, we can simply differentiate that relation twice: $\omega^2 = \omega_c^2 + k^2c^2$ has first derivative $2\omega = 2k[dk/d\omega]c^2$ and second derivative $2 = 2[dk/d\omega]^2c^2 + 2k[d^2k/d\omega^2]c^2$, so that the curvature at frequency ω is

$$\frac{d^2k}{d\omega^2} = \frac{1 - [dk/d\omega]^2c^2}{kc^2} = -\frac{[\omega^2/k^2c^2] - 1}{kc^2}$$
$$= -\frac{\omega_c^2}{c(\omega^2 - \omega_c^2)^{3/2}}. \tag{6.16}$$

Hence the distance the pulse can propagate before dispersion may become worrisome is given approximately by

$$z < 0.1\left[\frac{c}{\omega_c}\right]\left(\frac{\omega_c}{\Omega_m}\right)^2\left[\left(\frac{\omega_0}{\omega_c}\right)^2 - 1\right]^{3/2}. \tag{6.17}$$

We have stipulated that $\omega_0/\omega_c = 1.1$; suppose also that the waveguide cutoff frequency is $\omega_c/2\pi = 10$ GHz and that the highest frequency in the spectrum of the modulating pulse is $\Omega_m/2\pi = 1$ MHz; the latter implies that the pulse duration is of the order of 1 μs. Then $\omega_c/\Omega_m = 10^4$ and $0.1(c/\omega_c) = 0.477$ mm, so that, finally, $z < 4.6$ km keeps the phase factor near unity. The 1-μs pulse could travel up to 4.6 km along the waveguide before dispersion might begin to distort its shape significantly. ◆

Wave Velocities

We have encountered three velocities associated with the propagation of waves in dispersive media. We can summarize these as follows.

1. The phase velocity, v_p, is the velocity of a point of observation moving so as to maintain the phase of the wave at some fixed value:

$$v_p = \frac{\omega}{k}. \tag{6.18}$$

The direction of motion of the observer who keeps up with a fixed phase is along the wave vector $\mathbf{k} = k\hat{\mathbf{n}}$ in the plane-wave expression $f(\omega t - \mathbf{k} \cdot \mathbf{r})$, so that the vector phase velocity is given by

$$\mathbf{v}_p = \frac{\omega}{k}\,\hat{\mathbf{n}} = \frac{\omega}{k^2}\,\mathbf{k}. \tag{6.19}$$

2. The group velocity, v_g, is the velocity at which the slow modulation of a sinusoidal carrier wave propagates:

$$v_g = \frac{d\omega}{dk}, \tag{6.20}$$

where the derivative of $\omega = \omega(k)$ is evaluated at the carrier frequency. More generally, the frequency is a function of the wave vector $\mathbf{k}$ and the group velocity is then a vector:

$$\mathbf{v}_g = \frac{\partial\omega}{\partial\mathbf{k}}, \tag{6.21}$$

which means a vector whose components are $\partial\omega/\partial k_x$, $\partial\omega/\partial k_y$, $\partial\omega/\partial k_z$, or the gradient of the scalar $\omega = \omega(k_x, k_y, k_z)$ in the space of the wave vector $\mathbf{k}$.

3. The energy velocity, v_e, is the rate of flow of wave energy, defined as the ratio of the power flow to the energy density:

$$v_e = \frac{P}{W} \quad \text{or} \quad \mathbf{v}_e = \frac{\mathbf{E}\times\mathbf{H}}{\frac{1}{2}\mathbf{E}\cdot\mathbf{D} + \frac{1}{2}\mathbf{H}\cdot\mathbf{B}}. \tag{6.22}$$

In a vacuum, all three of these wave velocities are the same and equal in magnitude to c.

The notion of the group velocity is appropriate for a narrow-band signal, in a spectral region for which the dispersion relation is close to linear. If the dispersion curve departs significantly from a straight line near the carrier frequency, we say that we are in a region of "anomalous dispersion" and the Taylor series expansion of $k(\omega)$ requires more than just the linear terms. There is then significant distortion of the envelope signal and the concept of group velocity loses its meaning.

For the energy velocity, the ratio of power flow to energy density may well be highly oscillatory and the ratio of their time averages is then a more appropriate and useful measure of the velocity of flow of energy in the wave. We need to examine next how to extract quantities quadratically related to the fields, such as energy or power, particularly their time averages.

Time-Averaged Quadratic Quantities

With harmonic fields expressed in complex form in terms of their Fourier amplitude, as in

$$\mathscr{E}(\mathbf{r}, t) = \operatorname{Re}\{\mathbf{E}(\mathbf{r})e^{j\omega t}\}, \tag{6.23}$$

the results of applying any linear operator to the time-domain field $\mathscr{E}$ will leave a harmonic quantity of the same frequency, expressible in the same form. The linear operation will affect only the frequency-domain complex Fourier amplitude. For example, the time derivative of $\mathscr{E}$ retains the same form, but with $\mathbf{E}$ replaced by $j\omega\mathbf{E}$. As long as only linear operations are performed, it suffices to deal with the complex amplitude alone, in the frequency domain. Appending the $e^{j\omega t}$ factor and taking the real part is then necessary only to find the corresponding result in the time domain, particularly for purposes of interpretation. This step can be relegated to the end of the calculation after all the linear manipulations have been carried out on the complex amplitudes.

This is not the case for quantities related nonlinearly to the fields, in particular for quadratic quantities, such as energy or power. Nonlinear operations, including squaring or multiplying fields, should be performed only on the time-domain expressions. As an example, the power flow in the field expressed by Eq. (6.23) is given by the Poynting vector field

$$\mathscr{P}(\mathbf{r}, t) = \mathscr{E}(\mathbf{r}, t) \times \mathscr{H}(\mathbf{r}, t) = \text{Re}\,\{\mathbf{E}(\mathbf{r})e^{j\omega t}\} \times \text{Re}\,\{\mathbf{H}(\mathbf{r})e^{j\omega t}\}. \tag{6.24}$$

Since each factor involves a combination of $\cos \omega t$ and $\sin \omega t$, the product includes terms oscillating as $\cos^2 \omega t$, as $\sin^2 \omega t$, and as $\sin \omega t \cos \omega t$. The Poynting vector is not simply harmonic at frequency ω and is not expressible directly in the form of Eq. (6.23). In particular, the vector quantity $\mathbf{E} \times \mathbf{H}$ is not usable instead of the field in Eq. (6.24); it is not only a constant but a complex quantity as well, while the Poynting vector is real and oscillating. Nor is the quantity $\text{Re}\,\{\mathbf{E} \times \mathbf{H}\}$ appropriate as the power flow; it is real, but still a constant. Furthermore, $\text{Re}\,\{\mathbf{E} \times \mathbf{H}e^{j\omega t}\}$ is also not correct for the Poynting vector, which oscillates at 2ω, not at ω. Even $\text{Re}\,\{\mathbf{E} \times \mathbf{H}e^{j2\omega t}\}$ is not the correct expression; it averages to zero, while the Poynting vector has a nonzero time average. Only the fully expanded, time-domain expression in Eq. (6.24) can serve as the Poynting vector, because it is quadratically, not linearly, related to the harmonic fields.

The same applies to the energy in a harmonic signal expressed as $\mathscr{F}(t) = \text{Re}\,\{Fe^{j\omega t}\}$, with $F = |F|e^{j\varphi}$, for which the actual signal is given by $\mathscr{F}(t) = |F| \cos(\omega t + \varphi)$, while the energy is proportional to the square of the time-domain signal, $\mathscr{F}^2(t) = |F|^2 \cos^2(\omega t + \varphi)$. This is not correctly given by the complex constant F^2, which is $|F|^2 e^{j2\varphi} = |F|^2 \cos 2\varphi + j|F|^2 \sin 2\varphi$, nor by $\text{Re}\,\{F^2\}$, which is just $|F|^2 \cos 2\varphi$, nor even by $\text{Re}\,\{F^2 e^{j\omega t}\}$, which is $|F|^2 \cos(\omega t + 2\varphi)$ but still not the correct expression $|F|^2 \cos^2(\omega t + \varphi)$. The time-domain expression must be obtained before any nonlinear operation can safely be applied to a harmonic signal.

There is a short cut, however, to extracting certain important quantities quadratically related to harmonic fields from their complex expressions in the frequency domain. These quantities are the *time averages* of the power or energy associated with these signals. Not only are these averages of intrinsic interest and often sufficiently informative, they may well be the only measurable aspect of the power or energy in the signal, because the quadratic quantities oscillate rapidly, at twice the frequency of the harmonic signal. Unless the oscillations are sufficiently slow, ordinary instruments cannot follow the rapid variations of the energy in time and yield only their time average as the measurement of the energy in the signal.

We shall denote the time average of a signal $f(t)$ by angular brackets: $\langle f(t) \rangle$. Note that the time average of an oscillating signal is a constant, not a function of time. Note also that time averaging is, in itself, a linear operation. For a harmonic signal, or any signal linearly related to it, the time average of the sinusoidal oscillation is zero. For quantities quadratically related to the harmonic signal, however, we need the time average of, typically, $\cos^2(\omega t + \varphi)$. This is just $\frac{1}{2}$, as is clear from writing $\cos^2(\omega t + \varphi)$ as $\frac{1}{2}[1 + \cos 2(\omega t + \varphi)]$ and noting that the second-harmonic term averages to zero. Consequently, the time average of the energy in the harmonic signal $\mathscr{F}(t) = \text{Re}\{Fe^{j\omega t}\} = |F| \cos(\omega t + \varphi)$ is proportional to $\langle \mathscr{F}^2(t) \rangle$, which is just $\langle |F|^2 \cos^2(\omega t + \varphi) \rangle = \frac{1}{2}|F|^2$. As long as all we want in the end is the *time average* of the energy, not the oscillating energy signal itself, we may extract the result $\langle \mathscr{F}^2(t) \rangle = \frac{1}{2}|F|^2$ directly from the complex amplitude F, by calculating half its squared magnitude, without first obtaining the time-domain signal $\mathscr{F}(t)$, then squaring it, then averaging it.

The same short cut to extracting a time average is available for more general quadratic quantities associated with harmonic signals. Most generally, a product of two harmonic vectors is a sum of products of their components, each of which is itself a harmonic quantity. For a dot product of two harmonic vectors, such as the power density $\mathscr{E}(t) \cdot \mathscr{J}(t)$, the sum involves products of corresponding components; for a cross product of harmonic vectors, such as $\mathscr{E}(t) \times \mathscr{H}(t)$ to form the Poynting vector, the sum involves products of dissimilar components. It suffices to examine the time average of the product of any two harmonic (scalar) quantities $a(t)$ and $b(t)$ in terms of their complex amplitudes A and B; when the average of a product of vectors is needed, sums of such products of scalars can be formed. We will calculate the time average of any such product $a(t)b(t)$ in the time domain once and for all and see that there is a simple short cut to extracting the result directly from A and B in the frequency domain. Since

$$a(t) = \text{Re}[Ae^{j\omega t}] = \text{Re}[|A|e^{j\alpha}e^{j\omega t}] = |A| \cos(\omega t + \alpha) \tag{6.25}$$

$$b(t) = \text{Re}[Be^{j\omega t}] = \text{Re}[|B|e^{j\beta}e^{j\omega t}] = |B| \cos(\omega t + \beta), \tag{6.26}$$

the time average of the product is

$$\begin{aligned} \langle a(t)b(t) \rangle &= \langle |A| \cos(\omega t + \alpha) |B| \cos(\omega t + \beta) \rangle \\ &= |A||B| \langle \cos(\omega t + \alpha) \cos(\omega t + \beta) \rangle \end{aligned} \tag{6.27}$$

and we can readily obtain the time average of the product of two cosine signals by using the trigonometric identity

$$\cos P \cos Q = \tfrac{1}{2} \cos(P - Q) + \tfrac{1}{2} \cos(P + Q). \tag{6.28}$$

Because both $a(t)$ and $b(t)$ oscillate at exactly the same frequency ω, the difference $P - Q = (\omega t + \alpha) - (\omega t + \beta) = \alpha - \beta$ is independent of time and will yield a nonzero average, while the cosine of the sum will oscillate at twice the frequency and average to zero:

$$\begin{aligned}\langle a(t)b(t)\rangle &= \tfrac{1}{2}|A||B|\langle\cos(\alpha - \beta) + \cos(2\omega t + \alpha + \beta)\rangle \\ &= \tfrac{1}{2}|A||B|\cos(\alpha - \beta) + 0.\end{aligned} \tag{6.29}$$

Thus the time average of the product of the harmonic quantities $a(t)$ and $b(t)$, both of them oscillating at the same frequency, is obtainable in terms of their complex amplitudes as half the product of their magnitudes and of the cosine of the difference of their phase angles. But this is even more easily expressed in terms of $A = |A|e^{j\alpha}$ and $B = |B|e^{j\beta}$ by noting that $\cos(\alpha - \beta)$ is $\text{Re}\,[e^{j(\alpha-\beta)}]$ and that the exponential can be factored, so that

$$\begin{aligned}\langle a(t)b(t)\rangle &= \tfrac{1}{2}|A||B|\cos(\alpha - \beta) = \tfrac{1}{2}\,\text{Re}\,\{|A||B|e^{j(\alpha-\beta)}\} \\ &= \tfrac{1}{2}\,\text{Re}\,\{|A|e^{j\alpha}|B|e^{-j\beta}\} = \tfrac{1}{2}\,\text{Re}\,\{AB^*\},\end{aligned} \tag{6.30}$$

where B^* is the complex conjugate of B. Note also that AB^* and A^*B are complex conjugates of each other and hence have the same real part.

The final result for the time average of the product of two harmonic quantities oscillating at the same (nonzero) frequency is expressed by

$$\langle a(t)b(t)\rangle = \tfrac{1}{2}\,\text{Re}\,\{AB^*\} = \tfrac{1}{2}\,\text{Re}\,\{A^*B\} \tag{6.31}$$

and provides a direct route from the frequency-domain complex amplitudes A and B to the time-averaged product of the corresponding time-domain signals $a(t)$ and $b(t)$.

Since a product of vectors, whether it be a dot or a cross product (or even a more general dyadic product), involves a sum of products of their components, and since the real part of a sum is the sum of the real parts, the same result applies to the time average of a product of two harmonic vectors, both oscillating at the same frequency. For example,

$$\langle \mathscr{E}(t) \cdot \mathscr{J}(t)\rangle = \text{Re}\,[\tfrac{1}{2}\mathbf{E} \cdot \mathbf{J}^*] = \text{Re}\,[\tfrac{1}{2}\mathbf{E}^* \cdot \mathbf{J}] \tag{6.32}$$

and

$$\langle \mathscr{E}(t) \times \mathscr{H}(t)\rangle = \text{Re}\,[\tfrac{1}{2}\mathbf{E} \times \mathbf{H}^*]. \tag{6.33}$$

Provided that all we seek is the time average of the product of two harmonic signals of identical frequencies, these formulas are short cuts that avoid the lengthy process of first converting both of the complex amplitudes to time signals by appending the $e^{j\omega t}$ factor and taking the real part of each, then multiplying the oscillating signals, and then time averaging. We need only complex conjugate one of the two complex amplitudes before multiplying them, and then take one-half of the real part. This simplified calculation is performed entirely in the frequency-domain.

We will use this important result to interpret the even more important complex Poynting theorem.

Complex Poynting Theorem

Upon performing the manipulations that led to the Poynting theorem (Chapter 4) upon the Maxwell equations in the frequency domain, we are led to results that are similar to, yet go beyond, those in the time domain. The complex form of Maxwell's equations relates the complex amplitudes of the electromagnetic fields to that of the source current density. Time, t, does not appear in these equations, having been replaced by frequency, ω; in particular, time derivatives appear as $j\omega$ factors in the linear Maxwell equations, as in Eq. (5.6). We now replace one of the two Maxwell equations by its own complex conjugate, obtaining

$$\nabla \times \mathbf{E} = -j\omega\mathbf{B}, \qquad \nabla \times \mathbf{H}^* = -j\omega\mathbf{D}^* + \mathbf{J}^*. \tag{6.34}$$

We combine these relations as we did for the time-domain Poynting theorem earlier, using the same vector identity involving the divergence of a cross product, to write the field-source product $\mathbf{E} \cdot \mathbf{J}^*$ in terms of fields alone.

$$\begin{aligned} \mathbf{E} \cdot \mathbf{J}^* &= \mathbf{E} \cdot (\nabla \times \mathbf{H}^* + j\omega\mathbf{D}^*) \\ &= -\nabla \cdot (\mathbf{E} \times \mathbf{H}^*) + \mathbf{H}^* \cdot \nabla \times \mathbf{E} + j\omega\mathbf{E} \cdot \mathbf{D}^* \\ &= -\nabla \cdot (\mathbf{E} \times \mathbf{H}^*) - j\omega\mathbf{H}^* \cdot \mathbf{B} + j\omega\mathbf{E} \cdot \mathbf{D}^*. \end{aligned} \tag{6.35}$$

We rearrange the terms and multiply by one-half to get

$$-\nabla \cdot (\tfrac{1}{2}\mathbf{E} \times \mathbf{H}^*) = \tfrac{1}{2}\mathbf{E} \cdot \mathbf{J}^* + 2j\omega[\tfrac{1}{4}\mathbf{H}^* \cdot \mathbf{B} - \tfrac{1}{4}\mathbf{E} \cdot \mathbf{D}^*], \tag{6.36}$$

the differential form of the complex Poynting theorem. Its interpretation is easier after integration over some volume V bounded by closed surface S:

$$-\oint_S \tfrac{1}{2}\mathbf{E} \times \mathbf{H}^* \cdot d\mathbf{S} = \int_V \tfrac{1}{2}\mathbf{E} \cdot \mathbf{J}^* \, dV + 2j\omega \int_V [\tfrac{1}{4}\mathbf{H}^* \cdot \mathbf{B} - \tfrac{1}{4}\mathbf{E} \cdot \mathbf{D}^*] \, dV. \tag{6.37}$$

This is the *complex Poynting theorem.* It follows directly from just Maxwell's equations and is valid for harmonic electromagnetic fields at frequency ω, expressed in the frequency domain through the complex vector amplitudes $\mathbf{E}(\mathbf{r})$, $\mathbf{H}(\mathbf{r})$, and so on, for any volume V bounded by closed surface S, with $d\mathbf{S}$ directed outward. Its far-reaching utility will become clear after it is interpreted.

Interpretation

To interpret the complex Poynting theorem, consider first a medium in which the constitutive parameters ε, μ, and σ are real, at least at the frequency ω. Then each of the products of complex amplitudes, $\mathbf{E} \cdot \mathbf{D}^*$, $\mathbf{H}^* \cdot \mathbf{B}$, $\mathbf{E} \cdot \mathbf{J}^*$ is *real.* This is so since then, for example, $\mathbf{E} \cdot \mathbf{D}^* = \varepsilon\mathbf{E} \cdot \mathbf{E}^*$ and the dot product of any complex vector with its own complex conjugate vector is always real, being the sum of the squared magnitudes of its components. Consequently, each of the three integrands on the right side of the theorem is real, making it easy to separate the real and imaginary parts of the entire equation (6.37):

$$\operatorname{Re}\left\{-\oint_S \tfrac{1}{2}\mathbf{E} \times \mathbf{H}^* \cdot d\mathbf{S}\right\} = \int_V \tfrac{1}{2}\mathbf{E} \cdot \mathbf{J}^* \, dV, \tag{6.38}$$

$$\operatorname{Im}\left\{-\oint_S \tfrac{1}{2}\mathbf{E} \times \mathbf{H}^* \cdot d\mathbf{S}\right\} = 2\omega \int_V [\tfrac{1}{4}\mathbf{H}^* \cdot \mathbf{B} - \tfrac{1}{4}\mathbf{E} \cdot \mathbf{D}^*] \, dV. \tag{6.39}$$

But we know how to interpret a product such as $\frac{1}{2}\mathbf{E} \cdot \mathbf{J}^*$. Being real, it equals the time average of the product $\mathscr{E}(\mathbf{r}, t) \cdot \mathscr{J}(\mathbf{r}, t)$, which is the density of power dissipated at the point $\mathbf{r}$. Its integral is the total power expended within volume V, also averaged in time. Thus, in turn,

$$\int_V \tfrac{1}{2}\mathbf{E} \cdot \mathbf{J}^* \, dV = \left\langle \int_V \mathscr{E} \cdot \mathscr{J} \, dV \right\rangle = \langle P \rangle \tag{6.40}$$

is the time-averaged power dissipated in volume V,

$$\int_V \tfrac{1}{4}\mathbf{H}^* \cdot \mathbf{B} \, dV = \left\langle \int_V \tfrac{1}{2}\mathscr{H} \cdot \mathscr{B} \, dV \right\rangle = \langle W_m \rangle \tag{6.41}$$

is the time-averaged magnetic energy stored in volume V, and

$$\int_V \tfrac{1}{4}\mathbf{E} \cdot \mathbf{D}^* \, dV = \left\langle \int_V \tfrac{1}{2}\mathscr{E} \cdot \mathscr{D} \, dV \right\rangle = \langle W_e \rangle \tag{6.42}$$

is the time-averaged electric energy stored in volume V. Rewriting the complex Poynting theorem for the medium with real constitutive parameters in terms of these physical quantities leaves

$$-\oint_S \tfrac{1}{2}\mathbf{E} \times \mathbf{H}^* \cdot d\mathbf{S} = \langle P \rangle + j2\omega\{\langle W_m \rangle - \langle W_e \rangle\} \tag{6.43}$$

and allows the following interpretation of the complex vector $\frac{1}{2}\mathbf{E} \times \mathbf{H}^*$, which is called the *complex Poynting vector*. The inward flux of this complex Poynting vector over any closed surface is a complex number; that number's real part equals the time-averaged total power dissipation in the enclosed volume; its imaginary part equals twice the frequency, multiplied by the difference between the time-averaged total magnetic and electric energy stored in the volume.

Note from our discussion of field energetics in Chapter 4 that the rate at which energy is supplied to a volume across its bounding surface, from the exterior to the interior, is the negative of the surface integral of the time-domain Poynting vector $\mathscr{E} \times \mathscr{H}$ over the bounding surface. Its time average is hence, for the harmonic case,

$$\left\langle -\oint_S \mathscr{E} \times \mathscr{H} \cdot d\mathbf{S} \right\rangle = \operatorname{Re}\left\{-\oint_S \tfrac{1}{2}\mathbf{E} \times \mathbf{H}^* \cdot d\mathbf{S}\right\} = \langle P \rangle, \tag{6.44}$$

by Eq. (6.40). This merely confirms conservation of energy, since the influx of power must get balanced, after time averaging, by the power loss within the volume; the additional rate of storage of energy within the volume is an oscillating quantity that contributes nothing to the time average: For the time-domain Poynting theorem,

$$-\oint_S \mathscr{E} \times \mathscr{H} \cdot d\mathbf{S} = P + \frac{dW}{dt}, \qquad W = W_m + W_e, \tag{6.45}$$

the time average is

$$\left\langle -\oint_S \mathscr{E} \times \mathscr{H} \cdot d\mathbf{S} \right\rangle = \langle P \rangle + \left\langle \frac{dW}{dt} \right\rangle = \langle P \rangle, \tag{6.46}$$

because the time average of the derivative of any periodically oscillating quantity is necessarily zero.

Note also that the complex Poynting theorem, despite its formal similarity to the ordinary Poynting theorem, is not merely a special instance of it for harmonic signals and, in particular, is not obtainable from it by time averaging. First, the complex Poynting theorem is a relation between two complex constant numbers, not between real signals in time. Further, the complex theorem deals with the *difference* between magnetic and electric energies, while the time-domain Poynting theorem speaks of the *sum* of these two stored energies. The two theorems are distinct and independent.

Complex Permittivity

A medium may exhibit a permittivity ε that is complex at some frequency: $\varepsilon(\omega) = \varepsilon_r + j\varepsilon_i$. The complex Poynting theorem is powerful enough to allow us to interpret the behavior of the medium. Since the permittivity enters into the complex expression for the energy density, let us examine the corresponding term in the theorem: $\langle W_e \rangle$ becomes

$$\tfrac{1}{4}\mathbf{E} \cdot \mathbf{D}^* = \tfrac{1}{4}\mathbf{E} \cdot (\varepsilon_r - j\varepsilon_i)\mathbf{E}^* = \tfrac{1}{4}\varepsilon_r \mathbf{E} \cdot \mathbf{E}^* - j\tfrac{1}{4}\varepsilon_i \mathbf{E} \cdot \mathbf{E}^* \tag{6.47}$$

and is now a complex number, not a real one. Upon separating the real and imaginary parts of the complex Poynting theorem,

$$-\nabla \cdot (\tfrac{1}{2}\mathbf{E} \times \mathbf{H}^*) = \tfrac{1}{2}\mathbf{E} \cdot \mathbf{J}^* + 2j\omega[\tfrac{1}{4}\mathbf{H}^* \cdot \mathbf{B} - \tfrac{1}{4}\mathbf{E} \cdot \mathbf{D}^*], \tag{6.48}$$

in this case, the last term becomes a complex number with its own real and imaginary parts:

$$-2j\omega[\tfrac{1}{4}\mathbf{E} \cdot \mathbf{D}^*] = -\tfrac{1}{2}\omega\varepsilon_i \mathbf{E} \cdot \mathbf{E}^* - 2j\omega[\tfrac{1}{4}\varepsilon_r \mathbf{E} \cdot \mathbf{E}^*]. \tag{6.49}$$

The separation of the parts then appears as

$$-\nabla \cdot (\tfrac{1}{2}\mathbf{E} \times \mathbf{H}^*) = \tfrac{1}{2}(\sigma - \omega\varepsilon_i)\mathbf{E} \cdot \mathbf{E}^* + 2j\omega[\tfrac{1}{4}\mathbf{H}^* \cdot \mathbf{B} - \tfrac{1}{4}\varepsilon_r \mathbf{E} \cdot \mathbf{E}^*]. \tag{6.50}$$

We can see now that ε_r plays its usual role as part of the expression for the density of electric energy storage, while ε_i appears conjoined to the conductivity σ (if any) in the term $(\sigma - \omega\varepsilon_i)$. That is, the imaginary part of the complex permittivity, if it is negative and multiplied by the frequency ω, plays the role of an effective *conductivity* for the medium and provides a measure of the Joule heating loss or energy *dissipation* in the medium, rather than of the electric energy *storage*, which is given by the real part of the permittivity. When a medium is reported (after measurement or calculation) to have a complex permittivity, the real part ε_r corresponds to the usual type of permittivity and $-\omega\varepsilon_i$ represents the medium's conductivity; it is then superfluous to report a conductivity σ as a separate property of the medium. A negative imaginary part of the permittivity at a specified frequency corresponds to energy loss in the medium. If the imaginary part is positive, the medium actually generates energy, rather than dissipating it, and is then termed *active*.

Load Impedance

The complex Poynting theorem is especially useful for the calculation of what the source of a desired electromagnetic field configuration will be required to provide, energetically, to set up the field pattern. Both the real power (the power dissipation or expenditure) and the imaginary power (the reactive power, or imbalance in magnetic and electric energy storage) to be used within a volume must be furnished by the external source, generator, or antenna. Both the real and the imaginary power must flow across the bounding surface, from the exterior to the interior, at the rates measured by the real and imaginary parts of $\frac{1}{2}\mathbf{E} \times \mathbf{H}^*$ on the surface.

For example, if a sinusoidal antenna current given by complex amplitude I sets up an electromagnetic field pattern $\mathbf{E}$, $\mathbf{H}$ in the surrounding space, then the real and reactive powers expressed by $\oint_S \frac{1}{2}\mathbf{E} \times \mathbf{H}^* \cdot d\mathbf{S}$ must be supplied by the generator. There is then a "load" on the generator, which therefore "sees" an impedance Z such that the complex power the source supplies is

$$\tfrac{1}{2}|I|^2 Z = \tfrac{1}{2}|I|^2(R + jX) = +\oint_S \tfrac{1}{2}\mathbf{E} \times \mathbf{H}^* \cdot d\mathbf{S}, \tag{6.51}$$

or

$$Z = R + jX = \frac{\oint_S \mathbf{E} \times \mathbf{H}^* \cdot d\mathbf{S}}{|I|^2}. \tag{6.52}$$

This formula allows calculation of the load impedance, as seen by the generator, from the field pattern that it generates. Note that the plus sign is used for the integral in Eq. (6.51). Despite appearances, this is actually consistent with the complex Poynting theorem, which traces the flow of complex power across the bounding surface from the exterior to the interior of the field volume, and with the general convention that the vector element of area $d\mathbf{S}$ always points outward from a closed surface. This is so because the surface of integration

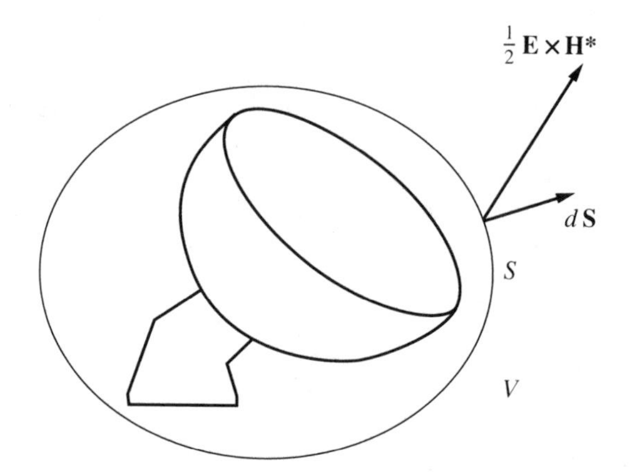

FIGURE 6–4 Complex Poynting vector on surface S around an antenna.

here surrounds and encloses the source antenna and the field volume extends *outside* the antenna volume; consequently, the "exterior" of the field volume V is actually the inside of the antenna volume, where the generator is located, and the "interior" of the field volume is the space surrounding the antenna, outside the bounding surface, where the fields are set up. It is therefore consistent to have the outwardly directed area element $+d\mathbf{S}$ point into the "interior" of the field volume V. Figure 6–4 illustrates this point.

EXAMPLE 6.3

Conceive of the infinitely extended, planar source "antenna" postulated in Chapter 4 to illustrate the emission and propagation of pulses of electromagnetic radiation (as in Figure 4–3) as excited by a collection of generators, each feeding only a finite rectangular area of dimensions l by w. Suppose that each such generator provides a total current $I = I_0 e^{j\omega t}$, distributed uniformly across the width w. What load impedance $Z = R + jX$ is seen by each such plane-wave generator?

The need to consider infinitely many generators is imposed, of course, by the fact that the plane wave is unrealistically extended throughout space and requires an infinite amount of power. A finite area $l \times w$, even if very large, could only approximate a plane-wave generator. By considering a collection of individual finite-power generators, we can have it both ways: We retain the plane wave but examine only the finite amount of power used for a finite portion of the full wave. We must first determine the field strength radiated by the given current distribution; both the electric and magnetic fields should be proportional to that current. We then form the complex Poynting vector, which will be proportional to the magnitude squared of the current, and integrate it over a surface that encloses the generator surface. Dividing out the squared current will leave the load impedance seen by each finite-area generator.

To relate the radiated field pattern to the current flowing on the plane, note first that the antenna is symmetrical: its front and back look identical and radiate the same plane wave on both sides, but in opposite directions. The source current for the electromagnetic field pattern would be given directly by applying Maxwell's equations to the fields, except that there must be a discontinuity in the field pattern, at the source plane itself, to allow the radiation to travel in opposite directions on its two sides. The integral versions of Maxwell's equations, Eqs. (3.7)–(3.8), can deal with discontinuities in fields and relate them to their source currents.

When a field discontinuity occurs across some surface, such as the source plane in question, integration of that field to form an emf or mmf can yield different values on the two sides of that surface. The *difference* between the two integrals along the open paths of integration on the two sides amounts to one overall integration over a closed path that straddles the discontinuity surface but hugs it tightly, as in Figure 6–5. The "enclosed" region then has no thickness, yet must allow for the corresponding source current and rate of change of flux. This places a rigorous constraint on the types of discontinuities that the electromagnetic fields may exhibit. The Faraday–Maxwell law does not permit a difference of emf on the two sides of the discontinuity plane, because that would entail a finite flux across a region devoid of thickness. Hence the electric field components tangential to the plane (the ones that enter into the emf calculation on the two sides) must be the same on both sides of the plane. The Ampère–Maxwell law, however, can allow for a discontinuity in tangential components of magnetic field, provided that a finite current can flow as a "current sheet" along the plane of discontinuity.

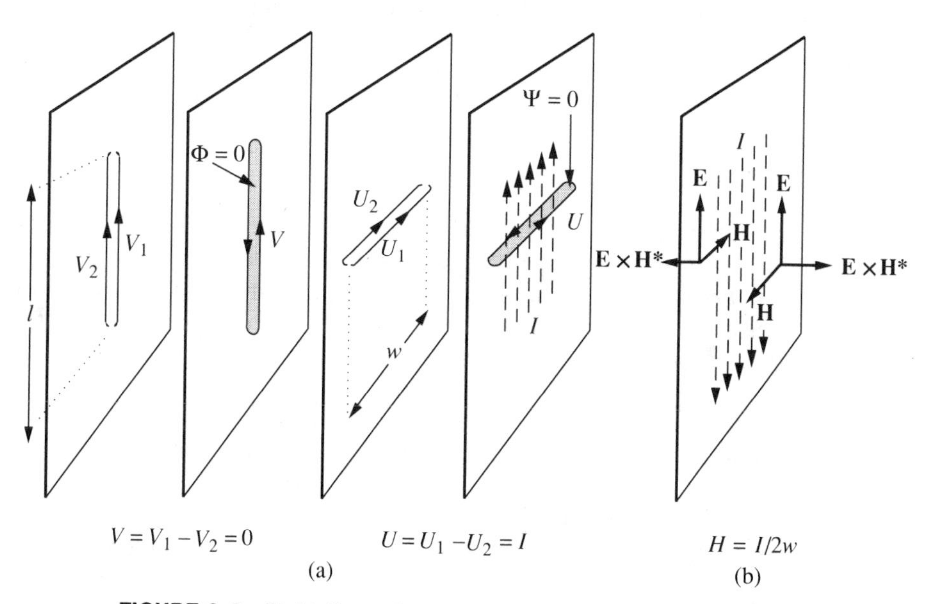

FIGURE 6–5 Field discontinuities and plane-wave generation.

For the case of the plane-wave generator, the electric field must be the same on both sides of the source plane, but the Poynting vector must be directed away from the plane on both sides. This requires that the magnetic field be in opposite directions, tangential to the source plane, on the two sides. The difference between the mmfs along a path of width w on the two sides equals twice that on either side and also equals the current flowing across a width w of the plane, at right angles to that width. Thus the discontinuity in tangential magnetic field equals the surface current per unit width that flows at right angles to that tangential field, directed as dictated by the right-hand rule. As indicated in the figure, the magnetic field on either side of the source plane has a strength equal to one-half of the surface current density: $H = I_0/2w$, oppositely directed on the two sides. From the properties of the plane wave, the electric field on each side has strength $E = \eta_0 H = \eta_0 I_0/2w$, directed the same way on both sides and, in fact, opposite to the direction of the surface current, in order to make the Poynting vector point away from the source plane.

The vector $\mathbf{E} \times \mathbf{H}^*$ points away from the plane and has the magnitude $\eta_0 |I_0|^2/4w^2$ on each side. Integration over an area $l \times w$ on both sides yields $2(lw)\eta_0 |I_0|^2/4w^2 = \eta_0 |I_0|^2 l/2w$ as the value of the closed surface integral $\oint_S \mathbf{E} \times \mathbf{H}^* \cdot d\mathbf{S}$. The load impedance seen by the generator that feeds the $l \times w$ area is hence $Z = \eta_0 l/2w$.

This result can be interpreted as the combination of two resistances $\eta_0 l/w$ in parallel, one for each side of the planar antenna. The impedance is real, representing power loss from the antenna to the radiation field in the surrounding space, which does carry power away to infinity. That the imaginary part is zero implies only that the magnetic and electric energies stored in space are exactly balanced, as was already known for a plane wave. Note that a *square* region of the antenna represents a load of $\eta_0/2$ on the generator that feeds that square, for *any* size $l = w$ of that square. ◆

Summary

We have examined how certain information about harmonic fields can be found directly from their complex expressions in the frequency domain, without the need to convert them first to the time domain. Such information includes properties of narrow-band signals and of the power and energy carried or conveyed by sinusoidal fields. We considered dispersive media, for which the phase velocity depends on the frequency, and found that the information carried by a narrow-band signal is propagated at the group velocity, not the phase velocity. We also found that there is a convenient short cut to extracting the time average of the power or energy in a harmonic signal directly from the complex amplitudes of the fields, by evaluating half the real part of the product of these amplitudes, one of them complex conjugated.

These observations led to the complex Poynting theorem, which was interpreted first for media with real constitutive parameters and then found to be useful for understanding media with complex permittivity or other parameters. Thus, an imaginary part of a permittivity actually represents a conductivity, and vice versa. The complex Poynting theorem also allows the engineer to calculate directly from an electromagnetic field pattern the load impedance presented to whatever generator or antenna is responsible for the existence of the field configuration. This is an important consideration in the design of the structure that can launch a desired wave; it is usually beneficial to arrange for the internal impedance of the wave generator to *match* the complex load impedance presented to it by the radiated fields.

Our time-domain study of plane waves in a vacuum allowed us to deal as well with propagation in idealized perfect dielectrics that have other values of permittivity and permeability, provided that these exhibit no frequency dependence. Our examination of dispersive media now permits us to consider more realistic dielectrics whose parameters do vary with frequency, by viewing the waves in the frequency domain, one frequency at a time. We will next find that we can incorporate conductivity of the medium within the same framework and understand propagation in conductors as well as insulators.

PROBLEMS

Dispersion of Amplitude-Modulated Signal

6.1 An amplitude-modulated signal with high-frequency carrier ω_0 and a modulation consisting of a pure tone of low-frequency ω_1, with modulation depth m, is written as

$$f(t) = [1 + m \cos(\omega_1 t + \varphi)] \cos \omega_0 t.$$

This combines three frequencies, equally spaced by ω_1:

$$f(t) = \cos \omega_0 t + \tfrac{1}{2}m \cos[(\omega_0 + \omega_1)t + \varphi] + \tfrac{1}{2}m \cos[(\omega_0 - \omega_1)t - \varphi].$$

In a dispersive medium, the phase constants at the three frequencies are not in the same proportion; they may not even be equally spaced. Let them be

$$k(\omega_0) = k_0, \quad k(\omega_0 + \omega_1) = k_0 + (k_1 + \kappa), \quad k(\omega_0 - \omega_1) = k_0 - (k_1 - \kappa),$$

so that the phase velocity of the medium at the carrier frequency is ω_0/k_0 and the group velocity would be uniquely ω_1/k_1 if κ were zero.

If the medium were nondispersive ($k_1/\omega_1 = k_0/\omega_0$ and $\kappa = 0$), the signal received at distance z would merely be delayed:

$$f(z, t) = [1 + m \cos(\omega_1 t - k_1 z + \varphi)] \cos(\omega_0 t - k_0 z) = f\left(t - \frac{k_0}{\omega_0} z\right).$$

If the medium were dispersive ($k_1/\omega_1 \neq k_0/\omega_0$) but with a unique group velocity ($\kappa = 0$), the signal received at distance z would still be an amplitude-modulated signal, but the carrier and modulation would be differently delayed:

$$f(z, t) = [1 + m \cos (\omega_1 t - k_1 z + \varphi)] \cos (\omega_0 t - k_0 z).$$

In the present case of unequally spaced phase constants ($\kappa \neq 0$), the received signal is not quite an amplitude-modulated carrier:

$$f(z, t) = \cos \Phi_0(z, t) + m \cos (\omega_1 t - k_1 z + \varphi) \cos \Phi(z, t).$$

How does $\Phi(z, t)$ differ from $\Phi_0(z, t) = (\omega_0 t - k_0 z)$?

Hyperbolic Dispersion Relation

6.2 What is the most general form of the dispersion relation $\omega = \omega(k)$ for which $v_p v_g = c^2$?

Frequency Dependence of Group Velocity

6.3 How much above the cutoff frequency of a waveguide does the carrier have to be for the group velocity of a narrow-band signal to be:
(a) $0.9c$?
(b) $0.5c$?

Dispersion of Gravity Waves

6.4 Gravity waves are characterized by the dispersion relation $\omega^2 = gk$, where $g = 9.8$ m/s^2 is the acceleration of gravity. For a gravity wave at a frequency $f = 0.5$ Hz, find:
(a) The wavelength λ;
(b) The phase velocity, v_p;
(c) The group velocity, v_g.

Arbitrary Dispersion Relation

6.5 The dispersion relation for a certain medium is expressed by

$$\frac{1}{\omega^2} = \frac{1}{\omega_0^2} + \frac{1}{k^2 c^2},$$

where ω_0 is a constant and c is the speed of light. Find, as functions of frequency:

(a) $\dfrac{v_p}{c}$;

(b) $\dfrac{v_g}{c}$.

Relation Between Phase and Group Velocities

6.6 The group velocity of a wave in a certain medium is proportional to frequency: $v_g(\omega) = a\omega$, where a is a constant. It is also known that at a special frequency ω_0, the phase velocity equals the group velocity. What is the phase velocity at other frequencies?

Exceptional Case of Time-Averaged Energy

6.7 The expression $\langle a(t)b(t)\rangle = \frac{1}{2}\operatorname{Re}[AB^*]$ is valid only for $a(t)$ and $b(t)$ oscillating at the same, nonzero frequency.

(a) What is the corresponding result at zero frequency?

(b) What is the result if $a(t)$ and $b(t)$ each includes several frequencies, as in

$$a(t) = \sum A_n e^{j\omega_n t} \quad \text{and} \quad b(t) = \sum B_n e^{j\omega_n t} \qquad \text{(including dc terms)?}$$

Time Average of Derivative of a Periodic Quantity

6.8 Prove that the time average of the time derivative of any periodic signal (not necessarily sinusoidal) must vanish, as mentioned in the text. The average means an average over one or any (whole) number of periods.

Complex Conductivity

6.9 Interpret both the real and imaginary parts of a complex conductivity $\sigma = \sigma_r + j\sigma_i$ of a medium, on the basis of its appearance in the complex Poynting theorem.

Complex Permeability

6.10 Interpret both the real and imaginary parts of a complex permeability $\mu = \mu_r + j\mu_i$ of a medium, on the basis of its appearance in the complex Poynting theorem.

Antenna with Reflector

6.11 Consider again the infinite, planar antenna with infinitely many generators, each feeding a rectangular area $l \times w$ with a current $I = I_0 e^{j\omega t}$, distributed uniformly across the width w. This time, however, a reflector, in the form of a parallel conducting plane, is placed behind the source plane, at distance s, as shown in Fig. P6–11. With $k = \omega/c$, the resultant fields are

$$\mathbf{E} = \hat{\mathbf{x}}E_0 e^{-jkz}, \qquad \eta_0\mathbf{H} = \hat{\mathbf{y}}E_0 e^{-jkz} \qquad (z > 0);$$

$$\mathbf{E} = \hat{\mathbf{x}}E_0 \frac{\sin k(z+s)}{\sin ks}, \qquad \eta_0\mathbf{H} = \hat{\mathbf{y}}E_0 j\frac{\cos k(z+s)}{\sin ks} \qquad (-s < z < 0).$$

(a) How is the complex amplitude E_0 of the radiated plane wave related to the complex generator current I_0?

(b) Obtain the load impedance on each generator, $Z = R + jX$.

(c) How close to the source plane can the reflector be placed if the load impedance is to be kept real?

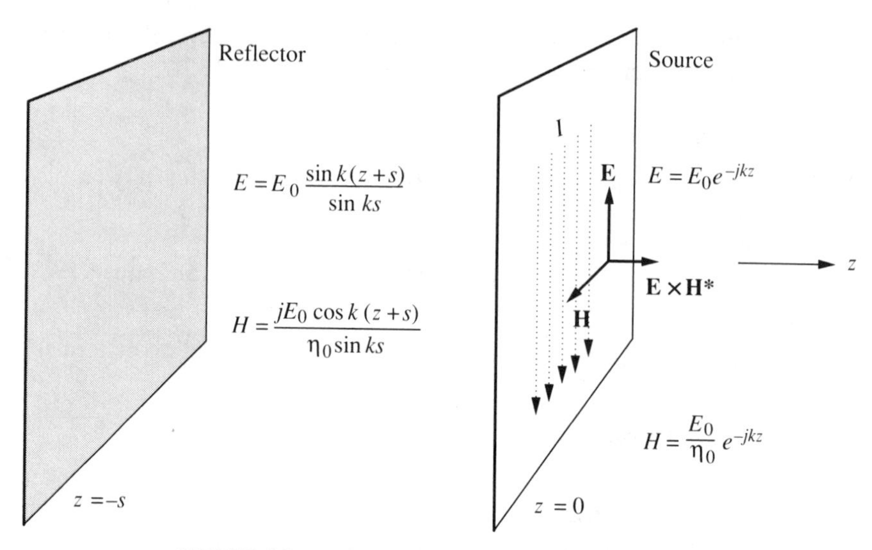

FIGURE P6–11 Plane-wave antenna with reflector.

(d) Find the time-averaged magnetic and electric energies stored between the source and the reflector, W_m and W_e, within the volume defined by the $l \times w$ area.

Pair of Plane-Wave Antennas

6.12 Consider two, parallel, infinite, planar antennas with infinitely many generators that feed a rectangular area $l \times w$, both at frequency ω, with currents I_1 for the first one, located at $z = 0$, and $I_2 = I_1 e^{j\varphi}$ for the other one, located at $z = s$, each current distributed uniformly across the width w. Let E_0 be the field strength generated by the first antenna alone.

(a) Obtain the field in each of the three regions $z > s$, $z < 0$, and $0 < z < s$.

(b) For what phase difference φ can the radiation on one side, say $z < 0$, be eliminated?

(c) For the antennas so phased, what spacing s can maximize the radiation on the other side, $z > s$?

(d) For the antennas so phased and spaced, how much energy is stored between them?

Phased Array of Plane-Wave Antennas

6.13 Consider an array of N equally spaced, parallel, infinite, planar antennas with infinitely many generators that feed a rectangular area $l \times w$, all at frequency ω, with progressively phased currents $I_m = I_0 e^{jm\varphi}$ for the mth one, located at $z = ms$ [with $0 \leq m \leq (N - 1)$], each current distributed uniformly across the width w. Let E_0 be the field strength generated by the first antenna alone.

(a) Obtain the field radiated in the region $z > [N - 1]s$, recalling that the finite sum

$$\sum_{m=0}^{N-1} x^m = \frac{1 - x^N}{1 - x} \qquad \text{if } x \neq 1 \text{ and } N \text{ if } x = 1.$$

(b) Obtain the field radiated in the region $z < 0$.

(c) Design a phasing φ and a spacing s that will minimize the radiation in $z < 0$ and maximize that in $z > [N - 1]s$.

Superposition of Waves of Different Polarization

6.14 Two waves, both at frequency ω and both propagating in air along the z-axis, have identical electromagnetic fields at $z = 0$ and $t = 0$, but one is linearly polarized along the x-axis while the other is RHCP.

(a) Express the electric and the magnetic fields of the superposition of these two waves at any z, t in complex form and also as a real, physical field.

(b) How is the total, time-averaged energy density of the superposition of the two waves related to that of the linearly polarized one alone?

CHAPTER 7

Waves in Conducting Media

To this point we have considered wave propagation in a vacuum and in perfect, lossless dielectrics. Actual dielectric materials always have some conductivity and the perfect insulator is only an idealization, the limit of zero conductivity. Materials with finite conductivity convert a portion of the field energy into thermal form, through Joule heating, so that waves that can propagate in imperfect insulators will lose energy as they travel in the medium. Metals represent another extreme, that of good conductors, in which mobile charge carriers rapidly rearrange themselves whenever electric fields appear, with the result that fields tend to be excluded from the interior of such media. The extreme version is the perfect conductor, the ideal limit of infinite conductivity. We wish to examine fields and waves in conducting media and contrast their behavior with that of their counterparts in perfectly insulating media.

Wave Equation in Conductors

Maxwell's equations applied to harmonic fields at frequency ω are, in the frequency domain,

$$\nabla \times \mathbf{E} = -j\omega\mathbf{B} \qquad \nabla \times \mathbf{H} = j\omega\mathbf{D} + \mathbf{J}, \tag{7.1}$$

where the complex fields depend on position $\mathbf{r}$ only. In a conducting medium, the current density $\mathbf{J}$ is not confined merely to the source antenna but appears additionally as an accompaniment to the electric field, in accordance with Ohm's law $\mathbf{J} = \sigma\mathbf{E}$, wherever $\mathbf{E}$ appears in space. We are considering a medium described by constitutive parameters $\mu = \mu(\omega)$, $\varepsilon = \varepsilon(\omega)$, and $\sigma = \sigma(\omega)$, each evaluated at the frequency ω and each independent of position and real.

In a sourceless region of the medium, the complex Maxwell equations become $\nabla \times \mathbf{E} = -j\omega\mu\mathbf{H}$ and $\nabla \times \mathbf{H} = j\omega\varepsilon\mathbf{E} + \sigma\mathbf{E} = (j\omega\varepsilon + \sigma)\mathbf{E}$. In the last equation, the two terms represent the displacement current and the conduction current. The two partial differential equations may be combined into a single one, of higher order, upon eliminating one of the fields, say $\mathbf{H}$, by taking the curl of the first equation and substituting the second.

$$\nabla \times \nabla \times \mathbf{E} = -j\omega\mu\nabla \times \mathbf{H} = -j\omega\mu(j\omega\varepsilon + \sigma)\mathbf{E} = (\omega^2\mu\varepsilon - j\omega\mu\sigma)\mathbf{E}. \tag{7.2}$$

Now the double curl operation can be simplified by invoking an identity of vector differential calculus that expresses it in terms of the Laplacian operator ∇^2:

$$\nabla \times \nabla \times \mathbf{E} \equiv \nabla\nabla \cdot \mathbf{E} - \nabla^2\mathbf{E}. \tag{7.3}$$

This identity actually defines ∇^2 as applied to a vector, but in rectangular coordinates, $\nabla^2\mathbf{E}$ turns out to be simply the sum of the second partial derivatives in the three coordinates, applied to each component of vector $\mathbf{E}$: $\nabla^2\mathbf{E} = (\partial^2/\partial x^2 + \partial^2/\partial y^2 + \partial^2/\partial z^2)\mathbf{E}$; this justifies the notation ∇^2, based on the components of the gradient operator ∇. In other coordinate systems, the Laplacian is a more complicated differential operator, defined by Eq. (7.3).

There is a further simplification of the double curl operation in Eq. (7.3), based on the fact that $\mathbf{E}$ has no divergence in this medium: $\nabla \cdot \mathbf{E} = 0$, because $\mathbf{E}$ is proportional to $\nabla \times \mathbf{H}$ and a curl never has a divergence. Consequently, in this medium, $\nabla \times \nabla \times \mathbf{E} = -\nabla^2\mathbf{E}$ and the two Maxwell equations combine into the single, second-order wave equation

$$\nabla^2\mathbf{E} + (\omega^2\mu\varepsilon - j\omega\mu\sigma)\mathbf{E} = 0 \tag{7.4}$$

for the vector $\mathbf{E}(\mathbf{r})$ in the conducting dielectric. This may be compared to the corresponding equation for a vacuum, for which $\sigma = 0$ and $\mu = \mu_0$, $\varepsilon = \varepsilon_0$:

$$\nabla^2\mathbf{E} + k^2\mathbf{E} = 0, \qquad k^2 = \omega^2\mu_0\,\varepsilon_0 = \frac{\omega^2}{c^2}. \tag{7.5}$$

The difference is that the coefficient in the case of a conductor is complex, rather than the real k^2. The magnetic field can be obtained from the solution to the equation by using one of Maxwell's equations, $\mathbf{H} = \nabla \times \mathbf{E}/(-j\omega\mu)$.

For simplicity of interpretation, let us once again stipulate that the fields are to vary along only one direction in space, the z-direction. Let us also again seek a linearly polarized electric field; more complicated polarizations will be superpositions of this type. Since $\nabla \cdot \mathbf{E} = 0$ or $dE_z/dz = 0$ for this case of only z-variation, the polarization cannot be along the direction, z, along which the field varies. Let us call the direction of the linear polarization the x-direction: $\mathbf{E} = E\hat{\mathbf{x}}$. Then the second-order wave equation in the conducting medium reduces to

$$\frac{d^2E}{dz^2} + (\omega^2\mu\varepsilon - j\omega\mu\sigma)E = 0. \tag{7.6}$$

This linear, constant-coefficient ordinary differential equation can be solved by an exponential trial function

$$E(z) = E_0\,e^{-\gamma z}, \tag{7.7}$$

provided that

$$\gamma^2 = -\omega^2\mu\varepsilon + j\omega\mu\sigma. \tag{7.8}$$

Since γ^2 is required to be complex, so is γ itself:

$$\gamma = \alpha + j\beta, \tag{7.9}$$

with α and β real and determined by

$$(\alpha + j\beta)^2 = \alpha^2 - \beta^2 + j2\alpha\beta = -\omega^2\mu\varepsilon + j\omega\mu\sigma. \tag{7.10}$$

Upon separating the real and imaginary parts, assuming real μ, ε, and σ at ω, this reduces to

$$\alpha^2 - \beta^2 = -\omega^2\mu\varepsilon, \tag{7.11}$$

$$2\alpha\beta = \omega\mu\sigma. \tag{7.12}$$

These are two equations for the two unknowns α and β and we shall proceed to solve them, after a pause for interpretation of what is being sought.

Interpretation

After $\gamma = \alpha + j\beta$ will have been found, the solution for the complex electric field will take the form

$$E(z) = E_0 e^{-\gamma z} = E_0 e^{-(\alpha + j\beta)z} = E_0 e^{-\alpha z} e^{-j\beta z}, \tag{7.13}$$

with E_0 a possibly complex constant coefficient, $E_0 = |E_0| e^{j\varphi_0}$.

To interpret this solution, the time-dependent harmonic factor $e^{j\omega t}$ is restored and the real part taken, so as to revert to the time domain. This yields

$$\begin{aligned}
\mathscr{E}(z, t) &= \text{Re}\,\{\mathbf{E}e^{j\omega t}\} = \text{Re}\,\{\hat{\mathbf{x}}Ee^{j\omega t}\} = \text{Re}\,\{\hat{\mathbf{x}}E_0 e^{-\alpha z} e^{-j\beta z} e^{j\omega t}\} \\
&= \text{Re}\,\{\hat{\mathbf{x}}|E_0| e^{j\varphi_0} e^{-\alpha z} e^{-j\beta z} e^{j\omega t}\} \\
&= \text{Re}\,\{\hat{\mathbf{x}}|E_0| e^{-\alpha z} e^{j(\omega t - \beta z + \varphi_0)}\} \\
&= \hat{\mathbf{x}}|E_0| e^{-\alpha z} \cos(\omega t - \beta z + \varphi_0).
\end{aligned} \tag{7.14}$$

In particular, at $z = 0$, this solution is just

$$\mathscr{E}(0, t) = \hat{\mathbf{x}}|E_0| \cos(\omega t + \varphi_0), \tag{7.15}$$

so that the outcome of this calculation is that a signal $|E_0| \cos(\omega t + \varphi_0)$ emitted at $z = 0$ will be received at any z as $|E_0| e^{-\alpha z} \cos(\omega t - \beta z + \varphi_0)$. Inasmuch as ωt has become $\omega t - \beta z$, this signal has propagated along z, with phase constant β and speed ω/β, but it has also suffered exponential attenuation of its amplitude, from $|E_0|$ at the emitter to $|E_0| e^{-\alpha z}$ at the receiver (this description is appropriate if α, β, and z are all positive). Figure 7–1 illustrates the received signal in time as a weakened version of the emitted one, and also the progressive attenuation in space of the signal, seen as a snapshot at one instant. Note that the signal is still periodic in time, with the usual period

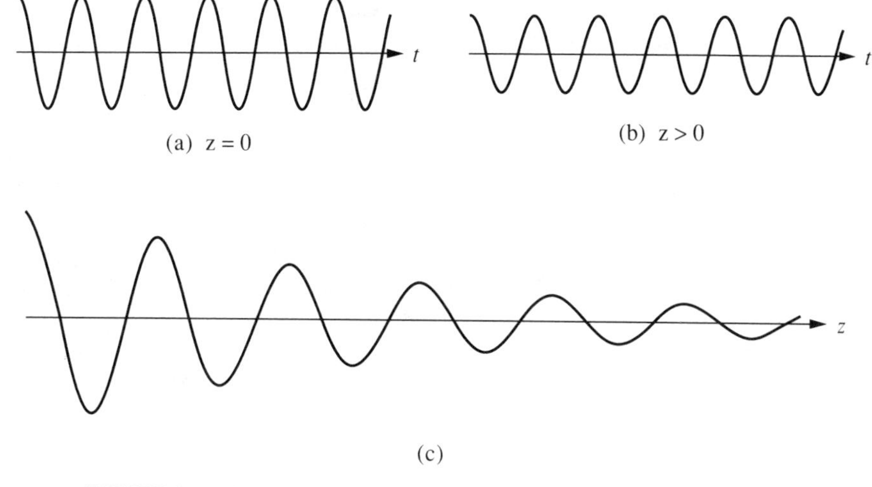

FIGURE 7–1 Spatially damped wave, versus time and versus space.

$\tau = 2\pi/\omega$, but it is now not periodic in space, along z. Nevertheless, the sinusoidal factor $\cos(\omega t - \beta z + \varphi_0)$ suggests that we still define the wavelength $\lambda = 2\pi/\beta$ as before. Now, however, this length is to be interpreted as the spacing between every other zero of the decaying exponential, or between crests; this spacing does remain constant despite the presence of the exponential factor, although the heights of the crests of the oscillatory waveshape do not repeat themselves. The coefficient $\beta = \text{Im}\,\gamma$ is the phase constant of the damped wave. The phase velocity is given by $v_p = \omega/\beta = \omega/(\text{Im}\,\gamma)$ and is still the speed at which one would have to travel along z to keep up with a particular null, or with a crest that gets weaker as the wave progresses.

The amplitude of the damped spatial oscillation decays exponentially as $e^{-\alpha z}$; this spatial variation of amplitude is termed the *envelope* of the waveshape. The coefficient $\alpha = \text{Re}\,\gamma$ is called the *attenuation constant.* The oscillation amplitude, or envelope, falls by a factor of $1/e$ in a distance $1/\alpha$. The diminution of field amplitude, and hence of field energy, is a manifestation of the energy lost from the wave to the ohmic medium, by Joule heating, as will be verified.

General Solution

We can now return to the task of solving Eqs. (7.11)–(7.12), the simultaneous, nonlinear algebraic equations for α and β in terms of the given ω, μ, ε, and σ:

$$\beta^2 - \alpha^2 = \omega^2 \mu \varepsilon, \qquad 2\beta\alpha = \omega\mu\sigma. \tag{7.16}$$

If we square and add the two equations, we can eliminate the cross term $2\beta\alpha$ and leave only the squares β^2 and α^2:

$$\beta^4 - 2\beta^2\alpha^2 + \alpha^4 = \omega^4\mu^2\varepsilon^2 \tag{7.17}$$

and

$$4\beta^2\alpha^2 = \omega^2\mu^2\sigma^2 \tag{7.18}$$

add to

$$(\beta^2 + \alpha^2)^2 = \omega^2\mu^2(\sigma^2 + \omega^2\varepsilon^2), \tag{7.19}$$

so that

$$\beta^2 + \alpha^2 = \omega\mu(\sigma^2 + \omega^2\varepsilon^2)^{1/2} = \omega^2\mu\varepsilon\left[1 + \left(\frac{\sigma}{\omega\varepsilon}\right)^2\right]^{1/2} \tag{7.20}$$

while

$$\beta^2 - \alpha^2 = \omega^2\mu\varepsilon. \tag{7.21}$$

Adding and subtracting the last two equations separates β^2 and α^2:

$$2\beta^2 = \omega^2\mu\varepsilon\{[1 + (\sigma/\omega\varepsilon)^2]^{1/2} + 1\}, \tag{7.22}$$

$$2\alpha^2 = \omega^2\mu\varepsilon\{[1 + (\sigma/\omega\varepsilon)^2]^{1/2} - 1\}. \tag{7.23}$$

Finally,

$$\beta = \omega\sqrt{\mu\varepsilon}\left\{\frac{[1 + (\sigma/\omega\varepsilon)^2]^{1/2} + 1}{2}\right\}^{1/2}, \tag{7.24}$$

$$\alpha = \omega\sqrt{\mu\varepsilon}\left\{\frac{[1 + (\sigma/\omega\varepsilon)^2]^{1/2} - 1}{2}\right\}^{1/2} \tag{7.25}$$

are the phase constant and attenuation constant for the conducting medium, at a general frequency ω.

Somewhat less formidable, but equivalent, expressions are obtainable by trigonometric substitution, using

$$\tan\theta = \frac{\sigma}{\omega\varepsilon}, \tag{7.26}$$

giving

$$\beta = \omega(\mu\varepsilon\sec\theta)^{1/2}\cos\frac{\theta}{2} \tag{7.27}$$

and

$$\alpha = \omega(\mu\varepsilon\sec\theta)^{1/2}\sin\frac{\theta}{2}. \tag{7.28}$$

The quantity $\sigma/\omega\varepsilon$ is often called the *loss tangent* of the medium. This designation is seen to be appropriate when the loss properties of the conducting medium are expressed through a complex permittivity ε^0, instead of specifying separately a real permittivity ε and a real conductivity σ. If

$$\varepsilon^0 = \varepsilon' - j\varepsilon'' = |\varepsilon^0| e^{-j\theta}, \tag{7.29}$$

then since $(-\omega \text{ Im } \varepsilon^0) = \omega\varepsilon''$ is equivalent to an ordinary conductivity σ, as was noted in Chapter 6, the ratio $\sigma/\omega\varepsilon$ (in which ε means the real permittivity, ε') is the same as $\varepsilon''/\varepsilon'$ and this is tan θ, the tangent of the (negative) polar angle when the complex permittivity ε^0 is written in terms of its magnitude $|\varepsilon^0| = \varepsilon' \sec\theta = \varepsilon \sec\theta$ and phase $(-\theta)$. Thus the θ in Eq. (7.29) is the same as the one in Eq. (7.26) and the factor $\varepsilon \sec\theta$ in Eqs. (7.27)–(7.28) is the magnitude of the equivalent complex permittivity.

Still another version is obtained by a hyperbolic substitution in Eqs. (7.24)–(7.25):

$$\sinh \xi = \frac{\sigma}{\omega\varepsilon} \tag{7.30}$$

gives

$$\beta = \omega\sqrt{\mu\varepsilon} \cosh \frac{\xi}{2}, \tag{7.31}$$

$$\alpha = \omega\sqrt{\mu\varepsilon} \sinh \frac{\xi}{2}. \tag{7.32}$$

Regardless of the form used, it is clear that the ratio $\sigma/\omega\varepsilon$ plays a key role in determining the wave propagation and attenuation characteristics of the conducting medium.

EXAMPLE 7.1

If a certain medium's constitutive parameters are such that $1/\sqrt{\mu\varepsilon} = \frac{1}{3}c$ and $\sigma/\omega\varepsilon = 1$ at an operating frequency for which the free-space wavelength is $\lambda_0 = 2$ m, what are the phase and attenuation constants, the wavelength, and the wave speed in the medium?

Using the last form of the equations for β and α, $\sinh \xi = 1$ at $\xi = 0.8814$ and $\xi/2 = 0.4407$, for which $\cosh(\xi/2) = 1.0987$ and $\sinh(\xi/2) = 0.4551$, so that $\beta = (\omega/c)3 \cosh(\xi/2) = (2\pi/\lambda_0)3 \cosh(\xi/2) = 3\pi(1.0987) = 10.355 \text{ m}^{-1}$ and $\alpha = (\omega/c)3 \sinh(\xi/2) = (2\pi/\lambda_0)3 \sinh(\xi/2) = 3\pi(0.4551) = 4.289 \text{ m}^{-1}$. The wavelength in the medium is $2\pi/\beta = \lambda_0/[3 \cosh(\xi/2)] = 0.6068$ m and the wave speed is $\omega/\beta = c/[3 \cosh(\xi/2)] = 0.3034c = (0.9095)10^8$ m/s. ◆

The relations between the phase and attenuation constants and the parameters of the medium are sufficiently complicated to bear examination in two limiting cases, based on whether the dimensionless quantity $\sigma/\omega\varepsilon$ is small or large compared to unity.

Waves in Good Insulators

For a good but imperfect insulator, the conductivity is small, in the sense that the dimensionless ratio $\sigma/\omega\varepsilon$ is much less than unity. This can occur either because the material has relatively low conductivity or because the operating frequency is relatively high. Permittivity varies much less from one material to another than does conductivity, so that σ and ω are the principal determinants of whether a material, at the given frequency, can be classified as a good insulator. Note also that σ and ε both vary with frequency, although they may be roughly constant over wide portions of the spectrum.

With $\sigma/\omega\varepsilon$ small, the inner square root in Eqs. (7.24)–(7.25), $[1 + (\sigma/\omega\varepsilon)^2]^{1/2}$, becomes $[1 + \frac{1}{2}(\sigma/\omega\varepsilon)^2]$, approximately, and

$$\beta \to \omega\sqrt{\mu\varepsilon}\left[1 + \tfrac{1}{4}\left(\frac{\sigma}{\omega\varepsilon}\right)^2\right]^{1/2} \to \omega\sqrt{\mu\varepsilon}\left[1 + \tfrac{1}{8}\left(\frac{\sigma}{\omega\varepsilon}\right)^2\right], \tag{7.33}$$

$$\alpha \to \omega\sqrt{\mu\varepsilon}\left[\tfrac{1}{4}\left(\frac{\sigma}{\omega\varepsilon}\right)^2\right]^{1/2} = \omega\sqrt{\mu\varepsilon}\left[\tfrac{1}{2}\left(\frac{\sigma}{\omega\varepsilon}\right)\right] = \tfrac{1}{2}\eta\sigma, \tag{7.34}$$

where $\eta = \sqrt{\mu/\varepsilon}$ would be the impedance of the dielectric if the conductivity were zero.

In this limit, the phase constant β is very slightly increased over the corresponding value for zero conductivity. The phase velocity ω/β is slightly less than the value for the perfect dielectric, $1/\sqrt{\mu\varepsilon}$. The waveform amplitude is attenuated spatially, as $\exp(-\alpha z) = \exp(-\frac{1}{2}\eta\sigma z)$. The attenuation rate is slight when compared to the oscillation scale length given by β, because $\alpha \ll \beta$, since $\alpha/\beta \approx \frac{1}{2}(\sigma/\omega\varepsilon)$ is small.

EXAMPLE 7.2

If the glass used to make an optical fiber is reported to have losses of 4 dB/km at a free-space wavelength of $\lambda_0 = 0.85\ \mu$m, and we are told that the wavelength in the glass is $\lambda = 0.56\ \mu$m at this operating frequency, what is the equivalent $\sigma/\omega\varepsilon$ for this glass?

The value 4 dB/km expresses the energy attenuation in terms of powers of $10^{0.1}$ (a decibel for energy) rather than powers of e (a neper), so that the conversion of 4 dB/km is given by $e^{-2\alpha z} = 10^{-(0.1)4z} = e^{-(0.230)4z} = e^{-0.92z}$, for z in kilometers, using $\ln 10 = 2.30$. Hence $2\alpha = 0.92$ Np/km. Assuming, as will be verified, that $\sigma/\omega\varepsilon$ is small, we can use $2\alpha = \beta(\sigma/\omega\varepsilon)$, which is $(2\pi/\lambda)(\sigma/\omega\varepsilon)$, so that $\sigma/\omega\varepsilon = 2\alpha\lambda/2\pi$. Substituting $2\alpha = 0.92\ \text{km}^{-1}$ and $\lambda = (0.56)10^{-9}$ km, we find $\sigma/\omega\varepsilon = (8.2)10^{-11}$, which is indeed much smaller than unity. This glass is an extremely low-loss dielectric. ◆

With $\alpha \ll \beta$, the waveform is nearly unaffected over short distances, of the order of a few wavelengths. It is only over a distance comprising a large number of wavelengths, say $l = (\omega\varepsilon/\sigma)\lambda$, that the wave amplitude is reduced by a significantly large amount, namely by

$$\exp(-\alpha l) = \exp\left[-\tfrac{1}{2}\beta\left(\frac{\sigma}{\omega\varepsilon}\right)l\right] = \exp\left[-\tfrac{1}{2}\left(\frac{\sigma}{\omega\varepsilon}\right)\left(\frac{\omega\varepsilon}{\sigma}\right)\beta\lambda\right]$$

$$= \exp(-\tfrac{1}{2}\beta\lambda) = \exp(-\pi) = 0.0432 = \frac{1}{23.14}. \tag{7.35}$$

For any damped oscillating system, the number of oscillations undergone while the amplitude attenuates by the factor $e^{-\pi}$ is called the Q of the system. The larger the Q, the less damped the oscillation. The Q is a readily observed quantity when the oscillations are viewed, say on an oscilloscope, because a simple count of the number of cycles seen before the amplitude drops to about 4% of the initial height (beyond which the oscillations are not easily distinguished anyway) provides an estimate of the parameter Q. This is illustrated in Figure 7–2, which exhibits $Q = 12$ cycles before the amplitude drops by a factor of $e^{-\pi}$. The operational definition of Q is consistent with the system definition for damped oscillations, $Q = \omega\langle W\rangle/\langle P\rangle$, or 2π times the ratio of the stored energy to the energy lost per cycle of oscillation. That the two definitions are consistent will be confirmed later.

For the imperfect insulator, the Q of the damped wave is high: $Q = \omega\varepsilon/\sigma$, the reciprocal of the small number $\sigma/\omega\varepsilon$. The wave is then only slightly damped; the attenuation due to the finite conductivity is only a small perturbation of the underlying oscillation.

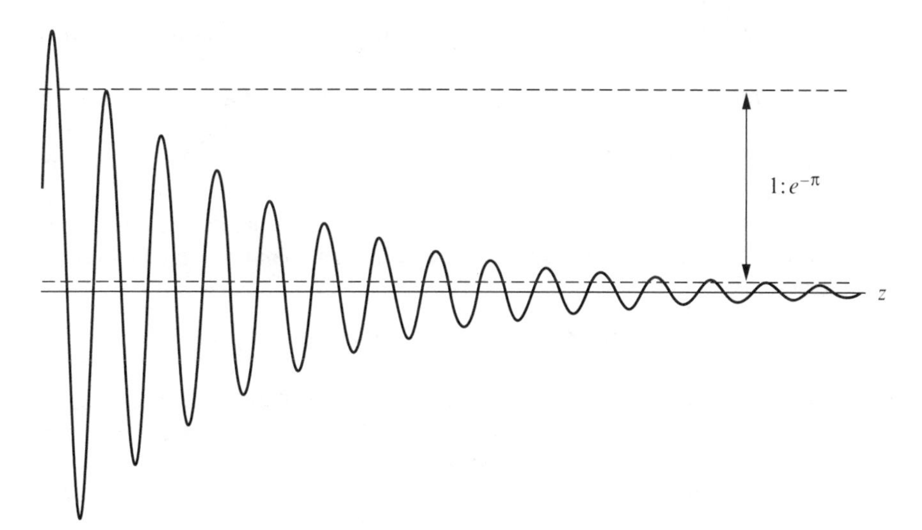

FIGURE 7.2 There are Q cycles with amplitudes in the range 1 to $e^{-\pi}$.

Another quantity of interest is the wave impedance, the relation between the complex amplitudes of the electric and magnetic fields of the wave. The magnetic field is related to the electric one by $\nabla \times \mathbf{E} = -j\omega\mu\mathbf{H}$ and when $\mathbf{E}$ varies as $\exp(-\gamma z)$, the complex amplitudes are related by the complex impedance

$$Z = \frac{E}{H} = \frac{j\omega\mu}{\gamma} = \frac{j\omega\mu}{\alpha + j\beta}. \tag{7.36}$$

For a perfect dielectric, $\alpha = 0$, $\beta = \omega\sqrt{\mu\varepsilon}$ and $Z = \omega\mu/\beta = \sqrt{\mu/\varepsilon} = \eta$, but for the imperfect one, in the limit of small $\sigma/\omega\varepsilon$ or $\alpha \ll \beta$, the impedance changes to

$$Z = \frac{j\omega\mu}{j\beta(1 - j\alpha/\beta)} \to \left(\frac{\omega\mu}{\beta}\right)\left[1 + j\left(\frac{\alpha}{\beta}\right)\right] = \eta\left[1 + j\tfrac{1}{2}\left(\frac{\sigma}{\omega\varepsilon}\right)\right], \tag{7.37}$$

in which the reciprocal of $(1 - j\alpha/\beta)$ has been approximated by $(1 + j\alpha/\beta)$, for small $\alpha/\beta = \frac{1}{2}(\sigma/\omega\varepsilon)$. This impedance is complex, instead of the real one η, but the imaginary part is very small. This indicates that E and H are slightly out of phase, instead of oscillating in perfect unison. This phase difference can be seen in the time domain, using in the limit of small α/β the complex impedance $Z = \eta/(1 - j\alpha/\beta) \to \eta e^{j(\alpha/\beta)}$:

$$\mathscr{E} = \hat{\mathbf{x}} \operatorname{Re}\left[E_0 e^{-\gamma z} e^{j\omega t}\right] = \hat{\mathbf{x}} E_0 e^{-\alpha z} \cos(\omega t - \beta z), \tag{7.38}$$

$$\mathscr{H} = \hat{\mathbf{y}} \operatorname{Re}\left[\frac{E_0}{Z} e^{-\gamma z} e^{j\omega t}\right] = \hat{\mathbf{y}} \frac{E_0}{\eta} e^{-\alpha z} \cos\left(\omega t - \beta z - \frac{\alpha}{\beta}\right), \tag{7.39}$$

where E_0 has been assumed real. The magnetic field is slightly delayed in time, compared to the electric field.

We conclude that the major effect of a small conductivity in what would otherwise be a perfect insulator is merely a gradual attenuation, by $e^{-\alpha z}$ in amplitude and $e^{-2\alpha z}$ in energy. The remaining effects, such as a slight increase in the phase constant, tend to be so slight as to be unnoticeable.

Once we realize that the only important effect of the finite but small conductivity of the imperfect insulator is an attenuation of the fields, the decay rate is more easily obtained from the properties of the medium by using the energy relation, the complex Poynting theorem, rather than the field equations themselves. We use

$$-\nabla \cdot (\tfrac{1}{2}\mathbf{E} \times \mathbf{H}^*) = \tfrac{1}{2}\mathbf{E} \cdot \mathbf{J}^* + 2j\omega(\tfrac{1}{4}\mathbf{H}^* \cdot \mathbf{B} - \tfrac{1}{4}\mathbf{E} \cdot \mathbf{D}^*) \tag{7.40}$$

and take advantage of the realization that, over short distances along z, the fields behave as they would in a perfect insulator: $E = \eta H$, $W_m = W_e$, and propagation as $\exp[j(\omega t - \beta_0 z)]$, with $\beta_0 = \omega\sqrt{\mu\varepsilon}$. It is only necessary to allow for a gradually varying amplitude of the field, $E_0(z)$ instead of a fixed E_0:

$$E(z) = E_0(z) e^{-j\beta_0 z}. \tag{7.41}$$

The plane wave is now nonuniform, because its amplitude is not constant. Since $W_m \approx W_e$, the complex Poynting theorem reduces to

$$-\nabla \cdot (\tfrac{1}{2}\mathbf{E} \times \mathbf{H}^*) = \tfrac{1}{2}\mathbf{E} \cdot \mathbf{J}^* \qquad \text{or} \qquad \frac{-d}{dz}\left[\frac{E_0 E_0^*}{\eta}\right] = E_0 \sigma E_0^*, \tag{7.42}$$

since the phase factor $e^{-j\beta_0 z}$ cancels its own complex conjugate. Hence

$$\frac{d}{dz}|E_0|^2 = -\eta\sigma|E_0|^2. \tag{7.43}$$

This differential equation is solved by

$$|E_0(z)|^2 = |E_0(0)|^2 e^{-\eta\sigma z}, \tag{7.44}$$

which agrees with the result

$$|E_0(z)| = |E_0(0)|e^{-\alpha z} \approx |E_0(0)| \exp(-\tfrac{1}{2}\eta\sigma z) \tag{7.45}$$

found more elaborately from Maxwell's equations in the limit of small $\sigma/\omega\varepsilon$.

Generally, for systems with only slight dissipation, it is most often convenient to use the dissipationless results, except for allowance for a gradually decaying amplitude, and to solve for the decay rate by use of the energy relation.

Waves in Good Conductors

For a good but imperfect conductor, the conductivity is high, in the sense that the dimensionless ratio $\sigma/\omega\varepsilon$ is much greater than unity. This can occur either because the material has relatively high conductivity or because the operating frequency is relatively low.

With $\sigma/\omega\varepsilon$ large, the inner square root in Eqs. (7.24)–(7.25), $[1 + (\sigma/\omega\varepsilon)^2]^{1/2}$, approaches $\sigma/\omega\varepsilon$, approximately, and

$$\beta \to \omega\sqrt{\mu\varepsilon}\left\{\frac{(\sigma/\omega\varepsilon) + 1}{2}\right\}^{1/2} \to \omega\sqrt{\mu\varepsilon}\left[\frac{\sigma/\omega\varepsilon}{2}\right]^{1/2}, \tag{7.46}$$

$$\alpha \to \omega\sqrt{\mu\varepsilon}\left\{\frac{(\sigma/\omega\varepsilon) - 1}{2}\right\}^{1/2} \to \omega\sqrt{\mu\varepsilon}\left[\frac{\sigma/\omega\varepsilon}{2}\right]^{1/2}. \tag{7.47}$$

Thus, α and β approach equality, at the value

$$\alpha = \beta = \sqrt{\frac{\omega\mu\sigma}{2}}, \tag{7.48}$$

although α is slightly less than β until the limit of infinite $\sigma/\omega\varepsilon$ is attained.

The phase constant β is substantially larger than for the case of the insulator with the same μ and ε, namely $\beta_0 = \omega\sqrt{\mu\varepsilon}$. The enhancement of β (or

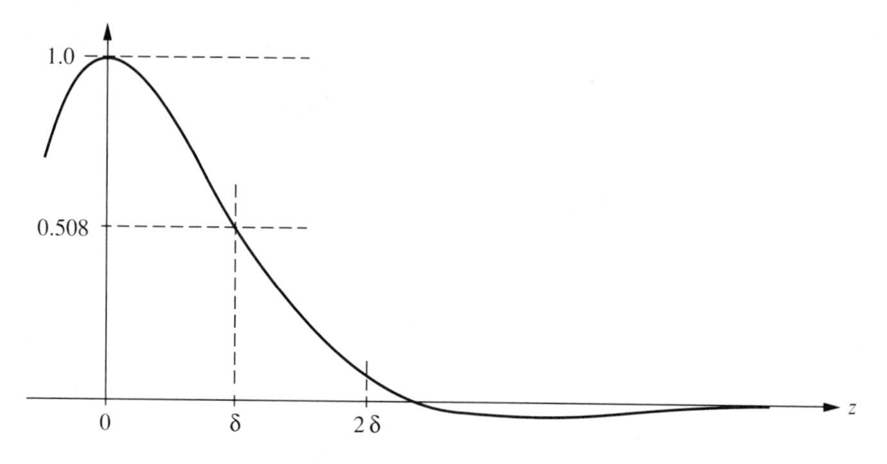

FIGURE 7–3 Decay of a wave in a good conductor.

diminution of the wave velocity ω/β) is not particularly large, however, since the factor $\sqrt{(\sigma/\omega\varepsilon)/2}$ is only moderately large for large $\sigma/\omega\varepsilon$. For example, if $\sigma/\omega\varepsilon$ is about 50, the factor is about 5 and if $\sigma/\omega\varepsilon$ doubles to about 100, the factor rises only to about 7.

What is overwhelmingly different about this case is that the attenuation constant α is very high, reaching equality with the phase constant β itself. For $\alpha = \beta$, the decaying oscillation $e^{-\alpha z} \cos(\omega t - \beta z)$ is reduced in amplitude by the factor $e^{-\pi}$ at a distance z such that $\alpha z = \pi = \beta z = 2\pi z/\lambda$ or at $z = \lambda/2$, which means that the amplitude is reduced to only 4.3% of its initial height within the space of just half an oscillation wavelength. The Q of this damped oscillation is only $\frac{1}{2}$; under these circumstances, the oscillation is barely noticeable at all, being overwhelmed by the attenuation. Figure 7–3 clearly illustrates this; it is a plot of the spatial variation of an attenuated wave whose decay rate equals its phase constant and which, for fair comparison with $\cos \beta_0 z$ or with the previous plot for a high value of Q, begins with unit value and zero slope at $z = 0$. This calls for a plot of $Ae^{-\alpha z} \cos(\beta z - \theta)$, with an amplitude $A = \sqrt{2}$ and with a phase of $\theta = 45°$; this corresponds to a plot of $e^{-\alpha z}[\cos \beta z + \sin \beta z]$, with $\alpha = \beta = 1/\delta$.

The quantity

$$\delta = \sqrt{\frac{2}{\omega\mu\sigma}}, \tag{7.49}$$

the reciprocal of α or β, is called the *skin depth* of the conductor. It is a measure of the depth of penetration of a wave in the conductor as it tries, but essentially fails, to propagate in it. As indicated in the figure, the amplitude of the wave falls to about half its initial height within one skin depth and the wave is left with virtually negligible amplitude beyond two skin depths or so.

The wave impedance, the relation between the complex amplitudes of the electric and magnetic fields of the wave, is again given by

$$Z = \frac{E}{H} = \frac{j\omega\mu}{\gamma} = \frac{j\omega\mu}{\alpha + j\beta}. \tag{7.50}$$

For a good conductor, $\alpha = \beta = 1/\delta$ and

$$Z = \frac{j\omega\mu\delta}{1+j} = \omega\mu\sqrt{\frac{2}{\omega\mu\sigma}}\,\frac{j}{1+j} = \sqrt{\frac{\omega\mu}{\sigma}}\,\frac{j\sqrt{2}}{1+j}$$

$$= \sqrt{\frac{\omega\mu}{\sigma}}\,\frac{1+j}{\sqrt{2}} = \sqrt{\frac{\omega\mu}{\sigma}}\,e^{j\pi/4}, \tag{7.51}$$

since $(1+j)^2 = 2j$. Thus $Z = R + jX$ includes resistance and inductive reactance in equal amounts $R = X = \sqrt{\omega\mu/2\sigma}$. Recall that the reactance is the imaginary part of an impedance and that a reactance X is inductive if $X > 0$, as it is for an inductor's impedance $j\omega L$, or else it is capacitive if $X < 0$, as it is for a capacitor's impedance $1/j\omega C$. From the last expression in Eq. (7.51), the electric field is $\pi/4$ or 45° ahead of the magnetic field in phase; the two fields do not oscillate in unison, but rather one-eighth of a period apart. In the time domain, using the limit of $\alpha = \beta = 1/\delta$ and the complex impedance $Z = \eta_\infty e^{j\pi/4}$,

$$\mathscr{E} = \hat{\mathbf{x}}\,\mathrm{Re}\,[E_0 e^{-\gamma z} e^{j\omega t}] = \hat{\mathbf{x}} E_0 e^{-z/\delta} \cos\left(\omega t - \frac{z}{\delta}\right), \tag{7.52}$$

$$\mathscr{H} = \hat{\mathbf{y}}\,\mathrm{Re}\left[\frac{E_0}{Z} e^{-\gamma z} e^{j\omega t}\right] = \hat{\mathbf{y}}\,\frac{E_0}{\eta_\infty} e^{-z/\delta} \cos\left(\omega t - \frac{z}{\delta} - \frac{\pi}{4}\right), \tag{7.53}$$

where $\eta_\infty = \sqrt{\omega\mu/\sigma}$ and E_0 has been assumed real. The magnetic field is significantly delayed in time, by one-eight of a period with respect to the electric field, at any position z. The amplitudes of the sinusoids for the two fields are related by $\eta_\infty = \sqrt{\omega\mu/\sigma} = \eta(\omega\varepsilon/\sigma)^{1/2}$, which is substantially smaller than the impedance $\eta = \sqrt{\mu/\varepsilon}$ of the insulator that has the same μ and ε but no conductivity. This means that the electric field is relatively weak, the magnetic one strong. Although electric and magnetic fields cannot be compared directly (they have different units), the energies stored in each field can be compared directly, as follows.

The time-averaged magnetic and electric energy densities in the good conductor are

$$\langle W_m \rangle = \tfrac{1}{4}\mu |H|^2 \qquad \text{and} \qquad \langle W_e \rangle = \tfrac{1}{4}\varepsilon |E|^2, \tag{7.54}$$

so that

$$\langle W_e \rangle = \tfrac{1}{4}\varepsilon\eta_\infty^2 |H|^2 = \tfrac{1}{4}\left(\frac{\omega\varepsilon}{\sigma}\right)\mu |H|^2 = \left(\frac{\omega\varepsilon}{\sigma}\right)\langle W_m \rangle, \tag{7.55}$$

or $\langle W_m \rangle / \langle W_e \rangle = \sigma/\omega\varepsilon \gg 1$. The wave energy is not equally divided between magnetic and electric forms, as it is in an insulator; in a good conductor, it resides nearly entirely in the magnetic field. Furthermore, the wave energy is depleted in the conductor, at the rate

$$\langle P \rangle = \tfrac{1}{2}\mathbf{E} \cdot \mathbf{J}^* = \tfrac{1}{2}\sigma |E|^2 = \tfrac{1}{2}\sigma\eta_\infty^2 |H|^2 = \tfrac{1}{2}\omega\mu |H|^2 = 2\omega\langle W_m \rangle . \quad (7.56)$$

The energy is being converted into heat in the good conductor, at a rate given by twice the frequency times the stored magnetic energy.

EXAMPLE 7.3

Can microwaves at 2.45 GHz (the operating frequency for microwave ovens) traverse aluminum foil 1 mil thick?

Aluminum has conductivity $\sigma = (3.54)10^7$ S/m and is nonmagnetic ($\mu \approx \mu_0$). Its permittivity is not well known but not much different from $\varepsilon_0 \approx 10^{-11}$ F/m. At $\omega \approx 10^{10}$ rad/s, $\sigma/\omega\varepsilon \approx 10^{7.5}/(10^{10} \times 10^{-11}) \approx 10^{8.5}$ is much greater than unity, confirming that the equations for a good conductor are applicable. The skin depth is therefore just $\delta = \sqrt{2/\omega\mu\sigma} = 1/\sqrt{\pi f \mu_0 \sigma} = 1.7\ \mu$m, while the foil is 25.4 μm thick, or about 15 skin depths. Any microwave field that might appear at the surface of the foil persists only within a thin "skin" and decays to negligible levels long before it can traverse the metal sheet. ◆

To generalize the results, note that the wave equation for harmonic fields in a vacuum or in a good insulator takes the form

$$\nabla^2 \mathbf{E} = -k^2 \mathbf{E}, \quad (7.57)$$

with a real but negative eigenvalue $-k^2$, formed by $(j\omega\mu_0)(j\omega\varepsilon_0)$ for a vacuum. By contrast, a medium such as a plasma behaves as does a good conductor if the eigenvalue becomes an imaginary quantity. The wave equation should then be written as

$$\nabla^2 \mathbf{E} = \frac{2j}{\delta^2} \mathbf{E}, \quad (7.58)$$

as is the case when $(j\omega\mu)\sigma$ is the appropriate eigenvalue, for an ohmic conductor. This form displays the skin depth δ directly in the wave equation.

Transition Frequencies

For metals, the skin depth is very small even at low frequencies. For copper at the power-line frequency of 60 Hz, the skin depth is $\delta = 8.5$ mm. At the frequency 100 MHz, in the FM radio band, the skin depth for copper is $\delta = 7.1\ \mu$m. These tiny distances should be compared to the free-space wavelengths $\lambda = 5000$ km at 60 Hz and $\lambda = 3$ m at 100 MHz. Metals are good conductors even at optical frequencies.

Other conductive materials behave as a good conductor at low frequencies but become good insulators at high frequencies. The transition between conductor and insulator occurs for a given material within a characteristic frequency range. The frequency f_0 for which $\sigma/\omega\varepsilon = 1$ is in the transition band.

The change from conductor to insulator is not abrupt at f_0, but for much lower frequencies, the material is definitely a conductor, while for much higher frequencies, it behaves as an insulator. The transition frequencies $f_0 = \sigma/2\pi\varepsilon$ for a few materials are listed below.

Pure water	0.2 MHz
Dry earth	1 MHz
Wet earth	5 MHz
Ocean water	900 MHz

These are given with no great precision, but they provide guidance as to which formulas are appropriate for determining the wave-propagating properties of the materials at a given operating frequency. The loss tangent $(\sigma/\omega\varepsilon)$ at a frequency $\omega = 2\pi f$ is just the ratio f_0/f if the conductivity and permittivity of the medium are approximately the same as at the transition frequency itself. Near the transition frequency, the full formulas for the phase and attenuation constants, wavelength, wave speed, and wave impedance should be used. For small f_0/f, the formulas applicable to an insulator are appropriate; for large f_0/f, those for a good conductor apply.

Summary

In materials with finite conductivity, the amplitudes of the fields attenuate exponentially as the wave propagates. This weakening of the wave is a manifestation of the loss of energy to the conductive medium, by Joule heating. The decay is slight in good insulators and severe in good conductors. The parameter that determines the severity of the attenuation and the classification of the medium as insulating or conducting is the loss tangent $\sigma/\omega\varepsilon$, a dimensionless quantity that depends on the frequency of the source of the wave, as well as on the constitutive parameters of the medium. Fundamentally, $\sigma/\omega\varepsilon$ measures the ratio of the amplitudes of the conduction and displacement currents in the medium.

When this parameter is small, the wave undergoes many oscillations before becoming significantly weaker; the Q of the damped oscillation is then the reciprocal of the small $\sigma/\omega\varepsilon$ parameter.

The system definition of Q for damped oscillations, $Q = \omega\langle W\rangle/\langle P\rangle$, meaning the ratio of stored energy to energy loss per radian of oscillation, is consistent with the operational one we have used, $Q = \beta/2\alpha$, meaning that the amplitude is reduced by $e^{-\pi}$ in Q oscillations (wavelengths). To see the equivalence, note that the total energy and power densities can be expressed in terms of the electric energy stored as

$$\begin{aligned}\langle W\rangle &= \langle W_m\rangle + \langle W_e\rangle = \tfrac{1}{4}\mu|H|^2 + \tfrac{1}{4}\varepsilon|E|^2 \\ &= \left\{\frac{\mu}{\varepsilon}\frac{|H|^2}{|E|^2} + 1\right\}\langle W_e\rangle = \left\{\frac{\eta^2}{|Z|^2} + 1\right\}\langle W_e\rangle \end{aligned} \tag{7.59}$$

and

$$\langle P \rangle = \frac{1}{2}\sigma |E|^2 = 2\left(\frac{\sigma}{\varepsilon}\right)\langle W_e \rangle, \tag{7.60}$$

so that the ratio that defines Q becomes

$$Q = \frac{\omega\langle W \rangle}{\langle P \rangle} = \frac{\omega\varepsilon}{\sigma} \frac{\eta^2/|Z|^2 + 1}{2}. \tag{7.61}$$

Since $Z = j\omega\mu/\gamma = j\omega\mu/(\alpha + j\beta)$, we have $\eta^2/|Z|^2 = (\alpha^2 + \beta^2)/\omega^2\mu\varepsilon$, leaving

$$\begin{aligned} Q = \frac{\omega\langle W \rangle}{\langle P \rangle} &= \frac{\omega\varepsilon/\sigma}{\omega^2\mu\varepsilon} \frac{\alpha^2 + \beta^2 + \omega^2\mu\varepsilon}{2} \\ &= \frac{\alpha^2 + \beta^2 + \omega^2\mu\varepsilon}{2\omega\mu\sigma} = \frac{\beta}{2\alpha} \end{aligned} \tag{7.62}$$

after substituting $\beta^2 - \alpha^2 = \omega^2\mu\varepsilon$ and $2\beta\alpha = \omega\mu\sigma$ from Eq. (7.16). This confirms that the two definitions of Q are consistent.

When $\sigma/\omega\varepsilon$ is large, the attenuation constant becomes equal to the phase constant and the decay effectively overwhelms the oscillation. The wave survives only over a distance of a few skin depths. The skin depth is given by $\delta = \sqrt{2/\omega\mu\sigma}$ in this case.

For a "perfect" conductor, an idealization defined by $\sigma = \infty$, the skin depth becomes zero and the wave is extinguished at zero distance from its source, meaning that the perfect conductor excludes time-varying magnetic fields, as well as electric fields, from its interior.

Vacuum is a perfect insulator, defined by $\sigma = 0$; in this limit, the wave can persist indefinitely without loss of its original energy.

The insulating or conductive character of the medium shows up in the frequency domain in the wave equation itself, in the guise of the algebraic nature of the eigenvalue Λ in the equation $\nabla^2\mathbf{E} = \Lambda\mathbf{E}$.

If Λ is real and negative, written as $\Lambda = -\beta^2$, the medium is an insulator with phase constant β and phase velocity ω/β.

If Λ is purely imaginary, written as $\Lambda = 2j/\delta^2$, the medium behaves as a good conductor, with skin depth δ. The diffusion equation in the frequency domain, $D\nabla^2 U = j\omega U$, is of this sort. Fields in a good conductor tend to diffuse, rather than propagate, with a diffusion constant $D = 1/\mu\sigma$.

If Λ is complex, written as $\Lambda = (\alpha + j\beta)^2$, the material supports an attenuating wave, with phase constant β and attenuation constant α. The damped wave then exhibits a Q given by $\beta/2\alpha$.

Finally, the case of Λ real and positive, written $\Lambda = \alpha^2$, applies to a medium in which wave propagation is precluded ($\beta = 0$), leaving only an oscillation in time (as $e^{j\omega t}$) that decays in space as $e^{-\alpha z}$, without the feature of wave motion at all. This behavior is not applicable to a medium with constitutive parameters μ, ε, and σ that are real and positive at the operating frequency, but it will be encountered in waveguides, for example, when they are used outside their normal range of operating frequencies, as will be seen.

Our next goal is to investigate waves that attempt to cross from one material to another.

PROBLEMS

Attenuation Away from Source

7.1 Consider again the infinite, planar antenna with infinitely many generators, each feeding a rectangular area $l \times w$ with a current $I = I_0 e^{j\omega t}$, distributed uniformly across the width w. This time, however, the medium is conducting, with parameters ε, μ, and σ.

(a) What are the fields on both sides of the source plane?

(b) What is the load impedance on a generator?

Plots of Attenuation and Phase Constants versus Frequency

7.2 If a medium had parameters ε, μ, and σ that were independent of frequency, how would the attenuation and phase constants α and β vary with frequency? A log-log plot of $\alpha/\sigma\eta$ and $\beta/\sigma\eta$ (where $\eta = \sqrt{\mu/\varepsilon}$) versus f/f_0 (where $f_0 = \sigma/2\pi\varepsilon$ is the transition frequency), over the range $f/f_0 = 0.01$ to 10, is most useful; include the asymptotic lines for low and high frequencies.

Attenuation in Terms of Loss Tangent

7.3 Plexiglass is nonmagnetic, has a relative permittivity of 2.5, and has a loss tangent of 0.005 at 10 GHz. What thickness of plexiglass would cause a 1-dB loss in a wave of that frequency traversing it?

Propagation in Seawater

7.4 Seawater has a conductivity of 3.5 S/m and a relative permittivity of 80 at 0.6 GHz.

(a) If the transmitter power and the receiver sensitivity are such that we can afford to lose 120 dB from the strength of a signal at the surface, how deep can the receiver get?

(b) If the frequency is reduced to 0.6 kHz and the other parameters are assumed unchanged, how deep can the receiver get?

(c) Why are low frequencies used to communicate with submarines?

Diffusion in Conductors

7.5 The diffusion equation is $D\nabla^2 U = \partial U/\partial t$, which becomes $D\nabla^2 U = j\omega U$ in the harmonic case. Show from Maxwell's equations (with ε, μ, and σ treated as constants) that this equation applies to the behavior of electric and magnetic fields in a good conductor, which implies that fields tend to diffuse within a metal. What is the diffusion coefficient D for the conductor, in terms of the parameters of the medium?

Complex Impedance in Conductor

7.6 What is the phase difference between the oscillations of the electric and magnetic fields in a conducting medium at the transition frequency $f = f_0$?

Vector Phase and Attenuation Constants

7.7 Solve Maxwell's equations in a medium with parameters ε, μ, and σ with the trial function $\mathbf{E} = \mathbf{E}_0 e^{-\mathbf{q}\cdot\mathbf{r}}$ and $\mathbf{H} = \mathbf{H}_0 e^{-\mathbf{q}\cdot\mathbf{r}}$, as was done in Chapter 5 for a nonconducting medium. Find the equations that relate the real and imaginary parts of the vector $\mathbf{q} = \boldsymbol{\alpha} + j\boldsymbol{\beta}$ to the source frequency and the parameters. Since there are now more unknowns than equations, what parts of $\boldsymbol{\alpha}$ and $\boldsymbol{\beta}$ should be considered the unknowns to be solved for, and what parts are to be assumed given by the source of the fields? Assume that the source lies in a plane.

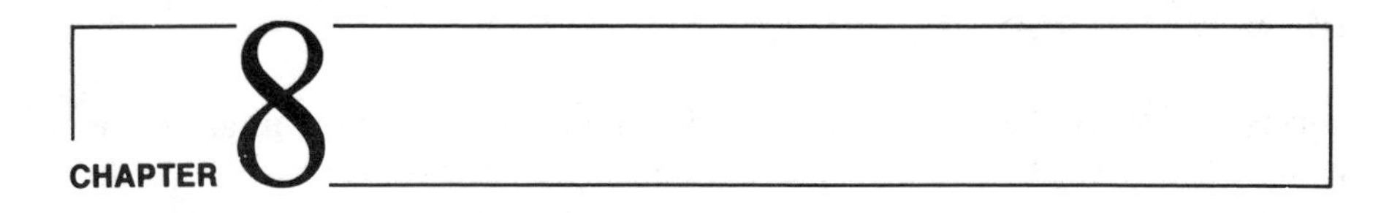

CHAPTER 8

Waves Across Interfaces

Until now, we have examined wave propagation in infinitely extended, uniform media; that is, the medium had the same, constant constitutive parameters μ, ε, and σ throughout the universe. We now wish to allow these parameters to be different at different points. The general case can be extremely difficult to deal with. The simplest case is that of just *two* uniform regions, with an *abrupt* change of parameters from one to the other, across a *planar* interface, as illustrated in Figure 8–1. Each region forms a half-space; one of them (region 1) has a source of waves, infinitely distant from the interface. The unit normal at the interface, $\hat{\mathbf{n}}$, points toward the unsourced region.

Region 1 can support waves at frequency ω, of the form $e^{j(\omega t - \mathbf{k} \cdot \mathbf{r})}$; the frequency is determined by the source antenna and the wave vector $\mathbf{k}$ is determined in direction by the source and in magnitude by both the source frequency and the constitutive parameters of the sourced region.

We have relegated the source antenna to a location infinitely remote from the interface and its details will remain mysterious. What we need to know about it will be specified as follows. We identify the source by saying that if the *entire* space were uniform (with the parameters of region 1), the source would emit a plane wave in a specified direction $\mathbf{k}$, with a specific power and polarization, at frequency ω. The phase velocity, attenuation (if any), and wave

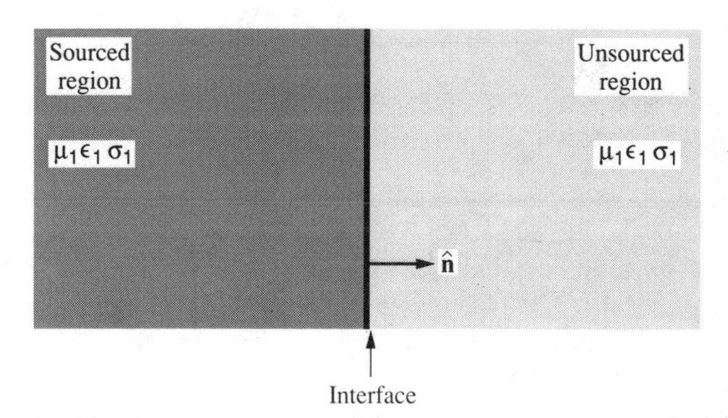

FIGURE 8–1 Planar interface between two uniform regions.

impedance for the wave we would have if region 2 were not present are determined entirely by the parameters of region 1. This specified wave is called the *incident wave.* Because of the interface and region 2, this wave is somehow affected and the fields on the two sides of the interface differ from those of the incident wave, not only beyond the interface but in front of it as well, as indicated in Figure 8–2. We wish to determine the fields in both regions.

Finding the fields in the two regions entails solving Maxwell's equations in all of space, given the specified source in region 1. Now solving Maxwell's equations in either of the two uniform regions is something we have already achieved: for a given frequency, we can form a plane wave, or a superposition of such waves, that will satisfy the equations, provided that we use the correct propagation constant $\gamma = \alpha + j\beta$, as determined by the properties of the medium. This means using γ_1 in region 1 and γ_2 in region 2. But our ability to solve the equations in either of the two regions does not entitle us to claim we have the solution everywhere. We still need to satisfy Maxwell's equations at the points on the interface itself. Should γ_1 or γ_2 be used at those points? Or should some compromise value be sought? What does it mean to satisfy Maxwell's equations at a collection of points at which the constitutive parameters that enter into the equations are discontinuous quantities? To answer these questions, we need to examine the field discontinuities permitted by Maxwell's equations at the boundary between two dissimilar regions of space.

Boundary Conditions

To satisfy Maxwell's equations at the points of a surface across which the constitutive parameters suffer an abrupt discontinuity, we cannot rely on the differential form of the equations, because we cannot readily differentiate discontinuous fields. Instead, we turn to the Maxwell equations in integral form,

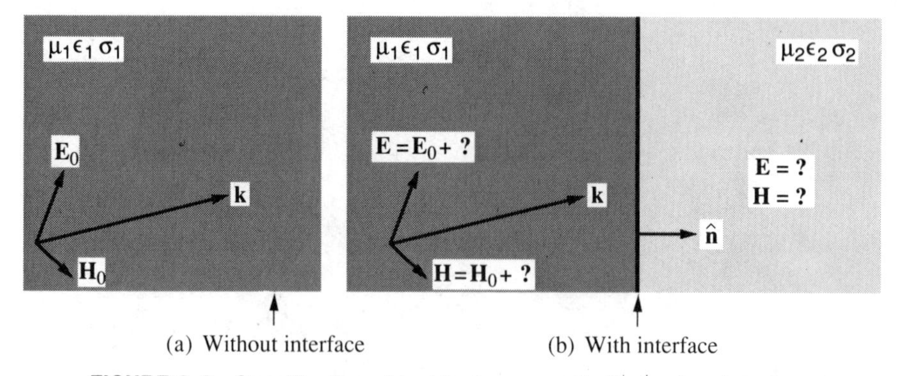

FIGURE 8–2 Specification of incident wave and effects of an interface.

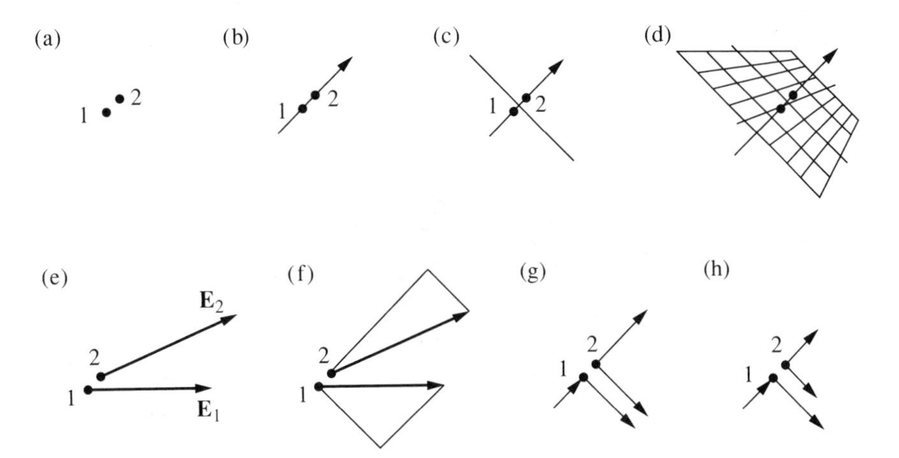

FIGURE 8–3 Two adjacent points and their bisecting plane.

$V = -d\Phi/dt$ and $U = I + d\Psi/dt$, which involve integrations in space, not differentiations, and hence are not troubled by spatial discontinuities. Applying these equations at the points of the interface results in *boundary conditions* that can be used to relate the fields on one side of the plane of discontinuity to those on the other side.

To obtain these boundary conditions, we first ask the question: Must fields vary continuously, or can they jump suddenly from one value at one point to another value at an immediately neighboring point? This question requires us to compare the fields, say $\mathbf{E}_1$ and $\mathbf{E}_2$, at two adjacent points. Now adjacent points automatically define a direction in space and also a bisecting plane that separates the two points, as in Figure 8–3. The direction is the one from one point to the other; the plane is the one that is perpendicular to and bisects the line that joins the two points. In the figure, part (a) shows two adjacent points and (b) depicts the direction from point 1 to point 2. The bisecting plane is shown on edge in (c) and obliquely in (d). In (e), two hypothetical values of an electric field, associated with the two neighboring points, are shown with a hypothetically finite difference between them; that is, the field suddenly jumps in its vector value from one point to the immediately adjacent one, instead of varying continuously from one to the other. Our goal is to determine what restrictions Maxwell's equations place on the possible discontinuity in the field. In (f), the two fields are shown decomposed into their components perpendicular to the bisecting plane and tangential to it; we will find that Maxwell's equations dictate the sorts of discontinuities these field components may undergo. A hypothetical case of fields at the two points that have the same tangential component but dissimilar normal components is given in (*g*), and another case, with equal normal components but with a discontinuity in tangential component, is shown in (h). The discontinuities allowed by Maxwell's equations can be determined by comparing the fields at adjacent points, as they enter into those equations.

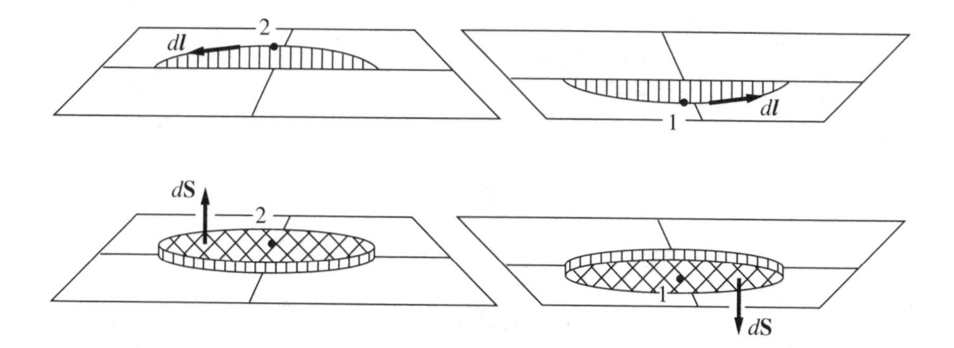

FIGURE 8–4 Closed curve and surface straddling the bisecting plane.

Now what the equations speak of are closed line and surface integrals of the various electromagnetic fields, so we should specify the curves or surfaces for the integrations. In order to learn something about the allowed discontinuities at adjacent points, we must see to it that the elements of length or area of these curves or surfaces pass through the two neighboring points. This puts one part of the curve or surface on one side of the bisecting plane and the rest on the other side. The curves and surfaces should hence straddle, and tightly hug, the bisecting plane, as suggested in Figure 8–4, which shows both the upper and lower sides of the plane. Consequently, the line elements $d\mathbf{l}$ along the curve of integration have directions tangential to the bisecting plane and the surface elements $d\mathbf{S}$ are directed perpendicular to that plane; at least, that becomes the case in the limit that the two neighboring points, 1 and 2, nearly merge, with the upper and lower portions of either the closed curve or the closed surface being then separated only infinitesimally. The most important consequence of the merging of the upper and lower portions of the curve or surface is that, in the limit, the surface that is surrounded by the closed curve can be merely a thin sliver, ultimately of zero area, and that the volume enclosed by the closed surface approaches a flat area on the bisecting plane, ultimately of zero volume.

Turning our attention first to the closed curve that straddles the plane, we have been led to choose curves of integration for the emf V and the mmf U such that each curve passes through the two points 1 and 2 and such that the surfaces of integration bounded by those curves, on which the electric and magnetic fluxes, Ψ and Φ, are to be evaluated, are infinitesimally thin. In the limit of zero separation, we deal with the electric and magnetic fields just at the interface, and on its two sides. For this infinitesimal separation, however, the surface bounded by the curve can be merely a thin sliver, with zero area in the limit. As a result, the flux or current across that thin surface must become zero in the limit, unless the current density were infinite. We postpone discussion of the extraordinary case of infinite current density for a moment and consider first the normal situation of finite densities, leading to zero total flux and current across the thin sliver. Thus Φ or Ψ or I must be zero in the limit of zero separation between the two halves of the closed curve. Then so are $d\Phi/dt$ and $d\Psi/dt$ zero and Maxwell's equations then require V and U to be zero along the closed curve. This means that the line integral of **E**, and also of **H**, along the curve must vanish, which implies that the integral along one side of the bisecting plane and that on the other side must be equal and opposite, to cancel to zero. This can happen for *every* closed curve that straddles and hugs the plane only if the *tangential* field components are the *same* on both sides. That only the tangential components are so restricted follows from the $V = \oint \mathbf{E} \cdot d\mathbf{l}$ or $U = \oint \mathbf{H} \cdot d\mathbf{l}$ integrals; these involve only the field components along $d\mathbf{l}$, which is itself tangential to the plane. The components of **E** and **H** normal to the plane do not enter into the line integrals and are not affected by the $V = 0$ and $U = 0$ requirements in the limit.

The result just obtained applies to any two neighboring points; they mandate *continuity* of the **E** and **H** field components *tangential* to the bisecting plane between the two adjacent points. When the bisecting plane is the interface between two media of dissimilar constitutive parameters, this continuity requirement becomes a boundary condition that restricts the discontinuities that the fields may suffer. Figure 8–5 shows allowable **E** and **H** field configurations across a discontinuity plane; the tangential components must match across the plane.

To summarize, in the ordinary case of finite fields, the boundary conditions at an interface between two regions are, for the field components tangential to the interface:

$$\text{Continuity of } \mathbf{E}_{\tan}: \qquad (\mathbf{E}_1)_{\tan} = (\mathbf{E}_2)_{\tan}, \tag{8.1}$$

$$\text{Continuity of } \mathbf{H}_{\tan}: \qquad (\mathbf{H}_1)_{\tan} = (\mathbf{H}_2)_{\tan}. \tag{8.2}$$

Imposing these conditions is equivalent to satisfying the two Maxwell equations $V = -d\Phi/dt$ and $U = I + d\Psi/dt$ at the points of the interface.

Turning next to the closed surface that straddles the plane, we have been led to choose surfaces of integration for the electric and magnetic fluxes Ψ and Φ such that each closed surface passes through the two points 1 and 2 and

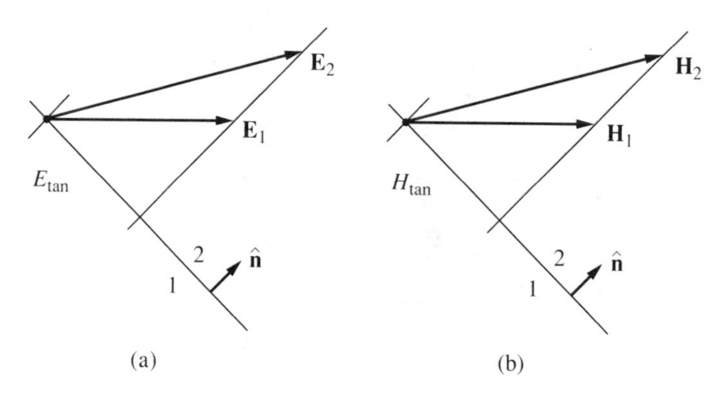

FIGURE 8–5 Permissible discontinuities of **E** and **H** fields.

such that the volumes of integration bounded by those surfaces are infinitesimally thin, with zero volume in the limit. As a result, the total charge enclosed by the surface must become zero in the limit, unless the charge density were infinite. We postpone discussion of the extraordinary case of infinite charge density for a moment and consider first the normal situation of finite charge density, leading to zero total charge Q enclosed by the surface. Thus $\Psi_0 = Q$ must be zero in the limit of zero separation between the two halves of the closed surface. Maxwell's equations also require Φ_0 to be zero over this, or any, closed surface. This means that the closed surface integral of **D**, and also of **B**, must vanish, which implies that the integral along one side of the bisecting plane and that on the other side must be equal and opposite, to cancel to zero. This can happen for *every* closed surface that straddles and hugs the plane only if the *normal* field components are the same on both sides. That only the normal components are so restricted follows from the $\Psi_0 = \oint \mathbf{D} \cdot d\mathbf{S}$ or $\Phi_0 = \oint \mathbf{B} \cdot d\mathbf{S}$ integrals; these involve only the field components along $d\mathbf{S}$, which is itself normal to the plane. The components of **D** and **B** tangential to the plane do not enter into the surface integrals and are not affected by the $\Psi_0 = 0$ and $\Phi_0 = 0$ requirements.

The result just obtained applies to any two neighboring points; they mandate *continuity* of the **D** and **B** field components *normal* to the bisecting plane between the two adjacent points. When the bisecting plane is the interface between two media of dissimilar constitutive parameters, this continuity requirement becomes a boundary condition that restricts the discontinuities that the fields may suffer. Figure 8–6 shows allowable **D** and **B** field configurations across a discontinuity plane; the normal components must match across the plane.

To summarize, in the ordinary case of finite charge density, the boundary conditions at an interface between two regions are, for the field components perpendicular to the interface:

$$\text{Continuity of } \mathbf{D}_{\text{nor}}: \qquad (\mathbf{D}_1)_{\text{nor}} = (\mathbf{D}_2)_{\text{nor}}, \tag{8.3}$$

$$\text{Continuity of } \mathbf{B}_{\text{nor}}: \qquad (\mathbf{B}_1)_{\text{nor}} = (\mathbf{B}_2)_{\text{nor}}. \tag{8.4}$$

Imposing these conditions is equivalent to satisfying the two subsidiary requirements of the Maxwell equations, $\Psi_0 = Q$ and $\Phi_0 = 0$ for closed surfaces, at the points of the interface.

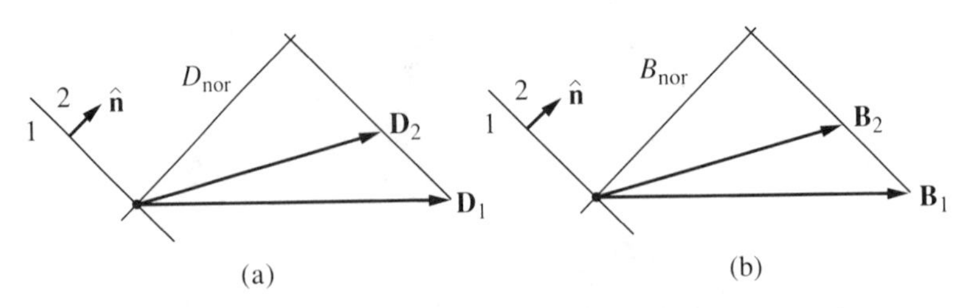

FIGURE 8–6 Permissible discontinuities of **D** and **B** fields.

Satisfying the continuity requirements on both the tangential components of **E** and the normal components of **D** at an interface between media of given, different permittivities leads to a determination of the full discontinuity of each of the vectors, as illustrated in the following example.

EXAMPLE 8.1

Let the interface between two dielectrics with $\varepsilon_1 = 2\varepsilon_0$ and $\varepsilon_2 = 6\varepsilon_0$ coincide with the *xy*-plane and suppose that the electric field at some point on side 1 at the plane were known to be $\mathbf{E}_1 = (2\hat{\mathbf{x}} + 5\hat{\mathbf{y}} - 6\hat{\mathbf{z}})E_0$ (V/m). What must the electric field be just on the other side of the plane, at the same location?

Since the *x*- and *y*-components are tangential to the interface plane, they are immediately known to be 2 and 5, respectively, on the other side as well. The *z*-component, which is normal to the plane, must be found. Now $\mathbf{D}_1 = \varepsilon_1(2\hat{\mathbf{x}} + 5\hat{\mathbf{y}} - 6\hat{\mathbf{z}})E_0$; its normal component, $D_{1z} = -6\varepsilon_1 E_0 = -12\varepsilon_0 E_0$, must be the same on the other side: $D_{2z} = -12\varepsilon_0 E_0 = -2(6\varepsilon_0)E_0$ or $D_{2z} = -2\varepsilon_2 E_0$, so that $E_{2z} = -2E_0$ and the electric field must jump from its value $\mathbf{E}_1 = (2\hat{\mathbf{x}} + 5\hat{\mathbf{y}} - 6\hat{\mathbf{z}})E_0$ on the first side to $\mathbf{E}_2 = (2\hat{\mathbf{x}} + 5\hat{\mathbf{y}} - 2\hat{\mathbf{z}})E_0$ on the other side.

Note that the **D** field's discontinuity is now also known: It jumps from $\mathbf{D}_1 = \varepsilon_0(4\hat{\mathbf{x}} + 10\hat{\mathbf{y}} - 12\hat{\mathbf{z}})E_0$ to $\mathbf{D}_2 = \varepsilon_0(12\hat{\mathbf{x}} + 30\hat{\mathbf{y}} - 12\hat{\mathbf{z}})E_0$. Also, the electric energy density $\frac{1}{2}\mathbf{E} \cdot \mathbf{D}$ is discontinuous, jumping from $\frac{1}{2}\mathbf{E}_1 \cdot \mathbf{D}_1 = 65\varepsilon_0 E_0^2$ to $\frac{1}{2}\mathbf{E}_2 \cdot \mathbf{D}_2 = 99\varepsilon_0 E_0^2$ from one side to the other of the plane at the point. ◆

To complete the development of boundary conditions, we should consider the extraordinary cases in which the limit of zero area or volume does *not* necessarily imply that the area must have zero current traversing it, or that the volume must enclose zero charge. We still exclude finite electric or magnetic flux Ψ or Φ over a sliver of infinitesimal area, because that would require an infinite **D** or **B** field, implying infinite energy density, which can entail infinite energy in a finite volume, a physical impossibility. However, we must not hastily exclude the possibility of infinite density of charge or current because, from a macroscopic viewpoint, charge *can* be concentrated to such an extent that a finite amount of charge can be smeared over a surface, with negligible volume. If that charge is moving, a finite current flows in a sheet along the surface, which has zero thickness. In those circumstances in which a surface charge or current sheet has been caused to appear on a surface of zero or infinitesimal thickness, the total charge Q within a volume that straddles and hugs that surface can be finite even within zero volume and the total current I crossing a sliver of area that straddles and hugs the surface can be finite even across zero area.

In those cases, the appropriate densities that describe the amount of charge or current on the surface are the surface charge density ρ_S (C/m^2) instead of volume charge density ρ (C/m^3) and the surface current density vector **K** in amperes per unit width (A/m) instead of the volume current density vector **J** (A/m^2). In Figure 8–7, the area A on the plane within the thin volume has

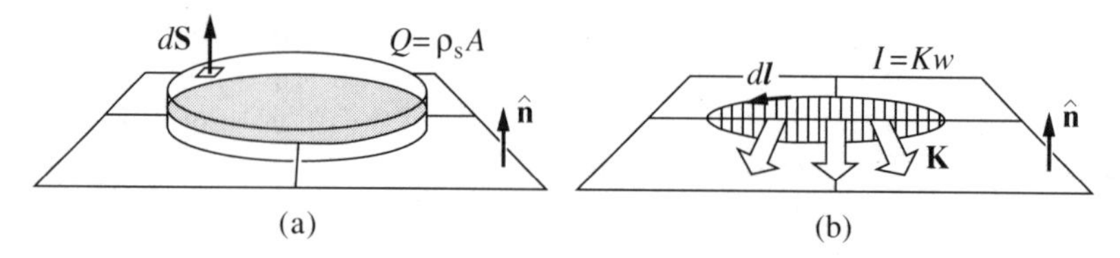

FIGURE 8–7 (a) Surface charge and (b) surface current sheet.

surface charge of density ρ_S, so that the total enclosed charge is the finite amount $Q = \rho_S A$ despite the lack of finite volume in the limit. The width w on the plane within the thin sliver of area straddling the plane carries current as a sheet with density K, so that the sliver has a finite current $I = Kw$ crossing it, along the plane and at right angles to the width w, despite the lack of finite thickness in the limit.

What happens to the boundary conditions when surface sources can be present? Gauss's law requires $\Psi_0 = Q$ and now $Q = \rho_S A$ remains finite even as the closed surface that passes through the neighboring points on the two sides of the charged surface loses all thickness. The electric flux Ψ_0 over the closed surface then becomes $\Psi_0 = \oint \mathbf{D} \cdot d\mathbf{S} = \mathbf{D}_2 \cdot \hat{\mathbf{n}}A + \mathbf{D}_1 \cdot (-\hat{\mathbf{n}})A = (\mathbf{D}_2 - \mathbf{D}_1) \cdot \hat{\mathbf{n}}A$ if, as shown, $d\mathbf{S}$ is along $+\hat{\mathbf{n}}$ on the side of point 2 but along $-\hat{\mathbf{n}}$ on the other side. (The area A has, for simplicity, been taken small enough for the field $\mathbf{D}$ not to vary significantly over either the top or the bottom part of the closed surface. Rigorously, we should consider the area A to be a first-order infinitesimal and the thickness to be a higher-order one.) Canceling the arbitrary area A from both sides of $\Psi_0 = Q$ leaves

$$(\mathbf{D}_2 - \mathbf{D}_1) \cdot \hat{\mathbf{n}} = \rho_S \tag{8.5}$$

as the more general boundary condition to replace the continuity of normal $\mathbf{D}$ at neighboring points. This relation states that the component of $\mathbf{D}$ normal to the bisecting plane between neighboring points is discontinuous by just the surface charge density on that plane, if any has been placed there. This boundary condition is equivalent to satisfying Gauss's law on the plane.

The Ampère–Maxwell law $U = I + d\Psi/dt$, applied to the closed curve that surrounds the thin sliver of area that can now carry a current sheet K, requires $U = I + 0$ ($\Psi = 0$ in the limit, since $\mathbf{D}$ will not be infinite) and $I = Kw$ remains finite even as the two parts of the closed curve that passes through the neighboring points on the two sides of the current-carrying surface become only infinitesimally separated. The mmf $U = \oint \mathbf{H} \cdot d\mathbf{l}$ along the closed curve becomes $(H_2 - H_1)w$ if, as shown, $d\mathbf{l}$ is along the direction of $\mathbf{K} \times \hat{\mathbf{n}}$ on the side of point 2 but along $-\mathbf{K} \times \hat{\mathbf{n}}$ on the other side. (The width w has, for simplicity, been taken small enough for the field $\mathbf{H}$ not to vary significantly over either the top or the bottom part of the closed curve. Rigorously, we should consider the width w to be a first-order infinitesimal and the thickness of the sliver to be a higher-order one.) Canceling the arbitrary width w from both sides of $U = I$ leaves

$$H_2 - H_1 = K \tag{8.6}$$

as the more general boundary condition to replace the continuity of tangential **H** at neighboring points. In this boundary condition, the component of **H** along the direction of $\mathbf{K} \times \hat{\mathbf{n}}$ is meant; note that the right-hand rule continues to relate the direction of **H** and of the current in the Ampère law. In vector form, the boundary condition can be stated as

$$\hat{\mathbf{n}} \times (\mathbf{H}_2 - \mathbf{H}_1) = \mathbf{K}, \tag{8.7}$$

since both the direction and magnitude of the discontinuity are thereby properly (i.e., by the right-hand rule) related to the surface current. This relation states that the component of **H** tangential to the bisecting plane between neighboring points and at right angles to the direction of the current sheet is discontinuous by just the surface current density on that plane, if any has been placed there. This boundary condition is equivalent to satisfying the Ampère–Maxwell law on the plane.

Satisfying the continuity requirements (or, if there is a current sheet, the discontinuity requirements) on the tangential components of **H** and the continuity requirements on normal components of **B** at an interface between media of given, different permeabilities leads to a determination of the full discontinuity of each of the vectors, as illustrated in the following example.

EXAMPLE 8.2

Let the interface between two media with $\mu_1 = 2\mu_0$ and $\mu_2 = 6\mu_0$ coincide with the xy-plane and suppose that the magnetic field at some point on the $z < 0$ side of the plane were known to be $\mathbf{H}_1 = (2\hat{\mathbf{x}} + 5\hat{\mathbf{y}} - 6\hat{\mathbf{z}})H_0$ (A/m). Suppose also that a current sheet $\mathbf{K} = 3\hat{\mathbf{y}}H_0$ is known to be flowing along the plane at that point. What must the magnetic field be just on the other side of the plane, at the same location?

The components of **H** tangential to the interface plane will jump discontinuously, in accordance with $\hat{\mathbf{n}} \times \mathbf{H}_2 = \hat{\mathbf{n}} \times \mathbf{H}_1 + \mathbf{K}$, with $\hat{\mathbf{n}} = \hat{\mathbf{z}}$. This yields information only on the tangential components of $\mathbf{H}_2$: $\hat{\mathbf{z}} \times \mathbf{H}_2 = [(2\hat{\mathbf{y}} - 5\hat{\mathbf{x}}) + 3\hat{\mathbf{y}}]H_0$, or $\hat{\mathbf{z}} \times \mathbf{H}_2 = (5\hat{\mathbf{y}} - 5\hat{\mathbf{x}})H_0 = \hat{\mathbf{z}} \times (5\hat{\mathbf{x}} + 5\hat{\mathbf{y}})H_0$; we still need to find the z-component of $\mathbf{H}_2$. But the normal component of **B** must be continuous: $\mu_1\hat{\mathbf{z}} \cdot \mathbf{H}_1 = \mu_2\hat{\mathbf{z}} \cdot \mathbf{H}_2$ or $2\mu_0(-6)H_0 = 6\mu_0\hat{\mathbf{z}} \cdot \mathbf{H}_2$, so that $\hat{\mathbf{z}} \cdot \mathbf{H}_2 = -2H_0$. Thus the magnetic field has jumped from $\mathbf{H}_1 = (2\hat{\mathbf{x}} + 5\hat{\mathbf{y}} - 6\hat{\mathbf{z}})H_0$ to $\mathbf{H}_2 = (5\hat{\mathbf{x}} + 5\hat{\mathbf{y}} - 2\hat{\mathbf{z}})H_0$ across the current-carrying xy-plane at the point in question.

Note that the **B** field also jumps there, from $\mathbf{B}_1 = (4\hat{\mathbf{x}} + 10\hat{\mathbf{y}} - 12\hat{\mathbf{z}})\mu_0 H_0$ to $\mathbf{B}_2 = (30\hat{\mathbf{x}} + 30\hat{\mathbf{y}} - 12\hat{\mathbf{z}})\mu_0 H_0$. Also, the magnetic energy density $\frac{1}{2}\mathbf{H} \cdot \mathbf{B}$ has a discontinuity, jumping from $\frac{1}{2}\mathbf{H}_1 \cdot \mathbf{B}_1 = 65\mu_0 H_0^2$ to $\frac{1}{2}\mathbf{H}_2 \cdot \mathbf{B}_2 = 162\mu_0 H_0^2$ from one side to the other of the plane at the point. ◆

Finally, the equation of conservation of charge, $I_0 = -dQ/dt$, relating the outflow of current I_0 across any closed surface to the enclosed charge Q, yields

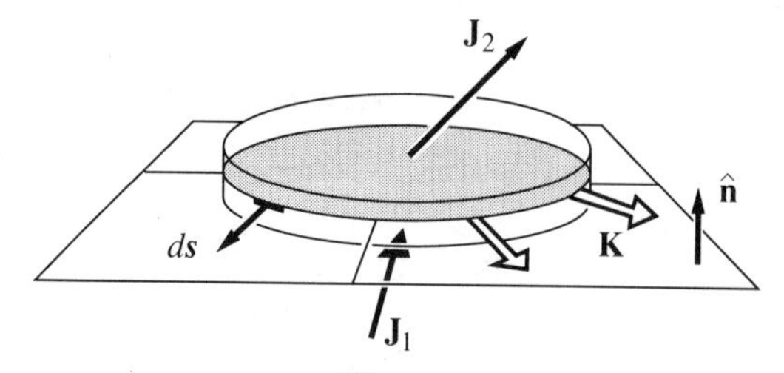

FIGURE 8–8 Outflow from a thin volume, at the sides and around the edge.

one further boundary condition, restricting discontinuities in electric current density. As indicated in Figure 8–8, the outflow I_0 of current from the closed surface that straddles the plane has three contributions: $\mathbf{J}_2 \cdot \hat{\mathbf{n}}A$ on the upper surface, $\mathbf{J}_1 \cdot (-\hat{\mathbf{n}})A$ on the lower one, and $\oint \mathbf{K} \cdot d\mathbf{s}$ around the periphery, where $d\mathbf{s}$ has the length of an element of the curve along the edge but is directed outward, in the plane. By the divergence theorem in the plane, $\oint \mathbf{K} \cdot d\mathbf{s} = \int \nabla \cdot \mathbf{K}\, dA$, which is here just $(\nabla \cdot \mathbf{K})A$; a two-dimensional divergence is used here, since $\mathbf{K}$ lies only in the plane. It follows that the total outflow is $I_0 = A\{(\mathbf{J}_2 - \mathbf{J}_1) \cdot \hat{\mathbf{n}} + \nabla \cdot \mathbf{K}\}$ and this must equal $-dQ/dt = -A\, d\rho_S/dt$. Canceling the small but arbitrary area A from both sides of the relation $I_0 = -dQ/dt$ leaves

$$(\mathbf{J}_2 - \mathbf{J}_1) \cdot \hat{\mathbf{n}} = -\left(\nabla \cdot \mathbf{K} + \frac{d\rho_S}{dt}\right). \tag{8.8}$$

This mandates *continuity* of normal electric current density at neighboring points, *unless* the bisecting plane carries a surface charge distribution or a surface current. In the latter case, the normal component of $\mathbf{J}$ jumps by the amount by which the surface current and surface charge density fail to satisfy the two-dimensional continuity relation on their own, as a result of leakage off the plane in the form of the current densities $\hat{\mathbf{n}} \cdot \mathbf{J}_2$ and $-\hat{\mathbf{n}} \cdot \mathbf{J}_1$.

How do we know when we are dealing with the ordinary cases that demand continuity of tangential **E** and **H** and of normal **D** and **B** and **J** at an interface between two media, rather than with the extraordinary cases that allow specific discontinuities in the presence of surface sources? For insulating media, unless we are told that we are to conceive of some given surface charge or current sheet that has deliberately been "painted" or smeared on some given surface, no such surface source should be present and continuity of the appropriate field components will reign. For conducting media, however, any charges that may have initially been introduced will tend to redistribute themselves; they may or may not accumulate on a boundary between conductors, depending on the rate at which they can move in the two media. Above all, we must ensure that Maxwell's equations be satisfied at all points, including the points that form an interface between two media, and we must also be sure that all the constitutive relations are satisfied on both sides of the interface. If either or both of the two media has nonzero conductivity, therefore, the opportunity exists for charges to be conveyed within the conductors, by whatever electric field is present, from the sources to the interface. These charges may accumulate or move along the boundary, forming a surface charge or a surface current and causing discontinuities in normal **D** and **J** and in tangential **H**, in accordance with the boundary conditions discussed above.

EXAMPLE 8.3

Let the interface between two conducting dielectrics with $\varepsilon_1 = 2\varepsilon_0$ and $\varepsilon_2 = 6\varepsilon_0$ coincide with the xy-plane and suppose that the complex electric field amplitude near some point on the $z < 0$ side of the plane were known to be $\mathbf{E}_1 = (2\hat{\mathbf{x}} + 5\hat{\mathbf{y}} - 6\hat{\mathbf{z}})E_0$ (V/m) at a given frequency ω. Let the conductivities of the two media be given by $\sigma_1 = 3\omega\varepsilon_0$ and $\sigma_2 = 4\omega\varepsilon_0$ (expressed in this way for convenience in maintaining the proper units). Can we find the electric field just on the other side of the plane, at that same location, at that frequency?

Since the x- and y-components are tangential to the interface plane, they are immediately known to be 2 and 5, respectively, on the other side as well. The z-component, which is normal to the plane, must be found. Now $\mathbf{D}_1 = \varepsilon_1(2\hat{\mathbf{x}} + 5\hat{\mathbf{y}} - 6\hat{\mathbf{z}})E_0$ and $\mathbf{J}_1 = \sigma_1(2\hat{\mathbf{x}} + 5\hat{\mathbf{y}} - 6\hat{\mathbf{z}})E_0$; their normal components, $D_{1z} = -6\varepsilon_1 E_0 = -12\varepsilon_0 E_0$ and $J_{1z} = -6\sigma_1 E_0 = -18\omega\varepsilon_0 E_0$, cannot both be made continuous: On side 2 of the plane, $D_{2z} = (6\varepsilon_0)E_{2z}$ and $J_{2z} = (4\omega\varepsilon_0)E_{2z}$ would be in the ratio $6/4\omega$, while the corresponding field components on the first side are in the ratio $12/18\omega$. We must therefore allow for the appearance of a surface charge at the frequency ω, swept onto the plane by the currents on the two sides. The boundary conditions dictate that $D_{2z} - D_{1z} = \rho_S$ and $J_{2z} - J_{1z} = -(\nabla \cdot \mathbf{K} + j\omega\rho_S)$; these combine into $(J_{2z} - J_{1z}) + j\omega(D_{2z} - D_{1z}) = -\nabla \cdot \mathbf{K}$, or

$$(\sigma_2 + j\omega\varepsilon_2)E_{2z} - (\sigma_1 + j\omega\varepsilon_1)E_{1z} = -\nabla \cdot \mathbf{K}, \tag{8.9}$$

or

$$(4 + j6)\omega\varepsilon_0 E_{2z} - (3 + j2)\omega\varepsilon_0 E_{1z} = -\nabla \cdot \mathbf{K}, \tag{8.10}$$

and we cannot obtain E_{2z} until we are given information about $\nabla \cdot \mathbf{K}$, which was not provided.

For the sake of completing the calculation, suppose we were given that $\nabla \cdot \mathbf{K} = 2\omega\varepsilon_0 E_0$ at the point in question (for this problem, the quantity $\omega\varepsilon_0 E_0$ provides convenient units for the divergence of the surface current density). From Eq. (8.10), $(4 + j6)E_{2z} = (3 + j2)E_{1z} - 2E_0 = (3 + j2)(-6)E_0 - 2E_0$ yields

$$E_{2z} = -\frac{(20 + j12)E_0}{4 + j6} = [(-2.923) + j(1.385)]E_0 \tag{8.11}$$

at the given frequency. The electric field jumps from $\mathbf{E}_1 = (2\hat{\mathbf{x}} + 5\hat{\mathbf{y}} - 6\hat{\mathbf{z}})E_0$ on the first side to $\mathbf{E}_2 = [2\hat{\mathbf{x}} + 5\hat{\mathbf{y}} + (-2.923 + j1.385)\hat{\mathbf{z}}]E_0$ on the other side.

There is a surface charge on the plane at the point, of density $D_{2z} - D_{1z}$, or

$$\rho_S = 6\varepsilon_0 E_{2z} - 2\varepsilon_0 E_{1z} = 6\varepsilon_0 E_{2z} + 12\varepsilon_0 E_0 = (-5.538 + j8.308)\varepsilon_0 E_0, \tag{8.12}$$

oscillating at the same frequency ω. The interpretation is that because the time constants $\tau_1 = \varepsilon_1/\sigma_1$ and $\tau_2 = \varepsilon_2/\sigma_2$ of the two media do not match, since $\omega\tau_1 = \frac{2}{3}$ while $\omega\tau_2 = \frac{3}{2}$, and because the surface current spreads the charge along the plane at the given rate $\nabla \cdot \mathbf{K} = 2\omega\varepsilon_0 E_0$, the currents on the two sides do not drain away the remaining charge at the same rate that it is brought to the interface plane. The charge of density ρ_S therefore accumulates (and oscillates).

How might we have learned about $\nabla \cdot \mathbf{K}$ if it had not arbitrarily been specified? An appropriate property of the surface would have to be known, such as its surface conductivity σ_S in the relation $\mathbf{K} = \sigma_S \mathbf{E}_{\text{tan}}$, expressing how readily charges on the surface can become a surface current, in response to a tangential electric field there that urges them to flow along it. Then the variation of the tangential electric field along the plane would have to be known, to yield $\nabla \cdot \mathbf{K}$ from the two-dimensional divergence of that field. ◆

To summarize the boundary conditions that apply at the interface between two media, they are expressed in vector form, in terms of the unit vector $\hat{\mathbf{n}}$ normal to the boundary and pointing toward medium 2, as

$$\hat{\mathbf{n}} \times \mathbf{E}_2 - \hat{\mathbf{n}} \times \mathbf{E}_1 = 0, \tag{8.13}$$

$$\hat{\mathbf{n}} \times \mathbf{H}_2 - \hat{\mathbf{n}} \times \mathbf{H}_1 = \mathbf{K}. \tag{8.14}$$

We also have the subsidiary relations

$$\hat{\mathbf{n}} \cdot \mathbf{D}_2 - \hat{\mathbf{n}} \cdot \mathbf{D}_1 = \rho_S, \tag{8.15}$$

$$\hat{\mathbf{n}} \cdot \mathbf{B}_2 - \hat{\mathbf{n}} \cdot \mathbf{B}_1 = 0, \tag{8.16}$$

$$\hat{\mathbf{n}} \cdot \mathbf{J}_2 - \hat{\mathbf{n}} \cdot \mathbf{J}_1 = -(\nabla \cdot \mathbf{K} + j\omega\rho_S), \tag{8.17}$$

as well as the constitutive parameters ε, μ, and σ for each of the two media *and* σ_S in the relation $\mathbf{K} = \sigma_S \mathbf{E}_{\text{tan}}$ for the surface itself.

Note that the units of the surface conductivity σ_S are siemens, while those of a bulk conductivity σ in $\mathbf{J} = \sigma\mathbf{E}$ are siemens/m. We should also be aware that surface conductivities are often reported (with or without a smile!) in "siemens per square" and its reciprocal, the surface resistivity, in "ohms per square." This designation reminds us that the size of a square area of the surface does not affect its conductance or resistance. This is because a rectangular area of the resistive plane, of length l along the electric field and width w across it, has a voltage–current relation $V = RI$ or $I = GV$ with $V = El$, $I = wK$, and $K = \sigma_S E$, giving $G = \sigma_S w/l$ or $R = l/\sigma_S w$. If the rectangular area becomes a square, of *any* size $l = w$, its conductance is $G = \sigma_S$

and its resistance is $R = 1/\sigma_S$, regardless of the size of the square, be it millimeters or meters or kilometers!

The boundary conditions are not all independent. Since the surface current **K** represents the motion of the surface charge ρ_S, the two are subject to their own equation of conservation of charge: the outflow across any closed loop on the surface must equal the rate of decrease of the total enclosed surface charge, by time variation or by leakage off the plane into the surrounding conductors. As a consequence, *the two boundary conditions that deal with the tangential components provide sufficient conditions to determine the fields at a boundary.* The additional ones that involve the normal components are subsidiary conditions that can determine the surface sources that make all the boundary conditions consistent with one another.

Armed with these relations, which are equivalent to Maxwell's equations as applied to the points on the boundary between dissimilar media, we can now resume our investigation of what happens to a wave that is incident onto a planar interface.

Normal Incidence with Matched Impedances

To approach the problem of an incident wave originating at a source infinitely remote from the planar interface between the sourced and the unsourced media in the simplest way, we first examine lossless (i.e., nonconducting) dielectrics, with an interface plane that also has no surface conductivity, and consider the wave to be propagating along the direction of $\hat{\mathbf{n}}$, normal to the interface. That is, the Poynting vector $\frac{1}{2}\mathbf{E} \times \mathbf{H}^*$ is parallel to $\hat{\mathbf{n}}$; this is termed *normal incidence.* We ask whether this wave can just cross the boundary and continue onward.

For normal incidence, both **E** and **H** of the incident wave are tangential to the planar boundary. If the wave is simply to cross the boundary, the same **E** and **H** fields must appear at the other side of the interface, to ensure continuity of the tangential (here, the complete) fields across the plane. On side 2, the Poynting vector is then the same, and still along $\hat{\mathbf{n}}$. This wave can then propagate away from the interface, into the second medium, provided that **E** and **H** are in the proper relationship to each other, as prescribed for region 2. In region 1, **E** and **H** were related by the impedance η_1 of the first medium: $E = \eta_1 H$. The same **E** and **H** fields can propagate in region 2 if it is true that $E = \eta_2 H$ as well. We conclude that pure transmission across the interface occurs if

$$\eta_1 = \eta_2, \tag{8.18}$$

that is, if the wave impedances of the two dielectrics are *matched*. This certainly happens in the trivial case that the two media are actually identical, so that the entire universe is filled with one medium, but it can also be the case for dissimilar dielectrics, with $\varepsilon_1 \neq \varepsilon_2$ and $\mu_1 \neq \mu_2$, provided that $\eta_1 = \sqrt{\mu_1/\varepsilon_1}$

equals $\eta_2 = \sqrt{\mu_2/\varepsilon_2}$. This requires $\mu_1/\varepsilon_1 = \mu_2/\varepsilon_2$ or, more simply, that $\mu_2/\mu_1 = \varepsilon_2/\varepsilon_1$: the two nonconducting media are matched if the ratio of their permeabilities equals the ratio of their permittivities.

In the case of dissimilar but *matched* dielectrics, the incident wave crosses the interface and continues to propagate in the second medium, but it is not entirely unaffected: it changes its wave speed, from $v_1 = 1/\sqrt{\mu_1\varepsilon_1}$ to $v_2 = 1/\sqrt{\mu_2\varepsilon_2}$. If μ and ε both increase by the factor $\chi = \varepsilon_2/\varepsilon_1$, the wave slows by that same factor χ. Also, the accompanying **D** and **B** fields are discontinuous across the plane, by the same factor χ. Finally, the Poynting vector $\frac{1}{2}\mathbf{E} \times \mathbf{H}^*$ is the same on both sides of the interface, so that all the incident power is transmitted across the boundary, into the second medium.

Impedance Mismatch

We now proceed to the case of a wave that is still normally incident onto the interface, but now with dielectrics whose wave impedances are mismatched: $\eta_1 \neq \eta_2$. The previous simple solution that satisfied Maxwell's equations on both sides of the interface *and* along the boundary, by just retaining the same **E** and **H** fields on both sides to ensure continuity of these tangential fields, is now no longer feasible. The incident wave's impedance ratio $E/H = \eta_1$ was appropriate for the first region, but is wrong (does not satisfy Maxwell's equations) in the second medium, which demands $E/H = \eta_2$ instead. The incident wave cannot simply cross the boundary plane and continue into the second medium, leaving the wave unaffected in the first region. We need to find another pair of solutions to Maxwell's equations within the two regions, consistent with the source of the incident wave *and* satisfying the boundary conditions at the interface. The latter requirement involves matching the tangential **E** and **H** fields on the two sides of the boundary plane; this matching of the fields must be achieved at every point of the interface, at every instant of time.

To discover how the fields of the incident wave are affected by the encounter with the interface, we ask what new, additional fields arise. Now the incident wave has frequency ω, determined directly by the source. The additional fields on both sides of the interface must also oscillate at this same frequency; otherwise, even if we succeeded in matching the total tangential fields across the boundary at one instant, they would not remain matched to each other at subsequent times if they were not to oscillate in unison. Furthermore, because the incident wave is directed normally to the interface, any value of the fields is attained simultaneously at every point of the boundary. Matching at one boundary point will therefore achieve matching at every point of the interface. But this requires the additional fields on the two sides also to attain their values simultaneously at every point of the plane. The additional fields can therefore also be normally directed waves.

But fields that vary along the direction of $\hat{\mathbf{n}}$ were found to be allowed by Maxwell's equations (or the wave equation) in the form of a superposition of *two* oppositely sensed traveling waves, both with the same wave speed but with oppositely directed Poynting vectors and propagation vectors. Using such superpositions of waves, all at frequency ω and with propagation constants determined by the parameters of the two media, should allow the necessary freedom to match the total tangential fields across the interface.

However, since region 2 is unsourced, it cannot carry a wave that travels *toward* the interface. If it did, there would have to be some source for it somewhere, even if only at infinity, but none has been allowed in that region. The boundary plane can *emit* or *scatter* fields, in the form of waves, into both regions, *away from* the interface; it cannot, however, "suck in" a wave from infinity toward itself, in the absence of a source that could emit such a wave toward it. This requirement, that sources can spew forth energy but not draw it in from a source-free region, is a separate physical principle, referred to as the *radiation condition*; it is not a mathematical requirement of the wave equation.

What we are left to deal with is a steady state with two waves, oppositely sensed, in region 1, plus one wave in region 2. One of the two waves in the sourced region is the incident wave; the *scattered* fields are the *reflected* wave, in the sourced region, and the *transmitted* wave, in the unsourced one. All the waves oscillate at the original frequency of the source, in order for the fields to match across the plane for all time (this statement would have to be modified if the interface plane were moving, instead of stationary). In order that the scattered waves, as well as the incident one, satisfy Maxwell's equations within the two regions, they must have propagation constants $k_1 = \omega\sqrt{\mu_1\varepsilon_1}$ in region 1 and $k_2 = \omega\sqrt{\mu_2\varepsilon_2}$ in region 2. The time and space dependence of the three waves must therefore be as follows, recalling that $\hat{\mathbf{n}}$ points into region 2.

$$\text{incident:} \quad \exp\left[j(\omega t - k_1\hat{\mathbf{n}}\cdot\mathbf{r})\right] \quad \text{in region 1}, \tag{8.19}$$

$$\text{reflected:} \quad \exp\left[j(\omega t + k_1\hat{\mathbf{n}}\cdot\mathbf{r})\right] \quad \text{in region 1}, \tag{8.20}$$

$$\text{transmitted:} \quad \exp\left[j(\omega t - k_2\hat{\mathbf{n}}\cdot\mathbf{r})\right] \quad \text{in region 2}. \tag{8.21}$$

Each of these waves has its own strength and polarization, given by its electric field vector $\mathbf{E}$, which is perpendicular to $\hat{\mathbf{n}}$ and to the corresponding magnetic field $\mathbf{H}$. As indicated in Figure 8–9, the incident wave has a given field amplitude $\mathbf{E}_0$ and a corresponding, known field $\mathbf{H}_0$ related to it by the wave impedance of the sourced region, $\mathbf{H}_0 = \hat{\mathbf{n}} \times \mathbf{E}_0/\eta_1$. The reflected wave has some unknown field amplitude $\mathbf{E}_1$, together with a magnetic field $\mathbf{H}_1$ related to it by the same wave impedance η_1 but directed so that the Poynting vector is along $-\hat{\mathbf{n}}$, instead of $\hat{\mathbf{n}}$. The transmitted wave has an unknown field $\mathbf{E}_2$; its magnetic field is oriented to make its Poynting vector point along $\hat{\mathbf{n}}$ but with a magnitude related to that of $\mathbf{E}_2$ by the wave impedance η_2 instead of η_1. There are hence two (vector) unknowns, $\mathbf{E}_1$ and $\mathbf{E}_2$, to be found in terms of the given $\mathbf{E}_0$ of the specified incident wave. There are two conditions to be imposed on these two unknowns: that the total $\mathbf{E}$ field and the total $\mathbf{H}$ field (which are tangential to the interface) both be continuous across the boundary plane. With two conditions for two unknowns, a solution should be forthcoming.

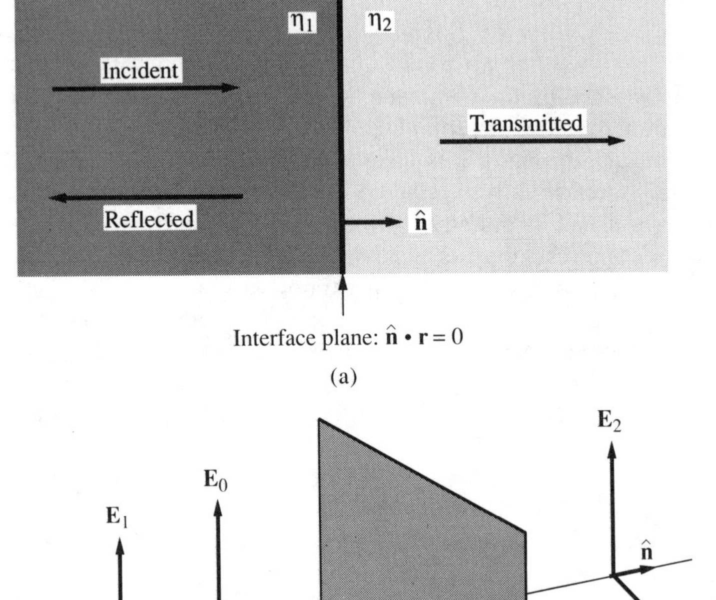

FIGURE 8–9 Field patterns of the incident and scattered waves.

The total electric field in region 1 is given by

$$\mathbf{E} = \mathbf{E}_0 \exp(-jk_1\hat{\mathbf{n}} \cdot \mathbf{r}) + \mathbf{E}_1 \exp(+jk_1\hat{\mathbf{n}} \cdot \mathbf{r}), \tag{8.22}$$

while that in region 2 is just

$$\mathbf{E} = \mathbf{E}_2 \exp(-jk_2\,\hat{\mathbf{n}} \cdot \mathbf{r}). \tag{8.23}$$

The corresponding magnetic fields in the two regions are

$$\mathbf{H} = \frac{\hat{\mathbf{n}} \times \mathbf{E}_0}{\eta_1} \exp(-jk_1\hat{\mathbf{n}} \cdot \mathbf{r}) + \frac{-\hat{\mathbf{n}} \times \mathbf{E}_1}{\eta_1} \exp(+jk_1\hat{\mathbf{n}} \cdot \mathbf{r}) \tag{8.24}$$

in medium 1 and

$$\mathbf{H} = \frac{\hat{\mathbf{n}} \times \mathbf{E}_2}{\eta_2} \exp(-jk_2\,\hat{\mathbf{n}} \cdot \mathbf{r}) \tag{8.25}$$

in medium 2. The boundary plane is given analytically by all those position vectors $\mathbf{r}$ such that $\hat{\mathbf{n}} \cdot \mathbf{r}$ is a constant, since $\hat{\mathbf{n}}$ is defined as being normal to the plane. If we choose to place the origin $\mathbf{r} = 0$ somewhere on the interface, rather than somewhere off it, that constant must be zero and this choice of origin simplifies the equations, since $\hat{\mathbf{n}} \cdot \mathbf{r} = 0$ makes all the exponentials become unity at every point of the interface.

The requirements of continuity of the tangential electric and magnetic fields at all points on the interface are then expressed by

$$\mathbf{E}_0 + \mathbf{E}_1 = \mathbf{E}_2, \tag{8.26}$$

$$\frac{\hat{\mathbf{n}} \times \mathbf{E}_0}{\eta_1} + \frac{-\hat{\mathbf{n}} \times \mathbf{E}_1}{\eta_1} = \frac{\hat{\mathbf{n}} \times \mathbf{E}_2}{\eta_2}. \tag{8.27}$$

Forming the cross product of the first of these with $\hat{\mathbf{n}}$ yields the pair

$$\hat{\mathbf{n}} \times \mathbf{E}_0 + \hat{\mathbf{n}} \times \mathbf{E}_1 = \hat{\mathbf{n}} \times \mathbf{E}_2, \tag{8.28}$$

$$\hat{\mathbf{n}} \times \mathbf{E}_0 - \hat{\mathbf{n}} \times \mathbf{E}_1 = \frac{\eta_1}{\eta_2} \hat{\mathbf{n}} \times \mathbf{E}_2, \tag{8.29}$$

and adding these last two versions of the two conditions eliminates the unknown $\mathbf{E}_1$:

$$2\hat{\mathbf{n}} \times \mathbf{E}_0 = \left(1 + \frac{\eta_1}{\eta_2}\right)\hat{\mathbf{n}} \times \mathbf{E}_2, \tag{8.30}$$

so that

$$\hat{\mathbf{n}} \times \mathbf{E}_2 = \left(\frac{2\eta_2}{\eta_2 + \eta_1}\right)\hat{\mathbf{n}} \times \mathbf{E}_0 \tag{8.31}$$

and Eq. (8.28) gives $\hat{\mathbf{n}} \times \mathbf{E}_1$ as $\hat{\mathbf{n}} \times \mathbf{E}_2 - \hat{\mathbf{n}} \times \mathbf{E}_0$ or

$$\hat{\mathbf{n}} \times \mathbf{E}_1 = \left(\frac{\eta_2 - \eta_1}{\eta_1 + \eta_2}\right)\hat{\mathbf{n}} \times \mathbf{E}_0. \tag{8.32}$$

Finally, by virtue of the general vector identity

$$\mathbf{E} \equiv (\hat{\mathbf{n}} \times \mathbf{E}) \times \hat{\mathbf{n}} + (\hat{\mathbf{n}} \cdot \mathbf{E})\hat{\mathbf{n}} \tag{8.33}$$

and the fact that for the waves in question, $\hat{\mathbf{n}} \cdot \mathbf{E} = 0$, we can extract the full vectors $\mathbf{E}$ from $\hat{\mathbf{n}} \times \mathbf{E}$ by crossing again with $\hat{\mathbf{n}}$ on both sides of the equations:

$$\mathbf{E}_1 = \frac{\eta_2 - \eta_1}{\eta_2 + \eta_1}\, \mathbf{E}_0, \tag{8.34}$$

$$\mathbf{E}_2 = \frac{2\eta_2}{\eta_2 + \eta_1}\, \mathbf{E}_0. \tag{8.35}$$

These are the electric field amplitudes of the scattered waves, in terms of the specified incident field. The total electric field in region 1 is given by

$$\mathbf{E} = \mathbf{E}_0\{\exp(-jk_1\hat{\mathbf{n}}\cdot\mathbf{r}) + \frac{\eta_2-\eta_1}{\eta_2+\eta_1}\exp(+jk_1\hat{\mathbf{n}}\cdot\mathbf{r})\}, \tag{8.36}$$

while that in region 2 is

$$\mathbf{E} = \mathbf{E}_0\frac{2\eta_2}{\eta_2+\eta_1}\exp(-jk_2\hat{\mathbf{n}}\cdot\mathbf{r}). \tag{8.37}$$

The associated magnetic fields in the two regions are, from Eqs. (8.24)–(8.25),

$$\mathbf{H} = \mathbf{H}_0\{\exp(-jk_1\hat{\mathbf{n}}\cdot\mathbf{r}) - \frac{\eta_2-\eta_1}{\eta_2+\eta_1}\exp(+jk_1\hat{\mathbf{n}}\cdot\mathbf{r})\} \tag{8.38}$$

in medium 1 and

$$\mathbf{H} = \mathbf{H}_0\frac{2\eta_1}{\eta_2+\eta_1}\exp(-jk_2\hat{\mathbf{n}}\cdot\mathbf{r}) \tag{8.39}$$

in medium 2, with $\mathbf{H}_0 = \hat{\mathbf{n}}\times\mathbf{E}_0/\eta_1$. These represent the solution to the problem of normal incidence onto the interface between mismatched media.

Reflection and Transmission Coefficients

The quantity E_1/E_0 or

$$\Gamma_e = \frac{\eta_2-\eta_1}{\eta_2+\eta_1} \tag{8.40}$$

is the electric-field amplitude *reflection coefficient* of the interface, for a wave normally incident from region 1 to region 2. The quantity E_2/E_0 or

$$T_e = \frac{2\eta_2}{\eta_2+\eta_1} \tag{8.41}$$

is the electric-field amplitude *transmission coefficient*, giving the amplitude of the transmitted electric field in terms of the incident one. The corresponding coefficients for the magnetic fields are readily derived from these, by using $H_2 = E_2/\eta_2 = (T_e E_0/\eta_2) = (T_e\eta_1/\eta_2)E_0/\eta_1 = (T_e\eta_1/\eta_2)H_0$, so that

$$T_h = \frac{2\eta_1}{\eta_2+\eta_1} \tag{8.42}$$

is the magnetic-field amplitude *transmission coefficient*, the ratio of the transmitted magnetic field to the incident one. For the reflected wave, the impedance η_1 is the same as for the incident wave, but the direction of either the electric or the magnetic field of the reflected wave is opposite to that of the incident one, to reverse the Poynting vector, so that $\Gamma_h = -\Gamma_e$ or

$$\Gamma_h = \frac{\eta_1 - \eta_2}{\eta_1 + \eta_2}. \tag{8.43}$$

Note that all these coefficients relate vector fields, so that both the magnitude and direction, or strength and polarization, of the scattered wave fields are given by these reflection and transmission coefficients. The scattered fields have the same orientation as the incident ones, either parallel or antiparallel to them, depending on which of the two mismatched impedances is the greater. Also note that $T = 1 + \Gamma$, since the transmitted field (electric or magnetic) is the sum of the incident and reflected ones at the interface; that is the essence of the boundary conditions there.

EXAMPLE 8.4

For normal incidence onto the interface between two nonmagnetic, lossless dielectrics with $\varepsilon_1 = 6.25\varepsilon_0$ and $\varepsilon_2 = 15.21\varepsilon_0$, what are the reflection and transmission coefficients?

For nonmagnetic media, $\mu_1 = \mu_2 = \mu_0$ and for lossless media $\sigma = 0$, so that the impedances are $\sqrt{\mu_0/\varepsilon}$. The impedance mismatch is therefore given by $\eta_2/\eta_1 = \sqrt{6.25/15.21} = 0.6410$. Hence the reflection coefficient is found as $\Gamma_e = (0.6410 - 1)/(0.6410 + 1) = -0.2188$ and the transmission coefficient is $T_e = 1 + \Gamma_e = 0.7812$, for the electric fields. The negative sign of Γ_e is due to the fact that $\eta_2 < \eta_1$ here; it means that the reflected electric field at the interface is directed oppositely to the incident one. Correspondingly, the reflected magnetic field has the same direction as the incident one, as is confirmed by $\Gamma_h = -\Gamma_e = +0.2188$. Also, $T_h = 1 + \Gamma_h = 1.2188$ indicates that the transmitted magnetic field is stronger than the incident one, and in the same direction. ◆

Mnemonic aids are easy to develop for these important results. The expression for the reflection coefficient, $\Gamma_e = (\eta_2 - \eta_1)/(\eta_2 + \eta_1)$, clearly exhibits the effects of the impedance mismatch. If the two media were matched ($\eta_2 = \eta_1$), Γ would be zero and there would be no reflected wave. Also, if the second region has zero impedance ($\eta_2 = 0$), interpreted as a medium that tolerates no electric field (as is the case for a perfect conductor), $\Gamma_e = -1$ for any value of η_1. The reflected electric field then is equal and opposite to the incident one, canceling it at the boundary, as required by the second medium. These two observations aid in remembering the form of the expression for the reflection coefficient: the difference between the impedances must be in the numerator (to yield zero reflection when the media are matched) and that difference must be $\eta_2 - \eta_1$, not $\eta_1 - \eta_2$ (to yield $\Gamma_e = -1$ at a perfect conductor). The other coefficients follow at once from Γ_e, because $T = 1 + \Gamma$ embodies the continuity requirements at the interface.

Still another mnemonic is obtained by noting that the "transfer impedance" that relates the *incident* electric field to the *transmitted* magnetic field is

$$\frac{E_0}{H_2} = \frac{1}{2}(\eta_1 + \eta_2), \tag{8.44}$$

which is merely the average of the two impedances and an easily remembered compromise between the two, giving the transmitted magnetic field generated by the incident electric field.

Energy Transmission and Reflection

Were it not for the interface, the source in region 1 would simply emit a wave of power density $\frac{1}{2}\mathbf{E}_0 \times \mathbf{H}_0^*$, propagating to infinity. Instead, in the presence of the interface at right angles to the incident wave direction, the power density that does reach infinity is $\frac{1}{2}\mathbf{E}_2 \times \mathbf{H}_2^*$. The two are easily related to each other, since $E_2 = T_e E_0$ and $H_2 = T_h H_0$, so that

$$\tfrac{1}{2}\mathbf{E}_2 \times \mathbf{H}_2^* = T_e T_h^* \tfrac{1}{2}\mathbf{E}_0 \times \mathbf{H}_0^* \tag{8.45}$$

exhibits the power transmission coefficient $T_p = T_e T_h^*$.

In region 1, the fields are

$$\mathbf{E} = \mathbf{E}_0\{\exp(-jk_1\hat{\mathbf{n}}\cdot\mathbf{r}) + \Gamma_e \exp(+jk_1\hat{\mathbf{n}}\cdot\mathbf{r})\} \tag{8.46}$$

and

$$\mathbf{H} = \mathbf{H}_0\{\exp(-jk_1\hat{\mathbf{n}}\cdot\mathbf{r}) - \Gamma_e \exp(+jk_1\hat{\mathbf{n}}\cdot\mathbf{r})\}. \tag{8.47}$$

One way to interpret this result is to decompose these fields into a part that continues into region 2, plus a remainder. The fields that reach and cross the interface are, at $\hat{\mathbf{n}}\cdot\mathbf{r} = 0$,

$$\mathbf{E} = (1 + \Gamma_e)\mathbf{E}_0, \qquad \mathbf{H} = (1 - \Gamma_e)\mathbf{H}_0. \tag{8.48}$$

Upon separating these from the total fields in region 1, we have

$$\mathbf{E} = \mathbf{E}_0\{\Gamma_e \exp(+jk_1\hat{\mathbf{n}}\cdot\mathbf{r}) - \Gamma_e \exp(-jk_1\hat{\mathbf{n}}\cdot\mathbf{r})\} + (1 + \Gamma_e)\mathbf{E}_0 \exp(-jk_1\hat{\mathbf{n}}\cdot\mathbf{r}), \tag{8.49}$$

$$\mathbf{H} = \mathbf{H}_0\{-\Gamma_e \exp(+jk_1\hat{\mathbf{n}}\cdot\mathbf{r}) + \Gamma_e \exp(-jk_1\hat{\mathbf{n}}\cdot\mathbf{r})\} + (1 - \Gamma_e)\mathbf{H}_0 \exp(-jk_1\hat{\mathbf{n}}\cdot\mathbf{r}), \tag{8.50}$$

or

$$\mathbf{E} = 2j\Gamma_e\mathbf{E}_0 \sin(k_1\hat{\mathbf{n}}\cdot\mathbf{r}) + (1 + \Gamma_e)\mathbf{E}_0 \exp(-jk_1\hat{\mathbf{n}}\cdot\mathbf{r}), \tag{8.51}$$

$$\mathbf{H} = -2j\Gamma_e\mathbf{H}_0 \sin(k_1\hat{\mathbf{n}}\cdot\mathbf{r}) + (1 - \Gamma_e)\mathbf{H}_0 \exp(-jk_1\hat{\mathbf{n}}\cdot\mathbf{r}) \tag{8.52}$$

as alternative expressions for the fields in region 1. Each field appears here as the sum of two types. One is a propagating wave

$$\mathbf{E}_p = (1 + \Gamma_e)\mathbf{E}_0 \exp(-jk_1\hat{\mathbf{n}}\cdot\mathbf{r}), \qquad \mathbf{H}_p = (1 - \Gamma_e)\mathbf{H}_0 \exp(-jk_1\hat{\mathbf{n}}\cdot\mathbf{r}) \tag{8.53}$$

with "compromise" amplitudes $(1 + \Gamma_e)\mathbf{E}_0 = T_e \mathbf{E}_0$ and $(1 - \Gamma_e)\mathbf{H}_0 = T_h \mathbf{H}_0$ that become the amplitudes of the transmitted wave (k_1 just changes to k_2 in region 2). The other is a field that does not propagate; it merely oscillates in time (at frequency ω) and is sinusoidally distributed in space:

$$\mathbf{E}_S = 2j\Gamma_e \mathbf{E}_0 \sin (k_1 \hat{\mathbf{n}} \cdot \mathbf{r}), \qquad \mathbf{H}_S = -2j\Gamma_e \mathbf{H}_0 \sin (k_1 \hat{\mathbf{n}} \cdot \mathbf{r}). \tag{8.54}$$

The first type is a traveling wave; the other is a standing wave, formed by the interference of the forward- and backward-traveling waves. At the interface, only the traveling-wave portion appears and crosses the plane. In front of the interface, the standing-wave portion just stores the energy that is not transmitted into region 2.

To confirm that energy is conserved in the process of reflection and transmission of the waves, we may calculate the complex power that crosses a closed surface that straddles the interface plane. Let this surface be cylindrical in shape, of cross-sectional area A, from $z_1 < 0$ to $z_2 > 0$, with the interface coinciding with the $z = 0$ plane. The quantity to be integrated over this cylinder is $\frac{1}{2}\mathbf{E} \times \mathbf{H}^*$; at z_2, this is just $\frac{1}{2}\mathbf{E}_2 \times \mathbf{H}_2^* = T_e T_h^* \frac{1}{2}\mathbf{E}_0 \times \mathbf{H}_0^*$ and $d\mathbf{S}$ is along $+z$, while at z_1 it is given by

$$\begin{aligned} &\tfrac{1}{2}\mathbf{E}_0\{e^{-jk_1z_1} + \Gamma_e e^{jk_1z_1}\} \times \mathbf{H}_0^*\{e^{jk_1z_1} - \Gamma_e^* e^{-jk_1z_1}\} \\ &\qquad = \tfrac{1}{2}\mathbf{E}_0 \times \mathbf{H}_0^*\{1 - |\Gamma_e|^2 + \Gamma_e e^{j2k_1z_1} - \Gamma_e^* e^{-j2k_1z_1}\} \end{aligned} \tag{8.55}$$

and $d\mathbf{S}$ is along $-z$. The total complex power that emerges from the enclosed volume is therefore

$$\begin{aligned} &\oint \tfrac{1}{2}\mathbf{E} \times \mathbf{H}^* \cdot d\mathbf{S} \\ &\qquad = \tfrac{1}{2}\mathbf{E}_0 \times \mathbf{H}_0^* \cdot \hat{\mathbf{z}}A\{T_e T_h^* - 1 + |\Gamma_e|^2 - \Gamma_e e^{j2k_1z_1} + \Gamma_e^* e^{-j2k_1z_1}\} \end{aligned} \tag{8.56}$$

and assuming real power flow in the incident wave, we have that

$$T_e T_h^* - 1 + |\Gamma_e|^2 = (1 + \Gamma_e)(1 - \Gamma_e^*) - 1 + |\Gamma_e|^2 = \Gamma_e - \Gamma_e^* = 2j \operatorname{Im} \Gamma_e \tag{8.57}$$

is purely imaginary, as is

$$-\Gamma_e e^{j2k_1z_1} + \Gamma_e^* e^{-j2k_1z_1} = -2j \operatorname{Im} (\Gamma_e e^{j2k_1z_1}), \tag{8.58}$$

so that the entire complex power outflow across the cylindrical surface is purely imaginary,

$$\oint \tfrac{1}{2}\mathbf{E} \times \mathbf{H}^* \cdot d\mathbf{S} = \tfrac{1}{2}\mathbf{E}_0 \times \mathbf{H}_0^* \cdot \hat{\mathbf{z}}A[2j \operatorname{Im} \Gamma_e - 2j \operatorname{Im} (\Gamma_e e^{j2k_1z_1})]. \tag{8.59}$$

Imaginary power represents only the difference between magnetic and electric energy storage within the enclosed volume, but no real power loss. Real power is therefore conserved in the process of reflection and transmission at the interface. In particular, for real values of the impedances η_1 and η_2 on the two sides of the interface, Γ_e is real too and the complex power is the purely imaginary quantity

$$\oint \tfrac{1}{2}\mathbf{E} \times \mathbf{H}^* \cdot d\mathbf{S} = \tfrac{1}{2}\mathbf{E}_0 \times \mathbf{H}_0^* \cdot \hat{\mathbf{z}} A \Gamma_e [-2j \sin(2k_1 z_1)], \qquad (8.60)$$

which is independent of z_2 ($z_2 > 0$), at which there is only the propagating transmitted wave, but does depend on z_1 ($z_1 < 0$), where there is a standing wave that stores electromagnetic energy.

Insulator–Conductor Interface

An important example of reflection and transmission occurs at the interface between a dielectric and a conductor. The relations previously obtained for general media hold for this case, but the impedance η_2 of the conductor is complex, in contrast to that of the dielectric η_1, which is real. We still restrict ourselves to normal incidence and we consider first the limiting case of a "perfect conductor." This means that we adopt the model $\sigma \to \infty$, implying that $E_2 = 0$ in the perfect conductor, which does not tolerate any electric field. It also implies a negligible skin depth, $\delta \to 0$ and makes $\eta_2 = 0$ (which incidentally masks the fact that η_2 is complex for an imperfect conductor, to be considered afterward).

Since $\eta_2 = 0$, the electric field amplitude reflection coefficient $\Gamma_e = (\eta_2 - \eta_1)/(\eta_2 + \eta_1)$ becomes -1 (regardless of the impedance of the dielectric in front of the interface). This makes the reflected electric field equal and opposite to the incident one, canceling it at the surface of the conductor. The amplitude transmission coefficient $T_e = 2\eta_2/(\eta_2 + \eta_1) = 0$, confirming that there is no transmitted electric field. But for the magnetic field, the reflection coefficient is $\Gamma_h = -\Gamma_e = +1$, which means that the reflected magnetic field equals the incident one and results in a doubled magnetic field in front of the conducting wall. Correspondingly, the magnetic field transmission coefficient is $T_h = 2\eta_1/(\eta_1 + \eta_2) = 2$ (regardless of the impedance of the dielectric in front of the interface). This means that there is a transmitted magnetic field just inside the perfect conductor, of magnitude twice that of the incident field, as required by continuity of the tangential magnetic field across the interface.

However, this doubled magnetic field that appears just inside the wall of the perfect conductor survives only on the surface of the conductor; it penetrates only to a negligible depth within the conductor, because the perfect conductor has negligible skin depth $\delta \to 0$. In this limiting case, we perceive a discontinuity in the magnetic field, from a finite value $2H_0$ just inside the conducting wall to zero value (after exponential attenuation with a negligible skin depth) at any nonzero depth within the perfect conductor. This discontinuity appears only because of our insistence that the attenuation within the conductor has to

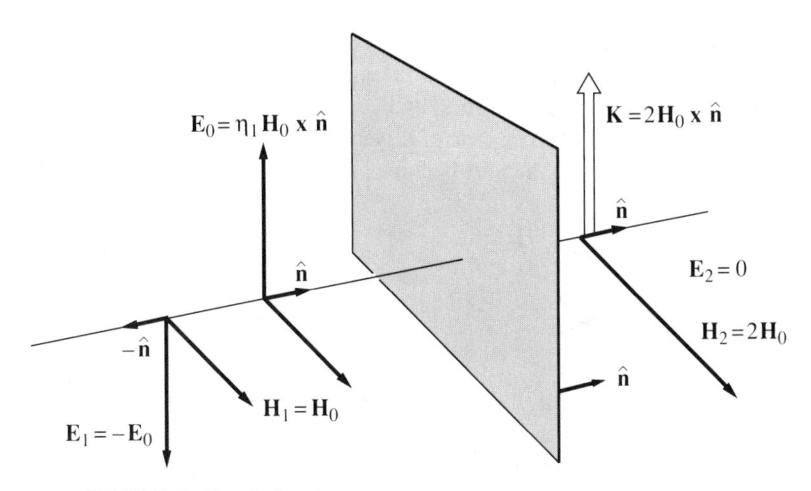

FIGURE 8–10 Reflection at a perfectly conducting mirror.

be abrupt instead of over an otherwise finite skin depth. It must be accompanied by a surface current K just inside the conductor's surface. The strength of this surface current equals the discontinuity, namely $2H_0$, and it is directed at right angles to the magnetic field at the surface, along the direction of the incident electric field $\mathbf{E}_0$, as indicated in Figure 8–10.

The perfectly conducting wall acts as a mirror. The incident electric field is reversed and the incident magnetic field is doubled at the wall. Since $\frac{1}{2}\mathbf{E}_1 \times \mathbf{H}_1^* = -\frac{1}{2}\mathbf{E}_0 \times \mathbf{H}_0^*$, all the incident power is reflected. A current flows along the surface of the conducting wall, induced by the incident electric field, of magnitude twice the incident magnetic field. The fields in the dielectric are

$$\mathbf{E} = \mathbf{E}_0 \exp(-jk_1\hat{\mathbf{n}} \cdot \mathbf{r}) - \mathbf{E}_0 \exp(+jk_1\hat{\mathbf{n}} \cdot \mathbf{r}) = -2j\mathbf{E}_0 \sin(k_1\hat{\mathbf{n}} \cdot \mathbf{r}), \quad (8.61)$$

$$\mathbf{H} = \mathbf{H}_0 \exp(-jk_1\hat{\mathbf{n}} \cdot \mathbf{r}) + \mathbf{H}_0 \exp(+jk_1\hat{\mathbf{n}} \cdot \mathbf{r}) = 2\mathbf{H}_0 \cos(k_1\hat{\mathbf{n}} \cdot \mathbf{r}). \quad (8.62)$$

This is a pure standing wave. Its time-domain version is

$$\mathscr{E}(\mathbf{r}, t) = 2\mathbf{E}_0 \sin(k_1\hat{\mathbf{n}} \cdot \mathbf{r}) \sin \omega t, \qquad \mathscr{H}(\mathbf{r}, t) = 2\mathbf{H}_0 \cos(k_1\hat{\mathbf{n}} \cdot \mathbf{r}) \cos \omega t, \quad (8.63)$$

if $\mathbf{E}_0$ is real. There is no propagation, only oscillation in a fixed, sinusoidal spatial pattern. The electric and magnetic fields are in time quadrature (90° out of phase) and there is no real, time-averaged power flow in the standing wave: For real incident power, $\frac{1}{2}\mathbf{E} \times \mathbf{H}^* = \frac{1}{2}\mathbf{E}_0 \times \mathbf{H}_0^*[-2j \sin(2k_1\hat{\mathbf{n}} \cdot \mathbf{r})]$ is purely imaginary; the standing wave in front of the mirror merely stores energy.

Let us now consider the case of normal incidence from a dielectric onto an imperfect conductor, with finite skin depth $\delta = \sqrt{2/\omega\mu\sigma}$. The impedance η_2 of the conductor is complex. For a good (but imperfect) conductor, with $\omega\varepsilon_2/\sigma \ll 1$, the impedance is $\eta_2 = (\omega\mu_2/\sigma)^{1/2}e^{j\pi/4}$ and the magnitude of this complex impedance is much smaller than the real impedance η_1 of the dielectric. Although our equations for reflection and transmission apply full well with complex impedances, the fact that $|\eta_2/\eta_1| \ll 1$ allows us to simplify the results, for easy comparison with the case of a perfect mirror.

Thus the reflection coefficient becomes

$$\Gamma_e = \frac{\eta_2 - \eta_1}{\eta_2 + \eta_1} = -1 + \frac{2\eta_2}{\eta_2 + \eta_1}$$
$$\approx -1 + 2\left(\frac{\eta_2}{\eta_1}\right) = -1 + 2\left|\frac{\eta_2}{\eta_1}\right| e^{j\pi/4}, \tag{8.64}$$

which is complex but only slightly different from -1: the phase shift of the electric field (the angle of the complex number Γ_e) is slightly less than the full 180° that occurs for a perfect mirror (since the real part of Γ_e is very nearly -1, while the imaginary part is small and positive).

The transmission coefficient T_e is also complex:

$$T_e = \frac{2\eta_2}{\eta_2 + \eta_1} \approx 2\left|\frac{\eta_2}{\eta_1}\right| e^{j\pi/4}; \tag{8.65}$$

the transmitted electric field is weak and shifted in phase by 45° relative to the incident electric field. The transmission coefficient for the magnetic field is not small, however:

$$T_h = \frac{2\eta_1}{\eta_2 + \eta_1} = 2 - T_e \approx 2 \tag{8.66}$$

and the incident magnetic field is still essentially doubled, as it is in the limiting case of the perfect conductor.

Finally, the magnitude squared of the reflection coefficient, $|\Gamma_e|^2$, is only slightly less than unity, indicating that almost all the incident energy is reflected. The little energy that does penetrate the conductor is dissipated within a skin depth or so.

Antireflection Coating

We have seen that normal incidence of a wave onto the interface between two media whose impedances are mismatched results in reflection as well as transmission. If our purpose is to transmit the electromagnetic energy into the second, unsourced medium, the reflection is an undesirable effect that reduces the efficiency of the process. We will now see that reflection from a mismatched medium can be overcome by interposing a layer of a suitable other medium. This result has many applications, notably in the coating of optical lenses to ensure that as much light as possible can enter the lens itself. What the antireflection coating does is to cancel the reflected wave, as will be seen.

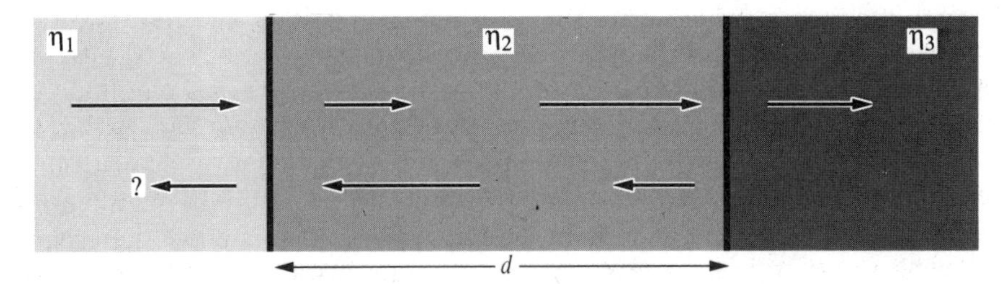

FIGURE 8–11 Antireflection coating between mismatched media.

With a layer of finite thickness interposed between two semi-infinite media, the system consists of three media, as indicated in Figure 8–11. There is the semi-infinite, sourced medium of impedance η_1; there is the layer of impedance η_2 and thickness d; finally, there is the semi-infinite, unsourced medium, of impedance η_3, into which we wish to transmit all the light incident from the first medium. There are now two interfaces, which are parallel to each other and perpendicular to the direction of propagation. The impedances of the first and third media are given and the third medium is mismatched to the first one ($\eta_3 \neq \eta_1$), or else there would be no need to interpose the antireflection coating. The task is to design the thickness d and the impedance η_2 of the layer to achieve zero reflection back into the first medium, and hence maximal transmission into the third one.

If we can arrange for the impedance η_1 of the sourced medium to be matched to the impedance that applies just beyond the interface between the first medium and the layer, the reflection at that interface will be zero and our goal will be achieved. However, the impedance just inside the layer is *not* just the intrinsic impedance η_2 of the layer itself, because the layer is not infinitely thick. Rather, the impedance at the first interface is affected by the existence of the second one at a distance d beyond the first one. The actual impedance that is to be matched to that of the semi-infinite first medium, η_1, can be expected to be some combination of both η_2 of the layer and η_3 of the medium beyond it. We need to find that corrected impedance and then set it equal to η_1 in order to match it to the first medium and thereby reduce the reflection to zero.

The matching of impedances at an interface simply ensures that the tangential electric and magnetic fields be continuous across that interface, with fewer than two waves on each side, by making the ratio of the tangential E and H fields conform to that of the incident wave alone. When there is only one wave, that ratio is just the intrinsic impedance η (in this case, η_1) of the medium. When, however, there are two oppositely traveling waves in a medium of intrinsic impedance η (here, η_2), the ratio Z of the tangential electric and magnetic fields becomes a function of the relative strengths of the two waves and varies from point to point along their direction of propagation.

When the incident wave encounters the interface with the layer, there should be both reflection and transmission; the latter results in a wave that travels forward within the intermediate layer. This wave then encounters the second interface, at which there should again be reflection and transmission. Of these, the reflected wave is a backward-traveling wave within the layer; upon reaching the first interface, it should itself result in transmission (into the original, sourced medium) and reflection (back into the layer). This last wave joins with the earlier one to form a modified, forward-going wave that encounters the second interface, repeating the process yet again to modify the backward-traveling wave as well. In the steady state, there are two oppositely traveling waves within the layer and one overall forward-going wave in the third medium, besides the incident wave and the overall reflected one in the first medium; the last of these is what we are trying to eliminate.

The expedient way to get the expression for the impedance (ratio of tangential E and H fields) anywhere in the system is to work backward from the region farthest from the source. Here, this is medium 3, which, being unsourced, carries only one wave (directed away from the interface with the layer) and therefore has a wave impedance equal to that of the medium, η_3. In the layer, however, there are two, oppositely directed waves, so that the wave impedance is not just η_2 of the medium but is affected by the presence of the third medium beyond the interface, acting as an electrical "load" on the "circuit." To get the ratio of E to H, we need to know the relative strengths of the two waves within the layer. But we already know how the reflected wave is related to the forward-traveling one at the last interface: the field structure at the last interface is exactly the three-wave situation that we have studied, with an incident wave within the layer (here of unknown amplitude, however) and a reflected wave of amplitude Γ times the unknown incident-wave amplitude and a transmitted wave in the last medium, of amplitude T times the unknown incident-wave amplitude. The matching of tangential fields at the last interface is identical to that for a two-medium, single-interface, three-wave problem and yields once again

$$\Gamma = \Gamma_{32} = \frac{\eta_3 - \eta_2}{\eta_3 + \eta_2} \quad \text{and} \quad T = T_{32} = \frac{2\eta_3}{\eta_3 + \eta_2}. \tag{8.67}$$

The double-subscript notation here indicates that the reflection and transmission coefficients apply to the interface between medium 2 and medium 3. We can therefore write the fields within the layer and beyond it in terms of the still-unknown amplitude E_0 of the forward-traveling wave in the layer: In medium 2,

$$E(z) = E_0 \exp(-jk_2 z) + \Gamma_{32} E_0 \exp(+jk_2 z), \tag{8.68}$$

$$\eta_2 H(z) = E_0 \exp(-jk_2 z) - \Gamma_{32} E_0 \exp(+jk_2 z). \tag{8.69}$$

In medium 3,

$$E(z) = \eta_3 H(z) = T_{32} E_0 \exp(-jk_3 z). \tag{8.70}$$

We have set the z-axis along the direction of propagation and put the origin $z = 0$ at the last interface, which then puts the first interface at $z = -d$. The unknown amplitude E_0 drops out from the ratio of $E(z)$ to $H(z)$; this ratio is the effective impedance in the layer and is a function of position, z:

$$Z_2(z) = \eta_2 \frac{\exp(-jk_2 z) + \Gamma_{32} \exp(+jk_2 z)}{\exp(-jk_2 z) - \Gamma_{32} \exp(+jk_2 z)}. \tag{8.71}$$

The impedance is complex. Note that at the last interface, this impedance reduces properly to

$$Z_2(0) = \eta_2 \frac{1 + \Gamma_{32}}{1 - \Gamma_{32}} = \eta_2 \frac{2\eta_3}{2\eta_2} = \eta_3, \tag{8.72}$$

to match the impedance beyond the interface. Moving now to the interface between media 1 and 2, the fields in medium 2 are: for $z = -d$,

$$E(-d) = E_0 \exp(+jk_2 d) + \Gamma_{32} E_0 \exp(-jk_2 d), \tag{8.73}$$

$$\eta_2 H(-d) = E_0 \exp(+jk_2 d) - \Gamma_{32} E_0 \exp(-jk_2 d), \tag{8.74}$$

and the impedance just beyond the first interface is

$$Z_2(-d) = \eta_2 \frac{\exp(+jk_2 d) + \Gamma_{32} \exp(-jk_2 d)}{\exp(+jk_2 d) - \Gamma_{32} \exp(-jk_2 d)}. \tag{8.75}$$

This corrected impedance, to be used instead of η_2 alone, exhibits the effect of loading by medium 3. The fields in the sourced region, in medium 1, are: for $z < -d$,

$$E(z) = E_1 \exp(-jk_1[z + d]) + \Gamma_{21} E_1 \exp(+jk_1[z + d]), \tag{8.76}$$

$$\eta_1 H(z) = E_1 \exp(-jk_1[z + d]) - \Gamma_{21} E_1 \exp(+jk_1[z + d]), \tag{8.77}$$

where E_1 is the amplitude of the incident wave at the interface, as given by the source, and Γ_{21} is the reflection coefficient that we are trying to force to zero. Imposing continuity of tangential fields at this interface results in the same expression for the reflection coefficient as for the two-medium case, except that the loaded impedance $Z_2(-d)$ replaces the unbounded-medium impedance η_2 in $\Gamma = (\eta_2 - \eta_1)/(\eta_2 + \eta_1)$:

$$\Gamma_{21} = \frac{Z_2(-d) - \eta_1}{Z_2(-d) + \eta_1}. \tag{8.78}$$

Our purpose is to eliminate reflection in medium 1, by adjusting the effective impedance $Z_2(-d)$ to match the impedance of the sourced medium:

$$Z_2(-d) = \eta_1, \tag{8.79}$$

or

$$\frac{\eta_1}{\eta_2} = \frac{e^{jk_2 d} + \Gamma_{32} e^{-jk_2 d}}{e^{jk_2 d} - \Gamma_{32} e^{-jk_2 d}}, \tag{8.80}$$

or

$$\frac{\eta_1}{\eta_2} = \frac{(\eta_3 + \eta_2)e^{jk_2d} + (\eta_3 - \eta_2)e^{-jk_2d}}{(\eta_3 + \eta_2)e^{jk_2d} - (\eta_3 - \eta_2)e^{-jk_2d}}, \tag{8.81}$$

or

$$\frac{\eta_1}{\eta_2} = \frac{\eta_3 \cos k_2 d + j\eta_2 \sin k_2 d}{\eta_2 \cos k_2 d + j\eta_3 \sin k_2 d}. \tag{8.82}$$

This matching condition requires that a real number be equated to a complex one, giving us two conditions on the two design variables η_2 and $k_2 d$, one from the real part, another from the imaginary part. By cross multiplying,

$$\eta_1\eta_2 \cos k_2 d + j\eta_1\eta_3 \sin k_2 d = \eta_2\eta_3 \cos k_2 d + j\eta_2^2 \sin k_2 d \tag{8.83}$$

and assuming that k_2 and all the η's are real, the matching conditions are

$$(\eta_1 - \eta_3)\eta_2 \cos k_2 d = 0 \tag{8.84}$$

and

$$(\eta_1\eta_3 - \eta_2^2) \sin k_2 d = 0. \tag{8.85}$$

Since the first and last media are mismatched (or else the antireflection layer would be superfluous), $\eta_1 \neq \eta_3$; also, the possibility $\eta_2 = 0$ (a perfectly conducting layer) would make the coating opaque. Hence the first of these two simultaneous matching conditions requires $\cos k_2 d = 0$ or

$$k_2 d = \frac{\pi}{2} \quad \left[\text{or} \quad k_2 d = \left(n + \frac{1}{2}\right)\pi, \quad n = \text{integer}\right] \tag{8.86}$$

and the second condition then requires

$$\eta_2 = \sqrt{\eta_1\eta_3}. \tag{8.87}$$

These are indeed real quantities, so that the matching is feasible. Since $k_2 = 2\pi/\lambda_2$, where λ_2 is the wavelength in the layer, the condition $k_2 d = \pi/2$ is the same as

$$d = \frac{\lambda_2}{4}, \tag{8.88}$$

[or, using $(n + \frac{1}{2})\pi$, $d = n\lambda_2/2 + \lambda_2/4$]. The antireflection coating is to have an impedance η_2 that is the geometric mean of the two mismatched impedances of the outer media and its thickness is to be a quarter-wavelength, as measured in the layer material, or an integral number of half-wavelengths more than that. This sort of layer is referred to as a quarter-wave matching section; for light, the wavelengths are short and the required layer is very thin, a mere coating, made of the appropriate material. For nonmagnetic materials, the requirement is for $\varepsilon_2 = \sqrt{\varepsilon_1\varepsilon_3}$.

The antireflection coating works by making the wave reflected from the first interface and the wave reflected from the second one (and then transmitted back from the layer to the sourced medium) exactly cancel each other. Note that a coating so designed will be 100% effective in eliminating reflection only at the design frequency and at other discrete frequencies at which the wavelength in the layer is $(n + \frac{1}{2})\lambda_2/2$, with n an integer, assuming that the materials are not lossy. When operated at other frequencies, the reflection coefficient, given in Eq. (8.78), will not be zero, although it may remain quite small over a rather broad band of frequencies. A succession of intervening layers between mismatched media can be designed to extend or shape that bandwidth.

Summary

We have examined waves that encounter planar interfaces between uniform media, at normal incidence, and have found that when the media have mismatched impedances, there is reflection back to the source as well as transmission across the boundary. The reflection and transmission coefficients were obtained as

$$\Gamma = \frac{\eta_2 - \eta_1}{\eta_2 + \eta_1}, \qquad T = \frac{2\eta_2}{\eta_2 + \eta_1} \tag{8.89}$$

at the interface between sourced medium 1 and unsourced medium 2, corresponding to a three-wave combination with only one wave incident onto the interface, the other two being scattered away from it. These expressions are based on continuity of tangential electric and magnetic fields across the planar boundary between media. This continuity condition follows from Maxwell's equations in integral form and allows those equations to be satisfied at points of a surface of discontinuity in constitutive parameters.

More general boundary conditions, allowing for the existence of surface charges and currents, were obtained as

$$\hat{\mathbf{n}} \times (\mathbf{E}_2 - \mathbf{E}_1) = 0, \qquad \hat{\mathbf{n}} \times (\mathbf{H}_2 - \mathbf{H}_1) = \mathbf{K}, \tag{8.90}$$

where $\hat{\mathbf{n}}$, the unit normal to the surface, points toward medium 2. The surface current density $\mathbf{K}$ is related to the surface charge density through a conservation-of-charge relation that allows for leakage off the surface; it will usually be related to the tangential electric field at the surface by some constitutive parameter, the surface conductivity or resistivity.

We examined energy transmission and reflection, analyzed the action of perfect and imperfect mirrors, and designed an antireflection coating for mismatched media. For the latter, we noted that when two waves are both incident onto an interface, resulting in a combination of four waves (two incident, two scattered) rather than just three, the expressions for reflection and transmission involve an effective impedance that depends on the relative strengths of the pairs of waves, not just on the medium's intrinsic impedance.

These results must now be extended to oblique incidence onto an interface; this case represents the mechanism for the trapping and propagation of light within a fiber and is therefore crucial to an understanding of the operation of optical fibers.

PROBLEMS

Discontinuity in Electric Field

8.1 Let the interface between two dielectrics with $\varepsilon_1 = 2\varepsilon_0$ and $\varepsilon_2 = 6\varepsilon_0$ coincide with the xy-plane and suppose that the electric field at some point on side 2 at the plane were known to be $\mathbf{E}_2 = (2\hat{\mathbf{x}} + 5\hat{\mathbf{y}} - 6\hat{\mathbf{z}})E_0$ (V/m).

(a) What must the electric field $\mathbf{E}_1$ be just on the other side of the plane, at that same location?

(b) What are the **D** fields on the two sides of the plane, at that same point?

(c) What are the values of the electric energy density on the two sides of the plane, at that same point?

Discontinuity in Magnetic Field

8.2 Let the interface between two media with $\mu_1 = 2\mu_0$ and $\mu_2 = 6\mu_0$ coincide with the xy-plane and suppose that the magnetic field at some point on the $z > 0$ side of the plane were known to be $\mathbf{H}_2 = (2\hat{\mathbf{x}} + 5\hat{\mathbf{y}} - 6\hat{\mathbf{z}})H_0$ (A/m). Suppose also that a current sheet $\mathbf{K} = 3\hat{\mathbf{y}}H_0$ is known to be flowing along the plane at that point.

(a) What must the magnetic field $\mathbf{H}_1$ be just on the other side of the plane, at that same location?

(b) What are the **B** fields on the two sides of the plane, at that same point?

(c) What are the values of the magnetic energy density on the two sides of the plane, at that same point?

Discontinuities at an Interface Between Conductors

8.3 Let the interface between two conducting dielectrics with $\varepsilon_1 = 2\varepsilon_0$ and $\varepsilon_2 = 6\varepsilon_0$ coincide with the xy-plane and suppose that the complex electric field amplitude near some point on the $z > 0$ side of the plane were known to be $\mathbf{E}_2 = (2\hat{\mathbf{x}} + 5\hat{\mathbf{y}} - 6\hat{\mathbf{z}})E_0$ (V/m) at a given frequency ω. Let the conductivities of the two media be given by $\sigma_1 = 3\omega\varepsilon_0$ and $\sigma_2 = 4\omega\varepsilon_0$. Suppose also that $\nabla \cdot \mathbf{K} = 2\omega\varepsilon_0 E_0$ at the point in question.

(a) Find the electric field $\mathbf{E}_1$ just on the other side of the plane, at that same location, at that frequency.

(b) What is the surface charge density on the plane at the point?

Incidence onto Resistive Sheet in Vacuum

8.4 A plane wave $\mathbf{E}_0 e^{-jkz}$ is incident onto a resistive sheet of surface conductivity σ_S. The sheet is coincident with the xy-plane and the media on the two sides of the sheet are both a vacuum.

(a) What are the scattered fields on the two sides?

(b) What is the surface current **K** on the resistive sheet?

Perfect Absorber of Plane Waves

8.5 A plane wave $\mathbf{E}_0 e^{-jkz}$ is incident onto a resistive sheet of surface conductivity σ_S. The sheet is coincident with the xy-plane and the media on the two sides of the sheet are both a vacuum. At a distance l beyond the sheet (i.e., at $z = l$), we place a perfectly conducting plane.

(a) Select the surface conductivity σ_S and the distance l to make the combination of resistive sheet and conducting plane a perfect absorber for the incident wave (no reflection back into the $z < 0$ region).

(b) What are the fields in the region $0 < z < l$?

(c) What is the surface current $\mathbf{K}$ on the resistive sheet?

(d) What is the surface current $\mathbf{K}_0$ on the conducting plane?

(e) What power is absorbed, per unit area, on the resistive sheet?

(f) What energy is stored, per unit transverse area, between the resistive sheet and the conducting plane?

Bandwidth of Perfect Absorber

8.6 The perfect absorber of a normally incident plane wave designed in the previous problem is fully effective only for certain frequencies.

(a) What frequencies are fully absorbed (no reflection)?

(b) What is the bandwidth, around any one such frequency, over which the power reflection is less than 5% of the incident power?

Mismatched Media with a Resistive Interface

8.7 Can reflection of a normally incident wave at the interface between mismatched media be averted by coating the interface plane with a resistive sheet of suitable surface conductivity? If so:

(a) What surface conductivity is suitable?

(b) What fraction of the incident power is transmitted?

If not, how small can the reflection coefficient be made?

Matched Dissimilar Conducting Media

8.8 Recall that the wave impedance in a conducting medium is $Z = j\omega\mu/(\alpha + j\beta)$ and that the condition $\mu_2/\mu_1 = \varepsilon_2/\varepsilon_1$ matches two dissimilar insulators.

(a) If the two dissimilar media also have some conductivities (σ_1, σ_2), what conditions on the ratios of the parameters ε, μ, and σ will match them?

(b) Can an imperfect insulator (ε, μ, σ, with $\sigma > 0$) be matched to a vacuum (ε_0, μ_0; $\sigma_0 = 0$) by suitably choosing its parameters?

Superposition of Opposed Waves

8.9 Each of two mismatched dielectrics (η_1 and η_2) has a source that generates a plane wave at the same frequency and directs it normally onto the interface plane. The amplitudes and phases are such that the electric fields of each (in the absence of the other) are identical ($\mathbf{E}_1 = \mathbf{E}_2 = \mathbf{E}_0$) at the interface (at $z = 0$).

(a) Obtain the electric and magnetic fields on both sides of the interface; show that these form a standing wave on both sides, by noting the value of $\Gamma_{21} + T_{12}$.

(b) What is the complex Poynting vector on both sides of the interface?

Maximum Mismatch for Given Reflection

8.10 If the power reflection coefficient for normal incidence onto the interface between two lossless, nonmagnetic dielectrics is to be kept no greater than 5%, what is the maximum ratio of permittivities that can be tolerated?

Sum of Partial Waves in Antireflection Coating

8.11 As an alternative to the text's derivation of the effective, loaded impedance within the antireflection coating, pretend that the transmission and reflection process in the layer is a transient, not a steady-state, phenomenon. This point of view results in an infinite sequence of partial waves, each transmitted or reflected at the two interfaces from "previous" partial waves as if the other interface did not exist. The resultant field is then the superposition of all the partial waves.

Thus, for unit incident wave, the reflected wave is comprised of Γ_{21}, plus T_{12} times the "first" transmitted partial wave T_{21} after it has made a round trip of the layer (including reflection Γ_{32} at the second interface and a phase delay of e^{-j2kd} in the round trip), plus T_{12} times the "second" forward wave in the layer, which is Γ_{12} times the "first" partial wave, after another round trip, plus T_{12} times the "third" one, and so on, to infinitely many round trips. We are here using the notation T_{nm} or Γ_{nm} to denote the transmission or reflection coefficient upon encountering the interface from unbounded medium m to unbounded medium n.

(a) Sum the infinitely many partial wave complex amplitudes that travel away from the first interface back into the sourced medium, recalling that the infinite geometric series $1 + x + x^2 + x^3 + \cdots$ sums to $1/(1 - x)$ if $|x| < 1$.

(b) Set the sum so found to zero to cancel the reflection and deduce the two conditions for the design of the antireflection coating.

Antireflection Coating at Other than the Design Frequency

8.12 An antireflection coating to be applied to glass of $\varepsilon/\varepsilon_0 = 4$ is achieved with a coating of $\varepsilon/\varepsilon_0 = 2$ and quarter-wave thickness at the design frequency. Find the power reflection coefficient when the coated glass is illuminated, from air, at normal incidence, at:

(a) Double the design frequency;

(b) Half the design frequency.

Bandwidth of Antireflection Layer

8.13 For a given thickness of the antireflection coating designed for a particular operating frequency, find the bandwidth Δf (around that frequency, f_0) over which the reflected power remains less than 5% of the incident power. The result can be expressed as $\Delta(kd) = \cos^{-1}(a - bR^2)$, where $R = (r^2 + 1)/(r^2 - 1)$ and $r = \eta_3/\eta_2 = \eta_2/\eta_1$; d is the coating thickness and $k = 2\pi f/c$.

(a) Find the coefficients a and b.

(b) For a quarter-wave coating that matches media with $\eta_3/\eta_1 = 2$, what is the fractional bandwidth $\Delta f/f_0$?

(c) For a quarter-wave coating that matches media with $\eta_3/\eta_1 = 1.5$, what is the fractional bandwidth $\Delta f/f_0$?

(d) Over what range of $r^2 = \eta_3/\eta_1$ is the bandwidth infinite?

Multiple Coatings

8.14 To match a dielectric with impedance $\eta_4 = 0.5\eta_0$ to air ($\eta_1 = \eta_0$), we would need a quarter-wave antireflection coating of impedance $\sqrt{\eta_1\eta_4} = 0.7071\eta_0$. If such material is not obtainable but two other dielectrics, with impedances $\eta_2 = 0.75\eta_0$ and $\eta_3 = 0.64\eta_0$, are available, two coatings can be used to reduce the reflection to zero. Design the pair of coatings (give the thicknesses d_2 and d_3) to achieve this; the suggested procedure to arrive at the design equations follows.

Let the coating of impedance η_2 extend from $z = -d_2$ to $z = 0$ (with air for $z < -d_2$) and the one of impedance η_3 from $z = 0$ to $z = d_3$ (with η_4 for $z > d_3$); let $\varphi_2 = k_2 d_2$ and $\varphi_3 = k_3 d_3$ be the phase changes on traversal of the two coatings.

(a) Since the impedance at $z = d_3$ is η_4, the reflection coefficient there is $\Gamma_{43} = (\eta_4 - \eta_3)/(\eta_4 + \eta_3)$ and the impedance at $z = 0$ is

$$Z_0 = \frac{\eta_3[e^{j\varphi_3} + \Gamma_{43} e^{-j\varphi_3}]}{e^{j\varphi_3} - \Gamma_{43} e^{-j\varphi_3}}.$$

Rewrite this Z_0 as a function of the unknown $\tan\varphi_3$ instead of φ_3.

(b) Since the impedance at $z = 0$ is Z_0, the reflection coefficient there is $\Gamma' = (Z_0 - \eta_2)/(Z_0 + \eta_2)$ and the impedance at $z = -d_2$ is

$$Z(-d_2) = \frac{\eta_2[e^{j\varphi_2} + \Gamma' e^{-j\varphi_2}]}{e^{j\varphi_2} - \Gamma' e^{-j\varphi_2}}.$$

Rewrite this $Z(-d_2)$ as a function of the unknown $\tan\varphi_2$ and of Z_0.

(c) Set the impedance $Z(-d_2)$ at the air interface to η_1 to reduce the reflection to zero; eliminate the quantity Z_0 between the two equations to obtain a relation between $\tan\varphi_2$ and $\tan\varphi_3$.

(d) Separate the real and imaginary parts of the relation, so as to obtain two equations for the unknowns $\tan\varphi_2$ and $\tan\varphi_3$. They are of the forms

$$\frac{[\eta_1\eta_4 - \eta_3^2]\tan\varphi_3}{\eta_3} = \frac{[\eta_2^2 - \eta_1\eta_4]\tan\varphi_2}{\eta_2}$$

and

$$\eta_1 - \eta_4 = A\,\frac{\tan\varphi_2}{\eta_2}\,\frac{\tan\varphi_3}{\eta_3}.$$

Find A in terms of the given impedances.

(e) Solve for φ_2 and φ_3, for the given numerical values of the impedances.

(f) Translate the phases φ_2 and φ_3 into thicknesses d_2 and d_3 of the nonmagnetic dielectric coatings, in terms of the free-space wavelength λ_0.

Standing Wave at a Mirror

8.15 A uniform plane wave traveling in free space is incident normal to the surface of a perfectly conducting plane. The resultant electric field is zero at a distance s in front of the mirror.

(a) What is the lowest possible frequency of the incident wave?

(b) What is the next lowest possible frequency?

Wave Dissipation Within a Conductor

8.16 A 10-V/m uniform plane wave at 4.5 MHz in free space is incident normally onto the surface of a conductor with $\varepsilon/\varepsilon_0 = 4$, $\mu/\mu_0 = 1$, $\sigma = 0.2$ S/m.

(a) What is the magnetic field just inside the surface of the conductor?

(b) Determine the time-averaged power dissipated in the conductor, within a volume consisting of a 3-m^2 area of the surface, 0.5 m deep.

Reflection of a Circularly Polarized Wave

8.17 A circularly polarized plane wave is incident normally from air onto a lossless, nonmagnetic dielectric.

(a) Are the reflected and transmitted waves also circularly polarized?

(b) Are the parities (right- or left-handedness) of the reflected and transmitted waves the same as that of the incident one?

(c) Are the answers for the reflected wave the same if the reflector is a perfect conductor instead?

Ordinary Mirror

8.18 A pane of glass (lossless, nonmagnetic, permittivity ε, thickness s) is silvered on one side (a perfectly conducting coating) to form an (idealized) ordinary mirror.

(a) Obtain the reflection coefficient at the air–glass interface, for normal incidence of a plane wave at frequency ω.

(b) What fraction of the incident power is reflected into the air?

CHAPTER 9

Oblique Incidence

For normal incidence onto the interface between dissimilar media, it is relatively easy to satisfy the boundary conditions of continuity of tangential electric and magnetic fields because both fields are parallel to the boundary plane in their entirety. Continuity of tangential fields then becomes simply continuity of the total fields, which are related by the impedance of each medium. When the plane wave is incident at an angle to the normal, however, the electric and magnetic fields cannot both be tangential to the interface; at most one of them can be. For such oblique incidence, as depicted in Figure 9–1, it is only the tangential components of the two fields that must be continuous, not the total fields, and the impedance that relates these components must first be established before the reflection and transmission properties can be found.

A change in viewpoint about the obliquely incident wave, however, can make this more challenging problem appear as a mere extension of the previously derived results for normal incidence. It is possible to trade the feature of obliqueness for uniformity; that is, we can make the uniform, oblique wave appear to be normally incident (transverse) but nonuniform. The nonuniformity is a small price to pay for reduction of the problem to a previously solved version.

Oblique Waves as Nonuniform Transverse Waves

The incident wave is a uniform one, meaning that its amplitude is the same everywhere: In

$$\mathbf{E}(\mathbf{r}) = \mathbf{E}_0 \exp(-j\mathbf{k}_0 \cdot \mathbf{r}) \qquad \mathbf{H}(\mathbf{r}) = \mathbf{H}_0 \exp(-j\mathbf{k}_0 \cdot \mathbf{r}), \tag{9.1}$$

the vector amplitudes $\mathbf{E}_0$ and $\mathbf{H}_0$ are constants. These two constant vectors are, in fact, related by the impedance η_1 of the sourced medium, $E_0 = \eta_1 H_0$. The field amplitudes $\mathbf{E}_0$ and $\mathbf{H}_0$ are perpendicular to each other and to the wave vector $\mathbf{k}_0$, forming a right-handed orthogonal triad. The interface plane, given by $\hat{\mathbf{n}} \cdot \mathbf{r} = 0$, is perpendicular to unit vector $\hat{\mathbf{n}}$, which points into the unsourced medium 2. That the wave is obliquely incident means that the wave vector $\mathbf{k}_0$ is not parallel to $\hat{\mathbf{n}}$; instead, it makes an angle θ with the normal to

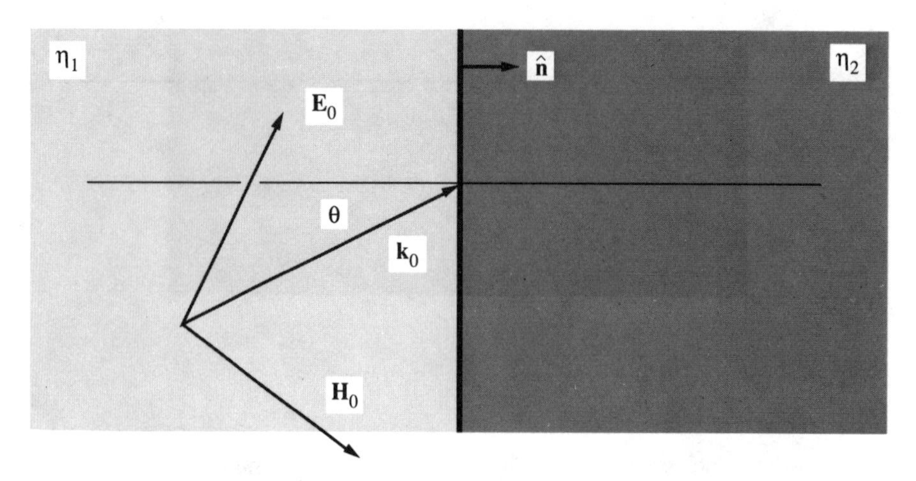

FIGURE 9–1 Oblique incidence onto interface between two media.

the interface, with $0 < \theta < \pi/2$. The plane that contains both $\mathbf{k}_0$ and $\hat{\mathbf{n}}$ is termed the *plane of incidence* of the wave.

Now a uniform plane wave that propagates along $\mathbf{k}_0$ can be viewed as a nonuniform plane wave that travels along $\hat{\mathbf{n}}$. For example, for $\hat{\mathbf{n}} = \hat{\mathbf{z}}$,

$$\begin{aligned}\mathbf{E}(\mathbf{r}) &= \mathbf{E}_0 \exp(-j\mathbf{k}_0 \cdot \mathbf{r}) = \mathbf{E}_0 \exp[-j(k_x x + k_y y + k_z z)] \\ &= \mathbf{E}_0 \exp[-j(k_x x + k_y y)] \exp(-jk_z z) \\ &= \{\mathbf{E}_0 e^{-j(k_x x + k_y y)}\} e^{-jk_z z} = \mathbf{E}_0'(x, y) e^{-jk_z z}. \end{aligned} \tag{9.2}$$

The last version has the appearance of a wave that propagates along z, hence is normally incident onto the interface, but with a complex amplitude that varies from point to point, instead of being constant. That is, the uniform plane wave along $\mathbf{k}_0$ appears as a nonuniform plane wave along z. The nonuniformity shows up in particular on the interface plane $z = 0$, on which the field is not constant but varies as $\mathbf{E}_0'(x, y) = \mathbf{E}_0 e^{-j(k_x x + k_y y)}$. The boundary condition on the interface is that the tangential components of both $\mathbf{E}_0'(x, y)$ and $\mathbf{H}_0'(x, y)$ must be continuous at *every* point of the xy-plane.

For true normal incidence, making the fields continuous at one point of the boundary plane automatically made it continuous at every point of the plane, since the fields were constant on the interface. For oblique incidence, we can *pretend* that the wave is still normally incident but is nonuniform; the variation on the interface requires us to ensure continuity at each point of the boundary plane.

More generally than for an interface that coincides with the xy-plane, the wave vector $\mathbf{k}_0$ can always be decomposed into components perpendicular and parallel to the normal to the interface, $\hat{\mathbf{n}}$:

$$\mathbf{k}_0 = \mathbf{p}_0 + \boldsymbol{\beta}_0 \qquad \text{with} \quad \mathbf{p}_0 = \hat{\mathbf{n}} \times \mathbf{k}_0 \times \hat{\mathbf{n}} \quad \text{and} \quad \boldsymbol{\beta}_0 = (\hat{\mathbf{n}} \cdot \mathbf{k}_0)\hat{\mathbf{n}}, \tag{9.3}$$

by an identity of vector algebra. Hence, the incident uniform, but oblique, wave can always be expressed as a nonuniform but normally incident one:

$$\mathbf{E}(\mathbf{r}) = \mathbf{E}_0 \exp(-j\mathbf{k}_0 \cdot \mathbf{r}) = \mathbf{E}_0 \exp(-j\mathbf{p}_0 \cdot \mathbf{r}) \exp(-j\boldsymbol{\beta}_0 \cdot \mathbf{r})$$
$$= \{\mathbf{E}_0 \exp(-j\mathbf{p}_0 \cdot \mathbf{r})\} \exp(-j\beta_0 \hat{\mathbf{n}} \cdot \mathbf{r}). \quad (9.4)$$

To satisfy Maxwell's equations, $\mathbf{E}_0$ and $\mathbf{k}_0$ are restricted to satisfy

$$\mathbf{E}_0 \cdot \mathbf{k}_0 = 0 \quad \text{and} \quad \mathbf{k}_0 \cdot \mathbf{k}_0 = \frac{\omega^2}{v_1^2}, \quad (9.5)$$

where v_1 is the phase velocity, at frequency ω, for medium 1. The last equation can be rewritten as

$$\mathbf{p}_0 \cdot \mathbf{p}_0 + \beta_0^2 = \frac{\omega^2}{v_1^2} \quad \text{or} \quad p_0^2 + \beta_0^2 = \frac{\omega^2}{v_1^2}. \quad (9.6)$$

The accompanying magnetic field is also expressible as a nonuniform plane wave along $\hat{\mathbf{n}}$:

$$\mathbf{H}(\mathbf{r}) = \mathbf{H}_0 \exp(-j\mathbf{k}_0 \cdot \mathbf{r}) = \{\mathbf{H}_0 \exp(-j\mathbf{p}_0 \cdot \mathbf{r})\} \exp(-j\beta_0 \hat{\mathbf{n}} \cdot \mathbf{r}), \quad (9.7)$$

where $\omega\mu_1\mathbf{H}_0 = \mathbf{k}_0 \times \mathbf{E}_0$, by the Faraday–Maxwell law. Note that, since $\hat{\mathbf{n}}$ and $\mathbf{k}_0$ are given as part of the specification of the interface and of the oblique incidence, both $\mathbf{p}_0$ and β_0 are known quantities. The source (infinitely remote from the interface) determines the frequency ω and the *direction* of the wave vector $\mathbf{k}_0$; the constitutive parameters of the sourced medium determine its phase velocity v_1 and hence the *magnitude* of the wave vector.

Snell's Laws

For the case of true normal incidence, the boundary conditions resulted in scattered waves, reflected and transmitted from the interface. For oblique incidence that appears as normal incidence of a nonuniform wave, it may be expected (and will be verified) that reflected and transmitted waves will again be generated at the interface, but now also nonuniform, to allow for continuity at each point of the boundary plane. The nonuniform scattered waves will also correspond to obliquely propagating uniform plane waves, but with new directions of propagation. The frequencies of the scattered waves must be identical to that of the incident one (assuming that the interface is stationary; otherwise, a Doppler shift arises). If the frequencies do not match, it becomes impossible to satisfy the boundary conditions at *all* times even if we succeed in satisfying them at any one time.

To verify these assertions, assume an obliquely reflected wave in medium 1 along some wave vector $\mathbf{k}_1$ (to be found),

$$\mathbf{E}_1(\mathbf{r}) = \mathbf{E}_1 \exp(-j\mathbf{k}_1 \cdot \mathbf{r}) = \{\mathbf{E}_1 \exp(-j\mathbf{p}_1 \cdot \mathbf{r})\} \exp(-j\boldsymbol{\beta}_1 \cdot \mathbf{r}), \quad (9.8)$$

and an obliquely transmitted wave in medium 2 along some wave vector $\mathbf{k}_2$ (also to be determined),

$$\mathbf{E}_2(\mathbf{r}) = \mathbf{E}_2 \exp(-j\mathbf{k}_2 \cdot \mathbf{r}) = \{\mathbf{E}_2 \exp(-j\mathbf{p}_2 \cdot \mathbf{r})\} \exp(-j\boldsymbol{\beta}_2 \cdot \mathbf{r}), \quad (9.9)$$

and confirm that these can be made to satisfy Maxwell's equations in the two media and also the boundary conditions at the interface. That $\mathbf{E}_1(\mathbf{r})$ is a reflected wave means that $\boldsymbol{\beta}_1$ is opposed in direction to $\boldsymbol{\beta}_0$ (i.e., $\boldsymbol{\beta}_1$ is along $-\hat{\mathbf{n}}$ to propagate back into the sourced medium, while $\boldsymbol{\beta}_0$ is along $\hat{\mathbf{n}}$) and that $\mathbf{E}_2(\mathbf{r})$ is a transmitted wave means that $\boldsymbol{\beta}_2$ has the same direction as $\boldsymbol{\beta}_0$ (i.e., $\boldsymbol{\beta}_2$ is along $+\hat{\mathbf{n}}$, to propagate onward in the second medium).

To satisfy Maxwell's equations within the two semi-infinite media, the scattered waves must conform to

$$\mathbf{E}_1 \cdot \mathbf{k}_1 = 0 \quad \text{and} \quad \omega\mu_1 \mathbf{H}_1 = \mathbf{k}_1 \times \mathbf{E}_1 \quad \text{and} \quad \mathbf{k}_1 \cdot \mathbf{k}_1 = \frac{\omega^2}{v_1^2}, \tag{9.10}$$

$$\mathbf{E}_2 \cdot \mathbf{k}_2 = 0 \quad \text{and} \quad \omega\mu_2 \mathbf{H}_2 = \mathbf{k}_2 \times \mathbf{E}_2 \quad \text{and} \quad \mathbf{k}_2 \cdot \mathbf{k}_2 = \frac{\omega^2}{v_2^2}. \tag{9.11}$$

The last relations in this pair are expressible in terms of the tangential and normal components of the wave vectors as

$$p_1^2 + \beta_1^2 = \frac{\omega^2}{v_1^2}, \qquad p_2^2 + \beta_2^2 = \frac{\omega^2}{v_2^2}, \tag{9.12}$$

corresponding to the incident wave's $p_0^2 + \beta_0^2 = \omega^2/v_1^2$. Note that, so far, only the right sides of the equations (9.12) are known, but both p_0 and β_0 are also known.

At the interface plane $\hat{\mathbf{n}} \cdot \mathbf{r} = 0$, the total electric fields are

$$\mathbf{E}_0(\mathbf{r}) + \mathbf{E}_1(\mathbf{r}) = \mathbf{E}_0 \exp(-j\mathbf{p}_0 \cdot \mathbf{r}) + \mathbf{E}_1 \exp(-j\mathbf{p}_1 \cdot \mathbf{r}) \quad \text{in medium 1}, \tag{9.13}$$

$$\mathbf{E}_2(\mathbf{r}) = \mathbf{E}_2 \exp(-j\mathbf{p}_2 \cdot \mathbf{r}) \quad \text{in medium 2}, \tag{9.14}$$

and these vary from point to point on the interface. The magnetic fields have exactly the same spatial dependences. The requirement is to ensure that the tangential components of both the electric and the magnetic fields be continuous across the interface, at every point of the plane. It is not sufficient to ensure this at just one point; continuity must hold at every point of the boundary plane.

The key result is the following one. The only way the tangential components of the fields can be matched across the plane at *every* point of the interface is for the spatial dependence along the plane to be *identical* for all three waves. This is not a sufficient condition (since the tangential components still need to be matched at some point) but it is surely a necessary one: if the spatial dependences were not identical, matching at one point would preclude matching at every other point. The exponential (actually sinusoidal) dependences will be identical only if

$$\mathbf{p}_0 = \mathbf{p}_1 = \mathbf{p}_2 \equiv \mathbf{p}. \tag{9.15}$$

The three wave vectors' tangential components are now all to be called simply $\mathbf{p}$. Note that $\mathbf{p}$ is known, being fully determined by the direction of the incident wave vector $\mathbf{k}_0$, in relation to the orientation of the interface, $\hat{\mathbf{n}}$; in fact, $\mathbf{p} = \hat{\mathbf{n}} \times \mathbf{k}_0 \times \hat{\mathbf{n}}$.

Since we know the magnitude of each of the three wave vectors and we now also know their tangential components, their normal components are imme-

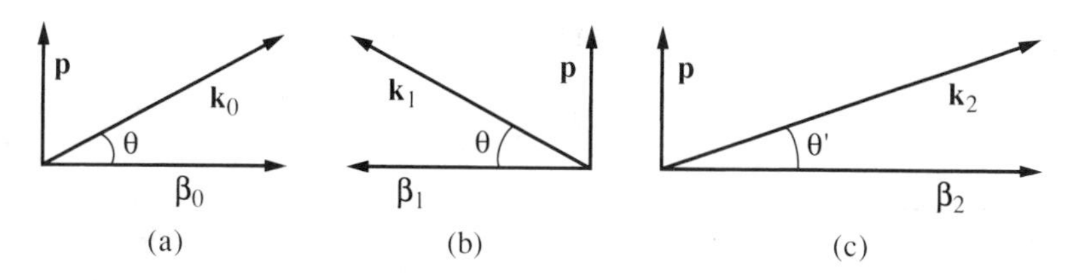

FIGURE 9–2 Wave vectors of incident, reflected, and transmitted waves.

diately obtainable, so that the scattered wave vectors are now fully determined. That is, we know the directions of the obliquely propagating reflected and transmitted waves. Since $k_1^2 = k_0^2 = \omega^2/v_1^2$ and $\boldsymbol{\beta}_1$ and $\boldsymbol{\beta}_0$ are opposed, the reflected wave vector must be

$$\mathbf{k}_1 = \mathbf{p}_1 + \boldsymbol{\beta}_1 = \mathbf{p} - \boldsymbol{\beta}_0 = \mathbf{p} - \beta_0\,\hat{\mathbf{n}} \tag{9.16}$$

(compare $\mathbf{k}_0 = \mathbf{p} + \beta_0\,\hat{\mathbf{n}}$), while the transmitted wave vector is

$$\mathbf{k}_2 = \mathbf{p}_2 + \boldsymbol{\beta}_2 = \mathbf{p} + \beta_2\,\hat{\mathbf{n}} \quad \text{with} \quad \beta_2 = \sqrt{\frac{\omega^2}{v_2^2} - p^2}\,. \tag{9.17}$$

Figure 9–2 shows how the oblique incident and scattered wave vectors are related. Equation (9.15) embodies the familiar Snell's laws of reflection and refraction, as follows.

The angles of incidence, of reflection, and of refraction are defined as the angles, measured in the plane of incidence (the plane of $\mathbf{k}_0$ and $\hat{\mathbf{n}}$), between $\mathbf{k}$ and $\boldsymbol{\beta}$ for each wave. Since, as shown in the figure, the tangential components of the $\mathbf{k}$'s are unique and $\boldsymbol{\beta}_1 = -\boldsymbol{\beta}_0$, the angles between $\mathbf{k}_0$ and $\boldsymbol{\beta}_0$ (or $\hat{\mathbf{n}}$) and between $\mathbf{k}_1$ and $\boldsymbol{\beta}_1$ (or $-\hat{\mathbf{n}}$) must be the same and we have:

Snell's Law of Reflection. The angle of incidence (θ in the figure) equals the angle of reflection *and* the reflected wave vector $\mathbf{k}_1$ is in the plane of incidence (of $\mathbf{k}_0$ and $\hat{\mathbf{n}}$).

Furthermore, the tangential component $\mathbf{p}$ of any of the wave vectors is given in terms of the angle to the normal, θ, by $p = k \sin\theta$ and, since all $\mathbf{p}$'s are the same, we have

$$k_2 \sin\theta' = k_0 \sin\theta\,, \tag{9.18}$$

to yield the angle θ' of the transmitted wave; the magnitudes of the wave vectors are given by $k_0 = \omega/v_1$ and $k_2 = \omega/v_2$. A dimensionless way of specifying the phase velocity in a medium is to give its *index of refraction n*, defined by

$$n = \frac{c}{v_p}\,. \tag{9.19}$$

For a dielectric, $n = \sqrt{\mu\varepsilon/\mu_0\varepsilon_0}$. Consequently, Eq. (9.18) can be expressed nondimensionally by multiplying by c/ω, leaving:

Snell's Law of Refraction. The angle of refraction (θ' in the figure) is related to the angle of incidence θ by

$$n_2 \sin \theta' = n_1 \sin \theta \tag{9.20}$$

and the refracted (transmitted) wave vector $\mathbf{k}_2$ is in the plane of incidence (of $\mathbf{k}_0$ and $\hat{\mathbf{n}}$).

Snell's law is most commonly stated as just Eq. (9.20), because that is what yields the angle of refraction, but it is important to realize that each of the two laws has two parts. All these laws follow from the fact that the incident and scattered waves share the tangential wave vector component $\mathbf{p}$.

TE and TM Polarizations

The requirements of Snell's laws make it *possible* to satisfy continuity of tangential E and H fields at every point of the interface *if* we succeed in satisfying continuity at one point. To *achieve* continuity requires that the amplitudes of the scattered waves be properly related to that of the incident wave.

Returning to Eqs. (9.13)–(9.14), at the interface plane $\hat{\mathbf{n}} \cdot \mathbf{r} = 0$, the total electric fields are

$$\mathbf{E}_0(\mathbf{r}) + \mathbf{E}_1(\mathbf{r}) = [\mathbf{E}_0 + \mathbf{E}_1] \exp(-j\mathbf{p} \cdot \mathbf{r}) \qquad \text{on side 1}, \tag{9.21}$$

$$\mathbf{E}_2(\mathbf{r}) = \mathbf{E}_2 \exp(-j\mathbf{p} \cdot \mathbf{r}) \qquad \text{on side 2}, \tag{9.22}$$

and the total magnetic fields are, correspondingly,

$$\mathbf{H}_0(\mathbf{r}) + \mathbf{H}_1(\mathbf{r}) = [\mathbf{H}_0 + \mathbf{H}_1] \exp(-j\mathbf{p} \cdot \mathbf{r}) \qquad \text{on side 1}, \tag{9.23}$$

$$\mathbf{H}_2(\mathbf{r}) = \mathbf{H}_2 \exp(-j\mathbf{p} \cdot \mathbf{r}) \qquad \text{on side 2}. \tag{9.24}$$

The magnetic field of each wave is perpendicular to both the wave vector and the electric field of that wave and its magnitude is related to that of the electric field by the impedance η of the medium. Since the $\exp(-j\mathbf{p} \cdot \mathbf{r})$ factor is common to the fields of all these waves, the requirement of continuity of tangential fields at every point of the plane is met by ensuring that the constant amplitudes be related by

$$\hat{\mathbf{n}} \times (\mathbf{E}_0 + \mathbf{E}_1) = \hat{\mathbf{n}} \times \mathbf{E}_2, \tag{9.25}$$

$$\hat{\mathbf{n}} \times (\mathbf{H}_0 + \mathbf{H}_1) = \hat{\mathbf{n}} \times \mathbf{H}_2. \tag{9.26}$$

The incident-wave field amplitudes $\mathbf{E}_0$ and $\mathbf{H}_0$ are given; for the scattered waves, the magnetic fields are related to the electric ones by the impedance of each medium, but there remain two vector unknowns, $\mathbf{E}_1$ and $\mathbf{E}_2$. Although Eqs. (9.25)–(9.26) provide no information at all about the normal components of the two unknown vectors, there is actually a sufficient number of equations to determine the vectors, because it is also known that $\mathbf{E}_1$ and $\mathbf{E}_2$ are perpendicular to $\mathbf{k}_1$ and $\mathbf{k}_2$, respectively, which are known from Snell's laws.

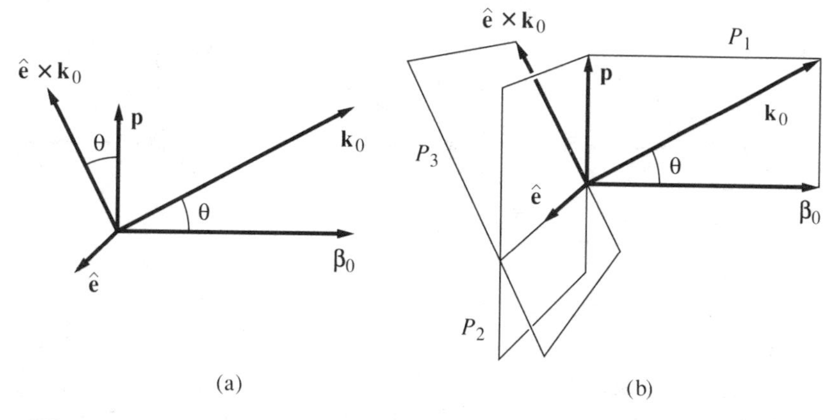

FIGURE 9–3 Planes of incidence P_1, of interface P_2, and of polarization P_3.

Elaborate matrix methods or complicated coordinate transformations could be used to extract the unknown scattered wave polarizations from the two continuity conditions, but a simpler approach is available. The difficulty to be overcome is that for oblique incidence, the natural coordinate systems for the wave (formed by the orthogonal vectors **E**, **H**, **k**) and for the interface (formed by the orthogonal vectors $\boldsymbol{\beta}$, **p**, $\boldsymbol{\beta} \times \mathbf{p}$) are not compatible. The feature of the problem that allows considerable simplification is that the unit vector $\hat{\mathbf{e}}$ along the direction of $\boldsymbol{\beta} \times \mathbf{p}$ is perpendicular to *both* $\hat{\mathbf{n}}$ and **k**. The vector $\hat{\mathbf{e}}$ therefore lies *in the plane of the interface* and also *in the plane of polarization* (the plane of the **E** and **H** fields, perpendicular to **k**) of each of the three waves. The vector $\hat{\mathbf{e}}$ therefore "belongs" to all the coordinate systems, of the interface and of all the waves. As illustrated in Figure 9–3, for the incident wave, the field vectors lie in the plane P_3 of $\hat{\mathbf{e}}$ and of $\hat{\mathbf{e}} \times \mathbf{k}_0$, both of which are orthogonal to $\mathbf{k}_0$. For any of the waves, all of the vectors $\hat{\mathbf{n}}$, $\boldsymbol{\beta}$, **k**, **p**, and $\hat{\mathbf{e}} \times \mathbf{k}$ lie in the plane of incidence P_1; the unit vector $\hat{\mathbf{e}}$ is perpendicular to all of these and lies in both the interface plane P_2 and the polarization plane P_3.

We can take advantage of this special status of the vector $\hat{\mathbf{e}}$ by decomposing the electric and magnetic fields of each of the three waves into components along $\hat{\mathbf{e}}$ and along $\hat{\mathbf{e}} \times \mathbf{k}$. More than a mere decomposition into orthogonal components is involved here, because if we pair the component of **E** along $\hat{\mathbf{e}}$ with the component of **H** along $-\hat{\mathbf{e}} \times \mathbf{k}$ and separately pair the component of **H** along $\hat{\mathbf{e}}$ with the component of **E** along $\hat{\mathbf{e}} \times \mathbf{k}$, we arrive at two pairs of fields that each satisfy Maxwell's equations for a wave that propagates along **k** and has the impedance η of the medium. This follows from the relation $\eta\mathbf{H} = \mathbf{k} \times \mathbf{E}/k$ demanded by Maxwell's equations, for any of the waves. If the operation $\mathbf{k} \times \mathbf{E}/k$ is applied to the decomposition $\mathbf{E} = E_e\hat{\mathbf{e}} + E_m\hat{\mathbf{e}} \times \mathbf{k}/k$, there results $E_m\hat{\mathbf{e}} - E_e\hat{\mathbf{e}} \times \mathbf{k}/k$, which is exactly the decomposition of $\eta\mathbf{H}$ called for above (i.e., $\eta H_e = E_e$ and $\eta H_m = E_m$). The result is that a wave propagating along **k** with *arbitrary* polarization can be decomposed into just *two*

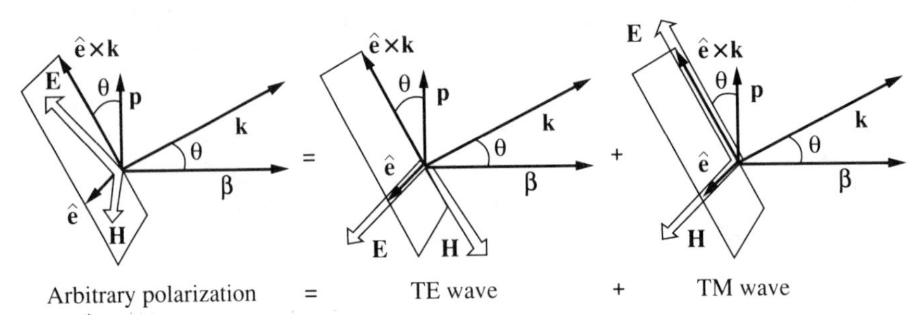

FIGURE 9–4 Arbitrary wave as superposition of TE and TM partial waves.

partial waves, each traveling along **k** but with special polarizations that put *either* **E** *or* **H** entirely in the plane of the interface, along **ê**.

This remarkable decomposition of any wave into two partial waves is illustrated in Figure 9–4. We designate the direction **n̂** normal to the interface "longitudinal" and that along **ê** "transverse." Then the partial wave with the electric field along **ê** is referred to as *transverse electric* (TE) and the partial wave with the magnetic field along **ê** is referred to as *transverse magnetic* (TM). The TE wave is also referred to as having "perpendicular" polarization (because its **E** is perpendicular to the plane of incidence), or "horizontal" polarization (appropriate if the interface is the ground), or "s" polarization (from the German word for perpendicular, *senkrecht*). The TM wave is also referred to as having "parallel" polarization (because its **E** is parallel to the plane of incidence), or "vertical" polarization (appropriate if the interface is the ground), or "p" polarization (from the German word for parallel, *parallel*).

The simplification in the boundary conditions after decomposition into TE and TM partial waves should now be clear. For each partial wave, the field that is the transverse one must be made continuous across the interface, as in the case of normal incidence.

$$\mathbf{E}_0 + \mathbf{E}_1 = \mathbf{E}_2 \quad \text{for TE;} \qquad \mathbf{H}_0 + \mathbf{H}_1 = \mathbf{H}_2 \quad \text{for TM.} \tag{9.27}$$

For each partial wave, the field that has a longitudinal component must have only its transverse components continuous across the interface. The field component tangential to the interface is

$$H \cos\theta \quad \text{for TE;} \qquad E\cos\theta \quad \text{for TM.} \tag{9.28}$$

The continuity conditions are the same as for normal incidence, for each partial wave. They involve the impedance mismatch, where impedance refers to the ratio of tangential electric and magnetic field components. For the TE and TM partial waves, the tangential fields are the complete transverse one and a projection of the one that has a longitudinal component. The tangential components are therefore related by equivalent impedances

$$\frac{E}{H\cos\theta} = \eta \sec\theta \quad \text{for TE,} \qquad \frac{E\cos\theta}{H} = \eta\cos\theta \quad \text{for TM,} \tag{9.29}$$

instead of just the impedance η of the medium in which the partial wave propagates.

The same continuity conditions, but with equivalent impedances, yield the same reflection and transmission coefficients, but using the new impedances

$$Z^{\text{TE}} = \eta \sec \theta, \qquad Z^{\text{TM}} = \eta \cos \theta. \tag{9.30}$$

Thus the reflection and transmission coefficients that apply to the fields that are transverse in each partial wave are given by

$$\Gamma_e^{\text{TE}} = \frac{Z_2^{\text{TE}} - Z_1^{\text{TE}}}{Z_2^{\text{TE}} + Z_1^{\text{TE}}} = \frac{\eta_2 \sec \theta_2 - \eta_1 \sec \theta_1}{\eta_2 \sec \theta_2 + \eta_1 \sec \theta_1}, \tag{9.31}$$

$$T_e^{\text{TE}} = \frac{2Z_2^{\text{TE}}}{Z_2^{\text{TE}} + Z_1^{\text{TE}}} = \frac{2\eta_2 \sec \theta_2}{\eta_2 \sec \theta_2 + \eta_1 \sec \theta_1} \tag{9.32}$$

for the electric field of the TE partial wave, and by

$$\Gamma_h^{\text{TM}} = \frac{Z_1^{\text{TM}} - Z_2^{\text{TM}}}{Z_1^{\text{TM}} + Z_2^{\text{TM}}} = \frac{\eta_1 \cos \theta_1 - \eta_2 \cos \theta_2}{\eta_1 \cos \theta_1 + \eta_2 \cos \theta_2}, \tag{9.33}$$

$$T_h^{\text{TM}} = \frac{2Z_1^{\text{TM}}}{Z_1^{\text{TM}} + Z_2^{\text{TM}}} = \frac{2\eta_1 \cos \theta_1}{\eta_1 \cos \theta_1 + \eta_2 \cos \theta_2} \tag{9.34}$$

for the magnetic field of the TM partial wave.

These are the Fresnel formulas, written for those fields of the partial waves that are entirely transverse. Their counterparts for those fields that have a longitudinal component as well (i.e., Γ_h^{TE}, T_h^{TE}, Γ_e^{TM}, T_e^{TM}), could also be written in this way, but they would apply only to the transverse projection of the total field that is not wholly transverse; these would then need additional trigonometric factors to get them to apply to the entire E field of the TM wave and the entire H field of the TE wave. But this is wholly unnecessary, since the reflection and transmission coefficients for the transverse fields suffice to yield the other field directly, by relating the entire E and H fields of either partial wave by the medium's impedance, η.

Note that, in the Fresnel equations, θ_1 is given for the incident wave and θ_2 must be precalculated from Snell's law of refraction. The major result is that the expressions for reflection and transmission coefficients for the tangential fields (which are the complete fields for the transverse ones) are given by the same mismatch equations as for normal incidence, that is,

$$\Gamma_e = \frac{Z_2 - Z_1}{Z_2 + Z_1}, \qquad T_e = \frac{2Z_2}{Z_2 + Z_1}, \tag{9.35}$$

$$\Gamma_h = \frac{Z_1 - Z_2}{Z_1 + Z_2}, \qquad T_h = \frac{2Z_1}{Z_1 + Z_2}, \tag{9.36}$$

but using the appropriate impedances, $\eta \sec \theta$ for TE and $\eta \cos \theta$ for TM, and the coefficients that apply to the transverse fields of each partial wave, Γ_e, T_e for TE, Γ_h, T_h for TM. If the given incident wave is neither TE nor TM, its given polarization should first be decomposed into the two partial transverse waves, by finding the field components along $\hat{\mathbf{e}}$ and along $\hat{\mathbf{e}} \times \mathbf{k}$; the reflected and transmitted partial waves can also, if desired, be added together, vectorially, to obtain the overall reflected and transmitted waves.

Note also that the impedance mismatch across the interface depends now not only on the two impedances η_1 and η_2 but also on the angle of incidence θ_1 and on the polarization (TE or TM). Two major consequences of this new dependence will be seen to be that, first, we can "tune" to a desired impedance, by tilting the interface with respect to the incident wave, and second, that an encounter with an interface can be used to favor one polarization (TE or TM) over another.

EXAMPLE 9.1

A plane wave is incident onto the interface between two nonmagnetic dielectrics at angle $\theta_1 = 36.87°$ to the normal. The permittivities of the media are $\varepsilon_1 = 6.25\varepsilon_0$ for the sourced one, $\varepsilon_2 = 15.21\varepsilon_0$ for the other. Obtain the reflection and transmission coefficients for both the TE and the TM polarizations; compare the results with the normal-incidence case.

The wave velocities in the two media are, since $\mu_1 = \mu_2 = \mu_0$ for nonmagnetic materials, $v_1 = c/\sqrt{6.25} = c/2.5$ and $v_2 = c/\sqrt{15.21} = c/3.9$, so that $n_1 = 2.5$ and $n_2 = 3.9$. Only their ratio is relevant here: $v_1/v_2 = \sqrt{\varepsilon_2/\varepsilon_1} = n_2/n_1 = 1.56 = \eta_1/\eta_2$. This impedance ratio is directly relevant to the case of normal incidence, but the effective impedances are different for the TE and TM components of the obliquely incident wave.

Snell's law yields the angle of refraction for both partial waves: $n_1 \sin\theta_1 = n_2 \sin\theta_2$, with $n_1 = 2.5$, $n_2 = 3.9$, and $\sin\theta_1 = 0.6$ yields $\sin\theta_2 = \frac{5}{13}$ or $\theta_2 = 22.62°$. We will need $\sec\theta_2 = \frac{13}{12}$, $\cos\theta_2 = \frac{12}{13}$, as well as $\sec\theta_1 = \frac{5}{4}$ and $\cos\theta_1 = \frac{4}{5}$.

The impedances for each partial wave are

$$Z_1^{\mathrm{TE}} = \eta_1 \sec\theta_1 = \frac{\eta_0}{2.5}\sec\theta_1 = 0.5\eta_0, \tag{9.37}$$

$$Z_2^{\mathrm{TE}} = \eta_2 \sec\theta_2 = \frac{\eta_0}{3.9}\sec\theta_2 = 0.27778\eta_0, \tag{9.38}$$

$$Z_1^{\mathrm{TM}} = \eta_1 \cos\theta_1 = \frac{\eta_0}{2.5}\cos\theta_1 = 0.32\eta_0, \tag{9.39}$$

$$Z_2^{\mathrm{TM}} = \eta_2 \cos\theta_2 = \frac{\eta_0}{3.9}\cos\theta_2 = 0.23669\eta_0, \tag{9.40}$$

so that the impedance mismatch for the given angle of incidence is

$$\left(\frac{Z_2}{Z_1}\right)^{\mathrm{TE}} = 0.555556, \qquad \left(\frac{Z_2}{Z_1}\right)^{\mathrm{TM}} = 0.739645 \tag{9.41}$$

for the two partial waves. This may be compared to the material impedance mismatch, which is relevant to normal incidence,

$$\left(\frac{Z_2}{Z_1}\right)^{\mathrm{TEM}} = \frac{\eta_2}{\eta_1} = \frac{2.5}{3.9} = 0.641026\,, \tag{9.42}$$

(the designation TEM, for transverse electromagnetic, is applied to the case that both the electric and magnetic fields are transverse, which occurs at normal incidence). Note that the TEM mismatch is intermediate between those of the TE and TM cases; in fact, it is the geometric mean of the two.

We obtain the reflection coefficients for the two partial waves as

$$\Gamma_e^{\mathrm{TE}} = \frac{(Z_2/Z_1)^{\mathrm{TE}} - 1}{(Z_2/Z_1)^{\mathrm{TE}} + 1} = -0.28571\,, \tag{9.43}$$

$$\Gamma_h^{\mathrm{TM}} = \frac{1 - (Z_2/Z_1)^{\mathrm{TM}}}{1 + (Z_2/Z_1)^{\mathrm{TM}}} = 0.14966 \tag{9.44}$$

and compare these with $\Gamma_e = -\Gamma_h = [(\eta_2/\eta_1) - 1]/[(\eta_2/\eta_1) + 1] = -0.21875$ for the TEM (normal incidence) case. These tell us that the reflected electric field of the TE partial wave is 29% in strength and opposed in direction, compared to the incident TE wave's electric field, while the reflected magnetic field of the TM partial wave is 15% in strength and with the same orientation, compared to the incident TM wave's magnetic field. Of course, the magnitude of the reflected magnetic field for the TE wave is obtainable from that of the reflected electric field by $H = E/\eta_1$ and the magnitude of the reflected electric field for the TM wave is related to that of the reflected magnetic field by $E = \eta_1 H$.

The transmission coefficients for the two partial waves are

$$T_e^{\mathrm{TE}} = \frac{2(Z_2/Z_1)^{\mathrm{TE}}}{(Z_2/Z_1)^{\mathrm{TE}} + 1} = 0.71429\,, \tag{9.45}$$

$$T_h^{\mathrm{TM}} = \frac{2}{1 + (Z_2/Z_1)^{\mathrm{TM}}} = 1.14966\,, \tag{9.46}$$

Compare these with $T_e = 2(\eta_2/\eta_1)/[(\eta_2/\eta_1) + 1] = 0.78125$ and with $T_h = 2/[1 + (\eta_2/\eta_1)] = 1.21875$ for the TEM (normal incidence) case. These tell us that the transmitted electric field of the TE partial wave is 71% in strength and in the same direction, compared to the incident TE wave's electric field, while the transmitted magnetic field of the TM partial wave is 115% in strength and with the same orientation, compared to the incident TM wave's magnetic field. Of course, the magnitude of the transmitted magnetic field for the TE wave is obtainable from that of the transmitted electric field by $H = E/\eta_2$ and the magnitude of the transmitted electric field for the TM wave is related to that of the transmitted magnetic field by $E = \eta_2 H$.

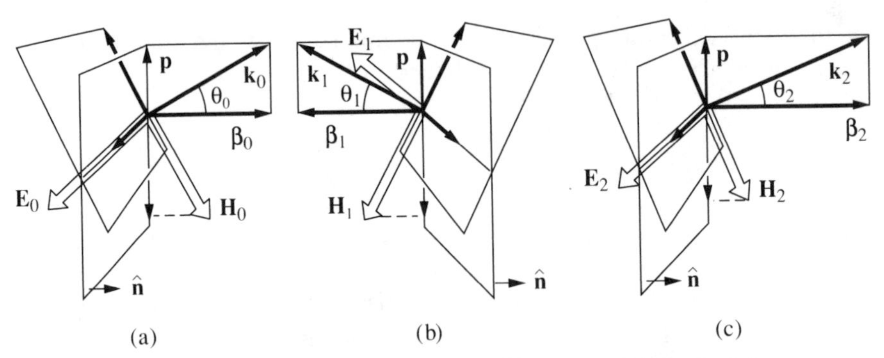

FIGURE 9–5 Incident and scattered TE waves of Example 9.1.

Knowing the reflected and transmitted wave vectors $\mathbf{k}_1$ and $\mathbf{k}_2$ from Snell's laws and having found the transverse field for both the reflected and the transmitted partial waves, the full fields of each partial wave can be constructed for the TE and the TM waves individually and, by superposition of the partial waves, for the complete reflected and transmitted waves. The incident, reflected, and refracted partial waves are depicted for this example in Figure 9–5 for the TE component and in Figure 9–6 for the TM part. (In these figures, the field vectors are not shown to scale, but their orientations are consistent with the results calculated above.)

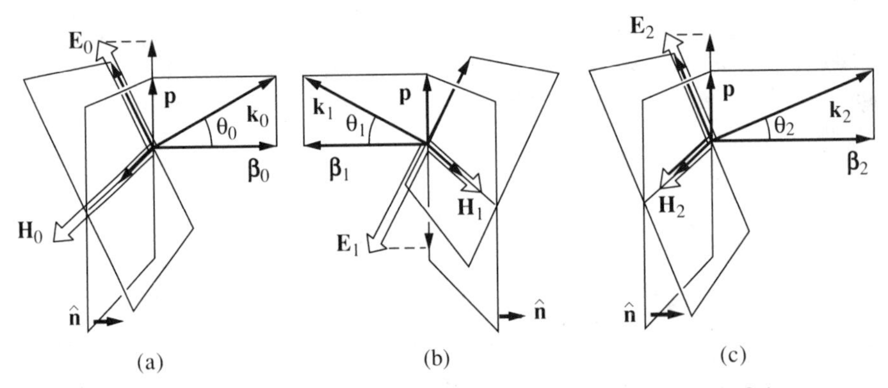

FIGURE 9–6 Incident and scattered TM waves of Example 9.1.

◆

Brewster's Angle

Since the effective impedance on each side of the interface depends on the angle of incidence, it may be possible to match otherwise mismatched media by judiciously selecting some particular angle at which an obliquely incident wave encounters the boundary plane. If we succeed, the refracted light should enter the sourceless medium without reflection and all of the incident energy should be transferred across the interface.

To match impedances for a TE wave, we need $Z_1^{TE} = Z_2^{TE}$, or

$$\eta_1 \sec \theta_1 = \eta_2 \sec \theta_2 \tag{9.47}$$

while, for a TM wave, matching occurs if $Z_1^{TM} = Z_2^{TM}$, or

$$\eta_1 \cos \theta_1 = \eta_2 \cos \theta_2 \,; \tag{9.48}$$

in either case, the angles θ_1 and θ_2 are related by Snell's law

$$n_1 \sin \theta_1 = n_2 \sin \theta_2 \,. \tag{9.49}$$

We are given the impedances η and indices of refraction n of the two mismatched media (for nonmagnetic materials, one of these suffices to determine the other) and we wish to choose an angle of incidence θ_1 that will make the reflection coefficient vanish, by matching the effective impedances for one or the other of the partial waves. To obtain θ_1, we need to eliminate θ_2 from the pair of equations (Snell's law and an impedance-matching condition) for each of the two partial waves. We can achieve this by squaring and adding the expressions for $\sin \theta_2$ and $\cos \theta_2$, as follows.

$$\text{For TE:} \qquad \cos^2 \theta_2 = \left(\frac{\eta_2}{\eta_1}\right)^2 \cos^2 \theta_1, \tag{9.50}$$

$$\text{For TM:} \qquad \cos^2 \theta_2 = \left(\frac{\eta_1}{\eta_2}\right)^2 \cos^2 \theta_1, \tag{9.51}$$

$$\text{For both:} \qquad \sin^2 \theta_2 = \left(\frac{n_1}{n_2}\right)^2 \sin^2 \theta_1. \tag{9.52}$$

Adding each pair and replacing $\cos^2 \theta_2 + \sin^2 \theta_2 = 1$ by $\cos^2 \theta_1 + \sin^2 \theta_1$ yields

$$\text{For TE:} \qquad 1 = \left(\frac{\eta_2}{\eta_1}\right)^2 \cos^2 \theta_1 + \left(\frac{n_1}{n_2}\right)^2 \sin^2 \theta_1 = \cos^2 \theta_1 + \sin^2 \theta_1, \tag{9.53}$$

$$\text{For TM:} \qquad 1 = \left(\frac{\eta_1}{\eta_2}\right)^2 \cos^2 \theta_1 + \left(\frac{n_1}{n_2}\right)^2 \sin^2 \theta_1 = \cos^2 \theta_1 + \sin^2 \theta_1. \tag{9.54}$$

Collecting the sine and cosine terms separately gives

$$\text{For TE:} \qquad \tan^2 \theta_1 = \frac{(\eta_2/\eta_1)^2 - 1}{1 - (n_1/n_2)^2} = \frac{(\mu_2/\mu_1)(\varepsilon_1/\varepsilon_2) - 1}{1 - (\mu_1/\mu_2)(\varepsilon_1/\varepsilon_2)}, \tag{9.55}$$

$$\text{For TM:} \qquad \tan^2 \theta_1 = \frac{(\eta_1/\eta_2)^2 - 1}{1 - (n_1/n_2)^2} = \frac{(\mu_1/\mu_2)(\varepsilon_2/\varepsilon_1) - 1}{1 - (\mu_1/\mu_2)(\varepsilon_1/\varepsilon_2)}. \tag{9.56}$$

Since, for the range of possible incidence angles ($0 < \theta_1 < \pi/2$), $\tan\theta_1$ ranges from zero to infinity, it will be possible to find a matching angle θ_1, provided merely that the right sides of these equations be positive.

In most practical cases in which such matching is used, the two media are nonmagnetic ($\mu_1 = \mu_2 = \mu_0$); significantly magnetic materials are not so likely to be transparent. The matching conditions are then reduced to

$$\text{For TE:} \qquad \tan^2\theta_1 = \frac{(\varepsilon_1/\varepsilon_2) - 1}{1 - (\varepsilon_1/\varepsilon_2)} = -1, \tag{9.57}$$

for which there can never (for any ε's) be a solution, and

$$\text{For TM:} \qquad \tan^2\theta_1 = \frac{(\varepsilon_2/\varepsilon_1) - 1}{1 - (\varepsilon_1/\varepsilon_2)} = \frac{\varepsilon_2}{\varepsilon_1}, \tag{9.58}$$

for which there is always (for any ε's) a solution. Thus nonmagnetic media can be matched and the reflection eliminated, but only for the TM partial wave and at the specific angle of incidence θ_B, called *Brewster's angle*, given by $\tan\theta_B = \sqrt{\varepsilon_2/\varepsilon_1}$ or

$$\theta_B = \tan^{-1}\frac{n_2}{n_1}. \tag{9.59}$$

For example, light can enter a plate of glass of refractive index 1.6, from air, without reflection if the light is polarized as a TM wave and is incident at an angle of 58° to the normal. If the light is polarized as a TE wave, there will be some reflection at this, and any other, angle of incidence. If the light is arbitrarily polarized and incident at the Brewster angle, then only the TE partial wave is reflected. When Brewster's angle is used in this way to select one of the two polarizations (TE) out of the mixture of both in an arbitrary incident wave and thereby achieve a reflected wave that has pure TE polarization and no TM component at all, θ_B is called the *polarizing angle*. Such reflected light could, for example, be made to impinge onto still another plate of glass, this time at TM polarization with respect to the new interface, whereupon that light is perfectly transmitted into the new plate.

We note that for incidence at Brewster's angle θ_B, the angle of refraction θ_2, given by Eq. (9.49), is found from

$$\sin\theta_2 = \frac{n_1}{n_2}\sin\theta_B = \cot\theta_B \sin\theta_B = \cos\theta_B \quad \text{or} \quad \theta_2 = \frac{\pi}{2} - \theta_B. \tag{9.60}$$

This indicates not only that the refracted light propagates at the angle that is complementary to the incident Brewster's angle but also that

$$\tan\theta_2 = \cot\theta_B = \frac{n_1}{n_2} = \tan\theta_B', \tag{9.61}$$

which means that the output light travels in the second medium at the angle that would be Brewster's angle θ_B' for transmission from the *second* medium to the *first*. That is, an interface at Brewster's angle will transmit in *either* direction without reflection, for TM incidence. The output window of a laser is usually set at Brewster's angle and the light properly polarized to take advantage of this perfect transmission.

Power Conservation

The interpretation of conservation of power is a slightly more subtle matter in the case of oblique incidence than it is for normal incidence. When we compare the powers in the scattered waves to the incident wave power, we expect that whatever power is not transmitted must be reflected, the two adding up to the incident power, for lossless media. This is correct, but we must be aware that it is not the power density, or magnitude of the Poynting vector, that satisfies the conservation principle; rather, it is the integral of the Poynting vector over a closed surface that maintains the balance between the power that enters the enclosed volume and the power that leaves it. This integral involves only the component of the Poynting vector normal to the surface of integration. When we examine incident and scattered plane waves at an interface plane, we find that the relevant component of the Poynting vector is only the one normal to the interface, as follows.

When a wave incident at angle θ_0 onto an interface is reflected at angle θ_1 and refracted at angle θ_2, the medium beyond the interface carries only one plane wave; its power density is given by Re $\frac{1}{2}\mathbf{E}_2 \times \mathbf{H}_2^*$, which has magnitude $\frac{1}{2}|E_2|^2/\eta_2 = \frac{1}{2}\eta_2|H_2|^2$ and is directed along θ_2 to the normal. For the TE polarization, the magnitude is $(\eta_1/\eta_2)|T_e|^2$ times that of the incident wave alone, which is $\frac{1}{2}|E_0|^2/\eta_1$; for the TM polarization, the magnitude is $(\eta_2/\eta_1)|T_h|^2$ times that of the incident wave alone, which is $\frac{1}{2}\eta_1|H_0|^2$. The sourced medium carries the superposition of two plane waves, the incident and reflected ones; these interfere with each other and the power density of the combined fields is

$$\begin{aligned}
\text{Re}\,\tfrac{1}{2}\mathbf{E} \times \mathbf{H}^* &= \text{Re}\,\tfrac{1}{2}(\mathbf{E}_0 e^{-j\mathbf{k}_0\cdot\mathbf{r}} + \mathbf{E}_1 e^{-j\mathbf{k}_1\cdot\mathbf{r}}) \times (\mathbf{H}_0^* e^{j\mathbf{k}_0\cdot\mathbf{r}} + \mathbf{H}_1^* e^{j\mathbf{k}_1\cdot\mathbf{r}}) \\
&= \text{Re}\,\tfrac{1}{2}\mathbf{E}_0 \times \mathbf{H}_0^* + \text{Re}\,\tfrac{1}{2}\mathbf{E}_1 \times \mathbf{H}_1^* \\
&\quad + \text{Re}\,\tfrac{1}{2}\mathbf{E}_0 \times \mathbf{H}_1^* \exp[-j(\mathbf{k}_0 - \mathbf{k}_1)\cdot\mathbf{r}] \\
&\quad + \text{Re}\,\tfrac{1}{2}\mathbf{E}_1 \times \mathbf{H}_0^* \exp[+j(\mathbf{k}_0 - \mathbf{k}_1)\cdot\mathbf{r}].
\end{aligned} \tag{9.62}$$

The first of these four terms is the power density of the incident wave alone; the second is that of the reflected wave alone. The last two terms represent the interference between the incident and reflected waves.

We often wish to speak of the power in each of the incident and reflected waves individually and compare these with that in the transmitted one. This means that we consider the first or the second term of the four, without summing them and without regard for the last two, the interference terms.

That this is meaningful is a result of the fact that the four terms have different vector directions and different spatial dependences. While all four terms should, in principle, be summed before the power is evaluated, it is actually possible to separate the four contributions and make a physical measurement of the power in each wave individually. Radiation detectors are usually sensitive to waves propagating in some direction, such as the normal to the detector, while quite insensitive to radiation along other directions; besides this, the integration of the Poynting vector over the surface of the detector involves integration of a constant for the first two terms, but a three-dimensional, spatial Fourier transformation of that surface when the interference terms are integrated. By orienting the detector properly, then, we can make it insensitive to all but the individual wave power that we wish to measure. This operation amounts to filtering out the spatial Fourier components of the overall radiation, other than that of the wave we want. This is all the more easy to achieve when the waves are not infinitely extended plane waves, but rather "beams" of radiation of finite, even if large, transverse extent; in that case, the interference appears only where the beams overlap and detectors outside that region can register the desired power in just one beam.

If, therefore, we calculate or measure the powers in the incident and the two scattered waves individually, we find that the reflected wave's power density is $|\Gamma_e|^2$ times that of the incident wave, for the TE case, or $|\Gamma_h|^2$ instead for the TM case. The magnitude of the transmitted wave's power density is $(\eta_1/\eta_2)|T_e|^2$ for TE, or $(\eta_2/\eta_1)|T_h|^2$ for TM, as already noted. The question to be addressed is the interpretation of the fact that the power densities of the scattered waves do not add to that of the incident wave: $|\Gamma_e|^2 + (\eta_1/\eta_2)|T_e|^2 \neq 1$ and $|\Gamma_h|^2 + (\eta_2/\eta_1)|T_h|^2 \neq 1$. That is, although the tangential fields are properly continuous, as expressed by $1 + \Gamma = T$ (which is the essence of the boundary condition), the powers appear not to add up in the oblique case, although they did do so in the case of normal incidence.

We have the correct interpretation, once we realize that it is not the power density, or magnitude of the Poynting vector, that should conform to the principle of power conservation, but rather that the *integral* of the scattered waves' Poynting vectors should balance that of the incident wave, over any closed surface that straddles the interface, as in Figure 9–7. For any such closed surface $S = S_1 + S_2$, the portion that extends into either the sourced or the unsourced region is an open surface; we can consider either one of the two open surfaces and close it by appending to it the area S_0 of the interface plane that lies within the volume enclosed by S. For either of these two newly closed surfaces, the integral of the Poynting vector for just one of the waves, being the integral of a constant over a closed surface, is zero, so that the integral over the open surface must be the opposite of the integral over the enclosed area on the interface. We can therefore get the integral of one wave's power density over any surface that straddles the interface by just integrating its Poynting vector over the interface area S_0 intercepted by the enclosed volume. For that intercepted area, the area element is $d\mathbf{S} = \hat{\mathbf{n}}\, dA$, so that the relevant component of the Poynting vector is only the one normal to the interface.

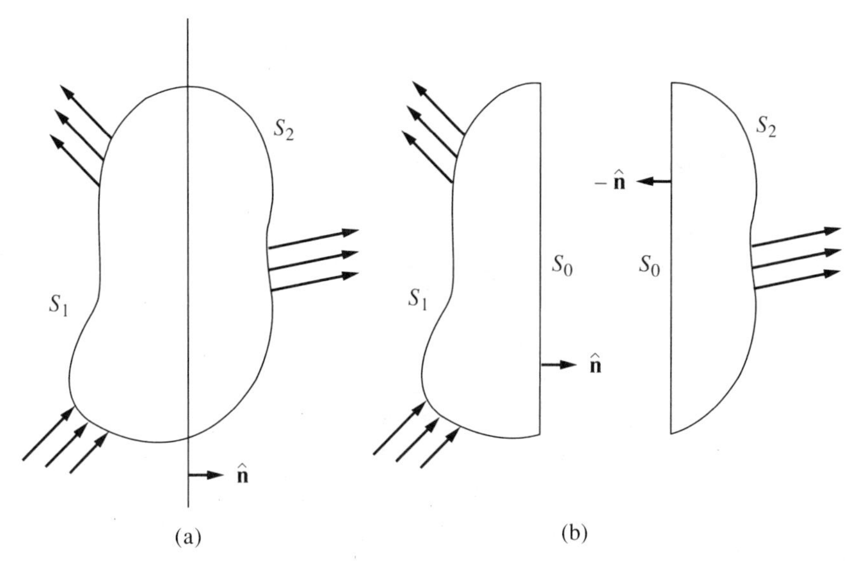

FIGURE 9–7 Power flow across a surface that straddles an interface.

Once we realize that only the Poynting vector component normal to the interface is relevant to the calculation of the power flow into or out of any closed surface across the interface, we find at once that the power flow of the scattered fields do add to the incident power flow. This is because the integral on S_0 introduces a factor of $\cos\theta_1$ or $\cos\theta_2$ on the two sides of the interface. This makes the incident power flow, per unit area of the interface, $\frac{1}{2}|E_0|^2\cos\theta_1/\eta_1$, or just $\frac{1}{2}|E_0|^2/Z_1$ for the TE polarization, or else $\frac{1}{2}\eta_1|H_0|^2\cos\theta_1$, or just $\frac{1}{2}|H_0|^2 Z_1$ for TM polarization. For the reflected wave, the power flow density is $\frac{1}{2}|E_1|^2\cos\theta_1/\eta_1$, or just $\frac{1}{2}|E_1|^2/Z_1 = |\Gamma_e|^2(\frac{1}{2}|E_0|^2/Z_1)$ for TE, or else $\frac{1}{2}\eta_1|H_1|^2\cos\theta_1$, or just $\frac{1}{2}|H_1|^2 Z_1 = |\Gamma_h|^2(\frac{1}{2}|H_0|^2 Z_1)$ for TM. For the refracted wave, the power flow density is $\frac{1}{2}|E_2|^2\cos\theta_2/\eta_2$, or just $\frac{1}{2}|E_2|^2/Z_2 = (Z_1/Z_2)|T_e|^2(\frac{1}{2}|E_0|^2/Z_1)$ for TE, or else $\frac{1}{2}\eta_2|H_2|^2\cos\theta_2$, or just $\frac{1}{2}|H_2|^2 Z_2 = (Z_2/Z_1)|T_h|^2(\frac{1}{2}|H_0|^2 Z_1)$ for TM. Conservation of power is hence preserved if

$$|\Gamma_e|^2 + \frac{Z_1}{Z_2}|T_e|^2 = 1 \quad \text{for TE}, \qquad |\Gamma_h|^2 + \frac{Z_2}{Z_1}|T_h|^2 = 1 \quad \text{for TM}. \tag{9.63}$$

These relations are, in fact, satisfied by $\Gamma_e = (Z_2 - Z_1)/(Z_2 + Z_1)$, $T_e = 2Z_2/(Z_2 + Z_1)$, using $Z = \eta\sec\theta$ for TE and by $\Gamma_h = (Z_1 - Z_2)/(Z_1 + Z_2)$, $T_h = 2Z_1/(Z_1 + Z_2)$, using $Z = \eta\cos\theta$ for TM, so that the sum of the power flows of the reflected and refracted waves does equal the incident power flow, provided that only the Poynting vector component normal to the interface is involved, not its magnitude. The following example should clarify the need to interpret conservation of power flow in this way.

EXAMPLE 9.2

Oblique incidence from air onto a lossless, nonmagnetic dielectric at a certain incidence angle is observed to result in 80% power transmission when TE polarization is used and in 100% power transmission when TM polarization is tried. What are the index of refraction n of the dielectric and the angle of incidence θ?

Since there is perfect transmission when TM polarization is used, the incidence must be at Brewster's angle, so that $\tan\theta_1 = n = \cot\theta_2$, as θ_1 and θ_2 are then complementary angles. For the TE wave, we can avoid the (slight) complication of dealing with the normal component of the power density if we use the reflected power fraction, instead of the given transmission, and invoke conservation of power flow. The simplification comes from the equality of the angles of reflection and of incidence, so that the $\cos\theta_1$ factor is the same for the incident and the reflected waves and cancels from the power ratio. Thus, we use 20% as the reflected power fraction, instead of 80% transmission, since power must be conserved. Hence $|\Gamma_e|^2 = 20\% = 0.2$. But $\Gamma_e = (Z_2 - Z_1)/(Z_2 + Z_1)$ and $Z = \eta \sec\theta$, with $\eta_2/\eta_1 = 1/n$ and $\sec\theta_2/\sec\theta_1 = 1/n$ (from $\tan\theta_1 = n = \cot\theta_2$), so that $Z_2/Z_1 = 1/n^2$ and $|\Gamma_e| = (n^2 - 1)/(n^2 + 1)$. The latter inverts to $n^2 = (1 + |\Gamma_e|)/(1 - |\Gamma_e|) = (1 + \sqrt{0.2})/(1 - \sqrt{0.2})$ or $n = 1.618$ and $\theta_1 = 58.3°$.

If we prefer to use the 80% power transmission fraction directly, we must recognize the $\cos\theta_1$ and $\cos\theta_2$ factors in the incident and refracted wave power flow expressions. Then $(|E_2|^2/\eta_2)/(|E_0|^2/\eta_1) = (\eta_1/\eta_2)|T_e|^2$ is *not* the ratio that equals $80\% = 0.8$; rather, it is $(|E_2|^2 \cos\theta_2/\eta_2)/(|E_0|^2 \cos\theta_1/\eta_1) = (\eta_1 \sec\theta_1/\eta_2 \sec\theta_2)|T_e|^2$ or $(Z_1/Z_2)|T_e|^2$ that is the 80% fraction. But $T_e = 2Z_2/(Z_2 + Z_1)$ gives $4Z_1Z_2/(Z_2 + Z_1)^2 = 0.8$; using $Z_1/Z_2 = n^2$, we get $4n^2/(n^2 + 1)^2 = 0.8$ or $2n/(n^2 + 1) = \sqrt{0.8}$; this quadratic equation is solved by $n = 1.618$ (as well as 0.618, but that is less than unity), giving the same answers as before. ◆

Summary

When an electromagnetic plane wave, such as light, impinges obliquely onto a planar interface between dissimilar media, the resulting reflection and transmission depend on modified, effective impedances on the two sides of the boundary plane. These impedances depend on the angle of incidence and on the polarization of the original wave, as well as on the constitutive properties of the media.

We found that we could extend the principles that govern scattering for normal incidence to the case of oblique incidence. In particular, the relationship between reflection and impedance mismatch could be maintained by a simple change of attitude. That is, a uniform plane wave obliquely incident onto the interface could equally well be considered to be normally incident, but nonuniform (with a particularly simple, exponential nonuniformity). This concept will be found useful again later, to ease the transition from transmission lines to waveguides.

We found that Snell's laws of reflection and refraction are a direct consequence of the electromagnetic boundary conditions at the interface. They simply allow continuity of the tangential electric and magnetic fields at all points of the interface, once continuity has been achieved at any one point. They require the tangential component of the wave vector, which describes the nonuniformity of the wave, to be identical for the incident, the reflected, and the refracted waves.

By choosing to polarize one or the other of the two fields along the unique direction common to both the plane of the interface and of polarization, we were able to impose continuity of the fields at the interface for each of two partial waves, the transverse electric (TE) and transverse magnetic (TM) polarizations. The continuity requirements led to the Fresnel formulas, which are of the same form as for normal incidence but use the effective impedances of the two polarizations, $\eta \sec \theta$ for TE and $\eta \cos \theta$ for TM. The concept of TE and TM waves will recur later, in our study of waveguiding.

We noted that the freedom provided by the dependence of the impedances on angle of incidence and on polarization allowed us to "tune" to a desired impedance by tilting the interface with respect to the incident wave. In particular, we are able to eliminate reflection at the interface between mismatched media, by matching their *effective* impedances. This is achieved by arranging for incidence at Brewster's angle and for the appropriate polarization (TM for nonmagnetic media).

Finally, we verified conservation of power by properly interpreting what we mean by incident, reflected, and transmitted power. Because only the integral of the Poynting vector over a surface gives power flow, we found that only the component of the Poynting vector normal to the interface is relevant to the density of power flow incident onto and scattered away from the boundary plane.

The basis for reflection and refraction calculations is Snell's laws, as we saw, but Snell's laws can fail, as we shall now see.

PROBLEMS

Scattering of Obliquely Incident TE Wave

9.1 Find the transmission and reflection coefficients T_e, Γ_e for incidence at 30° from a medium with $v_1 = \frac{1}{2}c$ to one with $v_2 = \frac{2}{3}c$, both media being lossless and nonmagnetic, for TE polarization.

Scattering of Obliquely Incident TM Wave

9.2 Find the transmission and reflection coefficients T_h, Γ_h for incidence at 30° from a medium with $v_1 = \frac{1}{2}c$ to one with $v_2 = \frac{2}{3}c$, both media being lossless and nonmagnetic, for TM polarization.

Bending of Fully Transmitted Wave

9.3 A plane wave is obliquely incident onto the planar interface between mismatched, lossless, nonmagnetic, uniform media, yet undergoes no reflection. If incidence is at 54° to the normal, at what angle to the normal does the transmitted wave travel?

Effect of Oblique Scattering on Polarization

9.4 A circularly polarized plane wave is incident from air onto a lossless, nonmagnetic dielectric, at Brewster's angle. Are the reflected and refracted waves also circularly polarized?

Power Transmission for Oblique Incidence

9.5 Oblique incidence from air onto a lossless, nonmagnetic dielectric at a certain incidence angle is observed to result in 75% power transmission when TE polarization is used and in 100% power transmission when TM polarization is used.

(a) Find the index of refraction of the dielectric.

(b) Find the angle of incidence.

Reflection of Unpolarized Light

9.6 Unpolarized light is composed of plane waves of all possible polarizations, all equally likely, so that half the total power is in the TE polarization and half in the TM. Consequently, the power reflection at an oblique interface is the average of those for the TE and TM waves. If 1 W of unpolarized light is incident at Brewster's angle from air onto a nonmagnetic glass of index $n = \sqrt{3}$, how much power is reflected?

Mistake in Polarization

9.7 An experimenter wants to transmit a plane wave across the interface between two different nonmagnetic dielectrics. Because only 50% of the power is transmitted at normal incidence, he decides to use incidence at the Brewster angle, which allows perfect transmission of a TM wave. Mistakenly, however, he shines a TE wave at this angle, instead of TM polarization. What fraction of the incident power is transmitted?

Oblique Incidence onto Resistive Sheet in Vacuum

9.8 A plane wave is incident at angle θ onto a resistive sheet of surface conductivity σ_S. The media on the two sides of the sheet are both a vacuum.

(a) Obtain the reflection and transmission coefficients, for TE polarization.

(b) What is the surface current K on the resistive sheet, for TE polarization?

(c) Obtain the reflection and transmission coefficients, for TM polarization.
(d) What is the surface current K on the resistive sheet, for TM polarization?

Perfect Absorber of Oblique Plane Waves

9.9 A plane wave is incident at angle θ onto a resistive sheet of surface conductivity σ_S. The sheet is coincident with the xy-plane and the media on the two sides of the sheet are both a vacuum. At a distance l beyond the sheet (i.e., at $z = l$), we place a perfectly conducting plane. Select the surface conductivity σ_S and the distance l to make the combination of resistive sheet and conducting plane a perfect absorber for the incident wave (no reflection back into the $z < 0$ region):
(a) For a TE wave;
(b) For a TM wave.

Superposition of Opposed TE Waves

9.10 Each of two mismatched dielectrics (η_1 and η_2) has a source that generates a plane wave at the same frequency and directs it obliquely onto the interface plane, at incidence angles θ_1 and θ_2. The amplitudes, phases, incidence angles, and polarizations are such that the incident electric fields of each (in the absence of the other) are identical ($\mathbf{E}_1 = \mathbf{E}_2 = \mathbf{E}_0 e^{-j\mathbf{p}\cdot\mathbf{r}}$) at the interface (at $z = 0$).
(a) How must the incidence angles θ_1 and θ_2 be related?
(b) Why must the polarization be TE?
(c) Obtain the electric fields on both sides of the interface; show that these form a standing wave on both sides, by noting the value of $\Gamma_{21} + T_{12}$ for such oblique incidence.

Superposition of Opposed TM Waves

9.11 Each of two mismatched dielectrics (η_1 and η_2) has a source that generates a plane wave at the same frequency and directs it obliquely onto the interface plane, at incidence angles θ_1 and θ_2. The amplitudes, phases, incidence angles, and polarizations are such that the incident magnetic fields of each (in the absence of the other) are identical ($\mathbf{H}_1 = \mathbf{H}_2 = \mathbf{H}_0 e^{-j\mathbf{p}\cdot\mathbf{r}}$) at the interface (at $z = 0$).
(a) How must the incidence angles θ_1 and θ_2 be related?
(b) Why must the polarization be TM?
(c) Obtain the magnetic fields on both sides of the interface; show that these form a standing wave on both sides, by noting the value of $\Gamma_{21} + T_{12}$ for such oblique incidence.

Maximum Mismatch for Given Reflection of Oblique Waves

9.12 The power reflection coefficient for incidence at angle θ onto the interface between two lossless, nonmagnetic dielectrics is to be kept no greater than 5%. What is the maximum ratio of refractive index that can be tolerated:

(a) If the wave is TE?

(b) If the wave is TM?

(c) Specialize these results to incidence at 45°, for both TE and TM waves.

Angular Bandwidth About Brewster's Angle

9.13 Over what range of angles of incidence from air onto a nonmagnetic dielectric of refractive index n, near Brewster's angle, does the power reflection coefficient for a TM wave remain less than 5%? Specialize the result to the case $n = 2$.

Antireflection Coating for a TE Wave

9.14 Design an antireflection coating for a TE wave incident at angle θ from air onto a nonmagnetic dielectric of refractive index n (give the index of refraction and the thickness of the coating).

Antireflection Coating for a TM Wave

9.15 Design an antireflection coating for a TM wave incident at angle θ from air onto a nonmagnetic dielectric of refractive index n (give the index of refraction and the thickness of the coating). Assume that θ is not the Brewster angle.

Oblique Standing Wave at a Mirror

9.16 A uniform plane wave traveling in free space is incident at angle θ to the surface of a perfectly conducting plane. The resultant electric field is zero at a distance s in front of the mirror.

(a) Why can the wave not be TM?

(b) What is the lowest possible frequency if the incident wave is TE?

Oblique Incidence onto Ordinary Mirror

9.17 A pane of glass (lossless, nonmagnetic, index of refraction n, thickness s) is silvered on one side (a perfectly conducting coating) to form an (idealized) ordinary mirror.

(a) Obtain the reflection coefficient at the air–glass interface, for incidence at angle θ of a plane wave at frequency ω, for TE polarization.

(b) What fraction of the incident TE power is reflected into the air?

(c) Obtain the reflection coefficient at the air–glass interface, for incidence at angle θ of a plane wave at frequency ω, for TM polarization.

(d) What fraction of the incident TM power is reflected into the air?

CHAPTER 10

Total Internal Reflection

There is the possibility of failure of Snell's laws, in the sense that the equation for the angle of refraction, $n_1 \sin \theta_1 = n_2 \sin \theta_2$, might have no solution under certain circumstances—at least not without reinterpretation of the results. The circumstances that lead to such failure actually represent an important optical effect, one that is crucial to the operation of optical fibers.

Failure of Snell's Laws

We first ask which way the wave that impinges obliquely on an interface will bend as it crosses the plane, toward or away from the normal to the boundary? That is, will the angle of refraction be smaller or larger than the angle of incidence? The answer is given by Snell's law, considered as an equation that yields the angle of refraction θ_2 as a function of a variable angle of incidence θ_1.

$$\theta_2 = \sin^{-1}\left[\frac{n_1}{n_2} \sin \theta_1\right]. \tag{10.1}$$

Whether θ_2 is smaller or larger than θ_1 depends on whether n_1 is smaller or larger than n_2, that is, on whether the wave slows down or speeds up on crossing the interface, from phase velocity $v_1 = c/n_1$ to $v_2 = c/n_2$.

If the wave travels from a medium of faster speed (optically less dense) to one of slower speed (optically denser), $v_1 > v_2$ or $n_1 < n_2$, the refracted wave bends toward the normal, $\theta_2 < \theta_1$. In crossing from a denser to a less dense medium, the wave bends away from the normal. This is illustrated in Figure 10–1, in which the semicircles represent the loci of the wave vectors as the angle of incidence varies. Their radii are $(\omega/c)n_1$ and $(\omega/c)n_2$ to the left and the right, respectively, of the interface. Since the tangential component $\mathbf{p}$ of each wave vector has to be the same, the shorter wave vector (smaller index n) needs to bend farther away from the normal to accommodate its tangential component.

Now the tangential component of all the wave vectors, $\mathbf{p}$, is determined by the incident wave and the refracted wave has to accommodate to it. But what

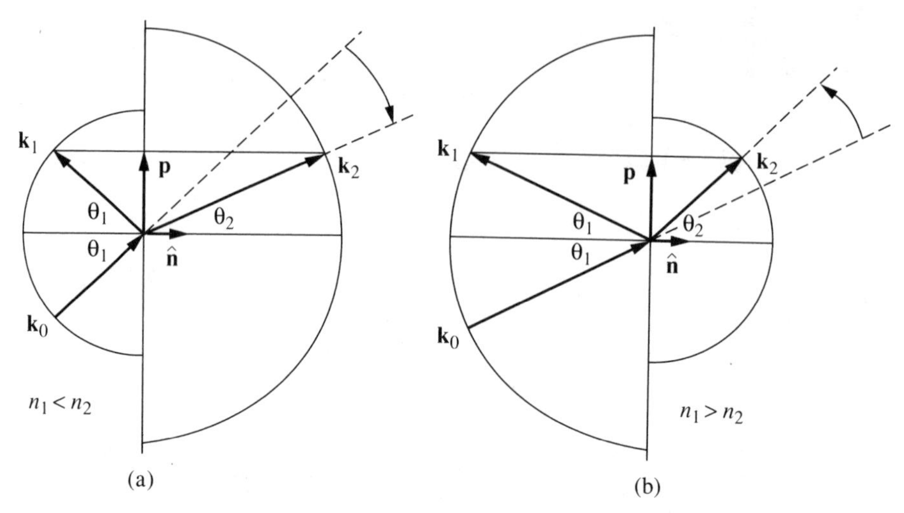

FIGURE 10–1 Refraction (a) toward ($n_1 < n_2$) or (b) away from ($n_1 > n_2$) the normal.

if the magnitude of the tangential component, p, exceeds that of the entire wave vector of the transmitted wave, $k_2 = (\omega/c)n_2$? How can the refracted wave vector $\mathbf{k}_2$ have a tangential component $\mathbf{p}$ larger than its own magnitude? This will be called for when $n_1 > n_2$ (transmission from a denser to a less dense medium) *and* the angle of incidence is too large for the $\mathbf{p}$ vector to fit into the smaller semicircle beyond the interface. This is illustrated in Figure 10–2, which shows first the limiting case, for which $\mathbf{k}_2$ becomes entirely tangential and equals $\mathbf{p}$, and then a case for which no refracted wave vector $\mathbf{k}_2$ can conform to the required tangential component $\mathbf{p}$.

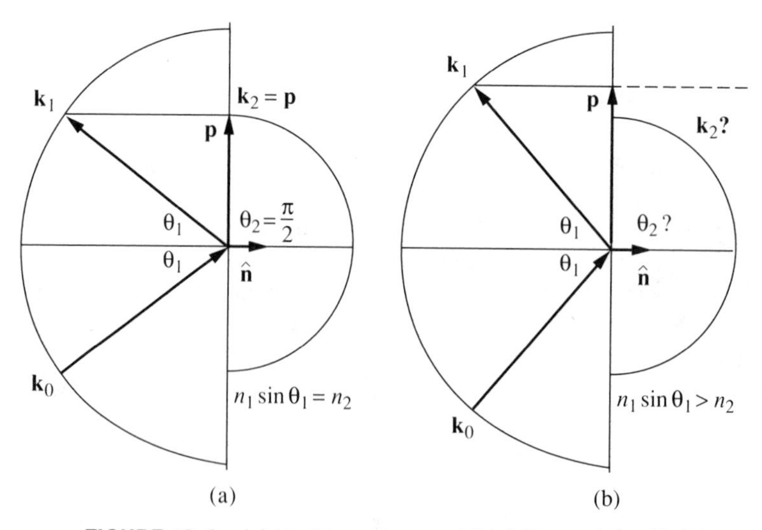

FIGURE 10–2 (a) Limiting case, and (b) failure, of Snell's law.

Mathematically, this failure to determine the refracted wave corresponds to the case that not only is $n_1 > n_2$ but the incidence angle is large enough that even $n_1 \sin \theta_1 > n_2$, whereupon Snell's law requests an angle of refraction θ_2 such that $\sin \theta_2 > 1$. There is no solution in such cases and we need to determine what happens then.

Reactive Impedances

What happens when Snell's law fails to yield a solution for the angle of refraction, and hence a solution for the transmitted wave vector $\mathbf{k}_2$, is that Maxwell's equations continue to hold, and so do the boundary conditions. The apparent incompatibility of the two is only a failure of our interpretation of the wave vector. The difficulty comes from our having decomposed the wave vector $\mathbf{k}_2$ into tangential and normal components at the interface, with the tangential component, prescribed by the boundary conditions to equal the tangential component of the incident $\mathbf{k}_0$, too large for $\mathbf{k}_2$, as

$$\mathbf{k}_2 = \mathbf{p} + \boldsymbol{\beta}_2, \qquad p > k_2 = \frac{\omega}{c} n_2. \tag{10.2}$$

That is, the boundary conditions require $\mathbf{p}$ to be large, while Maxwell's equations still demand that

$$\mathbf{k}_2 \cdot \mathbf{k}_2 = p^2 + \beta_2^2 = \left(\frac{\omega}{c}\right)^2 n_2^2, \qquad \text{despite} \quad p^2 > \left(\frac{\omega}{c}\right)^2 n_2^2. \tag{10.3}$$

The only way to preserve both Maxwell's equations and the boundary conditions that they imply is to make β_2^2 negative:

$$\beta_2^2 = -\alpha^2 \qquad \text{with} \quad \alpha^2 = p^2 - \left(\frac{\omega}{c}\right)^2 n_2^2. \tag{10.4}$$

This reconciles the two requirements, but it leaves β_2 imaginary, which requires reinterpretation of the vector $\boldsymbol{\beta}_2 = \beta_2 \hat{\mathbf{n}} = \pm j\alpha\hat{\mathbf{n}}$. Note that α is known to us, from Eq. (10.4) with p determined by the incident wave, but we do not yet know how to choose the sign of the square root of α^2.

To interpret the result and choose the proper sign for $\sqrt{\alpha^2}$, we note that the transmitted wave takes the form

$$\begin{aligned}\mathbf{E}_2(\mathbf{r}) &= \mathbf{E}_2 e^{-j\mathbf{k}_2 \cdot \mathbf{r}} = \mathbf{E}_2 e^{-j(\mathbf{p}+\boldsymbol{\beta}_2)\cdot \mathbf{r}} = \mathbf{E}_2 e^{-j\mathbf{p}\cdot\mathbf{r}} e^{-j\boldsymbol{\beta}_2\cdot\mathbf{r}} \\ &= \mathbf{E}_2 \exp[-j\mathbf{p}\cdot\mathbf{r}] \exp[-j(\pm j\alpha\hat{\mathbf{n}})\cdot\mathbf{r}] = \mathbf{E}_2 \exp[-j\mathbf{p}\cdot\mathbf{r}] \exp[\pm\alpha\hat{\mathbf{n}}\cdot\mathbf{r}] \\ &= \{\mathbf{E}_2 \exp[\pm\alpha\hat{\mathbf{n}}\cdot\mathbf{r}]\} \exp[-j\mathbf{p}\cdot\mathbf{r}].\end{aligned} \tag{10.5}$$

This is seen to be a *nonuniform plane wave* that propagates along the vector $\mathbf{p}$ but with an amplitude that varies from point to point within medium 2.

With the $e^{j\omega t}$ factor restored, the field is the propagating wave $e^{j(\omega t - \mathbf{p}\cdot\mathbf{r})}$ that progresses along the direction of **p**, but with the varying amplitude $\mathbf{E}_2 \exp[\pm\alpha\hat{\mathbf{n}}\cdot\mathbf{r}]$. We see that the nonuniformity of the wave is here essential; it is not a mere rewriting of a uniform but obliquely propagating wave as a nonuniform but normally propagating one. We also note that medium 2 is the semi-infinite region $\hat{\mathbf{n}}\cdot\mathbf{r} > 0$, so that at an infinite distance from the interface, the factor $\exp[\pm\alpha\hat{\mathbf{n}}\cdot\mathbf{r}]$ either becomes infinitely strong if the upper sign is used, or else becomes zero if the lower one is adopted. The former choice is physically not admissible and we are left with the exponentially attenuating nonuniform plane wave

$$\mathbf{E}_2(\mathbf{r}) = \mathbf{E}_2\, e^{-\boldsymbol{\alpha}\cdot\mathbf{r}} e^{-j\mathbf{p}\cdot\mathbf{r}} \tag{10.6}$$

as the electric field that is transmitted into the unsourced medium when Snell's law "fails," where we define the attenuation vector $\boldsymbol{\alpha}$ as

$$\boldsymbol{\alpha} = \alpha\hat{\mathbf{n}} = \sqrt{p^2 - \left(\frac{\omega}{c}\right)^2 n_2^2}\,\hat{\mathbf{n}}\,. \tag{10.7}$$

This field propagates parallel to the interface plane, along **p**, but attenuates exponentially in the direction perpendicular to that plane; it does not propagate (obliquely or normally) *into* the second medium and neither the field nor the energy reaches to infinite distance from the plane, in the less dense, faster-phase-velocity medium 2. In medium 1, there are still the incident and reflected waves of the usual, obliquely propagating type

$$\mathbf{E}_0(\mathbf{r}) = \mathbf{E}_0\, e^{-j\boldsymbol{\beta}_0\cdot\mathbf{r}} e^{-j\mathbf{p}\cdot\mathbf{r}}, \qquad \mathbf{E}_1(\mathbf{r}) = \mathbf{E}_1 e^{-j\boldsymbol{\beta}_1\cdot\mathbf{r}} e^{-j\mathbf{p}\cdot\mathbf{r}}, \tag{10.8}$$

with $\boldsymbol{\beta}_1 = -\boldsymbol{\beta}_0$. The component of each wave vector normal to the interface, β if real or α if imaginary, satisfies the relations

$$p^2 + \beta_0^2 = p^2 + \beta_1^2 = \left(\frac{\omega}{c}\right)^2 n_1^2, \qquad p^2 - \alpha^2 = \left(\frac{\omega}{c}\right)^2 n_2^2\,. \tag{10.9}$$

Figure 10–3 contrasts the configuration of wave vectors for the cases $p < (\omega/c)n_2$ and $p > (\omega/c)n_2$.

On the interface plane $\hat{\mathbf{n}}\cdot\mathbf{r} = 0$, all three waves vary as $e^{-j\mathbf{p}\cdot\mathbf{r}}$, so that the tangential electric and magnetic fields will be continuous at all points of the boundary plane if they are made to match at one of its points. To achieve this matching, the continuity conditions can again be expressed in terms of the mismatch of impedances on the two sides of the interface. However, when the exponential variation of the wave represents propagation on one side and attenuation on the other, the impedances on the two sides must be defined properly, in conformity with Maxwell's equations.

To extend the definitions of the wave impedances for the TE and TM polarizations from the cases that feature propagation normal to the interface (as well as tangentially), with $\mathbf{k} = \mathbf{p} + \boldsymbol{\beta}$, to the ones that demand attenuation instead, using $\mathbf{k} = \mathbf{p} - j\boldsymbol{\alpha}$, we must reconcile our impedance designations in the

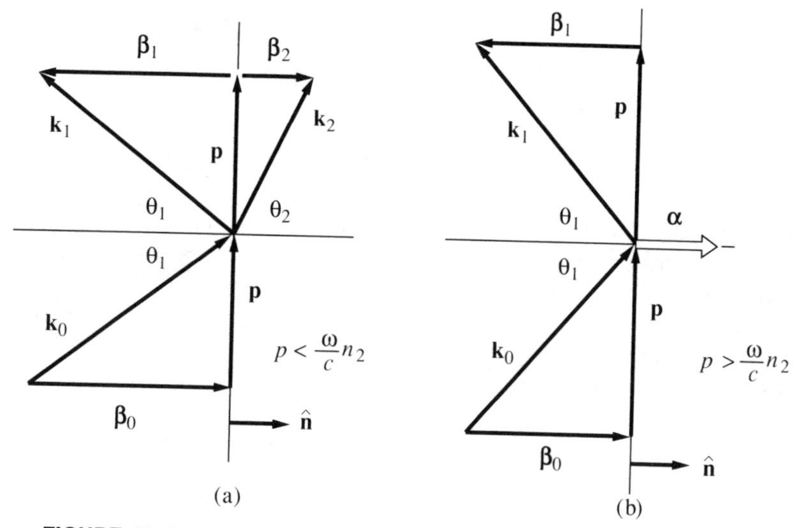

FIGURE 10–3 (a) Propagation versus (b) attenuation when $n_2 < n_1$.

natural coordinate system of the interface,

$$\text{For TE waves:} \qquad \mathbf{E} = Z^{\text{TE}}\mathbf{H} \times \hat{\mathbf{n}}, \tag{10.10}$$

$$\text{For TM waves:} \qquad Z^{\text{TM}}\mathbf{H} = \hat{\mathbf{n}} \times \mathbf{E}, \tag{10.11}$$

with the requirements of Maxwell's equations for a plane wave $e^{-j\mathbf{k}\cdot\mathbf{r}}$, with $\mathbf{k}$ complex, as $j\mathbf{k} = \boldsymbol{\alpha} + j\mathbf{p}$. The two Maxwell equations become

$$[\boldsymbol{\alpha} + j\mathbf{p}] \times \mathbf{E} = j\omega\mu\mathbf{H}, \qquad -[\boldsymbol{\alpha} + j\mathbf{p}] \times \mathbf{H} = j\omega\varepsilon\mathbf{E} \tag{10.12}$$

and these apply to both the TE and TM partial waves. We cross these two equations with $\hat{\mathbf{n}}$ and note that $\hat{\mathbf{n}} \cdot [\boldsymbol{\alpha} + j\mathbf{p}] = \alpha$. We also note that $\hat{\mathbf{n}} \cdot \mathbf{E}^{\text{TE}} = 0$ and $\hat{\mathbf{n}} \cdot \mathbf{H}^{\text{TM}} = 0$ reduce the triple cross product to just α times the field. We therefore find for the TE waves

$$\{[\boldsymbol{\alpha} + j\mathbf{p}] \times \mathbf{E}\} \times \hat{\mathbf{n}} = j\omega\mu\mathbf{H} \times \hat{\mathbf{n}} = \alpha\mathbf{E} = \frac{j\omega\mu\mathbf{E}}{Z^{\text{TE}}} \tag{10.13}$$

and for the TM waves

$$\hat{\mathbf{n}} \times \{-[\boldsymbol{\alpha} + j\mathbf{p}] \times \mathbf{H}\} = j\omega\varepsilon\hat{\mathbf{n}} \times \mathbf{E} = \alpha\mathbf{H} = j\omega\varepsilon Z^{\text{TM}}\mathbf{H}. \tag{10.14}$$

The extended definitions of the TE and TM wave impedances when the waves attenuate along $\hat{\mathbf{n}}$ are therefore

$$Z^{\text{TE}} = \frac{j\omega\mu}{\alpha}, \qquad Z^{\text{TM}} = \frac{\alpha}{j\omega\varepsilon}. \tag{10.15}$$

To interpret these results, we note first that these wave impedances do reduce to our previous expressions when the transmitted wave does propagate; that is, when $\mathbf{k} = \mathbf{p} + \boldsymbol{\beta}$ instead of $\mathbf{k} = \mathbf{p} - j\boldsymbol{\alpha}$, we can replace α with $j\beta$ to recover the earlier versions

$$Z^{\mathrm{TE}} = \frac{j\omega\mu}{j\beta} = \frac{\omega\mu}{k \cos\theta} = \eta \sec\theta, \tag{10.16}$$

$$Z^{\mathrm{TM}} = \frac{j\beta}{j\omega\varepsilon} = \frac{k \cos\theta}{\omega\varepsilon} = \eta \cos\theta. \tag{10.17}$$

We note next that the modified impedances for the attenuating waves, $Z^{\mathrm{TE}} = j\omega\mu/\alpha$ and $Z^{\mathrm{TM}} = \alpha/j\omega\varepsilon$ are purely *reactive* impedances ($Z = jX$), inductive ($X > 0$) for the TE wave and capacitive ($X < 0$) for the TM polarization, instead of the purely resistive impedances $Z^{\mathrm{TE}} = \eta \sec\theta$, $Z^{\mathrm{TM}} = \eta \cos\theta$ of the obliquely propagating cases.

It is also interesting to note that even in the case of the attenuated waves, the geometric mean of $Z^{\mathrm{TE}} = j\omega\mu/\alpha$ and $Z^{\mathrm{TM}} = \alpha/j\omega\varepsilon$ is just the impedance η of the medium, as in the propagating case.

Total Internal Reflection

We have obtained reactive impedances for the TE and TM partial waves in the cases for which Snell's laws fail to yield a propagating refracted wave. These impedances still represent the ratio of tangential electric and magnetic fields at the interface; therefore, applying the boundary conditions that demand continuity of those fields, we once again get reflection and transmission coefficients that involve the mismatch in impedances across the interface.

The reflection coefficient for the electric fields is, once again,

$$\Gamma = \frac{Z_2 - Z_1}{Z_2 + Z_1}, \tag{10.18}$$

but now the mismatch is between a resistive impedance $Z_1 = R_1$ (which is $R_1 = \eta_1 \sec\theta_1$ for TE and $R_1 = \eta_1 \cos\theta_1$ for TM) and a reactive impedance $Z_2 = jX_2$ (which is $X_2 = \omega\mu_2/\alpha$ for TE and $X_2 = -\alpha/\omega\varepsilon_2$ for TM). The reflection coefficient is therefore a complex number, of the form

$$\Gamma = \frac{jX_2 - R_1}{jX_2 + R_1} \tag{10.19}$$

for either partial wave. Consequently, the complex numerator and denominator have the same magnitude, so that

$$|\Gamma|^2 = 1. \tag{10.20}$$

This states that the magnitude of the reflection coefficient is unity; that is, the reflection coefficient is merely a phase factor. But $|\Gamma|^2$ is the power reflection coefficient; that it is unity indicates that 100% of the incident power is reflected back into the denser of the two media. The process is called *total internal reflection* (internal to the denser medium of the incident wave), abbreviated as

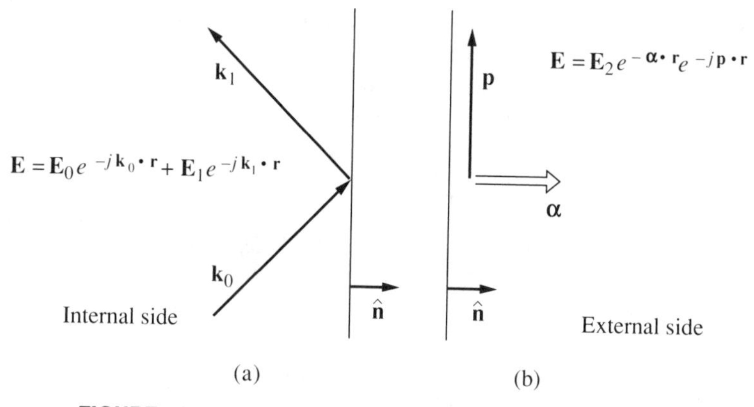

FIGURE 10–4 Fields on the two sides of the interface in TIR.

TIR. No real power is transmitted into the medium beyond the interface; all of it is reflected.

Under conditions of TIR, the interface between two lossless dielectrics acts as a perfect mirror. However, there do exist fields in the less dense medium that carries the attenuated wave. These fields store energy but do not carry real power to infinity. They extend to a depth given by the *e*-folding distance $1/\alpha$; this depth depends not only on the constitutive parameters of the medium but also on the angle of incidence on the other side, via p in $\alpha^2 = p^2 - (\omega/c)^2 n_2^2 > 0$ for TIR. By contrast, a perfectly conducting mirror reflects perfectly and has zero field beyond its surface, but is an idealization. An imperfectly conducting mirror also has attenuating fields within a skin depth of the surface, but those fields propagate as they decay, while TIR features pure attenuation beyond the interface. Figure 10–4 shows the field propagation and attenuation vectors on the two sides of the interface, under conditions of total internal reflection. The two sides are shown separated, for clarity.

TIR for TE and TM Polarizations

Just as the first step toward determining the mismatch for oblique waves involved finding the angle of refraction from Snell's law, that step is also first when the law fails; it then yields the attenuation rate, which enters also into the reactive impedances for the two polarizations when total internal reflection is confirmed. Thereafter, the calculations of reflection and transmission coefficients proceed in the usual manner, except that complex numbers enter the calculations and the transmitted wave is a nonuniform, attenuating wave.

EXAMPLE 10.1

We reconsider an earlier example of oblique incidence onto the interface between two dissimilar media, but now with transmission attempted from the denser side, from a nonmagnetic dielectric with refractive index $n_1 = 3.9$ to one with index $n_2 = 2.5$, at incidence angle $\theta_0 = 43°$. What are the reflected and transmitted waves, for both polarizations?

Attempting to find the angle of refraction from Snell's law $n_1 \sin\theta_1 = n_2 \sin\theta_2$ yields $n_1 \sin\theta_1 = 2.6598$, which exceeds $n_2 = 2.5$, so that this is indeed a case of total internal reflection. The resistive impedance of side 1 is

$$Z_1 = \eta_1 \sec\theta_1 = \frac{\eta_0}{3.9} \sec 43° = 0.3506\eta_0 \text{ for TE}, \tag{10.21}$$

or

$$Z_1 = \eta_1 \cos\theta_1 = \frac{\eta_0}{3.9} \cos 43° = 0.1875\eta_0 \text{ for TM}. \tag{10.22}$$

To obtain the reactive impedances of side 2, we need the attenuation coefficient

$$\alpha = \sqrt{p^2 - \left(\frac{\omega}{c}\right)^2 n_2^2} = \frac{\omega}{c}\sqrt{n_1^2 \sin^2\theta_1 - n_2^2} = 0.9080\left(\frac{\omega}{c}\right). \tag{10.23}$$

Then the reactances are

$$Z_2^{\text{TE}} = \frac{j\omega\mu}{\alpha} = \frac{j\omega\mu_0}{\alpha} = \frac{j\eta_0}{\alpha c/\omega} = \frac{j\eta_0}{0.9080} = j(1.1013)\eta_0, \tag{10.24}$$

$$Z_2^{\text{TM}} = \frac{\alpha}{j\omega\varepsilon} = \frac{\alpha}{j\omega\varepsilon_0 n_2^2} = -j\left(\frac{\alpha c}{\omega}\right)\frac{\eta_0}{n_2^2} = -j\left(\frac{0.9080}{2.5^2}\right)\eta_0 = -j(0.1453)\eta_0. \tag{10.25}$$

(As a check on the calculations, we may verify that $Z_2^{\text{TE}} Z_2^{\text{TM}} = \eta_2^2 = \eta_0^2/n_2^2 = 0.1600\eta_0^2$.) The reflection coefficients are

$$\Gamma_e^{\text{TE}} = \frac{Z_2 - Z_1}{Z_2 + Z_1} = \frac{j1.1013 - 0.3506}{j1.1013 + 0.3506} = e^{j0.6164} \tag{10.26}$$

for the electric field of the TE wave and

$$\Gamma_h^{\text{TM}} = \frac{Z_1 - Z_2}{Z_1 + Z_2} = \frac{0.1875 + j0.1453}{0.1875 - j0.1453} = e^{j1.3183} \tag{10.27}$$

for the magnetic field of the TM wave. In each case, the reflected field has the same amplitude as the incident one, but is shifted in phase. The corresponding transmission coefficients are

$$T_e^{\mathrm{TE}} = 1 + \Gamma_e^{\mathrm{TE}} = 1 + e^{j0.6164} = 1.8160 + j0.5781\,, \tag{10.28}$$

$$T_h^{\mathrm{TM}} = 1 + \Gamma_h^{\mathrm{TM}} = 1 + e^{j1.3183} = 1.2498 + j0.9683 \tag{10.29}$$

and these give the transverse fields for each polarization. We cannot simply use the medium's impedance $\eta_2 = \eta_0/2.5$ to get the magnetic field of the transmitted TE wave or the electric field of the transmitted TM wave, because we are dealing not with a uniform wave in medium 2, but with an attenuating one. The reactive wave impedances yield only the transverse part of the attenuating wave. To get the complete H^{TE} or E^{TM} from E^{TE} or H^{TM}, we use one or the other of Maxwell's equations, in the forms

$$[\boldsymbol{\alpha} + j\mathbf{p}] \times \mathbf{E} = j\omega\mu\mathbf{H}\,, \qquad \mathbf{H} \times [\boldsymbol{\alpha} + j\mathbf{p}] = j\omega\varepsilon\mathbf{E}\,, \tag{10.30}$$

for the TE and the TM partial waves, respectively. Note that we have already found both $\boldsymbol{\alpha}$ and $\mathbf{p}$; their magnitudes are $\alpha = (\omega/c)0.9080$ and $p = (\omega/c)2.6598$ and their directions are normal and tangential to the plane and both are perpendicular to the transverse fields. Thus if we let $\hat{\mathbf{n}} = \hat{\mathbf{z}}$ and $\mathbf{p} = p\hat{\mathbf{x}}$, the transverse fields lie along $\hat{\mathbf{y}}$. The fields that have a longitudinal component (along z) are then

$$\begin{aligned} \mathbf{H}_2^{\mathrm{TE}} &= (2.66\hat{\mathbf{z}} + j0.908\hat{\mathbf{x}})\,\frac{E_2^{\mathrm{TE}}}{\eta_0} \\ &= (2.66\hat{\mathbf{z}} + j0.908\hat{\mathbf{x}})(1.816 + j0.578)\,\frac{E_0^{\mathrm{TE}}}{\eta_0}\,, \end{aligned} \tag{10.31}$$

$$\begin{aligned} \mathbf{E}_2^{\mathrm{TM}} &= \frac{-(2.66\hat{\mathbf{z}} + j0.908\hat{\mathbf{x}})\eta_0\, H_2^{\mathrm{TM}}}{6.25} \\ &= \frac{-(2.66\hat{\mathbf{z}} + j0.908\hat{\mathbf{x}})(1.250 + j0.968)\eta_0\, H_0^{\mathrm{TM}}}{6.25} \\ &= -(2.66\hat{\mathbf{z}} + j0.908\hat{\mathbf{x}})(0.200 + j0.155)\eta_0\, H_0^{\mathrm{TM}}, \end{aligned} \tag{10.32}$$

upon substituting the transmission coefficients. These are the fields at $x = 0$, $z = 0$; elsewhere in medium 2, they propagate along x and decay along z.

We can examine the Poynting vectors for this case. If the incident wave is entirely TE, its complex Poynting vector is

$$\begin{aligned} \frac{1}{2}\,\mathbf{E}_0 \times \mathbf{H}_0^* &= [\cos 43°\hat{\mathbf{z}} + \sin 43°\hat{\mathbf{x}}]\,\frac{|E_0|^2}{2\eta_1} \\ &= [0.731\hat{\mathbf{z}} + 0.682\hat{\mathbf{x}}]3.9\,\frac{|E_0|^2}{2\eta_0}\,. \end{aligned} \tag{10.33}$$

For the reflected wave,

$$\frac{1}{2}\,\mathbf{E}_1 \times \mathbf{H}_1^* = [-0.731\hat{\mathbf{z}} + 0.682\hat{\mathbf{x}}]3.9\,\frac{|E_0|^2}{2\eta_0}\,. \tag{10.34}$$

These are purely real and constant Poynting vectors, along the oblique directions of incidence and reflection, and of equal magnitudes $|E_0|^2/2\eta_1$. The transmitted Poynting vector is formed for the TE polarization from

$$\mathbf{E}_2 = (1.816 + j0.578)E_0\,\hat{\mathbf{y}} f(x, z), \tag{10.35}$$

$$\mathbf{H}_2 = (1.816 + j0.578)(2.66\hat{\mathbf{z}} + j0.908\hat{\mathbf{x}}) f(x, z)\,\frac{E_0}{\eta_0}, \tag{10.36}$$

where $f(x, z) = e^{-0.9080(\omega z/c)} e^{-j2.6598(\omega x/c)}$, as

$$\begin{aligned}\frac{1}{2}\,\mathbf{E}_2 \times \mathbf{H}_2^* &= 3.632[(2.66\hat{\mathbf{x}} + j0.908\hat{\mathbf{z}})]e^{-1.816(\omega z/c)}\,\frac{|E_0|^2}{2\eta_0} \\ &= [(9.660\hat{\mathbf{x}} + j3.298\hat{\mathbf{z}})]e^{-1.816(\omega z/c)}\,\frac{|E_0|^2}{2\eta_0}.\end{aligned} \tag{10.37}$$

This transmitted TE-wave Poynting vector is complex; it shows real power flow density only along $\hat{\mathbf{x}}$, parallel to the interface. It is also an exponentially decaying function of z; its divergence is purely imaginary,

$$\begin{aligned}-\nabla \cdot \left(\frac{1}{2}\,\mathbf{E}_2 \times \mathbf{H}_2^*\right) &= j(\omega/c)(1.816)(3.298)e^{-1.816(\omega z/c)}\,\frac{|E_0|^2}{2\eta_0} \\ &= 2j\omega[5.989]e^{-1.816(\omega z/c)}\,\frac{\varepsilon_0 |E_0|^2}{4}\end{aligned} \tag{10.38}$$

and does equal $2j\omega[\langle w_m\rangle - \langle w_e\rangle]$, indicating no power loss (the medium has no conductivity) but an excess of magnetic over electric energy density stored near the interface in medium 2.

If the incident wave is entirely TM instead, we find the transmitted complex Poynting vector to be

$$\tfrac{1}{2}\mathbf{E}_2 \times \mathbf{H}_2^* = [(1.064\hat{\mathbf{x}} - j0.3632\hat{\mathbf{z}})]e^{-1.816(\omega z/c)}\tfrac{1}{2}\eta_0 |H_0|^2. \tag{10.39}$$

This again shows real power flow density only along $\hat{\mathbf{x}}$, parallel to the interface; the z-component is now imaginary and negative, indicating an excess of electric over magnetic energy density stored near the interface in medium 2. ◆

Significance for Dielectric Waveguides

Oblique incidence from an optically dense medium (index n_1) onto a less dense one (index $n_2 < n_1$) results in transmission at a steeper angle θ_2 if the incidence angle θ_1 is less than the critical angle θ_c given by

$$\theta_c = \sin^{-1}\left(\frac{n_2}{n_1}\right). \tag{10.40}$$

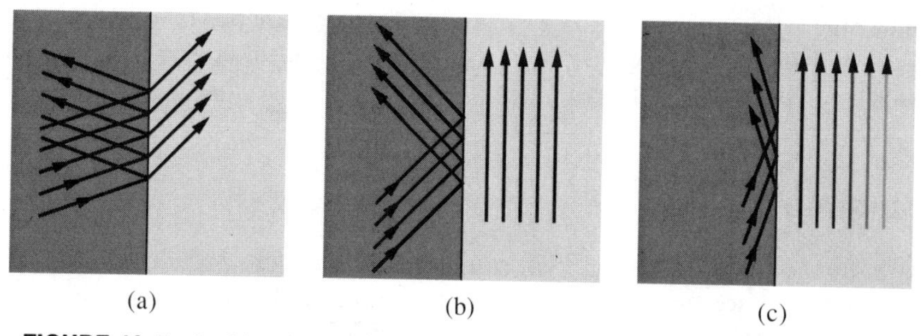

FIGURE 10–5 Incidence angles less than, equal to, and greater than critical.

For incidence at the critical angle $\theta_1 = \theta_c$, θ_2 attains its maximum value of $\pi/2$ and the refracted wave travels parallel to the interface. Beyond the critical angle, so that the incident wave is more grazing to the interface than θ_c, there results *total internal reflection.* All the incident power is reflected into the denser medium; no real power is transmitted across the interface to infinite distance normal to the boundary plane, although there are fields beyond the plane, propagating parallel to the interface and decaying in the direction away from it. Figure 10–5 compares the three cases of incidence at $\theta < \theta_c$, at $\theta = \theta_c$, and at $\theta > \theta_c$. In the third part of the figure, the fading of the propagation vectors is intended to convey the notion of evanescence of the strength of the transmitted wave, in the direction normal to the interface.

Total internal reflection has applications in optical systems when perfect mirror action (neglecting conductive losses) is needed; prisms in binoculars are one example. More important for our purposes, TIR is the fundamental process that allows guided propagation of light in dielectric waveguides, including optical fibers. As will be seen when we study these systems in detail, if we can arrange for the light to impinge on the edge of the dielectric waveguide at a sufficiently grazing angle, the light should be totally reflected into the dielectric and will be prevented from escaping into the medium surrounding the guide. When the reflected wave encounters another wall of the dielectric waveguide, it can again bounce back, perfectly, into the waveguide and remain confined, and guided, by the structure. Light that strikes the boundary at too small an angle of incidence, however, can cross the interface and leak energy away from the waveguide. We will confirm these suggestions, which are loosely based on a single, planar interface between dielectrics, for the cases of a pair of parallel interfaces and, ultimately, for the cylindrical fiber.

The fact that, despite the 100% power reflection under conditions of total internal reflection, fields do appear on the other side but attenuate at right angles to the plane can be verified by placing another dense medium close to, but not touching the original interface, leaving a gap. The decaying fields (what remains of them at the other side of the gap) can then cross the new interface and may propagate away. Total internal reflection has then been thwarted within the first medium and power "tunnels" across the otherwise "forbidden" region of the gap. This process can be used to tap some of the light otherwise confined to the waveguide. The structure has two parallel interfaces and involves three media; it can be examined after the dielectric slab waveguide has been analyzed.

Summary

Refraction of light that is sent from a denser to a less dense medium across a planar interface turns into the phenomenon of total internal reflection when the angle of incidence exceeds the critical angle, the angle beyond which Snell's law fails to yield a real angle of refraction. The formalism that yields the reflection and transmission coefficients in terms of the effective wave impedances on the two sides of the interface is valid even beyond the critical angle. At sufficiently grazing angles. the impedance of the outside medium becomes reactive instead of resistive, inductive for the TE partial wave and capacitive for the TM polarization. For the TE case, this corresponds to an excess of magnetic over electric energy density stored near but beyond the interface; for TM, electric energy predominates.

In either case, electromagnetic fields do penetrate to the less dense outer medium, but they do not carry real power perpendicularly away from the interface; instead, they attenuate in the direction normal to the plane while conveying power parallel to the plane. The attenuation depends on the angle of incidence: at angles just beyond critical, the fields decay only gradually and are loosely coupled to the interface; for more nearly grazing angles, the fields persist over only a short range beyond the boundary plane and are tightly bound to the interface.

This sort of binding of a wave to a surface is an instance of the guiding of electromagnetic waves along a structure, in this case the interface between two dielectrics. Such guiding occurs also at an impenetrable wall formed by a conductor. We need to study such waveguiding further, first along the exterior of wires, then in the interior of a pipe, and ultimately by flat or round interfaces between dielectrics.

PROBLEMS

Scattering of Obliquely Incident TE Wave

10.1 Find the transmission and reflection coefficients T_e, Γ_e for incidence at 60° from a medium with $v_1 = \frac{1}{2}c$ to one with $v_2 = \frac{2}{3}c$, both media being lossless and nonmagnetic, for TE polarization.

Scattering of Obliquely Incident TM Wave

10.2 Find the transmission and reflection coefficients T_h, Γ_h for incidence at 60° from a medium with $v_1 = \frac{1}{2}c$ to one with $v_2 = \frac{2}{3}c$, both media being lossless and nonmagnetic, for TM polarization.

TIR for TE and for TM Waves

10.3 If an obliquely incident TE wave is totally internally reflected at an interface, will a TM wave incident at the same angle also be totally reflected? Why?

Effect of TIR on Polarization

10.4 A circularly polarized plane wave is totally internally reflected at the interface between a lossless, nonmagnetic dielectric and air. Is the reflected wave also circularly polarized?

Full Power Transmission Versus Full Reflection

10.5 Oblique incidence from air onto a lossless, nonmagnetic dielectric at a certain incidence angle is observed to result in 100% power transmission, while incidence from the dielectric at the same incidence angle results in 100% power reflection. What is the minimum value that the index of refraction n of the dielectric can attain?

Transmitted Complex Poynting Vector of TM Wave in TIR

10.6 Fill in the steps in the evaluation of the complex Poynting vector transmitted into the medium with $n_2 = 2.5$ from the one with $n_1 = 3.9$ for TM polarization at incidence angle 43°, as in Example 10.1.

(a) $|T_h|^2$ appears to be the same as n_2. Is this based on theory or coincidental?

(b) Confirm that $\frac{1}{2}\mathbf{E}_2 \times \mathbf{H}_2^* = [(1.064\hat{\mathbf{x}} - j0.3632\hat{\mathbf{z}})]e^{-1.816(\omega z/c)}\eta_0 |H_0|^2/2$ if the interface faces $\hat{\mathbf{z}}$, the magnetic field is along $\hat{\mathbf{y}}$, and $\mathbf{p}$ is along $\hat{\mathbf{x}}$.

(c) Determine the difference between magnetic and electric energy density stored near the interface for the TM case, in terms of $\mu_0 |H_0|^2/4$.

TIR for TE Wave at Edge of Air Gap to Mirror

10.7 Let a glass medium of refractive index $n = 1.2$ end at the plane $z = -s$ in front of a perfectly conducting plane mirror at $z = 0$, with an air gap between the two. A TE wave is incident onto the interface from within the glass at 60°. Let the air gap be one free-space wavelength thick, $s = \lambda_0$.

(a) Find the reflection coefficient at the interface.

(b) How is the power reflection at the interface affected by the presence of the mirror?

TIR for TM Wave at Edge of Air Gap to Mirror

10.8 Let a glass medium of refractive index $n = 1.2$ end at the plane $z = -s$ in front of a perfectly conducting plane mirror at $z = 0$, with an air gap between the two. A TM wave is incident onto the interface from within the glass at 60°. Let the air gap be one free-space wavelength thick, $s = \lambda_0$.

(a) Find the reflection coefficient at the interface.

(b) How is the power reflection at the interface affected by the presence of the mirror?

Reflection at the Slant Face of a Prism

10.9 A prism to be used to redirect a beam of light at right angles to its original direction is formed of glass of refractive index n, in the shape of an isosceles right triangle; the legs of the triangle have antireflection coatings and incidence onto a leg is to be normal (Fig. P10–9).

(a) What is the minimum value of n that can be used for this purpose?

(b) What is the minimum value of n that will assure that the field strength in the air beyond the hypotenuse of the prism is no more than 1% of the strength at the surface, at one free-space wavelength from the interface?

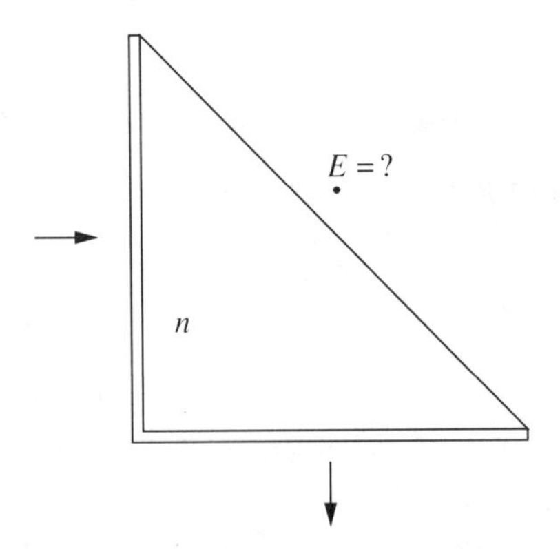

FIGURE P10–9 Prism of 45°, with antireflection coatings.

CHAPTER 11

Transmission Lines

We have reached a point where we need to review the concepts and terminology of wave propagation guided by transmission lines, before going on to metal and then dielectric waveguides and optical fibers. In these systems, waves are confined and guided by wires, pipes, or rods, instead of roaming freely in infinite or semi-infinite spaces. The concept of nonuniform waves, which we invoked to deal with obliquely propagating uniform plane waves, or else needed to describe attenuating waves, becomes essential to the analysis of guided wave transmission.

Nonuniform Waves

An obliquely propagating uniform plane wave $\mathbf{E}_0 e^{-j\mathbf{k}\cdot\mathbf{r}}$ was advantageously considered to be a nonuniform wave that propagates along a specific direction, say the z-axis, in order to reduce the equations to the simpler ones that govern axial propagation onto a transverse interface.

$$\mathbf{E}_0 e^{-j\mathbf{k}\cdot\mathbf{r}} = [\mathbf{E}_0 e^{-j\mathbf{p}\cdot\mathbf{r}}]e^{-j\beta z}, \qquad \text{with} \quad \mathbf{k} = \mathbf{p} + \beta\hat{\mathbf{z}}. \tag{11.1}$$

We also encountered a wave that propagates in one direction but attenuates in another. The complex wave

$$\mathbf{E}_0 e^{-j\mathbf{k}\cdot\mathbf{r}} = [\mathbf{E}_0 e^{-\alpha z}]e^{-j\mathbf{p}\cdot\mathbf{r}} \qquad \text{with} \quad \mathbf{k} = \mathbf{p} - j\alpha\hat{\mathbf{z}}, \tag{11.2}$$

is a nonuniform wave that propagates along $\mathbf{p}$ but decays along z; it can be treated as if it were a uniform plane wave, but with a complex wave vector. We now ask what other forms of nonuniform wave can propagate. That is, what transverse variation of the amplitude of an axially propagating wave is allowed by Maxwell's equations?

To determine what forms are permitted, we treat a nonuniform wave

$$\mathbf{E} = \mathbf{E}_0(x, y)e^{-j\beta z} \tag{11.3}$$

as a trial solution in Maxwell's equations. This is a product of a vector function of x, y with a scalar, exponential factor $e^{-j\beta z}$; by an identity of vector calculus, the curl of a product of a scalar and a vector reduces to the gradient of the scalar crossed with the vector, plus the scalar times the curl of the vector:

$$\nabla \times \mathbf{E} = \nabla \times [e^{-j\beta z}\mathbf{E}_0] = (\nabla e^{-j\beta z}) \times \mathbf{E}_0 + e^{-j\beta z}\nabla \times \mathbf{E}_0 \tag{11.4}$$

and the gradient of a function is the function's derivative, multiplied by the gradient of its argument:

$$\nabla \times \mathbf{E} = e^{-j\beta z}(-j\beta\hat{\mathbf{z}}) \times \mathbf{E}_0 + e^{-j\beta z}\nabla \times \mathbf{E}_0 = e^{-j\beta z}\{-j\beta\hat{\mathbf{z}} \times \mathbf{E}_0 + \nabla \times \mathbf{E}_0\}, \tag{11.5}$$

so that the exponential factor survives the operation. Since Maxwell requires this to be $-j\omega\mu\mathbf{H}$, we see that the magnetic field also has the form of our arbitrary nonuniform axial wave trial function:

$$\mathbf{H} = \mathbf{H}_0(x, y)e^{-j\beta z}, \tag{11.6}$$

with

$$\nabla \times \mathbf{E} = e^{-j\beta z}\{-j\beta\hat{\mathbf{z}} \times \mathbf{E}_0 + \nabla \times \mathbf{E}_0\} = -j\omega\mu\mathbf{H} = -j\omega\mu\mathbf{H}_0(x, y)e^{-j\beta z}, \tag{11.7}$$

so that the nonuniform amplitudes in our trial functions must satisfy

$$\nabla \times \mathbf{E}_0 = -j\omega\mu\left\{\mathbf{H}_0 - \frac{\beta}{\omega\mu}\hat{\mathbf{z}} \times \mathbf{E}_0\right\}. \tag{11.8}$$

In exactly the same way, the other of Maxwell's two equations, $\nabla \times \mathbf{H} = j\omega\varepsilon\mathbf{E}$, requires

$$\nabla \times \mathbf{H}_0 = j\omega\varepsilon\left\{\mathbf{E}_0 + \frac{\beta}{\omega\varepsilon}\hat{\mathbf{z}} \times \mathbf{H}_0\right\} \tag{11.9}$$

when the same trial functions are used. We now seek solutions for these simultaneous partial differential equations for the unknown nonuniform amplitudes $\mathbf{E}_0(x, y)$ and $\mathbf{H}_0(x, y)$.

Solutions to these equations abound; they fall into one class of very simple solutions and another of more complicated ones. The simple solutions are relevant to the description of propagation along transmission lines and the more complex ones involve waveguides, to be considered later.

Electrostatic Solutions

The simplest, but by no means the only nonuniform field $\mathbf{E}_0(x, y)$, $\mathbf{H}_0(x, y)$ that can satisfy the two equations just found is the type that makes both sides of each equation not only equal, but equal to zero:

$$\nabla \times \mathbf{E}_0 = 0 \quad \text{and} \quad \nabla \times \mathbf{H}_0 = 0. \tag{11.10}$$

This will indeed satisfy the equations, provided that the amplitudes $\mathbf{E}_0$ and $\mathbf{H}_0$ are related by

$$\mathbf{H}_0 = \frac{\beta}{\omega\mu}\,\hat{\mathbf{z}} \times \mathbf{E}_0 \qquad \text{and} \qquad \mathbf{E}_0 = \frac{\beta}{\omega\varepsilon}\,\mathbf{H}_0 \times \hat{\mathbf{z}}. \tag{11.11}$$

From the last pair, we conclude immediately that such solutions must be *transverse*; that is, both $\mathbf{E}_0$ and $\mathbf{H}_0$ are perpendicular to z, the axial direction of propagation. The fields $\mathbf{E}_0$, $\mathbf{H}_0$, and $\hat{\mathbf{z}}$ form an orthogonal triad and, furthermore, the magnitudes of $\mathbf{E}_0$ and $\mathbf{H}_0$ must be related by *both*

$$\frac{H_0}{E_0} = \frac{\beta}{\omega\mu} \qquad \text{and} \qquad \frac{E_0}{H_0} = \frac{\beta}{\omega\varepsilon}. \tag{11.12}$$

In turn, this requires that the assumed propagation constant β be related to the frequency ω by

$$\omega^2\mu\varepsilon = \beta^2 \qquad \text{or} \qquad \beta = \pm kn, \tag{11.13}$$

where $k = \omega/c$ and $n = \sqrt{\mu\varepsilon/\mu_0\varepsilon_0}$ is the medium's index of refraction. Also, the wave impedance, E_0/H_0, must be

$$\frac{E_0}{H_0} = \frac{\beta}{\omega\varepsilon} = \frac{\omega\mu}{\beta} = \pm\sqrt{\mu/\varepsilon} = \pm\eta \qquad (= \pm\eta_0 \text{ for a vacuum}). \tag{11.14}$$

We recognize the phase velocity $\omega/\beta = c/n$ and the wave impedance $E_0/H_0 = \eta$ and the orthogonal field configuration to be the same as for the uniform plane wave that propagates along z, except that now the amplitude of the field is nonuniform instead of constant:

$$\mathbf{E}_0 = \mathbf{E}_0(x, y) \qquad \text{subject to} \quad \nabla \times \mathbf{E}_0(x, y) = 0, \tag{11.15}$$

with $\mathbf{H}_0(x, y) = \pm\hat{\mathbf{z}} \times \mathbf{E}_0(x, y)/\eta$. The equation $\nabla \times \mathbf{E}_0(x, y) = 0$ is the condition of *electrostatics*; it allows the field to be expressed as the gradient of a scalar *potential*, as

$$\mathbf{E}_0(x, y) = -\nabla\varphi(x, y). \tag{11.16}$$

Note that the potential φ cannot depend on z, since we already know that $\mathbf{E}_0$, being transverse, has no z-component.

What we are left with is a *two-dimensional electrostatics* problem, to be solved for the potential $\varphi(x, y)$ or for the transverse field $\mathbf{E}_0(x, y)$, from which the transverse magnetic field $\mathbf{H}_0(x, y) = \pm\hat{\mathbf{z}} \times \mathbf{E}_0(x, y)/\eta$ can be deduced. These then become the nonuniform amplitudes of a wave that propagates along $\pm z$, at the speed of light (in the medium). The alternate signs allow for propagation either forward or backward along the z-direction.

We conclude that any purely two-dimensional electrostatics field configuration converts to a nonuniform propagating wave, of phase velocity $v_p = 1/\sqrt{\mu\varepsilon} = c/n$, transmitted along the direction perpendicular to the two-dimensional plane, by appending the propagation factor $e^{-j\beta z}$, with $\beta = \pm kn$, to the two-dimensional, transverse field pattern $\mathbf{E}_0 = -\nabla\varphi(x, y)$, together with a transverse magnetic field $\mathbf{H}_0 = \pm\hat{\mathbf{z}} \times \mathbf{E}_0\sqrt{\varepsilon/\mu}$. The complete pattern is a TEM (transverse electromagnetic) wave.

For this to be valid for all z, the spatial configuration of conductors and dielectrics that comprises the original two-dimensional electrostatics problem in the xy-plane must be extended *uniformly* into the third dimension, along z, thereby forming a *transmission line* whose cross section exactly matches the configuration of the electrostatics problem.

We recall that the two-dimensional electrostatics problem leads only to the trivial zero solution, unless the space whose constitutive parameters are ε and μ is bounded by at least a pair of (two-dimensional) conductors that are maintained at different potentials. Upon conceiving of these conductors as being extruded into the third dimension, they become the conducting boundaries, or the conductors, of the uniform transmission line.

We note also that in (two-dimensional) electrostatics, nonzero conductivity of the dielectric medium leaves only a zero electric field, in the static case, unless the charges that leak away are continuously replenished by a steady current (which involves magnetostatics instead). Also, if the conductors are imperfect, with only finite conductivity instead of infinite, the field pattern becomes at least slightly three-dimensional. We conclude that pure TEM propagation occurs for *lossless, uniform* transmission lines, comprised of perfect dielectrics bounded by perfect conductors.

Before examining an example of TEM waves on uniform, lossless transmission lines, we note that our conclusion about conversion of a purely electrostatic, two-dimensional problem into a field pattern of a TEM propagating wave at frequency ω can also be reached from a comparison of the three-dimensional wave equation with the two-dimensional Laplace equation of electrostatics:

$$\nabla^2\psi(x, y, z, t) = \frac{1}{c^2}\frac{\partial^2\psi(x, y, z, t)}{\partial t^2} \quad \text{vs.} \quad \nabla^2\varphi(x, y) = 0. \tag{11.17}$$

If we use a solution $\varphi(x, y)$ of the Laplace equation to construct a trial function for the wave equation as

$$\psi(x, y, z, t) = \varphi(x, y)e^{j(\omega t - kz)}, \tag{11.18}$$

then

$$\begin{aligned} \nabla^2\psi - \frac{1}{c^2}\frac{\partial^2\psi}{\partial t^2} &= [\nabla^2\varphi]e^{j(\omega t - kz)} - \left(k^2 - \frac{\omega^2}{c^2}\right)\varphi e^{j(\omega t - kz)} \\ &= -\left(k^2 - \frac{\omega^2}{c^2}\right)\psi = 0 \quad \text{if } k^2 = \frac{\omega^2}{c^2}, \end{aligned} \tag{11.19}$$

as found earlier. Constructing a solution to Maxwell's equations from this one of the wave equation, as

$$\mathbf{E}(x, y, z, t) = -[\nabla\varphi(x, y)]e^{j(\omega t - kz)} \quad \text{with} \quad \mathbf{H}(x, y, z, t) = \hat{\mathbf{z}} \times \frac{\mathbf{E}}{\eta_0}, \tag{11.20}$$

yields the TEM waves of a transmission line (for vacuum as the dielectric).

Coaxial Line

As an example of the conversion of a two-dimensional electrostatics problem into a three-dimensional configuration for its extruded transmission line version, we examine the fields and properties of a coaxial transmission line, shown in cross section in Figure 11–1.

In the electrostatics version, the conductors are equipotentials; the outer conductor is at zero potential (grounded) while the inner one is kept at fixed potential V. The conductors and the dielectric are perfect (infinite and zero conductivity, respectively). The fields exist between the conductors, in the dielectric space, from radius a to radius b. We wish to find the electrostatic field between the coaxial conductors and then to convert the solution into a TEM wave, at any frequency, along the coaxial line.

The geometry is here so symmetrical that we could readily obtain the field pattern from Gauss' law. For the sake of illustration, however, we shall proceed by solving Laplace's equation for the potential. Combining $\nabla \cdot \mathbf{E} = 0$ with $\mathbf{E} = -\nabla\varphi$ gives $\nabla^2\varphi = 0$ as the partial differential equation for $\varphi(x, y)$, but here the polar coordinate system is more appropriate because the boundaries of the dielectric space are given by constant values of the radius. For $\varphi(r, \theta)$, the differential equation takes the equivalent form

$$\nabla^2\varphi = \frac{1}{r}\frac{\partial}{\partial r}\left(r\frac{\partial\varphi}{\partial r}\right) + \frac{1}{r^2}\frac{\partial^2\varphi}{\partial\theta^2} = 0. \tag{11.21}$$

Because the geometry and also the boundary conditions are azimuthally symmetric, the potential cannot depend on the angle θ. This leaves the ordinary differential equation

$$\frac{1}{r}\frac{d}{dr}\left(r\frac{d\varphi}{dr}\right) = 0 \qquad \text{with} \quad \varphi(b) = 0, \quad \varphi(a) = V, \tag{11.22}$$

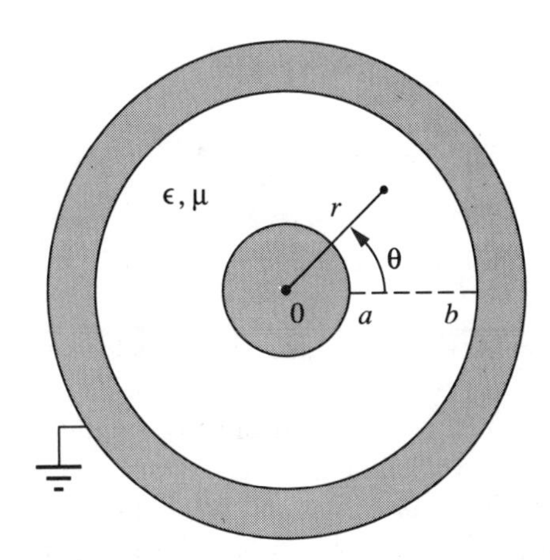

FIGURE 11–1 Coaxial line: outer shell grounded, inner wire at V volts.

which implies in turn that

$$r\frac{d\varphi}{dr} = C, \qquad \frac{d\varphi}{dr} = \frac{C}{r}, \qquad \varphi(r) = C \ln r + B, \tag{11.23}$$

with the constants C and B determined from the boundary conditions

$$\varphi(b) = 0 = C \ln b + B \quad \text{or} \quad \varphi(r) = -C \ln \frac{b}{r}, \tag{11.24}$$

$$\varphi(a) = V = -C \ln \frac{b}{a} \quad \text{or} \quad \varphi(r) = \frac{V \ln (b/r)}{\ln (b/a)}. \tag{11.25}$$

This is the electrostatic potential between the conductors; the electrostatics problem is completed by deriving the electric field from $\varphi(r)$. This has only a radial component, given by

$$E_r = -\frac{\partial\varphi}{\partial r} = \frac{V/\ln (b/a)}{r}. \tag{11.26}$$

If we now conceive of the two-dimensional geometry of the concentric conducting rings as extruded, intact and uniformly, into the third dimension to form a coaxial transmission line, then the TEM wave that can propagate along that line at frequency ω has this electrostatic field with the factor $e^{-j(\omega z/v)}$ appended, together with the magnetic field $\mathbf{H} = \hat{\mathbf{z}} \times \mathbf{E}/\eta$, where $v = 1/\sqrt{\mu\varepsilon} = c/n$ and $\eta = \sqrt{\mu/\varepsilon}$. The magnetic field has only an azimuthal component; the nonuniform wave field pattern is given in $a < r < b$ by

$$\mathbf{E}(r, \theta, z) = \hat{\mathbf{r}}\left[\frac{V}{\ln (b/a)}\right]\frac{1}{r}\, e^{-j(\omega z/v)}, \tag{11.27}$$

$$\eta\mathbf{H}(r, \theta, z) = \hat{\boldsymbol{\theta}}\left[\frac{V}{\ln (b/a)}\right]\frac{1}{r}\, e^{-j(\omega z/v)}. \tag{11.28}$$

The transmission-line fields can propagate in the opposite direction as well:

$$\mathbf{E}(r, \theta, z) = \hat{\mathbf{r}}\left[\frac{V}{\ln (b/a)}\right]\frac{1}{r}\, e^{+j(\omega z/v)}, \tag{11.29}$$

$$\eta\mathbf{H}(r, \theta, z) = -\hat{\boldsymbol{\theta}}\left[\frac{V}{\ln (b/a)}\right]\frac{1}{r}\, e^{+j(\omega z/v)} \tag{11.30}$$

are also a solution to Maxwell's equations. The fields vanish inside the perfect conductors, of course.

The general solution for TEM transmission within the coaxial line is a superposition of the forward-going and the backward-traveling waves. A TEM wave propagating in the coaxial line and encountering some discontinuity in the otherwise uniform line will be reflected back, as well as transmitted onward. For example, as illustrated in Figure 11–2, an abrupt change from

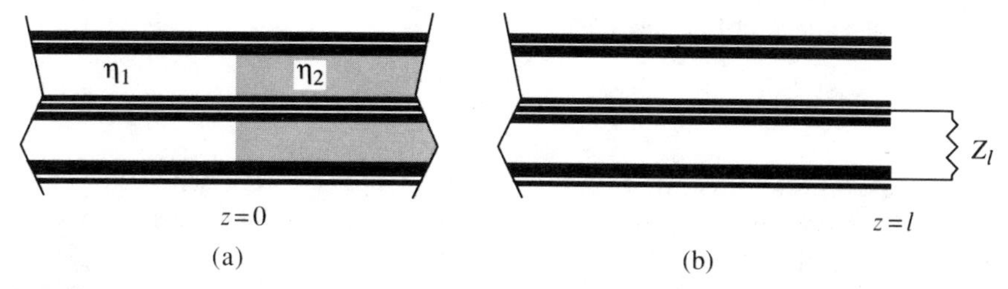

FIGURE 11–2 Coaxial line discontinuities: (a) change of dielectric and (b) termination.

one dielectric to another at $z = 0$, without change of geometry, results in the same sort of reflection and transmission that applies to infinitely extended plane waves. The mismatch of impedances, from η_1 for $z < 0$ to η_2 for $z > 0$, generates a reflected wave with amplitude reflection coefficient $\Gamma_e = (\eta_2 - \eta_1)/(\eta_2 + \eta_1)$, as before.

But the wave can encounter another type of discontinuity along a transmission line: the line can terminate at some distance l; some lumped "load impedance" can be attached at the end of the line to receive the power that flows in the transmission line. This is also shown in the figure, but only schematically, as a resistor or other impedance element connected by wires between the center and outer conductors; a symmetrical load structure would be preferable, to preserve the field pattern without distortion. Before considering the disposition of the propagating power when it encounters the load impedance, we should examine the power, voltage, and current relations in the line.

The power flow in a wave that propagates along a transmission line in the z-direction has a time-averaged density $\langle \mathscr{E} \times \mathscr{H} \rangle = \text{Re}\,[\frac{1}{2}\mathbf{E} \times \mathbf{H}^*]$, in watts/m^2. The *total* power that flows across a transverse plane of the line is $P = \int \text{Re}\,[\frac{1}{2}\mathbf{E} \times \mathbf{H}^*] \cdot d\mathbf{S}$. Since $\mathbf{E}$ and $\mathbf{H}$ are transverse, the Poynting vector is along $\hat{\mathbf{z}}$, as is $d\mathbf{S}$ for a transverse plane at z. For the coaxial line, for example, $\mathbf{E} \times \mathbf{H}^* = \hat{\mathbf{z}} E_r H_\theta^*$ and, from Eqs. (11.27)–(11.28),

$$E_r H_\theta^* = \frac{|V|^2}{\eta[\ln(b/a)]^2} \frac{1}{r^2} \qquad \text{for} \quad a < r < b \text{ only}, \tag{11.31}$$

so that

$$P = \int_0^{2\pi} \int_a^b \frac{|V|^2}{2\eta[\ln(b/a)]^2} \frac{1}{r^2}\, r\, dr\, d\theta = \frac{2\pi |V|^2}{2\eta[\ln(b/a)]^2} \int_a^b \frac{dr}{r}$$
$$= \frac{\frac{1}{2}|V|^2}{(\eta/2\pi)\ln(b/a)}. \tag{11.32}$$

This power P that crosses the transverse plane is independent of z, the location of the plane, as required by conservation of power in a lossless system. The power flow along the line is the same as if the voltage V across the coaxial conductors appeared across an equivalent, lumped impedance, called the *char-*

acteristic impedance of the line,

$$Z_0 = \frac{\eta}{2\pi} \ln \frac{b}{a}. \tag{11.33}$$

This represents an integrated, global impedance associated with the TEM wave and the coaxial structure. On a point-by-point basis, however, the local impedance is still $E_r/H_\theta = \eta$ between the conductors.

Voltage and Current Waves

The electromagnetic fields of the TEM wave in the transmission line are accompanied by a voltage across the line and a current along it, at any position z along the line. These propagate as waves also. At a fixed position z, the voltage is related to the electric field by

$$V(z) = \int_C \mathbf{E} \cdot d\mathbf{l} \tag{11.34}$$

along some path from the inner to the outer conductor. As long as the path C lies entirely in a transverse plane at z, the emf is independent of the path, so that $V(z)$ is unique when so defined. This uniqueness holds despite the time variation of the electric field, because two distinct paths that define $V(z)$ enclose no magnetic flux, since $\mathbf{H}$ and $\mathbf{B}$ are also transverse, so that $\oint \mathbf{E} \cdot d\mathbf{l} = 0$ and the two paths must yield the same voltage.

For example, for the coaxial line,

$$V(z) = \int_a^b E_r(r, z)\, dr = \frac{V}{\ln (b/a)} e^{-jknz} \int_a^b \frac{dr}{r} = Ve^{-jknz}, \tag{11.35}$$

in which V, which was originally the potential difference between the inner and outer conductors in the two-dimensional electrostatic problem, is now seen to have become the amplitude of a propagating voltage wave at frequency ω, after the two-dimensional structure has been extended into the third dimension. The actual, physically measurable voltage is given by $v(z, t) = \text{Re}\,[V(z)e^{j\omega t}] = \text{Re}\,[Ve^{j(\omega t - knz)}] = |V| \cos(\omega t - knz + \varphi_0)$ for complex V.

At position z, the current in one conductor is related to the magnetic field by the Ampère–Maxwell law

$$I(z) = \oint_{C'} \mathbf{H} \cdot d\mathbf{l}, \tag{11.36}$$

for a path C' that encircles the inner conductor and lies in the dielectric space where there is a magnetic field. As long as the path C' lies entirely in a transverse plane at z, the mmf is independent of the path, so that $I(z)$ is unique when so defined. This uniqueness holds despite the time variation of the magnetic field, because two distinct closed paths that define $I(z)$ surround no axially directed displacement flux, since **E** and **D** are also transverse.

Note also that under normal operating conditions, the fields are confined to the dielectric region between the conductors. Hence, if C' were to encircle both conductors of the coaxial line, the integrand would be zero and we conclude that there is no net current in the pair of conductors taken together. There are therefore equal and opposite currents $I(z)$ in each, when the line is operated normally. We could, of course, cause a unidirectional, additional current to flow in either or both conductors as a separate, independent effect. This would unbalance the currents of the TEM wave alone, but the superimposed magnetic field would then not be confined to the space between the coaxial conductors.

As an example, the current in the center conductor of the coaxial line is

$$I(z) = \int_0^{2\pi} H_\theta(r, z) r \, d\theta = \frac{V}{\eta \ln (b/a)} e^{-jknz} \frac{2\pi r}{r}$$

$$= \frac{V}{(\eta/2\pi) \ln (b/a)} e^{-jknz}, \tag{11.37}$$

which has the form

$$I(z) = Ie^{-jknz} \qquad \text{with} \quad I = \frac{V}{(\eta/2\pi) \ln (b/a)} = \frac{V}{Z_0}. \tag{11.38}$$

This is a current wave, propagating along z at the speed of light in the dielectric medium; its amplitude is related to that of the voltage wave by the characteristic impedance of the transmission line.

Characteristic Impedance

For a unidirectionally propagating TEM wave traveling along $+z$, the characteristic impedance Z_0, which we originally defined by the power relation $P = \frac{1}{2} |V|^2/Z_0$, can be regarded also as

$$Z_0 = \frac{V}{I} = \frac{\int_C \mathbf{E} \cdot d\mathbf{l}}{\oint_{C'} \mathbf{H} \cdot d\mathbf{l}}, \tag{11.39}$$

the ratio of the voltage from the inner to the outer conductor to the current along z in the inner conductor. Note that the ratio of the characteristic impedance Z_0 to the dielectric medium's impedance η is a quantity that depends only on the geometry of the structure, such as the sizes of the conductors, as in $Z_0/\eta = (1/2\pi) \ln (b/a)$ for the coaxial line. For the wave that propagates along $-z$, **E** and V are the same but **H** and I are reversed, so that the ratio of voltage to current is $-Z_0$ for the backward-traveling wave.

EXAMPLE 11.1

A typical coaxial line may have metal conductors, with the inner one having outer diameter $2a = 0.411$ cm and the outer one having inner diameter

$2b = 1.143$ cm; the conductors are separated with polyethylene foam, for which $\varepsilon = 1.5\varepsilon_0$. Its characteristic impedance is

$$Z_0 = \frac{\eta_0 \ln [1.143/0.411]}{2\pi\sqrt{1.5}} = 0.1329\eta_0 = 50\ \Omega. \qquad \blacklozenge$$

Corresponding to the general solution for the **E** and **H** fields as a superposition of waves along $+z$ and $-z$, the general voltage and current along any transmission line are

$$V(z) = V_1 e^{-jknz} + V_2 e^{jknz}, \tag{11.40}$$

$$Z_0 I(z) = V_1 e^{-jknz} - V_2 e^{jknz}, \tag{11.41}$$

superpositions of oppositely traveling voltage and current waves, each propagating at the phase velocity $v_p = \omega/kn = 1/\sqrt{\mu\varepsilon} = c/n$, which is the speed of light in the dielectric medium between the conductors. The fundamental principle for transmission lines is that:

> At any position, the voltage is the *sum* of a forward and a backward wave and the characteristic impedance times the current is the *difference* of the same two waves.

The constants V_1 and V_2 are to be determined from boundary conditions, typically at the two ends of the transmission line.

The impedance along the line, defined by the ratio of complex voltage to complex current, varies from point to point. It is a specific function of z, however, with a single parameter:

$$Z(z) = \frac{V(z)}{I(z)} = \frac{Z_0[V_1 e^{-jknz} + V_2 e^{jknz}]}{V_1 e^{-jknz} - V_2 e^{jknz}}$$

$$= \frac{Z_0[1 + (V_2/V_1)e^{2jknz}]}{1 - (V_2/V_1)e^{2jknz}}, \tag{11.42}$$

or

$$\frac{Z(z)}{Z_0} = \frac{1 + \Gamma(z)}{1 - \Gamma(z)}, \tag{11.43}$$

where

$$\Gamma(z) = \frac{V_2 e^{jknz}}{V_1 e^{-jknz}} = \Gamma_0 e^{2jknz} \tag{11.44}$$

is the ratio of the complex amplitude of the backward-traveling wave to that of the forward one, at point z along the line; it is called the *voltage reflection coefficient* and varies along the line as the specific function e^{2jknz}, with an undetermined constant coefficient Γ_0.

While the expressions for the voltage and current waves exhibit two undetermined constants V_1 and V_2, the ratio of voltage to current, which is the impedance along the line, involves only one such constant, Γ_0, the voltage reflection coefficient at $z = 0$:

$$\frac{Z(z)}{Z_0} = \frac{1 + \Gamma_0 e^{2jknz}}{1 - \Gamma_0 e^{2jknz}}. \tag{11.45}$$

In this expression, the characteristic impedance Z_0 is known for the line; it is determined by the dielectric and the geometry of the line. What determines the reflection coefficient Γ_0?

Any information that prescribes the value of the impedance $Z(z_0)$ at some particular location z_0 will allow the equation for $Z(z_0)$ to be inverted to yield the unknown Γ_0, and hence determine the values of $Z(z)$ everywhere else. In practice, such information is provided by the boundary condition at the end of the line, $z = l$.

Two-conductor transmission lines afford an opportunity to attach a lumped impedance at the end of the extended structure. This then appears as a *load impedance* Z_l at the end $z = l$ of the line. The boundary condition at the end is then just that the ratio of voltage to current there must conform to the requirements of the load impedance that has been attached across the conductors [i.e., that $Z(l) = Z_l$]. Upon inverting

$$Z(l) = \frac{Z_0[1 + \Gamma_0 e^{2jknl}]}{1 - \Gamma_0 e^{2jknl}}, \tag{11.46}$$

we get $\Gamma_l = \Gamma(l) = \Gamma_0 e^{2jknl}$ as

$$\Gamma_l = \frac{Z_l - Z_0}{Z_l + Z_0}. \tag{11.47}$$

It is the mismatch $(Z_l - Z_0)$ between the load impedance Z_l that has been connected to the end of the line and the characteristic impedance Z_0 of the transmission line itself that determines the voltage reflection coefficient Γ_l at the end of the line. This then determines the constant Γ_0, hence $\Gamma(z)$, hence $Z(z)$ everywhere along the line. The reflection coefficient gives the ratio V_2/V_1; V_1 and V_2 become known individually when the additional information about the source connected to the line at $z = 0$ is given. These then determine the voltage and current, and the fields, and the power flow, everywhere along the transmission line.

Mismatched Loads

Since the reflection coefficient and all that follows from it are determined by the load at $z = l$, it is convenient to refer all relevant quantities to their values at that location, simply by measuring position along the line in terms of distance to the load, $(l - z)$, rather than distance from the source, z.

The relation between Γ_l and Γ_0 is that $\Gamma_l = \Gamma_0 e^{2jknl}$, so that

$$\Gamma(z) = \Gamma_l e^{-2jkn(l-z)} \tag{11.48}$$

gives the voltage reflection coefficient anywhere, in terms of its value at the load. Similarly, the incident voltage wave is written as $V_0 e^{jkn(l-z)}$, instead of $V_1 e^{-jknz}$. The total voltage and current at any position are

$$V(z) = V_0[e^{jkn(l-z)} + \Gamma_l e^{-jkn(l-z)}] \tag{11.49}$$

$$Z_0 I(z) = V_0[e^{jkn(l-z)} - \Gamma_l e^{-jkn(l-z)}], \tag{11.50}$$

with the reflection coefficient Γ_l determined by the load impedance from

$$Z_l = Z_0 \frac{1+\Gamma_l}{1-\Gamma_l} \quad \text{or} \quad \Gamma_l = \frac{Z_l - Z_0}{Z_l + Z_0}. \tag{11.51}$$

The remaining constant V_0 is determined when the source voltage, or current, is given at $z = 0$, or any equivalent information is provided.

EXAMPLE 11.2

Matched line If we choose to connect at the end $z = l$ of the line a lumped load impedance that is exactly equal to the characteristic impedance of the transmission line; that is,

$$\text{if} \quad Z_l = Z_0, \qquad \text{then} \quad \Gamma_l = 0. \tag{11.52}$$

The line is *matched* and there is then no reflected wave. The voltage and current anywhere along the line are then

$$V(z) = V_0 e^{jkn(l-z)},$$

$$I(z) = \frac{V_0}{Z_0} e^{jkn(l-z)}. \tag{11.53}$$

Recalling that the $e^{j\omega t}$ factor has been elided, these are recognized as a pure propagating wave, traveling in the direction of decreasing values of $(l - z)$ or of increasing distance from the source, z, at the speed $\omega/kn = c/n = 1/\sqrt{\mu\varepsilon}$. They constitute the incident wave, sent by the source at $z = 0$ to the matched load at $z = l$. The wave is absorbed by the matched load; there is no reflected wave. The impedance at any position z is $Z(z) = V(z)/I(z) = Z_0$, independent of z and equal to both the characteristic impedance and the matched load.

The amplitude V_0 is determined by the source: If the source voltage is given as the complex amplitude V_s, then $V(0) = V_0 e^{jknl} = V_s$ and the voltage and current anywhere along the line are just $V(z) = V_s e^{-jknz}$, $I(z) = (V_s/Z_0)e^{-jknz}$. The source voltage is delivered to the load intact, except for a phase lag of $knl = \omega nl/c$ radians, which corresponds to merely a delay of $\tau = nl/c$ seconds.

The power along the line, $P(z) = \frac{1}{2}V(z)I^*(z)$ is here the same everywhere, equal to $\frac{1}{2}|V_s|^2/Z_0$ for all z from $z = 0$ to $z = l$; it is supplied by the source and dissipated in the matched load. The matched line acts as a pure delay element, with all the incident power absorbed by the load. ◆

EXAMPLE 11.3

Shorted line If we choose to connect a short circuit at the end $z = l$ of the line, it acts as a load impedance $Z_l = 0$. Then $\Gamma_l = -1$, regardless of the characteristic impedance of the line. This means that there is a reflected wave, with the same strength but opposite polarity, as compared to the incident wave at the location of the short circuit, canceling the incident voltage but doubling the incident current there.

The voltage and current distributions along the shorted line are

$$V(z) = V_0[e^{jkn(l-z)} - e^{-jkn(l-z)}] = 2jV_0 \sin kn(l-z), \tag{11.54}$$

$$I(z) = \frac{V_0[e^{jkn(l-z)} + e^{-jkn(l-z)}]}{Z_0} = 2\left(\frac{V_0}{Z_0}\right) \cos kn(l-z). \tag{11.55}$$

These distributions oscillate, at frequency ω, but do not propagate. They form a *standing wave*, comprised of oppositely traveling waves of equal amplitudes. There is no real power flow: assuming real Z_0 (lossless line), the complex power is $P(z) = \frac{1}{2}V(z)I^*(z) = j(|V_0|^2/Z_0) \sin 2kn(l-z)$, which is purely imaginary and represents storage of electromagnetic energy.

In terms of the source voltage $V(0) = V_s$, the voltage and current are

$$V(z) = \frac{V_s[\sin kn(l-z)]}{\sin knl}, \qquad I(z) = \frac{V_s}{jZ_0} \frac{\cos kn(l-z)}{\sin knl}. \tag{11.56}$$

The impedance at position z is

$$Z(z) = jZ_0 \tan kn(l-z) \tag{11.57}$$

and the impedance seen at the source is

$$Z_s = Z(0) = jZ_0 \tan knl, \tag{11.58}$$

which is reactive and can attain any magnitude if the distance to the short circuit, l, is allowed to vary. ◆

For a transmission line with an arbitrary load Z_l, the impedance at any position is

$$Z(z) = \frac{V(z)}{I(z)} = Z_0 \frac{e^{jkn(l-z)} + \Gamma_l e^{-jkn(l-z)}}{e^{jkn(l-z)} - \Gamma_l e^{-jkn(l-z)}}, \tag{11.59}$$

with

$$\Gamma_l = \frac{Z_l - Z_0}{Z_l + Z_0}, \tag{11.60}$$

so that

$$Z(z) = Z_0 \frac{(Z_l + Z_0)e^{jkn(l-z)} + (Z_l - Z_0)e^{-jkn(l-z)}}{(Z_l + Z_0)e^{jkn(l-z)} - (Z_l - Z_0)e^{-jkn(l-z)}}, \tag{11.61}$$

or

$$Z(z) = Z_0 \frac{Z_l \cos kn(l-z) + jZ_0 \sin kn(l-z)}{Z_0 \cos kn(l-z) + jZ_l \sin kn(l-z)}, \tag{11.62}$$

or, finally,

$$Z(z) = Z_0 \frac{Z_l + jZ_0 \tan [kn(l-z)]}{Z_0 + jZ_l \tan [kn(l-z)]}. \tag{11.63}$$

In particular, the input impedance seen by the source is

$$Z(0) = \frac{V_s}{I_s} = Z_0 \frac{Z_l + jZ_0 \tan knl}{Z_0 + jZ_l \tan knl}. \tag{11.64}$$

Although such elaborate but explicit equations may comfort some, we recommend that routine transmission line problems be solved by obtaining the reflection coefficient and then the impedance in succession, from the more palatable set of relations

$$\Gamma_l = \frac{Z_l - Z_0}{Z_l + Z_0}, \tag{11.65}$$

$$\Gamma(z) = \Gamma_l e^{-2jkn(l-z)}, \tag{11.66}$$

$$Z(z) = Z_0 \frac{1 + \Gamma(z)}{1 - \Gamma(z)}. \tag{11.67}$$

The reader who would struggle to remember the combined, explicit equation for the impedance but who has understood the concepts of impedance mismatch, of reflection coefficient as a ratio of opposed wave amplitudes, and of impedance as the ratio of sum to difference of the opposed waves should have no difficulty reconstructing these equations when needed.

For theoretical purposes, however, the explicit equation for the impedance at any point in terms of the load impedance, Eq. (11.63), makes certain properties clear. We see that impedance values along the line are a periodic function of position, with period $\lambda/2$ (since the tangent function has period π). We note too that if the length of the line is a multiple of a half-wavelength, $l = m\lambda/2$, then $knl = m\pi$ and $\tan knl = 0$, which leaves $Z(0) = Z_l$. That is, the source then sees the load impedance as the input impedance. Also, if the length is an odd multiple of a quarter-wavelength, $l = m_0 \lambda/4$ with m_0 an odd integer, then $knl = m_0 \pi/2$ and $\tan knl = \infty$, whereupon the formula yields $Z(0) = Z_0^2/Z_l$. This means that the input impedance $Z(0)$ is an inverted version (with respect to the characteristic impedance Z_0) of the actual load Z_l: a capacitive load is seen as inductive, a short is seen as an open circuit, a large resistance appears small (compared to Z_0), and so on.

Standing-Wave Ratio

In practice, direct impedance measurements along a transmission line are difficult to make. The quantities that are readily measurable are the magnitude of a (sinusoidal) voltage, such as $|V(z)|$, and distances (or distance increments) along the line, such as z or $(l - z)$.

For access to the fields inside a transmission line, such as a coaxial line, a *slotted line* is used. This is a section of transmission line with a narrow slot cut

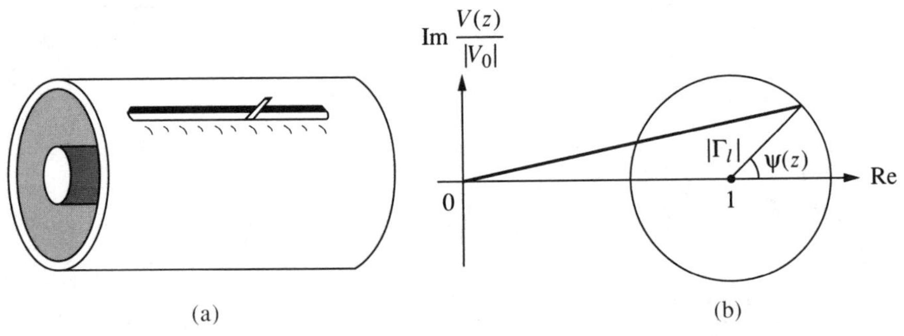

FIGURE 11–3 (a) Coaxial slotted line and (b) crank diagram.

along it to allow a probe to penetrate just enough to pick up a signal proportional to the electric field, without disturbing the field pattern too much. The probe is connected to a voltmeter, which then provides a reading proportional to the rms voltage or field $\langle \mathscr{E}^2(t) \rangle^{1/2}$. In turn, this is proportional to $|\mathbf{E}|$ or $|V|$ at the location of the probe, which can be moved along the slot. The observable quantity is then proportional to $|V(z)|$. Figure 11–3 shows the essentials of a coaxial section of slotted line.

Now the complex voltage distribution along the line is the sum of an incident and a reflected wave:

$$V(z) = V_0[e^{jkn(l-z)} + \Gamma_l e^{-jkn(l-z)}] = V_0 e^{jkn(l-z)}[1 + \Gamma_l e^{-2jkn(l-z)}] \quad (11.68)$$

and its magnitude is

$$|V(z)| = |V_0||1 + \Gamma_l e^{-2jkn(l-z)}| = |V_0||1 + |\Gamma_l| e^{j\Psi(z)}|, \quad (11.69)$$

where we define the variable phase angle

$$\Psi(z) = \varphi_l - 2k\underset{\cdot}{n}(l - z) \quad (11.70)$$

in terms of the phase φ_l of the reflection coefficient at the load, Γ_l. The figure also shows the phasor $1 + |\Gamma_l| e^{j\Psi(z)}$ in the complex plane of the ratio $V(z)/|V_0|$; this phasor is the displacement from the origin to a typical point on the circle of radius $|\Gamma_l|$ centered at (1, 0). The plot is known as a crank diagram, because one end of the phasor cranks around the circle as the observation point z changes. As the probe moves along the slot, the voltmeter reading is proportional to the magnitude of the phasor; this ranges from a peak of $1 + |\Gamma_l|$ to a minimum of $1 - |\Gamma_l|$. At an arbitrary point, the magnitude is

$$\begin{aligned}\frac{|V(z)|}{|V_0|} &= |1 + |\Gamma_l| e^{j\Psi(z)}| \\ &= \{1 + 2|\Gamma_l| \cos \Psi(z) + |\Gamma_l|^2\}^{1/2}. \quad (11.71)\end{aligned}$$

This function of z is plotted in Figure 11–4, for the particular case of $|\Gamma_l| = 0.7$. What is observed is a standing-wave pattern, the resultant of the interference between the forward and backward waves along the line. If there were

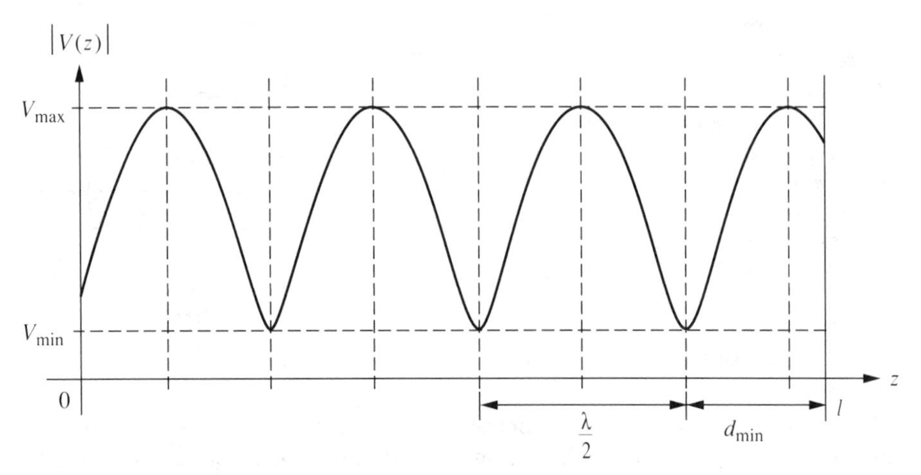

FIGURE 11–4 Observed standing-wave pattern on slotted line.

no reflected wave, then $|V(z)|$ would be constant (the circle in the crank diagram would have zero radius). For a pure standing wave, for which the reflected wave has the same strength as the incident one, the minima would reach zero (the circle would pass through the origin). The general case involves a partial standing wave, with $0 < |\Gamma_l| < 1$.

It is a particularly easy measurement to determine $|V|_{max}$ and $|V|_{min}$ from the voltmeter readings as the probe travels along the slot; the location of a particular minimum-voltage point along the line, at a distance d_{min} from the load, is also readily measured. These readings suffice to determine the complex reflection coefficient Γ_l for the line and, from this, the complex load impedance, as follows.

Since $|V|_{max} = |V_0|\{1 + |\Gamma_l|\}$ and $|V|_{min} = |V_0|\{1 - |\Gamma_l|\}$, the unknown $|V_0|$ can be eliminated by forming the ratio of the maximum to the minimum voltage readings, known as the *voltage standing-wave ratio* (VSWR):

$$\text{VSWR} = \frac{|V|_{max}}{|V|_{min}}. \tag{11.72}$$

Note that the VSWR can range from a minimum value of unity for a matched line to infinity when there is a pure standing wave. It follows that

$$\text{VSWR} = \frac{1 + |\Gamma_l|}{1 - |\Gamma_l|} \quad \text{or} \quad |\Gamma_l| = \frac{\text{VSWR} - 1}{\text{VSWR} + 1}, \tag{11.73}$$

so that the easily measured VSWR immediately determines the magnitude of the complex reflection coefficient along the line.

To obtain the phase φ_l of the reflection coefficient at the load, use is made of the distance d_{min} from the load to some minimum point of the interference pattern, in relation to the wavelength λ along the line. Even if the wavelength is not known directly from the operating frequency and the constitution of the dielectric medium, it is readily observed from the standing-wave pattern as twice the interval between successive minima. From the crank diagram, the phase angle $\Psi(z)$ at the minimum-voltage point at $z = l - d_{min}$ must have the value π, or an odd multiple of π: $\Psi = m_0 \pi$, with m_0 an odd integer. Since $\Psi(z) = \varphi_l - 2kn(l - z)$ becomes $\Psi_{min} = \varphi_l - 2knd_{min}$ at the minimum point and $kn = 2\pi/\lambda$, we have

$$\Psi_{min} = m_0 \pi = \varphi_l - 2knd_{min} = \varphi_l - \frac{4\pi d_{min}}{\lambda} \tag{11.74}$$

and

$$\varphi_l = \pi\left[m_0 + \frac{4d_{min}}{\lambda}\right]. \tag{11.75}$$

Because additive multiples of 2π have no significance to the phase of a complex number, this does provide the phase of the reflection coefficient, and hence the complete complex voltage reflection coefficient at the load.

Impedance Measurements

Slotted-line measurements allow the determination of an unknown load impedance that terminates the transmission line, in relation to the known characteristic impedance of the line. Since the complex reflection coefficient at the load, Γ_l, is obtainable from the observed standing-wave pattern along the slotted line in front of the unknown load, the load impedance Z_l is derivable from this as

$$Z_l = Z_0 \frac{1 + \Gamma_l}{1 - \Gamma_l}. \tag{11.76}$$

Before electronic calculators and computers became ubiquitous, the tedious calculations with complex numbers were eased by use of a Smith chart, which is a plot of the unit circle in the complex plane of $\Gamma(z)$, labeled by the corresponding values of the complex impedance ratio $Z(z)/Z_0$. (On this chart, loci of constant values of either the real or the imaginary part of that ratio are circular, as indicated for just a few such values in Figure 11–5; also, moving along the transmission line translates into tracing a circle of radius $|\Gamma_l|$ on the chart. Some details concerning this chart are left to the problems.) With or without the Smith chart, we can extract the complex load impedance from slotted-line measurements, as in the following example.

EXAMPLE 11.4

On a certain (lossless) transmission line with a characteristic impedance of 50 Ω, the measured VSWR is 3.60 and a voltage minimum occurs at a distance 2.90 wavelengths in front of the load. Find the terminating impedance at the operating frequency.

The magnitude of the reflection coefficient is obtained immediately as $|\Gamma| = (3.60 - 1)/(3.60 + 1) = 0.5652$ and the location of the minimum (which

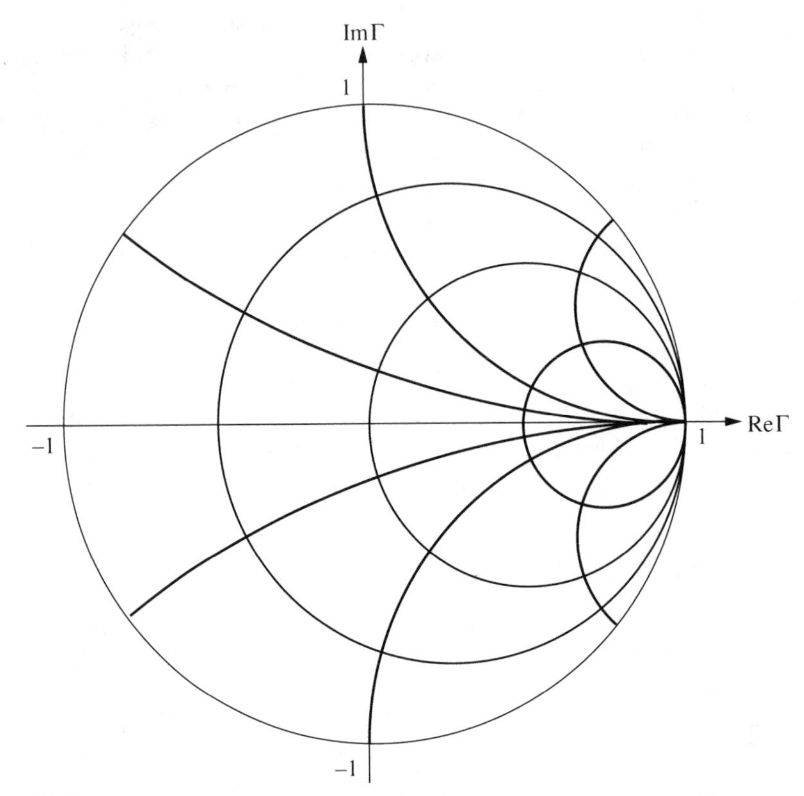

FIGURE 11–5 Smith chart: constant-R and constant-X lines in the Γ-plane.

could be diminished by a multiple of $\lambda/2$ for convenience, because of the periodicity of the interference pattern) yields the phase as

$$\varphi_l = \pi\left[m_0 + \frac{4d_{\min}}{\lambda}\right] = \pi[m_0 + 4(2.90)] = \pi[m_0 + 11.60] \qquad (11.77)$$

or $\varphi_l = 0.60\pi$ after reducing the phase to a value between 0 and 2π. The reflection coefficient at the load is therefore

$$\Gamma_l = 0.5652e^{j0.60\pi} = -0.1747 + j0.5376, \qquad (11.78)$$

so that the load impedance, normalized to the characteristic impedance, is

$$\begin{aligned}\frac{Z_l}{Z_0} &= \frac{1+\Gamma_l}{1-\Gamma_l} = \frac{0.8253 + j0.5376}{1.1747 - j0.5376} \\ &= \frac{0.9850e^{j0.5773}}{1.2918e^{-j0.4292}} = 0.7625e^{j1.0065} \\ &= 0.4078 + j0.6442 \end{aligned} \qquad (11.79)$$

and the load impedance is $Z_l = (20.39 + j32.21)\ \Omega$, a combination of a resistive and an inductive load. ◆

Summary

Transmission lines allow propagation of TEM waves within the dielectric space between the conductors, thereby guiding the fields and the power they convey from the source to the load. The TEM waves are a special sort of nonuniform wave, formed from an electrostatic field pattern associated with the planar cross section of the line. The waves can travel in either direction along the line, at the speed of light in the dielectric. For different geometries, the field patterns differ, as do the associated characteristic impedances that distinguish one line from another.

The fundamental principle governing the operation of transmission lines is that, at any position, the voltage is the sum of a forward-traveling and a backward-traveling wave and the characteristic impedance times the current is the difference of the same two waves. Questions involving phenomena on transmission lines and their interconnections in circuits can be answered by determining the two oppositely traveling waves on each uniform section, from information about the source at one end and the electrical load impedance at the other.

The reflected wave is determined from the incident one by the mismatch between the load impedance and the characteristic impedance of the line. That result is the same as the one for unbounded waves that encounter an interface between mismatched media. For the transmission line, there is the opportunity for a lumped load to be connected to the end of the line that is fed from the other end. When the load impedance matches the characteristic impedance of the line, there is no reflection and the line acts as a pure delay for the signal transmitted from the source to the load.

The lossless transmission line serves as an approximation to the practical cases of slightly lossy lines, for which the characteristic impedance may be complex and the propagation constant is not purely real.

Although transmission lines are designed to convey TEM waves, these represent only a special type of nonuniform propagating wave, with a transverse field pattern that is purely electrostatic. Coaxial and other lines, along with pipes and more general structures, can also carry other forms of propagating waves, not TEM, associated with the wider class of *waveguides*, which are to be studied next.

PROBLEMS

Trivial Solutions for One-Conductor Electrostatics

11.1 Show that, as claimed in the text, the electrostatic field enclosed by a single hollow conducting boundary maintained at a prescribed voltage, as in the case of a coaxial line with its center conductor missing, must vanish, as follows.

(a) Obtain the divergence of the quantity $\varphi\nabla\varphi$, where φ satisfies Laplace's equation of electrostatics, $\nabla^2\varphi = 0$, to show that $\nabla \cdot [\varphi\nabla\varphi] = |\nabla\varphi|^2$.

(b) Integrate this relation over the region bounded by the conductor and apply the divergence theorem to obtain

$$\oint_S \varphi\nabla\varphi \cdot d\mathbf{S} = \int_V |\nabla\varphi|^2 \, dV.$$

(c) Any boundary condition on surface S that causes the surface integral to vanish must make the volume integral vanish. Why does this imply that the electric field in the entire enclosed volume must be zero?

(d) By using $\varphi'(\mathbf{r}) = \varphi(\mathbf{r}) - V_0$ instead of $\varphi(\mathbf{r})$ for the case that the boundary value of the potential φ is a nonzero constant V_0 on the conducting boundary, show that the enclosed electric field must be zero.

Calculation of Characteristic Impedance for Confocal Line

11.2 If the conducting boundaries of the cross section of a transmission line are of simple, analytically described shapes, it may well be easier to describe the potential distribution implicitly, in inverted form, by giving the position vector $\mathbf{r} = \mathbf{r}(\varphi)$ instead of the potential $\varphi = \varphi(\mathbf{r})$. The explicit inversion need not be carried out to extract quantities such as the characteristic impedance of the line. Consider the transmission line with cross section formed by confocal ellipses, as in Fig. P11–2. The potential $\varphi(x, y)$ within the space between the ellipses is described

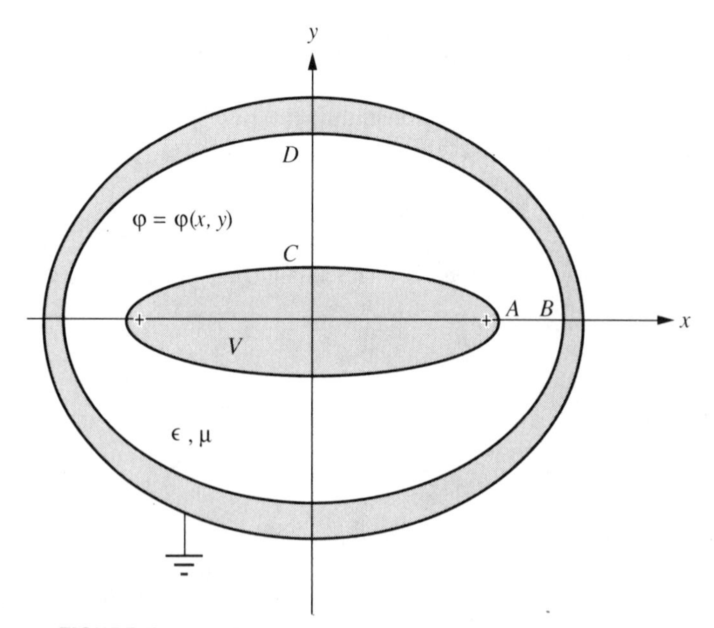

FIGURE P11–2 Confocal-ellipse transmission line.

implicitly by

$$x = x(\varphi, \theta) = b \cosh\left(\delta - \frac{\xi\varphi}{V}\right) \cos\theta$$

$$y = y(\varphi, \theta) = b \sinh\left(\delta - \frac{\xi\varphi}{V}\right) \sin\theta,$$

where b, δ, ξ, and V are fixed parameters. (Analytic functions of a complex variable are an inexhaustible supply of such solutions to Laplace's equation.)

(a) Verify that the curve that corresponds to $\varphi = 0$ (the grounded conductor) is an ellipse; give its semiaxes in terms of the parameters.

(b) Verify that the curve that corresponds to $\varphi = V$ (the conductor maintained at voltage V) is an ellipse; give its semiaxes in terms of the parameters.

(c) Verify that the two vectors $\partial\mathbf{r}/\partial\varphi$ and $\partial\mathbf{r}/\partial\theta$ are orthogonal. As a consequence, the differential $d\mathbf{r} = [\partial\mathbf{r}/\partial\varphi]\, d\varphi + [\partial\mathbf{r}/\partial\theta]\, d\theta$ implies that

$$d\mathbf{r} \cdot \frac{\partial\mathbf{r}}{\partial\varphi} = \left|\frac{\partial\mathbf{r}}{\partial\varphi}\right|^2 d\varphi$$

and the definition of the gradient as $d\varphi \equiv d\mathbf{r} \cdot \nabla\varphi$ (for *all* $d\mathbf{r}$) yields

$$\nabla\varphi = \frac{\partial\mathbf{r}/\partial\varphi}{|\partial\mathbf{r}/\partial\varphi|^2},$$

so that it is not necessary to invert $\mathbf{r} = \mathbf{r}(\varphi, \theta)$ to extract $\nabla\varphi$.

(d) We want to calculate $I = \oint \mathbf{H} \cdot d\mathbf{l} = \oint [-1/\eta]\hat{\mathbf{z}} \times \nabla\varphi \cdot d\mathbf{l}$, for given voltage V from the inner to the outer conductor, so as to obtain Z_0 in $V = Z_0 I$. Show that

$$\hat{\mathbf{z}} \times \nabla\varphi \cdot d\mathbf{l} = \hat{\mathbf{z}} \cdot [\partial\mathbf{r}/\partial\varphi] \times [\partial\mathbf{r}/\partial\theta]\, d\theta / |\partial\mathbf{r}/\partial\varphi|^2.$$

(e) Obtain the characteristic impedance Z_0 for the confocal line, in terms of the parameters $\eta = \sqrt{\mu/\varepsilon}$, b, δ, and ξ.

(f) Verify that the result agrees with the characteristic impedance for a coaxial line (concentric circular conductors) in the limit $b \to 0$, $\delta \to \infty$ that reduces the confocal ellipses to concentric circles.

Discontinuity in Coaxial Line

11.3 A 60-Ω coaxial line with inner and outer radii 2 mm and 6 mm is joined to another such line with the same dimensions of its conductors but with a different dielectric, of permittivity $\varepsilon = 1.8\varepsilon_0$; the second line is terminated in its own matched impedance.

(a) What is the terminating impedance?

(b) Obtain the reflection coefficient at the interface.

Open-Circuited Line

11.4 If the end $z = l$ of a transmission line (phase velocity c/n, characteristic impedance Z_0) is left open-circuited:

(a) Express the voltage and current distributions $V(z)$ and $I(z)$ in terms of the incident wave amplitude V_0.

(b) Obtain the complex power $P(z)$ along the line.

(c) Express the voltage and current distributions $V(z)$ and $I(z)$ in terms of the source voltage V_s at $z = 0$.

(d) Find the impedance at position z and, in particular, at the source.

Impedance at Given Distance from Given Load

11.5 If the load impedance is $Z_l = (3 + j2)Z_0$ and observations are made at a distance 3.2λ from the load:

(a) What is the reflection coefficient at the load?

(b) What is the reflection coefficient at the observation point?

(c) What is the impedance (in terms of Z_0) at the observation point?

Load Impedance from VSWR Measurements

11.6 The VSWR along a 50-Ω lossless line is measured as 3.2 and two successive minima of the standing wave are found at distances 4.2 cm and 5.6 cm from the unknown load.

(a) Find the magnitude of the reflection coefficient.

(b) Find the phase of the reflection coefficient.

(c) Find the load impedance.

Load Impedance from Reflection Coefficient Measurements

11.7 The reflection coefficient measured at the load on a 50-Ω transmission line is found to be $\Gamma = \frac{1}{2} + j\frac{2}{3}$.

(a) What is the load impedance, Z_l?

(b) What is the VSWR on this line?

Standing Wave for a Given Load

11.8 The load on a 50-Ω lossless line is $(50 + j10)$ Ω and the wavelength along the line is 1.25 m.

(a) What is the VSWR along the line?

(b) Where is the minimum of the standing wave nearest the load?

Smith Chart Fundamentals

11.9 If the impedance at any point along a lossless line is normalized to the characteristic impedance, as $r + jx = (R + jX)/Z_0$, and curves of constant r or constant x are drawn within the unit circle of the complex Γ plane, the resultant construction is a Smith chart, shown for just a few values of r and x in Fig. P11–9. We find that the constant-r loci are full circles centered along the real axis and the constant-x loci are arcs of

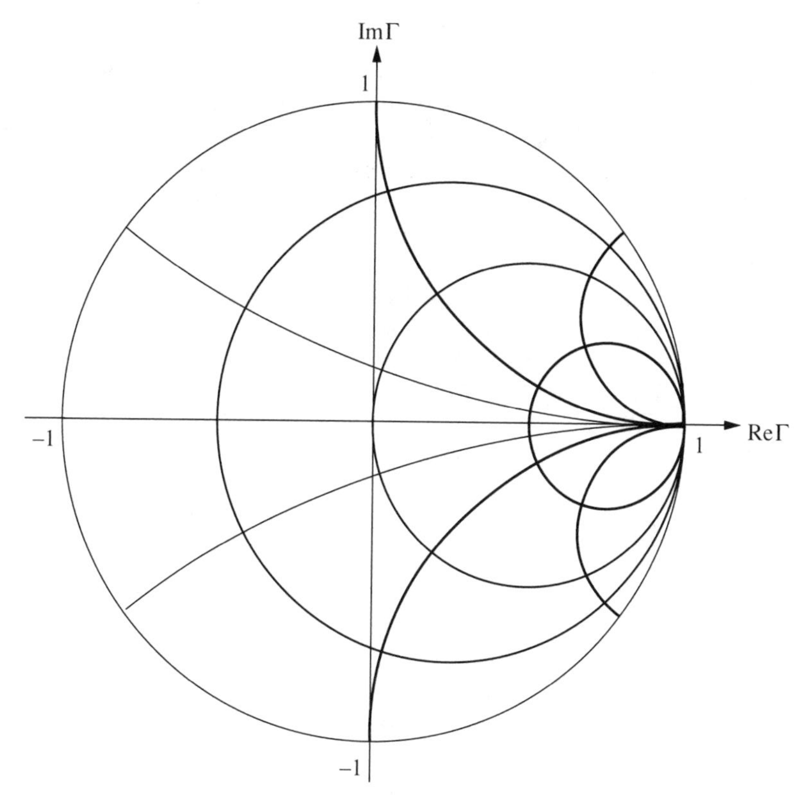

FIGURE P11–9 Rudimentary Smith chart.

circles centered along the line parallel to the imaginary axis, passing through the point $\Gamma = 1$.

(a) Find the center and radius of the circle $r = r_0$.

(b) Find the center and radius of the circle $x = x_0$.

(c) If the point on the chart corresponding to normalized load impedance $r_0 + jx_0$ has been located, where on the chart can be found the point that corresponds to the impedance seen at $\lambda/8$ in front of the load?

(d) What is the locus of points on the chart corresponding to a given VSWR?

Characteristic Impedance from Measured Impedances

11.10 Calculate the characteristic impedance Z_0 of a lossless transmission line that presents an impedance of $(40 - j30)\ \Omega$ at a point $\lambda/8$ away from the load, when terminated in a resistive load of $100\ \Omega$. (*Note:* A quadratic equation is to be solved. Are both solutions valid?)

Transmission Line with Source in the Middle

11.11 An ideal parallel-wire transmission line, with characteristic speed of propagation u_0, characteristic impedance Z_0, and length $2l$, is shorted at the end $z = 0$, open-circuited at the end $z = 2l$, and has a voltage source V_0 at frequency ω attached across it at the middle position $z = l$, as in Fig. P11–11.

(a) What boundary conditions apply at $z = 0$, at $z = 2l$, and at the source at $z = l$?

(b) Obtain the transverse voltage $V(z)$ and longitudinal current $I(z)$, on both sides of the source ($z < l$ and $z > l$).

(c) Find the current I_0 through the source.

(d) What are the VSWR values on both sides of the source ($z < l$ and $z > l$)?

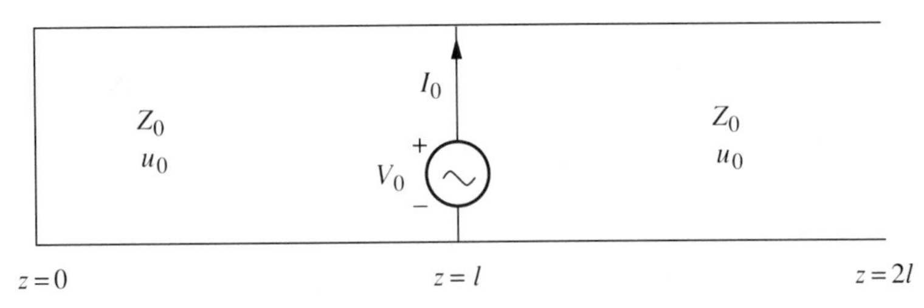

FIGURE P11–11 Parallel-wire line with source in the middle.

Matching with a Shunt Susceptance

11.12 When a transmission line feeds a mismatched load, the resultant inefficiency of power transfer to the load can be overcome by attaching a section of shorted line (a tuning stub) across the original line, at a suitable location in front of the load.

In Fig. P11–12, a parallel-wire line (wave velocity c, real characteristic impedance Z_0) feeds the mismatched impedance $Z_l = (3 + j2)Z_0$. At a suitable distance d in front of this load, a shorted section of the

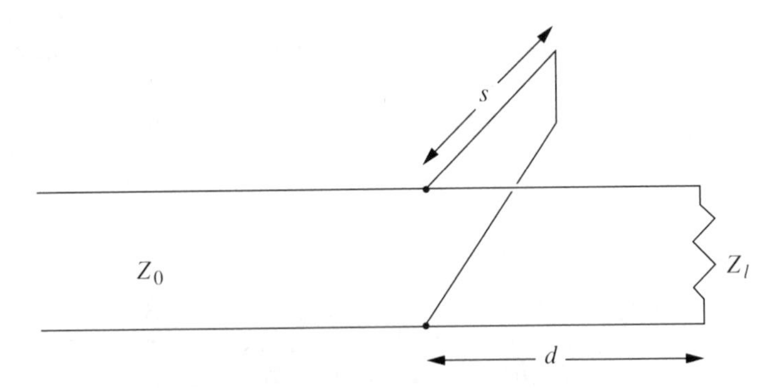

FIGURE P11–12 Matching with a tuning stub.

same type of line, of length s, is attached across the original line. Since the shorted stub represents a shunt susceptance in parallel with the admittance $Y = G + jB$ seen at location d in front of Z_l, matching can be achieved if the conductance G there is already $1/Z_0$ and the susceptance B can be canceled by the stub.

(a) Find the normalized distance d/λ at which the real part of the admittance Y is $1/Z_0$.

(b) Find the normalized stub length s/λ that will cancel the imaginary part of the admittance Y and thereby match the line.

(c) Why does this procedure guarantee 100% power transfer from source to mismatched load?

CHAPTER 12

Conducting Waveguides

The waves on a transmission line are TEM waves, with both the electric and magnetic fields transverse to the direction of propagation. The transverse variation of the nonuniform fields is that of an electrostatic pattern. Neither of these two features is a necessity; other nonuniform waves can travel along the z-axis of a waveguiding structure, in the form

$$\mathbf{E} = \mathbf{E}_0(x, y)e^{-j\beta z}, \tag{12.1}$$

without imposing the electrostatics condition $\nabla \times \mathbf{E}_0 = 0$. The more general types of waves are related to the TEM type in much the same way that oblique waves can be viewed as TE and TM normally incident waves.

Generalized Nonuniform Waves

To determine what nonuniform waves are permitted by Maxwell's equations, other than the TEM waves of transmission lines, we again use as trial functions for the equations

$$\mathbf{E} = \mathbf{E}_0(x, y)e^{-j\beta z}, \qquad \mathbf{H} = \mathbf{H}_0(x, y)e^{-j\beta z}; \tag{12.2}$$

these are waves that travel along z at phase velocity ω/β and have a nonuniform amplitude in the transverse plane. Once again, we obtain directly from Maxwell's equations the following relations between the electric and magnetic field amplitudes:

$$\nabla \times \mathbf{E}_0 = -j\omega\mu\left\{\mathbf{H}_0 - \frac{\beta}{\omega\mu}\,\hat{\mathbf{z}} \times \mathbf{E}_0\right\}, \tag{12.3}$$

$$\nabla \times \mathbf{H}_0 = j\omega\varepsilon\left\{\mathbf{E}_0 + \frac{\beta}{\omega\varepsilon}\,\hat{\mathbf{z}} \times \mathbf{H}_0\right\}. \tag{12.4}$$

This time, however, we do not ask for these equations to be satisfied by making both sides of each be zero, which is what led to the electrostatic field patterns and the TEM waves of transmission lines. We keep the equations general and seek solutions to these two simultaneous vector partial differential equations.

Helmholtz Solutions

An alternative to the two first-order partial differential equations is the single second-order wave equation for either the electric or the magnetic field, specialized for harmonic time variation at frequency ω. This is obtained by combining the two Maxwell equations:

$$\nabla \times \mathbf{E} = -j\omega\mu\mathbf{H}, \qquad \nabla \times \mathbf{H} = j\omega\varepsilon\mathbf{E}. \tag{12.5}$$

Taking the curl of one of the equations and substituting the other yields

$$\nabla \times \nabla \times \mathbf{E} = -j\omega\mu\nabla \times \mathbf{H} = -j\omega\mu j\omega\varepsilon\mathbf{E} = \omega^2\mu\varepsilon\mathbf{E} = \left(\frac{\omega}{c}\right)^2 n^2\mathbf{E}, \tag{12.6}$$

where n is the index of refraction for the medium in which the fields exist. But an identity of vector calculus states that

$$\nabla \times \nabla \times \mathbf{E} = \nabla\nabla \cdot \mathbf{E} - \nabla^2\mathbf{E}. \tag{12.7}$$

This defines the ∇^2 operator as applied to a vector; in a rectangular coordinate system, this operator is just the sum of the three partial second derivatives of the vector. But the second of the equations in (12.5) shows that $\nabla \cdot \mathbf{E} = 0$, so that $\nabla \times \nabla \times \mathbf{E} = -\nabla^2\mathbf{E}$ and the wave equation becomes

$$\nabla^2\mathbf{E} + k^2n^2\mathbf{E} = 0, \tag{12.8}$$

where $k = \omega/c$, the vacuum propagation constant. The same equation, known as the Helmholtz equation, holds for $\mathbf{H}$ as well, as is verified by finding $\nabla \times \nabla \times \mathbf{H}$. The Helmholtz equation is the wave equation, specialized to $e^{j\omega t}$ time variation.

When our nonuniform propagating wave trial solution for the fields is substituted into the Helmholtz equation, a similar equation emerges for the amplitudes $\mathbf{E}_0(x, y)$ and $\mathbf{H}_0(x, y)$. Applying $\nabla^2\mathbf{E}$ or $\partial^2\mathbf{E}/\partial x^2 + \partial^2\mathbf{E}/\partial y^2 + \partial^2\mathbf{E}/\partial z^2$ to the trial function $\mathbf{E} = \mathbf{E}_0(x, y)e^{-j\beta z}$ yields $\partial^2\mathbf{E}/\partial x^2 + \partial^2\mathbf{E}/\partial y^2 - \beta^2\mathbf{E}$, so that the Helmholtz equation becomes for such waves $\partial^2\mathbf{E}/\partial x^2 + \partial^2\mathbf{E}/\partial y^2 - \beta^2\mathbf{E} + k^2n^2\mathbf{E} = 0$ or, upon canceling the factor $e^{-j\beta z}$, $\nabla^2\mathbf{E}_0 + (k^2n^2 - \beta^2)\mathbf{E}_0 = 0$, or

$$\nabla^2\mathbf{E}_0 + p^2\mathbf{E}_0 = 0, \tag{12.9}$$

where ∇^2 is now only two-dimensional ($\nabla^2 = \partial^2/\partial x^2 + \partial^2/\partial y^2$) when applied to $\mathbf{E}_0(x, y)$ and with p^2 defined by

$$k^2n^2 = p^2 + \beta^2. \tag{12.10}$$

Equation (12.9) is the two-dimensional vector Helmholtz equation for the electric field amplitude $\mathbf{E}_0(x, y)$; the same equation holds for $\mathbf{H}_0(x, y)$.

Note that β in $e^{-j\beta z}$ is an assumed phase constant, which will give the wavelength, phase velocity, and group velocity of the nonuniform wave when we find out what its value is for the given operating frequency ω, but it is as yet an unknown quantity. So is p^2 unknown; only $k = \omega/c$ and the medium's refractive index $n = \sqrt{\varepsilon\mu/\varepsilon_0\mu_0}$ are known, so that the sum of the two unknowns p^2 and β^2 is a known quantity. The value of p, and hence of β, will have to emerge from the solution to the vector Helmholtz equation for the field amplitudes.

TE and TM Waves

Equations (12.3)–(12.4) for the wave amplitudes $\mathbf{E}_0(x, y)$ and $\mathbf{H}_0(x, y)$, and also the pair of Helmholtz equations for these fields, are vector equations, with a total of six unknown dependent variables. We show now that if just the axial components of $\mathbf{E}_0$ and of $\mathbf{H}_0$ become known, the entire pair of vector fields is obtainable directly from these two variables, merely by algebraic manipulation and differentiation. This means that it will suffice to solve the differential equations for the axial components of the field amplitudes; thereafter, the transverse components will be derivable from the axial ones.

To demonstrate this remarkable result, let the transverse parts of the two field amplitudes be denoted $\mathbf{E}_t$ and $\mathbf{H}_t$; that is,

$$\mathbf{E}_t = \hat{\mathbf{z}} \times \mathbf{E}_0 \times \hat{\mathbf{z}}, \qquad \mathbf{H}_t = \hat{\mathbf{z}} \times \mathbf{H}_0 \times \hat{\mathbf{z}}. \tag{12.11}$$

Upon taking the cross product of each of Eqs. (12.3)–(12.4) with $\hat{\mathbf{z}}$, we get

$$\hat{\mathbf{z}} \times \nabla \times \mathbf{E}_0 = -j\omega\mu\left\{\hat{\mathbf{z}} \times \mathbf{H}_0 + \frac{\beta}{\omega\mu}\mathbf{E}_t\right\}, \tag{12.12}$$

$$\hat{\mathbf{z}} \times \nabla \times \mathbf{H}_0 = j\omega\varepsilon\left\{\hat{\mathbf{z}} \times \mathbf{E}_0 - \frac{\beta}{\omega\varepsilon}\mathbf{H}_t\right\}. \tag{12.13}$$

The right sides involve only the transverse field components, since $\hat{\mathbf{z}} \times \mathbf{E}_0$ is the same as $\hat{\mathbf{z}} \times \mathbf{E}_t$. On the other hand, the left sides turn out to involve only the axial components, as follows from the vector identity for any vector function of only x, y:

$$\hat{\mathbf{z}} \times \nabla \times \mathbf{F}(x, y) = \nabla[\hat{\mathbf{z}} \cdot \mathbf{F}(x, y)], \tag{12.14}$$

which is just ∇F_z. It follows that

$$\nabla E_z = -j\omega\mu\left\{\hat{\mathbf{z}} \times \mathbf{H}_t + \frac{\beta}{\omega\mu}\mathbf{E}_t\right\}, \tag{12.15}$$

$$\nabla H_z = j\omega\varepsilon\left\{\hat{\mathbf{z}} \times \mathbf{E}_t - \frac{\beta}{\omega\varepsilon}\mathbf{H}_t\right\}. \tag{12.16}$$

What we want is the inverse of these equations. That is, we consider these to be two simultaneous equations for $\mathbf{E}_t$ and $\mathbf{H}_t$ in terms of the two axial components E_z and H_z that we suppose to have been solved for already. To invert these equations, we can combine them so as to eliminate $\mathbf{H}_t$ as

$$j\omega\mu\hat{\mathbf{z}} \times \nabla H_z - j\beta\nabla E_z = (k^2n^2 - \beta^2)\mathbf{E}_t = p^2\mathbf{E}_t \tag{12.17}$$

and recombine them so as to eliminate $\mathbf{E}_t$ as

$$-j\omega\varepsilon\hat{\mathbf{z}} \times \nabla E_z - j\beta\nabla H_z = (k^2n^2 - \beta^2)\mathbf{H}_t = p^2\mathbf{H}_t. \tag{12.18}$$

These equations confirm what we sought to demonstrate: that the transverse field amplitudes $\mathbf{E}_t$ and $\mathbf{H}_t$ are indeed derivable directly from the axial components E_z and H_z (more precisely, from their gradients) alone.

But these equations also demonstrate another important property of the field amplitudes. They represent the transverse fields as linear combinations of the gradients of the two axial components. Hence, they allow the general transverse fields $\mathbf{E}_t$ and $\mathbf{H}_t$ to be expressed as a superposition of two simpler types, one that has no axial component of **E** (a TE wave) and another that has no axial component of **H** (a TM wave):

For the TE wave ($E_z = 0$):

$$p^2\mathbf{E}_t^{\mathrm{TE}} = j\omega\mu\hat{\mathbf{z}} \times \nabla H_z \qquad \text{and} \qquad p^2\mathbf{H}_t^{\mathrm{TE}} = -j\beta\nabla H_z. \tag{12.19}$$

For the TM wave ($H_z = 0$):

$$p^2\mathbf{H}_t^{\mathrm{TM}} = -j\omega\varepsilon\hat{\mathbf{z}} \times \nabla E_z \qquad \text{and} \qquad p^2\mathbf{E}_t^{\mathrm{TM}} = -j\beta\nabla E_z. \tag{12.20}$$

It therefore suffices to solve for H_z to obtain a TE wave and, separately, to solve for E_z to extract a TM wave; the general solution is a superposition of both types. The axial field components are to be found by solving the two-dimensional scalar Helmholtz equations

$$\nabla^2 H_z + p^2 H_z = 0 \qquad \text{for TE waves}, \tag{12.21}$$

$$\nabla^2 E_z + p^2 E_z = 0 \qquad \text{for TM waves}. \tag{12.22}$$

This separation into transverse electric and transverse magnetic waves, derivable separately and from scalar instead of vector Helmholtz equations, represents a considerable simplification of the original combined vector partial differential equation problem.

The program should now be clear. We first solve the two-dimensional Helmholtz equation for either H_z or E_z, each separately, for some given configuration of conductors and dielectrics in a transverse plane. From each solution for the axial fields, we can then construct a full TE or TM wave that propagates in the third dimension as $e^{-j\beta z}$, as follows.

For the TE wave ($E_z = 0$):

$$\mathbf{H}^{\mathrm{TE}} = \left\{\hat{\mathbf{z}}H_z - \frac{j\beta}{p^2}\nabla H_z\right\}e^{-j\beta z}, \qquad \mathbf{E}^{\mathrm{TE}} = Z^{\mathrm{TE}}\mathbf{H}^{\mathrm{TE}} \times \hat{\mathbf{z}}. \tag{12.23}$$

For the TM wave ($H_z = 0$):

$$\mathbf{E}^{\mathrm{TM}} = \left\{\hat{\mathbf{z}}E_z - \frac{j\beta}{p^2}\nabla E_z\right\}e^{-j\beta z}, \qquad Z^{\mathrm{TM}}\mathbf{H}^{\mathrm{TM}} = \hat{\mathbf{z}} \times \mathbf{E}^{\mathrm{TM}}. \tag{12.24}$$

The wave impedances, the ratio of the transverse electric and magnetic field magnitudes, are

$$Z^{\mathrm{TE}} = \frac{\omega\mu}{\beta}, \qquad Z^{\mathrm{TM}} = \frac{\beta}{\omega\varepsilon}. \tag{12.25}$$

For both cases, $\beta^2 = k^2n^2 - p^2$. The value of the unknown constant p will emerge from the solution to the Helmholtz equation for either H_z or E_z; this partial differential equation is the same for both cases, but the associated boundary conditions will differ for the TE and TM configurations.

The TEM waves of transmission lines correspond here to the special case of $p^2 = 0$, whereupon the Helmholtz equation reduces to the Laplace equation $\nabla^2\varphi = 0$ of electrostatics and $\beta^2 = k^2n^2$ yields propagation at the speed of light in the dielectric medium, c/n. We now exclude that case.

Whereas, for an electrostatic field pattern, we needed at least a pair of conductors with a dielectric between them to avoid a trivial, zero-field solution, we can now look for nontrivial field patterns even in a space enclosed by a single, hollow conductor that surrounds a dielectric. For the wave solutions to be valid for all z, the spatial configuration that comprises the original two-dimensional hollow-conductor problem in the xy-plane must be extended *uniformly* into the third dimension, along z, thereby forming a hollow pipe whose cross section exactly matches the configuration of the two-dimensional geometry. This will be seen to confine and guide the TE and TM waves; any such pipe is hence called a *waveguide.*

Rectangular Waveguide

The simplest hollow pipe to analyze has a rectangular cross section, as shown in Figure 12–1. The perfectly conducting walls are spaced apart by distances a and b in the x- and y-directions and enclose a perfect dielectric with constitutive parameters ε, μ (or material impedance η and refractive index n). We seek the TE and TM waves for this waveguide geometry.

We need to solve the two-dimensional boundary value problem

$$\nabla^2\psi + p^2\psi = 0, \tag{12.26}$$

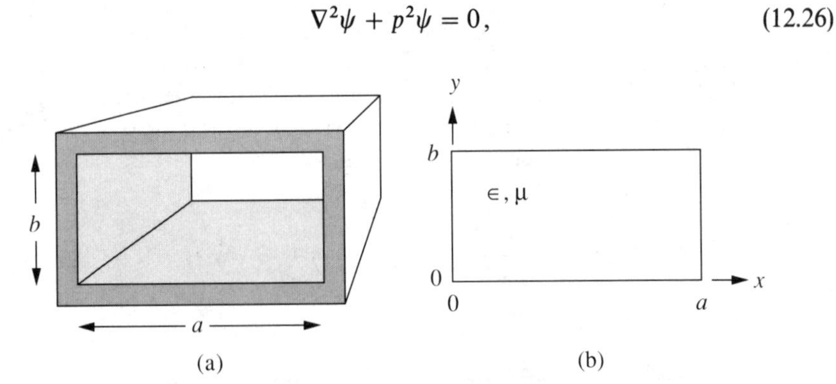

FIGURE 12–1 Rectangular waveguide geometry.

where $\psi = \psi(x, y)$ will be E_z for TM waves and H_z for TE waves. For either case,

$$\frac{\partial^2 \psi}{\partial x^2} + \frac{\partial^2 \psi}{\partial y^2} + p^2 \psi = 0 \tag{12.27}$$

is the partial differential equation to be solved in the space $0 < x < a$, $0 < y < b$. The sovereign approach is to try separation of variables; if it works (here, it does), it yields solutions with relative ease. We assume that a solution exists in the form of a product of a function $X(x)$ of x alone and another function $Y(y)$ of y alone; if such solutions can be found, superpositions of these special solutions can form more general solutions. Our trial function is therefore

$$\psi(x, y) = X(x)Y(y); \tag{12.28}$$

substituting this into the differential equation, we find, after dividing by ψ,

$$\frac{1}{X}\frac{d^2 X}{dx^2} + \frac{1}{Y}\frac{d^2 Y}{dy^2} + p^2 = 0. \tag{12.29}$$

Because the first term depends only on x and the second only on y, each term in this equation must be a constant, as becomes obvious upon differentiating the entire equation with respect to one or the other of x, y. Furthermore, the sum of the three constants must be zero, to satisfy the equation itself, so that we choose to write p^2 as

$$p^2 = p_x^2 + p_y^2 \tag{12.30}$$

and identify these two constant constituents of p^2 with the negatives of the first two terms in Eq. (12.29), obtaining two ordinary differential equations for the unknown functions $X(x)$ and $Y(y)$:

$$\frac{d^2 X}{dx^2} + p_x^2 X(x) = 0, \qquad \frac{d^2 Y}{dy^2} + p_y^2 Y(y) = 0. \tag{12.31}$$

Before proceeding to solve these rather simple differential equations, we should review what is known and what is unknown in them. In fact, the only thing known in these equations is that p_x and p_y are constants, but their values are unknown; as yet, they might not even be real. The sum of their squares, p^2, is also an unknown constant, as is β^2 in the relation

$$p^2 + \beta^2 = k^2 n^2, \tag{12.32}$$

in which, for a given operating frequency, the right side is known, since $k^2 = \omega^2/c^2$ and $n^2 = \mu\varepsilon/\mu_0 \varepsilon_0$ is given. We will find that the boundary conditions will determine p_x and p_y, hence p, hence β, hence the wavelength and phase and group velocities, as well as the field patterns in the dielectric space, in short, everything we need to know about the waveguide. The boundaries of the space in which we are solving the differential equation are $x = 0$, a and $y = 0$, b and these boundaries are perfectly conducting walls.

The physical boundary condition is that the *tangential electric field must vanish at the conducting walls.* To convert this requirement into a mathematical boundary condition on $\psi(x, y)$ and on $X(x)$ and $Y(y)$, we must consider TM and TE waves separately, because $\mathbf{E}$ is obtained differently for the two types of wave.

For the TM case, the axial component E_z is tangential on all four walls; E_x is tangential on the "floor" and "ceiling" $y = 0, b$ and E_y is tangential on the two side walls $x = 0, a$. But the transverse components E_x and E_y are derived from the axial component E_z by use of

$$\mathbf{E}^{\mathrm{TM}} = \hat{\mathbf{z}}E_z - \frac{j\beta}{p^2}\nabla \mathbf{E}_z, \tag{12.33}$$

or

$$E_x = -\frac{j\beta}{p^2}\frac{\partial E_z}{\partial x}, \qquad E_y = -\frac{j\beta}{p^2}\frac{\partial E_z}{\partial y}. \tag{12.34}$$

We require that $E_z = 0$ on all four sides, which already makes $\partial E_z/\partial x$ and $\partial E_z/\partial y$ vanish on the walls. Therefore, the condition $E_z = 0$ or

$$\psi = 0 \qquad \text{(TM case)} \tag{12.35}$$

on each wall suffices to guarantee that the tangential electric field duly vanish on all the conducting boundaries, for the TM case.

For the TE case, there is no axial component of the electric field, but E_x is tangential and must vanish on the bottom and top walls, $y = 0, b$, while E_y is tangential and must vanish on the two side walls, $x = 0, a$. But the transverse components E_x and E_y are derived from the axial component H_z by use of

$$\begin{aligned}\mathbf{E}^{\mathrm{TE}} &= Z^{\mathrm{TE}}\mathbf{H}^{\mathrm{TE}} \times \hat{\mathbf{z}} = -\frac{\omega\mu}{\beta}\hat{\mathbf{z}} \times \mathbf{H} = -\frac{\omega\mu}{\beta}\hat{\mathbf{z}} \times \left[-\frac{j\beta}{p^2}\nabla H_z\right] \\ &= \frac{j\omega\mu}{p^2}\hat{\mathbf{z}} \times \nabla H_z,\end{aligned} \tag{12.36}$$

so that

$$E_x = 0 \quad \text{requires that} \quad \frac{\partial H_z}{\partial y} = 0 \quad \text{at} \quad y = 0, b, \tag{12.37}$$

$$E_y = 0 \quad \text{requires that} \quad \frac{\partial H_z}{\partial x} = 0 \quad \text{at} \quad x = 0, a. \tag{12.38}$$

Therefore, the condition that the *normal derivative* of ψ vanish or

$$\hat{\mathbf{n}} \cdot \nabla\psi = 0 \qquad \text{(TE case)} \tag{12.39}$$

on each wall, where $\hat{\mathbf{n}}$ is normal to the boundary, suffices to guarantee that the tangential electric field duly vanish on all the conducting boundaries, for the TE case.

We can now proceed with the solution to the boundary value problem by separation of variables, for the TM and TE cases separately. Assuming that

$\psi(x, y) = X(x)Y(y)$, we found that X and Y have to satisfy

$$\frac{d^2X}{dx^2} + p_x^2 X(x) = 0, \qquad \frac{d^2Y}{dy^2} + p_y^2\, Y(y) = 0. \tag{12.40}$$

These constant-coefficient ordinary differential equations are satisfied by trigonometric functions, $\sin p_x x$ and $\cos p_x x$ for $X(x)$, $\sin p_y y$ and $\cos p_y y$ for $Y(y)$. The coefficients of these independent solutions are to be found from the boundary conditions, which differ for the TM and TE cases.

For TM waves, we need $\psi(x, 0) = 0$ and $\psi(x, b) = 0$ for all x in $0 < x < a$, which, for $\psi(x, y) = X(x)Y(y)$, can be achieved only by requiring that $Y(0) = 0$, $Y(b) = 0$. We also need $\psi(0, y) = 0$ and $\psi(a, y) = 0$ for all y in $0 < y < b$, which demands that $X(0) = 0$, $X(a) = 0$. The trigonometric function that is zero at zero argument has the form $X(x) = A \sin p_x x$ and this is required to satisfy $X(a) = A \sin p_x a = 0$. If we comply by making $A = 0$, the entire $X(x)$ factor becomes the trivial zero solution. For a nontrivial solution, we need $\sin p_x a = 0$. Similarly, $Y(y) = B \sin p_y y$ with $Y(b) = B \sin p_y b = 0$ and without $B = 0$ leaves the conditions

$$\sin p_x a = 0 \qquad \text{and} \qquad \sin p_y b = 0 \qquad \text{(TM)}. \tag{12.41}$$

These are constraints on the unknowns p_x and p_y; they determine permissible values of these constants as the discrete set

$$p_x = \frac{l\pi}{a}, \qquad p_y = \frac{m\pi}{b}, \qquad (l, m = \text{integer}). \tag{12.42}$$

The product solutions for $\psi(x, y) = X(x)Y(y)$ are therefore any one of the set

$$\psi(x, y) = AB \sin p_x x \sin p_y y = C \sin \frac{l\pi x}{a} \sin \frac{m\pi y}{b}, \tag{12.43}$$

(C is a combined arbitrary constant amplitude) with

$$p^2 = p_x^2 + p_y^2 = \left(\frac{l\pi}{a}\right)^2 + \left(\frac{m\pi}{b}\right)^2 = k^2n^2 - \beta^2. \tag{12.44}$$

Thus the waveguide geometry alone, through the boundary conditions at the walls, determines p, hence $\beta = \beta(\omega)$, hence the wavelength and the phase and group velocities. A different possible solution exists for each pair of integers l, m (except either $l = 0$ or $m = 0$, for which $\psi = 0$ identically). The field pattern derived from the axial component

$$E_z(x, y) = \psi(x, y) = C \sin \frac{l\pi x}{a} \sin \frac{m\pi y}{b} \qquad \text{(TM)} \tag{12.45}$$

for a particular choice of integers l, m is called a *mode* of propagation, denoted TM_{lm}. Superpositions of such modes, with different amplitude coefficients C for each pair of integers, form more general TM solutions.

For TE waves, we need $\partial\psi(x, 0)/\partial y = 0$ and $\partial\psi(x, b)/\partial y = 0$ for all x in $0 < x < a$ which, for $\partial\psi(x, y)/\partial y = X(x)\, dY(y)/dy$, can be achieved only by requiring that $dY(0)/dy = 0$, $dY(b)/dy = 0$. We also need $\partial\psi(0, y)/\partial x = 0$ and

$\partial\psi(a, y)/\partial x = 0$ for all y in $0 < y < b$, which demands that $dX(0)/dx = 0$, $dX(a)/dx = 0$. The trigonometric function that has zero slope at zero argument has the form $X(x) = A \cos p_x x$ and this is required to satisfy $X'(a) = -p_x A \sin p_x a = 0$. If we comply by making $A = 0$, the entire $X(x)$ factor becomes the trivial zero solution. For a nontrivial solution, we need $\sin p_x a = 0$. Similarly, $Y(y) = B \cos p_y y$ with $Y'(b) = -p_y B \sin p_y b = 0$ and without $B = 0$ leaves the conditions

$$\sin p_x a = 0 \qquad \text{and} \qquad \sin p_y b = 0 \qquad (\text{TE}). \tag{12.46}$$

These are constraints on the unknowns p_x and p_y; they determine permissible values of these constants as the discrete set

$$p_x = \frac{l\pi}{a}, \qquad p_y = \frac{m\pi}{b}, \qquad (l, m = \text{integer}). \tag{12.47}$$

The product solutions for $\psi(x, y) = X(x)Y(y)$ are therefore any one of the set

$$\psi(x, y) = AB \cos p_x x \cos p_y y = C \cos \frac{l\pi x}{a} \cos \frac{m\pi y}{b}, \tag{12.48}$$

(C is a combined arbitrary constant amplitude) with

$$p^2 = p_x^2 + p_y^2 = \left(\frac{l\pi}{a}\right)^2 + \left(\frac{m\pi}{b}\right)^2 = k^2 n^2 - \beta^2. \tag{12.49}$$

Again, the waveguide geometry alone, through the boundary conditions at the walls, determines p, hence $\beta = \beta(\omega)$, hence the wavelength and the phase and group velocities. A different possible solution exists for each pair of integers l, m (except both $l = 0$ and $m = 0$, for which $\psi = C$ and $\nabla\psi = 0$ identically, giving zero field; that would be the $p = 0$ electrostatic solution, which vanishes inside a hollow conductor). The field pattern derived from the axial component

$$H_z(x, y) = \psi(x, y) = C \cos \frac{l\pi x}{a} \cos \frac{m\pi y}{b} \qquad (\text{TE}) \tag{12.50}$$

for a particular choice of integers l, m is called a *mode* of propagation, denoted TE_{lm}. Superpositions of such modes, with different amplitude coefficients C for each pair of integers, form more general TE solutions. Superpositions of both TE and TM modes form the most general solutions. In fact, we recognize such superpositions to be Fourier series, which can represent any reasonable distribution of axial fields that satisfy the boundary conditions.

Interpretation

The simplest of the rectangular waveguide modes we have just found is the TE_{10} mode. With $l = 1$, $m = 0$, the axial magnetic field and its gradient are

$$H_z = \psi_{10}(x, y) = C \cos \frac{\pi x}{a}, \qquad \nabla H_z = -\hat{\mathbf{x}} C \frac{\pi}{a} \sin \frac{\pi x}{a}, \tag{12.51}$$

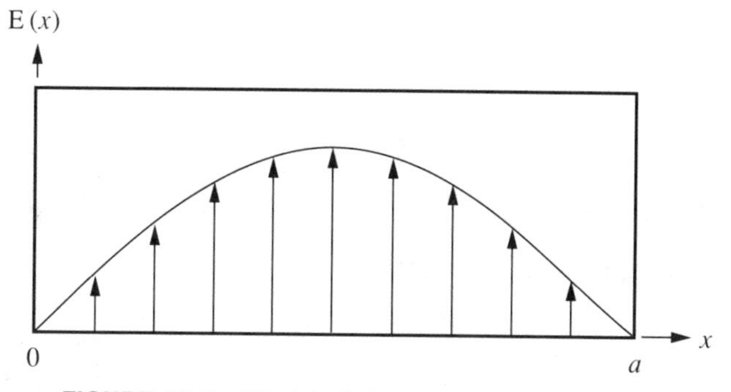

FIGURE 12–2 Electric field pattern of TE_{10} mode.

with $p = \pi/a$, and the complete field pattern is given by

$$\mathbf{H} = \hat{\mathbf{z}}H_z - \frac{j\beta}{p^2}\nabla H_z, \qquad \mathbf{E} = Z^{\mathrm{TE}}\mathbf{H} \times \hat{\mathbf{z}}, \tag{12.52}$$

with $Z^{\mathrm{TE}} = \omega\mu/\beta$ and the factor $e^{-j\beta z}$ appended; more explicitly,

$$\mathbf{H} = C[\hat{\mathbf{z}} \cos px + \hat{\mathbf{x}}j\frac{\beta}{p} \sin px], \qquad \mathbf{E} = -\frac{j\omega\mu}{p} C\hat{\mathbf{y}} \sin px. \tag{12.53}$$

That is, the electric field is transverse,

$$\mathbf{E} = \hat{\mathbf{y}}E_0 \sin px, \tag{12.54}$$

with a sinusoidal distribution across the waveguide, peaked in the middle of the span and vanishing at the two walls, as plotted in Figure 12–2. The transverse part of the magnetic field has the same sinusoidal distribution but is directed along x; the axial magnetic field is in time quadrature to the transverse part and has a cos px distribution instead, which peaks at the walls and is zero in the middle of the waveguide, at $x = a/2$.

The sinusoidal transverse distribution can be considered a standing wave, a superposition of oppositely traveling waves of equal strength along the x-axis; the complete pattern propagates axially as a traveling wave, as $e^{-j\beta z}$. This view of the field can be made explicit by writing the sinusoidal pattern as a sum of two exponentials, as in

$$\mathbf{E} = -\frac{j\omega\mu}{p} C\hat{\mathbf{y}} \sin px = C\frac{\omega\mu}{2p}\hat{\mathbf{y}}[e^{-jpx} - e^{jpx}] \tag{12.55}$$

$$\begin{aligned}\mathbf{H} &= C\left[\hat{\mathbf{z}} \cos px + \hat{\mathbf{x}}j\frac{\beta}{p} \sin px\right] \\ &= \frac{1}{2}C\hat{\mathbf{z}}[e^{-jpx} + e^{jpx}] - \frac{1}{2}C\frac{\beta}{p}\hat{\mathbf{x}}[e^{-jpx} - e^{jpx}],\end{aligned} \tag{12.56}$$

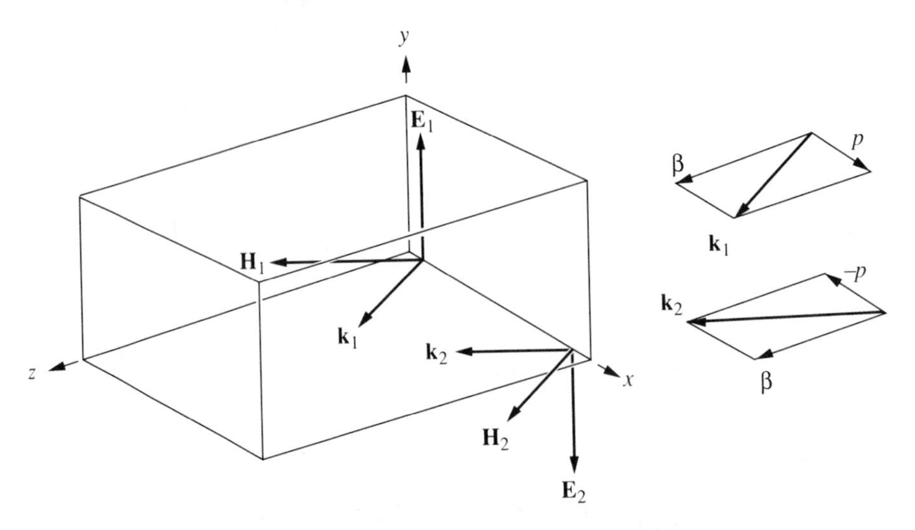

FIGURE 12–3 TE_{10} mode as a pair of oblique waves.

so that, with the axial propagation factor, the entire field is seen to be a superposition of two obliquely traveling plane waves:

$$\mathbf{E} = C\frac{\omega\mu}{2p}\,\hat{\mathbf{y}}[e^{-j(px+\beta z)} - e^{j(px-\beta z)}], \tag{12.57}$$

$$\mathbf{H} = \frac{C}{2p}[\hat{\mathbf{z}}p - \hat{\mathbf{x}}\beta]e^{-j(px+\beta z)} + \frac{C}{2p}[\hat{\mathbf{z}}p + \hat{\mathbf{x}}\beta]e^{j(px-\beta z)}. \tag{12.58}$$

The first of these oblique waves travels along $\mathbf{k}_1 = p\hat{\mathbf{x}} + \beta\hat{\mathbf{z}}$ and the other along $\mathbf{k}_2 = -p\hat{\mathbf{x}} + \beta\hat{\mathbf{z}}$; they are therefore directed at equal and opposite angles to the waveguide's axis. They reflect and bounce back and forth between the parallel walls at $x = 0$ and $x = a$, each becoming the other upon reflection at either wall, while both oblique waves progress along the z-axis. Figure 12–3 shows how the two oblique waves that comprise the TE_{10} mode are related to the waveguide geometry.

Waveguide Dispersion

The dispersion relation for the rectangular waveguide is determined for both TE_{lm} and TM_{lm} modes by the same value of $p = p_{lm}$; this is a coincidence traceable to the symmetry of a rectangle. The relation $\omega = \omega(\beta)$ is expressed by

$$k^2n^2 = p^2 + \beta^2 \qquad \text{or} \qquad \frac{\omega^2 n^2}{c^2} = \left(\frac{l\pi}{a}\right)^2 + \left(\frac{m\pi}{b}\right)^2 + \beta^2. \tag{12.59}$$

The time and axial dependence of a mode is as exp $[j(\omega t - \beta z)]$, so that the wavelength along the waveguide is

$$\lambda_g = \frac{2\pi}{\beta} \tag{12.60}$$

instead of the free-space value $\lambda_0 = 2\pi/k$ or that for an unbounded medium of refractive index n, $\lambda = 2\pi/(kn)$. For the TE_{10} mode in particular, the dispersion relation is

$$k^2 n^2 = \left(\frac{\pi}{a}\right)^2 + \beta^2 \tag{12.61}$$

and can be expressed in terms of the wavelengths $\lambda = \lambda_0/n$ and λ_g as

$$\frac{1}{\lambda^2} = \frac{1}{(2a)^2} + \frac{1}{\lambda_g^2}. \tag{12.62}$$

The dispersion relation for a waveguide is of the type that was discussed in Chapter 6, the type for which the squares of the frequency and of the propagation constant have a constant shift between them, as in

$$\omega^2 = \omega_c^2 + \beta^2 v^2. \tag{12.63}$$

For the rectangular waveguide, the asymptotic phase velocity v is c/n and the *cutoff frequency* below which no real value of the propagation constant β can be found is given for either the TE_{lm} or the TM_{lm} mode by

$$\omega_c = pv = \left\{\left(\frac{l\pi v}{a}\right)^2 + \left(\frac{m\pi v}{b}\right)^2\right\}^{1/2}. \tag{12.64}$$

The dispersion relation plots as a hyperbola, with vertex at the cutoff frequency and asymptotic to the dispersion relation for the corresponding unbounded medium, $\omega = \beta v$; it is illustrated in Figure 12–4.

The phase velocity at frequency ω above the cutoff frequency is

$$v_p = \frac{\omega}{\beta} = \frac{c}{n}\left[1 - \left(\frac{\omega_c}{\omega}\right)^2\right]^{-1/2}. \tag{12.65}$$

This is asymptotic to the phase velocity for waves in the unbounded medium, when the frequency is far above cutoff. As the frequency approaches cutoff, however, the phase velocity increases indefinitely; it is always greater than the speed of light in the dielectric (or the vacuum speed of light, c, if the waveguide is empty) at any frequency for which propagation can occur, but recall that no signal is transmitted at the phase velocity, which is defined only geometrically. On the other hand, the group velocity, obtainable by differentiating the dispersion relation with respect to β and solving for $d\omega/d\beta$, is

$$v_g = \frac{d\omega}{d\beta} = \frac{c}{n}\left[1 - \left(\frac{\omega_c}{\omega}\right)^2\right]^{1/2}, \tag{12.66}$$

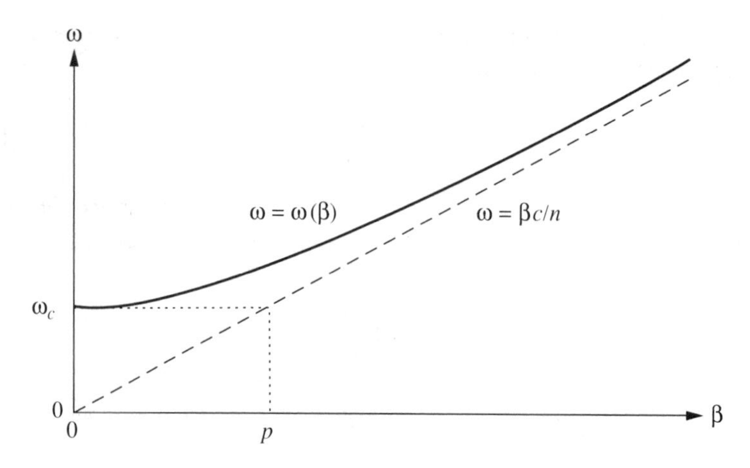

FIGURE 12–4 Dispersion curve for a waveguide.

and is less than the speed of light; narrow-band signals are conveyed along the waveguide at the group velocity. As the frequency drops to the cutoff frequency, the group velocity approaches zero. In this regime, the oblique waves that comprise the waveguide mode propagate nearly perpendicularly to the waveguide axis, bouncing back and forth between the side walls without making significant progress along the guide axis.

EXAMPLE 12.1

One standard microwave rectangular waveguide has inside dimensions $a = 0.9$ in. by $b = 0.4$ in. and is air filled. Find its cutoff frequency for the TE_{10} mode and the guide wavelength and phase and group velocities if it is operated at frequency $f = 9.0$ GHz.

From $\omega_c = pc$ with $p = \pi/a$ for $l = 1$, $m = 0$, we get for the cutoff frequency $f_c = \omega_c/2\pi = c/2a = [(29.98)\ \text{cm/ns}]/[2(0.9\ \text{in.})(2.54\ \text{cm/in.})] = 6.557$ GHz, so that $\omega_c/\omega = f_c/f = 0.7286$ and the phase velocity is then $v_p = c/[1 - (f_c/f)^2]^{1/2} = c/0.6850 = 1.460c = 43.77$ cm/ns, while the group velocity is $v_g = c^2/v_p = 0.6850c = 20.53$ cm/ns. The guide wavelength is then $\lambda_g = v_p/f = 1.460(c/f) = 1.460\lambda_0 = (1.460)(3.331\ \text{cm}) = 4.863$ cm. ◆

For a given waveguide geometry, there is a family of modes, both TE and TM. Each has its own cutoff frequency, which must be exceeded for that mode to propagate. At any particular operating frequency, however, only a finite number of waveguide modes are above cutoff and can propagate. Figure 12–5 shows part of the family of dispersion curves for a rectangular waveguide with the width-to-height ratio $a/b = 9/4$. The cutoff frequencies have been labeled with the subscripts lm for the modes. Not all the modes that fit into the illus-

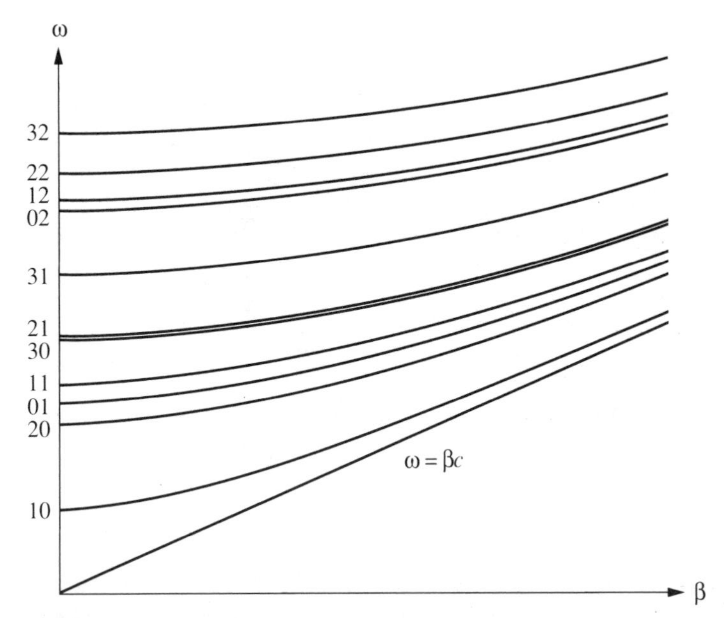

FIGURE 12–5 Family of dispersion curves for a rectangular waveguide.

trated range of frequencies have been shown; the 40- and 50-modes, for example, have been omitted. Note also that for this a/b ratio, the 30- and 21-modes have cutoff frequencies that are quite close to each other, at 3.0000 and 3.0104 ($=\sqrt{l^2 + (ma/b)^2}$ for $l = 2$, $m = 1$) times the cutoff for the TE_{10} mode. All the dispersion curves are eventually asymptotic to the same straight line, $\omega = \beta c$ for an empty waveguide.

As the operating frequency is increased from dc, there is first no mode that is above cutoff and can propagate. The mode with the lowest cutoff frequency is the TE_{10} mode (the TE_{01} mode has a higher cutoff frequency if $a > b$ and TM modes do not appear until the TM_{11} mode is above cutoff). Its cutoff is at $\omega_c = p_{10}\, c = \pi c/a$ (for an empty guide); this corresponds to a frequency such that the free-space wavelength has just become less than $2a$. The interpretation is that a half-wavelength (in unbounded space) fits across the waveguide, corresponding to the picture of a wave that propagates along the guide but is formed of a standing wave across it. After attaining frequencies high enough for the TE_{10} mode to be above cutoff, that mode is the only one that does propagate, until the cutoff for the next-lowest-cutoff mode is reached. Thereafter, both these modes can propagate, sharing the available power between them in some proportion determined by the way they have been generated. At still higher frequencies, more and more modes can propagate, of both the TE and the TM type. In Figure 12–6, three modes can propagate at the operating frequency ω_{op} shown, namely the TE_{10}, TE_{20}, and TE_{01} modes; their respective phase constants β are indicated (along with the free-space one, k). The TE_{11} and TM_{11} modes are, however, still below cutoff at that frequency.

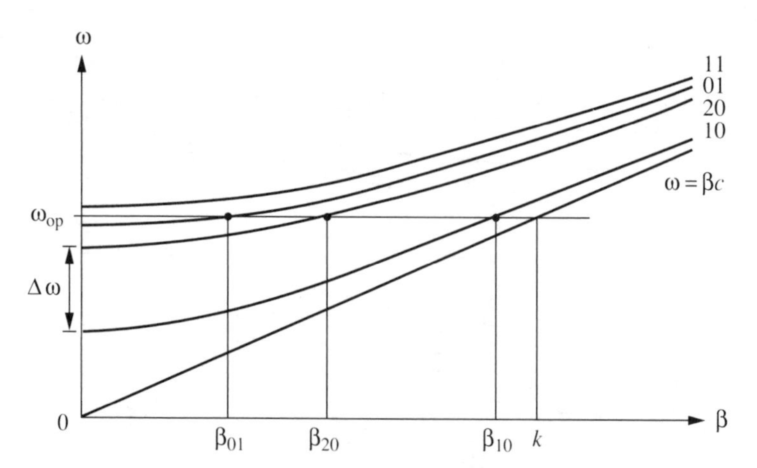

FIGURE 12–6 Three modes are above cutoff at frequency ω_{op}.

It is often desirable to have only one mode be capable of propagating, so that the energy is not shared among different ones with different group velocities and the generating and detection schemes are eased. If the operating frequency is designed to be between the cutoff for the TE_{10} mode and the next-lowest cutoff, then only the TE_{10} mode can propagate. This mode is called the *dominant* mode; it is always there if any mode can be. Under dominant-mode operation, the propagating field pattern is unique, making it easier to generate and detect. As soon as other modes are above cutoff, what propagates can be any superposition of these modes and the resultant field pattern is more difficult to predict and utilize. In Figure 12–6, the frequency range for dominant-mode operation is indicated by $\Delta\omega$.

For the TE_{10} mode, the transverse electric field pattern is a half-cycle of a sinusoid across the broad width of the guide. For the TE_{20} mode, a full cycle fits across the guide. For the TE_{lm} or TM_{lm} modes, the pattern has $l/2$ cycles across the width and $m/2$ cycles along the height, with $(l-1)$ and $(m-1)$ nodes, respectively, between the waveguide walls, as illustrated for $l = 2$ and $l = 5$ in Figure 12–7. Each mode has its own, distinct field pattern, even if several modes happen to share a single cutoff frequency, a "degeneracy" that can arise from the symmetry of the waveguide cross section.

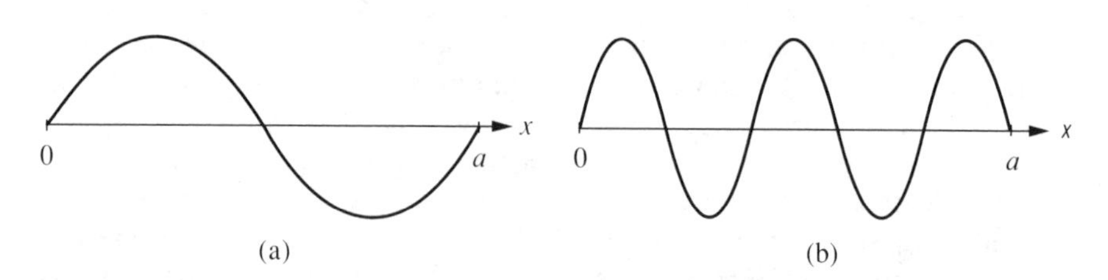

FIGURE 12–7 Rectangular waveguide mode field patterns for $l = 2, 5$.

Waves Below Cutoff

The waveguide dispersion relation

$$\omega^2 = \omega_c^2 + \beta^2 v^2 \qquad \text{or} \qquad k^2n^2 = p^2 + \beta^2 \tag{12.67}$$

(with $k = \omega/c$, $v = c/n$, $\omega_c = pv$, and p determined for each mode by the geometry of the waveguide's cross section) indicates that the operating frequency ω must exceed the cutoff frequency ω_c in order for the mode to propagate with phase constant β. What happens if we operate at a frequency below the cutoff frequency for a particular mode?

Below the cutoff frequency, $\omega < \omega_c$ or $kn < p$ and the assumed $e^{-j\beta z}$ factor still provides a solution with p unchanged for the mode, since p depends only on the geometry through the boundary conditions, but now β^2 is negative and β is not real:

$$\beta^2 = -(p^2 - k^2n^2) \qquad \text{or} \qquad \beta = -j\alpha = -j\sqrt{p^2 - k^2n^2}, \tag{12.68}$$

which means that the exp $[j(\omega t - \beta z)]$ dependence is changed to $e^{j\omega t}e^{-\alpha z}$. This corresponds to oscillation (at frequency ω) without propagation but with attenuation of the field amplitude with decay rate α along the waveguide. The sign of the square root in Eq. (12.68) is selected to yield attenuation in the direction away from the source. The wave gets weaker as distance from the source increases; it is said to be an *evanescent* mode, or to be "cut off" when the frequency is below ω_c.

High-order modes, those with large values of the integers l and m, have large values of p and hence high cutoff frequencies. The further below cutoff we set the operating frequency, the greater the difference $p^2 - k^2n^2$ and the stronger the decay rate $\alpha = \sqrt{p^2 - k^2n^2}$ for the mode; the wave amplitude then has a shorter e-folding distance $1/\alpha$ and survives only near its source.

EXAMPLE 12.2

For the waveguide previously considered, 0.9 in. by 0.4 in. and empty, what is the frequency range for dominant-mode operation and what are the decay rates of the TE_{20} and TM_{11} modes at $f = 9.0$ GHz?

We found in the previous example that the dominant mode (TE_{10}) for this waveguide has cutoff frequency $f_c = f_{10} = 6.557$ GHz. Other modes, TE_{lm} and TM_{lm}, have cutoff frequencies $f_{lm} = f_{10}\sqrt{l^2 + m^2(a/b)^2}$; here, $a/b = 2.25$. Examining these for small values of the integers l, m, we find that the next smallest cutoff frequency is $f_{20} = 2f_{10} = 13.114$ GHz. For the TM_{11} mode, the cutoff frequency is $f_{11} = f_{10}\sqrt{1 + (9/4)^2} = 2.4622f_{10} = 16.145$ GHz. The range of frequencies for dominant-mode operation is from f_{10} to f_{20}, which is from 6.557 to 13.114 GHz. The operating frequency $f = 9.0$ GHz is within this range.

The decay rate for a mode below cutoff is $\alpha = (2\pi/\lambda)\sqrt{(f_c/f)^2 - 1}$, where λ is the wavelength in the unbounded medium; here $\lambda = \lambda_0 = c/f = 3.331$ cm at $f = 9.0$ GHz. For the TE_{20} mode, $f_c/f = 13.114/9.0 = 1.4571$ and $\alpha = (2\pi/\lambda)1.0598 = 1.999\ \text{cm}^{-1}$. For the TM_{11} mode, $f_c/f = 16.145/9.0 = 1.794$ and $\alpha = (2\pi/\lambda)1.489 = 2.809\ \text{cm}^{-1}$. ◆

Power Flow

The time-averaged total power flowing along a waveguide is the real part of the integral of the Poynting vector over a transverse plane across the guide:

$$P = \text{Re} \int_A \tfrac{1}{2}\mathbf{E} \times \mathbf{H}^* \cdot \hat{\mathbf{z}}\, dA. \tag{12.69}$$

This can be simplified for each of the two wave types, because only the transverse parts of the fields enter into the integrand's scalar triple product. For TM waves, these are related by $Z^{\text{TM}}\mathbf{H} = \hat{\mathbf{z}} \times \mathbf{E}$, so that upon reordering the triple product,

$$\begin{aligned} P &= \text{Re} \int_A \tfrac{1}{2}\hat{\mathbf{z}} \times \mathbf{E} \cdot \mathbf{H}^*\, dA = \text{Re} \int_A \tfrac{1}{2} Z^{\text{TM}} |\mathbf{H}|^2\, dA \\ &= \text{Re}\, \frac{1}{2}\left(\frac{\beta}{\omega\varepsilon}\right) \int_A |\mathbf{H}|^2\, dA \qquad \text{(TM)}. \end{aligned} \tag{12.70}$$

For TE waves, $\mathbf{E} = Z^{\text{TE}}\mathbf{H} \times \hat{\mathbf{z}}$ and another reordering, together with complex conjugation, gives

$$\begin{aligned} P &= \text{Re} \int_A \frac{1}{2}\mathbf{E}^* \cdot \mathbf{H} \times \hat{\mathbf{z}}\, dA = \text{Re} \int_A \frac{1}{2}\frac{|\mathbf{E}|^2}{Z^{\text{TE}}}\, dA \\ &= \text{Re}\, \frac{1}{2}\left(\frac{\beta}{\omega\mu}\right) \int_A |\mathbf{E}|^2\, dA \qquad \text{(TE)}. \end{aligned} \tag{12.71}$$

We note that there is real power flow only when β is real, which means above cutoff for the mode in question. We also note that the z-dependence of the fields, in $e^{-j\beta z}$, disappears from $|\mathbf{E}|^2 = \mathbf{E} \cdot \mathbf{E}^*$ or from $|\mathbf{H}|^2$ when β is real, implying that P is then independent of which transverse plane's power flow is being calculated. There is conservation of power in a lossless waveguide.

As an example, the power flow along the rectangular waveguide that carries the TE_{10} mode $\mathbf{E} = \hat{\mathbf{y}}E_0 \sin px$ above cutoff, with $p = \pi/a$, is found as

$$\begin{aligned} P &= \frac{1}{2}\left(\frac{\beta}{\omega\mu}\right) \int_A |\mathbf{E}|^2\, dA = \frac{1}{2}\left(\frac{\beta}{\omega\mu}\right) \int_A E_0^2 \sin^2 px\, dA \\ &= \frac{1}{2}\left(\frac{\beta}{\omega\mu}\right) E_0^2 \int_0^b \int_0^a \sin^2 \frac{\pi x}{a}\, dx\, dy = \frac{ab}{4}\frac{\beta}{\omega\mu} E_0^2. \end{aligned} \tag{12.72}$$

The amplitude E_0 of the mode is determined by the power P it carries.

EXAMPLE 12.3

If the 0.9-in. by 0.4-in. waveguide considered earlier carries 1 W of power at 9.0 GHz, what is the peak field strength?

Since the operating frequency is in the dominant-mode regime, the wave can only be the TE_{10} mode. The area of the waveguide is $ab = (0.9)(0.4)(25.4)^2 = 232.3$ mm^2 and the inverse impedance $\beta/\omega\mu = (\beta/k)/\eta_0 = \sqrt{1-(f_c/f)^2}/\eta_0 = 0.6850/\eta_0$ at 9.0 GHz. Hence $1\ W = (232.3)(0.6850)E_0^2/4\eta_0$ and $E_0 = 3.077$ V/mm. ◆

Cylindrical Waveguide

A round pipe or cylindrical waveguide, as shown in Figure 12–8, shares many properties with the rectangular version, but has different field patterns and different cutoff frequencies. The perfectly conducting cylindrical wall has inner diameter $2a$ and encloses a perfect dielectric with constitutive parameters ε and μ (or material impedance η and refractive index n). We seek the TE and TM waves for this waveguide; we want $\exp[j(\omega t - \beta z)]$ dependence and ask for the phase constant β for a given frequency ω. Once again, the dispersion relation will be

$$k^2 n^2 = p^2 + \beta^2, \tag{12.73}$$

with $k = \omega/c$, and the cutoff value p will be determined as part of the solution of the two-dimensional boundary value problem

$$\nabla^2\psi + p^2\psi = 0, \tag{12.74}$$

where ψ will be E_z for TM modes, or H_z for TE waves. For the circular geometry, polar coordinates are appropriate: $\psi = \psi(r, \theta)$ and the Helmholtz equation appears as

$$\frac{1}{r}\frac{\partial}{\partial r}\left(r\frac{\partial\psi}{\partial r}\right) + \frac{1}{r^2}\frac{\partial^2\psi}{\partial\theta^2} + p^2\psi = 0. \tag{12.75}$$

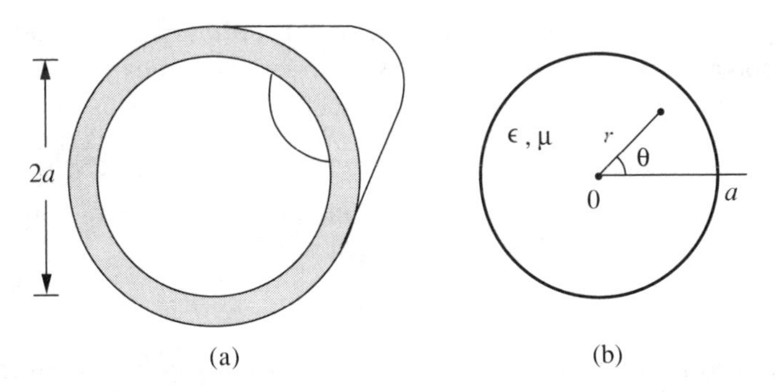

FIGURE 12–8 Cylindrical waveguide geometry.

We try separation of variables, in the form $\psi(r, \theta) = R(r)T(\theta)$ and, after dividing through by RT, we find that

$$\frac{1}{Rr}\frac{d}{dr}\left[r\frac{dR}{dr}\right] + \frac{1}{r^2 T}\frac{d^2T}{d\theta^2} + p^2 = 0. \tag{12.76}$$

At first glance, this is disappointing, because the variables are not fully separated in the three terms, as the middle one depends on both r and θ. Yet, differentiating this equation with respect to θ shows at once that $(1/T)\, d^2T/d\theta^2$ must be a constant. This means that $d^2T/d\theta^2$ is proportional to T itself, which implies exponential functions of θ (including hyperbolic and trigonometric functions, which are combinations of exponentials). But θ is the azimuthal angle, so that the solution *must* repeat itself whenever θ is incremented by 2π, since the same point in space is reached thereby. That is, the solution must be periodic in θ, with period 2π. Thus $T(\theta)$ must be trigonometric and with an integer coefficient in its argument: $T(\theta)$ is a combination of $\cos l\theta$ and $\sin l\theta$, or $e^{\pm jl\theta}$, with $l =$ integer. We choose the complex exponential form (the $e^{j\omega t}$ factor makes everything complex anyway) and write

$$T(\theta) = Ae^{-jl\theta} + Be^{jl\theta}. \tag{12.77}$$

Consequently, $(1/T)d^2T/d\theta^2 = -l^2$ and this completes the separation of variables in Eq. (12.76) as

$$\frac{1}{Rr}\frac{d}{dr}\left[r\frac{dR}{dr}\right] - \frac{l^2}{r^2} + p^2 = 0, \tag{12.78}$$

or

$$\frac{1}{r}\frac{d}{dr}\left[r\frac{dR}{dr}\right] + \left(p^2 - \frac{l^2}{r^2}\right)R = 0, \tag{12.79}$$

which reduces to

$$\frac{d^2R}{dr^2} + \frac{1}{r}\frac{dR}{dr} + \left(p^2 - \frac{l^2}{r^2}\right)R = 0. \tag{12.80}$$

This is a second-order, nonconstant-coefficient, ordinary differential equation and is solvable, for example, by power series. The equation is known as Bessel's equation and its solutions are Bessel functions.

If we divide the equation through by p^2, we see at once that the solution $R(r)$ actually depends on the product $x = pr$, not on r and p separately, and also on the integer l. The two independent solutions to Bessel's equation are denoted $J_l(x)$ and $Y_l(x)$ and we write the general solution as

$$R(r) = CJ_l(pr) + DY_l(pr). \tag{12.81}$$

We now need to review a few of the most important aspects and properties of Bessel functions.

Bessel Functions

Both types of Bessel functions, $J_l(x)$ and $Y_l(x)$, are *oscillatory* and *damped*, except near $x = 0$, where they behave as x^l and x^{-l}, respectively, and with the further exception that if $l = 0$, they behave near $x = 0$ as a constant and as $\ln x$, respectively. For any l, $Y_l(x) \to \infty$ as $x \to 0$. Figure 12–9 shows graphs of a typical Bessel function of each type. We will shortly need to call attention to a few more features of these functions but we now know enough about the radial functions to continue the development of the solution by separation of variables.

Since $\psi(r, \theta)$ will be either E_z or H_z, neither of which can be infinitely strong within the waveguide, the $Y_l(pr)$ solution cannot be permitted to have a nonzero coefficient when the coordinate axis ($r = 0$) is within the region in which the wave equation is being solved. Both the $J_l(pr)$ and $Y_l(pr)$ functions *would* be needed, however, if the waveguide cross section were that of the coaxial line, for example, because we would then be solving the equation for the TE and TM waves (not the transmission-line TEM waves of the coaxial structure) in the dielectric space between the conductors and $r = 0$ would never be reached within that space. For the present case of the *empty* cylindrical waveguide, we must exclude the $Y_l(pr)$ function to avoid infinite fields and the radial solution is then just $R(r) = J_l(pr)$, with an arbitrary coefficient.

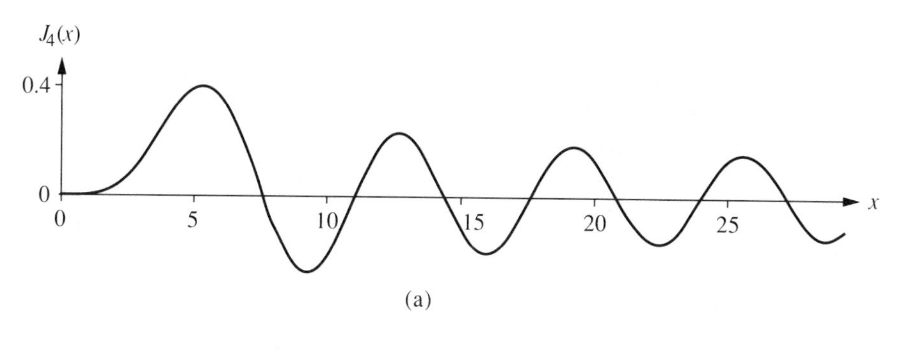

(a)

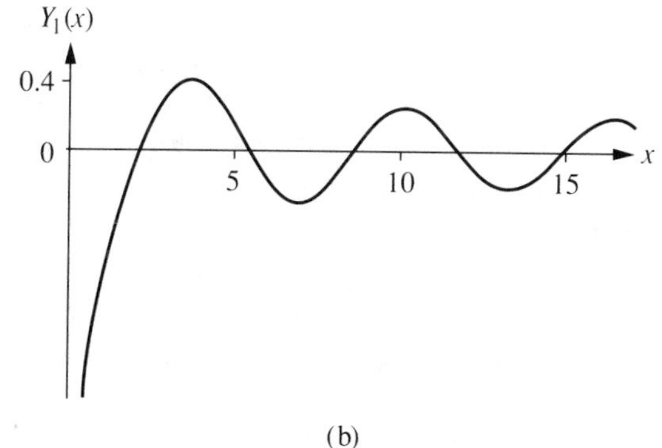

(b)

FIGURE 12–9 Bessel functions $J_4(x)$ and $Y_1(x)$.

Before completing this development, we should interpret what we have already found. The solution

$$\psi(r, \theta) = J_l(pr)[Ae^{-jl\theta} + Be^{jl\theta}] \tag{12.82}$$

combines with the exp $[j(\omega t - \beta z)]$ factor as

$$\psi(r, \theta) = J_l(pr)\{A \exp [j(\omega t - \beta z - l\theta)] + B \exp [j(\omega t - \beta z + l\theta)]\}. \tag{12.83}$$

These are waves that propagate along z *and* along $\pm\theta$ (provided that $l \neq 0$). They twist around the axis as they progress along it, in a right- or left-handed rotation (for $l = 0$, the waves move only axially, without rotation). We can view the $J_l(pr)$ factor as the radial nonuniformity of this twisting wave, or we can consider the $J_l(pr)e^{\pm jl\theta}$ factor as the transverse nonuniformity of a plane wave exp $[j(\omega t - \beta z)]$ that travels along z only.

Note that the phase constant β is not yet known, nor is p, but $p^2 + \beta^2 = k^2n^2$ is given as $\omega^2\mu\varepsilon$. The boundary condition at $r = a$ will determine p and hence β. The boundary condition is that $E_{\tan} = 0$ at $r = a$, where there is a conductor. However, $\mathbf{E}$ is derived differently from ψ for the TM and the TE waves and these two cases should be considered separately.

For the TM waves, E_z is tangential to the conducting wall and must vanish there, along with E_θ (but not E_r). From $\mathbf{E}^{TM} = \hat{\mathbf{z}}E_z - (j\beta/p^2)\nabla E_z$, we find that $E_\theta = -(j\beta/p^2r)\,\partial E_z/\partial\theta$, so that the condition $E_z = 0$ at $r = a$ automatically makes $\partial E_z/\partial\theta = 0$ and $E_\theta = 0$; alternatively, note that $E_\theta = \mp(l\beta/p^2r)E_z$, which makes it obvious that $E_z = 0$ entrains $E_\theta = 0$. For TM waves, then, the boundary condition is just $E_z(a, \theta) = 0$ or $\psi(a, \theta) = 0$ for all θ; that requirement can only be met by the $R(r)$ factor in $\psi(r, \theta)$, by imposing $R(a) = 0$ or

$$J_l(pa) = 0 \qquad \text{(TM case)}. \tag{12.84}$$

This is a condition on the unknown constant p, namely that the product pa be such that $J_l(pa)$ be zero.

As already indicated, the Bessel function is oscillatory; it vanishes at infinitely many discrete points. These nulls of the function are different for different integers l and are not evenly spaced, unlike the nulls of the sinusoids cos x and sin x (although the nulls of the Bessel functions do approach even spacing, by π, for large argument). The actual nulls of Bessel functions are not difficult to find and have been tabulated. We define the mth null of the Bessel function of order l as j_{lm} (exclusive of the null at $x = 0$, which yields only the trivial, electrostatic solution); that is,

$$J_l(j_{lm}) \equiv 0 \tag{12.85}$$

and it follows that the set of solutions of Eq. (12.84) is given by

$$p = \frac{j_{lm}}{a} \qquad \text{(TM case)}. \tag{12.86}$$

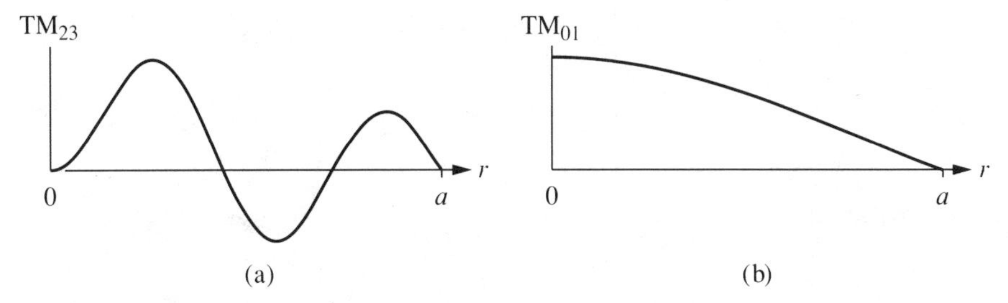

FIGURE 12–10 Radial variation of cylindrical waveguide TM modes.

From this set of allowable values of p, we can form

$$\beta^2 = k^2n^2 - p^2 = k^2n^2 - \frac{j_{lm}^2}{a^2} \tag{12.87}$$

and get the phase constant, wavelength, and phase and group velocities of the TM_{lm} mode, for which

$$E_z = \psi(r, \theta, z) = J_l\left(\frac{j_{lm} r}{a}\right) \exp\left[-j(l\theta + \beta z)\right]. \tag{12.88}$$

The solution that twists in the direction of decreasing θ, as $e^{-j(-l\theta+\beta z)}$, is also valid. To interpret the subscripts that identify and distinguish the modes, note that the subscript l tells us the azimuthal variation (there are l azimuthal cycles around the axis), while m gives the number of oscillatory swings the axial field undergoes along a radius, from the axis to the wall. Figure 12–10 illustrates this radial variation for the TM_{23} and TM_{01} modes, which involve the nulls $j_{23} = 11.6198$ and $j_{01} = 2.4048$.

For the TE waves, $\psi(r, \theta)$ is H_z and $\mathbf{E}^{TE} = (j\omega\mu/p^2)\hat{\mathbf{z}} \times \nabla H_z$ has only the E_r and E_θ components, of which E_θ is tangential to the conducting wall and must vanish at $r = a$. The boundary condition is just $E_\theta(a, \theta) = 0$ or $\hat{\boldsymbol{\theta}} \cdot \hat{\mathbf{z}} \times \nabla H_z = 0$, or $\hat{\mathbf{r}} \cdot \nabla H_z = 0$ or $\partial\psi(a, \theta)/\partial r = 0$ for all θ; that requirement can only be met by the $R(r)$ factor in $\psi(r, \theta)$, by imposing $dR(a)/dr = 0$ for $R(r) = J_l(pr)$, or

$$J_l'(pa) = 0 \qquad \text{(TE case)}. \tag{12.89}$$

This is a condition on the unknown constant p, namely that the product pa be such that $J_l(x)$ have zero slope at $x = pa$.

As we know, the Bessel function is oscillatory; its slope vanishes at infinitely many discrete points. These points of zero slope are different for different integers l and are not evenly spaced. The zero-slope points of Bessel functions have been tabulated. We define the mth zero-slope point of the Bessel function of order l as j_{lm}' (exclusive of the one at $x = 0$, which yields only the trivial, electrostatic solution); that is,

$$J_l'(j_{lm}') \equiv 0 \tag{12.90}$$

and it follows that the set of solutions of Eq. (12.89) is given by

$$p = \frac{j'_{lm}}{a} \qquad \text{(TE case)}. \tag{12.91}$$

From this set of allowable values of p, we can form

$$\beta^2 = k^2n^2 - p^2 = k^2n^2 - \frac{j'^2_{lm}}{a^2} \tag{12.92}$$

and get the phase constant, wavelength, and phase and group velocities of the TE_{lm} mode, for which

$$H_z = \psi(r, \theta, z) = J_l\left(\frac{j'_{lm}r}{a}\right) \exp\left[-j(l\theta + \beta z)\right]. \tag{12.93}$$

The solution that twists in the direction of decreasing θ, as $e^{-j(-l\theta+\beta z)}$, is also valid; once again, there are l azimuthal cycles around the axis and m gives the number of oscillatory swings the axial field undergoes along a radius, from the axis to the wall. Figure 12–11 illustrates this radial variation for the TE_{23} and TE_{11} modes, which involve $j'_{23} = 9.9695$ and $j'_{11} = 1.8412$.

The dispersion relation for a cylindrical waveguide is given by

$$\omega^2\mu\varepsilon = k^2n^2 = p^2 + \beta^2 = \begin{cases} \dfrac{j^2_{lm}}{a^2} + \beta^2 & \text{for TM}, \\ \dfrac{j'^2_{lm}}{a^2} + \beta^2 & \text{for TE}. \end{cases} \tag{12.94}$$

The waves can propagate only for frequencies greater than the cutoff frequency $\omega_c = pc/n$ for each mode. There is a sequence of such cutoff frequencies and, below a cutoff frequency, the phase constant β turns imaginary, as $\beta =$

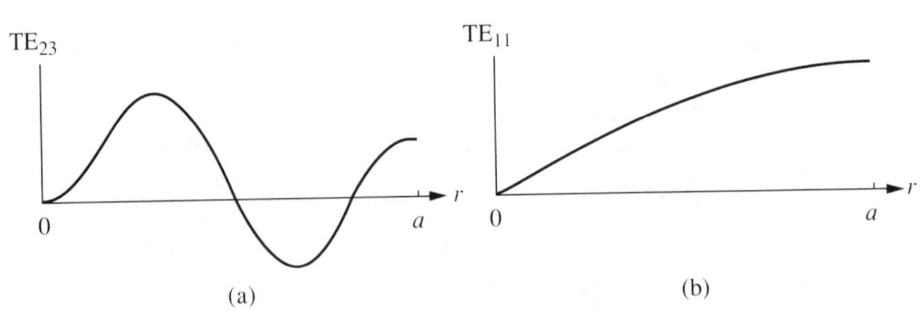

FIGURE 12–11 Radial variation of cylindrical waveguide TE modes.

$-j\alpha = -j\sqrt{p^2 - k^2n^2}$, which leaves for the axial field

$$\psi(r, \theta, z) = J_l(pr)e^{-jl\theta}e^{-\alpha z}. \tag{12.95}$$

This means attenuation along the direction of the waveguide, while there is still propagation transversely, along the azimuth θ, if $l \neq 0$. The wave then spins about the axis but does not travel along it. The wave is evanescent when the operating frequency is below cutoff. The dominant mode, the first to propagate as the frequency increases, is the TE_{11} mode, since $j'_{11} = 1.8412$ is smaller than all the other null or zero-slope points of Bessel functions.

Summary

We have found nonuniform waves more general than the TEM wave of a uniform transmission line. They can propagate within a dielectric region enclosed by a hollow conducting pipe of uniform cross section and they are of two types, transverse electric (TE) and transverse magnetic (TM), with either **H** or **E** having an axial component. Both types are derived from solutions of a two-dimensional Helmholtz equation appropriate to the cross sectional geometry and both conform to the dispersion relation $k^2n^2 = p^2 + \beta^2$, where $k = \omega/c$, n is the refractive index of the dielectric, β is the axial phase constant, and p is the constant in the Helmholtz equation that determines the transverse behavior. The difference between the TM and TE waves lies in the boundary condition applied to the axial field component ψ: for TM waves, the condition is that ψ be zero at the conducting boundary; for TE waves, the requirement is that ψ have zero slope at the conducting wall. In both cases, the condition ensures that the tangential electric field vanish at the wall.

Either boundary condition on ψ results in an infinite family of modes of propagation, each with its own field pattern and allowed value of the parameter p. The latter determines a cutoff frequency, $\omega_c = pc/n$, below which propagation of the wave cannot be sustained; the wave is evanescent, decaying exponentially along the axis of the waveguide and carrying no real power, when the mode is below cutoff. The geometry of the waveguide cross section determines the field pattern and the cutoff frequency for each mode.

We examined the modes of a rectangular and of a circularly cylindrical waveguide. The former involve sinusoidal nonuniformities of the fields; the latter are formed from Bessel functions radially and sinusoids azimuthally. The general solution for the fields in a waveguide is a superposition of all the TE and TM modes.

We interpreted the rectangular waveguide modes in a way that reveals that the underlying mechanism of propagation along the pipe involves repeated reflections of a plane wave at the walls of the guide. This mechanism confines the fields within the pipe and guides the wave along its length. The question now arises as to whether the pair of conductors in a transmission line or the single one in a waveguide are really necessary to achieve guided wave propagation. Can waves be guided by a dielectric alone?

PROBLEMS

Cutoff Frequency of Empty Waveguide

12.1 At frequency $f = 9$ GHz, the guide wavelength along a certain air-filled hollow conducting waveguide is found to be $\lambda = 3.456$ cm, for a particular mode. What is the cutoff frequency of that mode?

Cutoff Frequency of Dielectric-Filled Waveguide

12.2 At frequency $f_1 = 9$ GHz, the guide wavelength along a certain dielectric-filled conducting waveguide is found to be $\lambda_1 = 3.456$ cm, for a particular mode. At frequency $f_2 = 10$ GHz, the wavelength is $\lambda_2 = 2.345$ cm, for the same mode.

(a) What is the cutoff frequency f_0 of that mode?

(b) What is the relative permittivity ε of the dielectric?

Modes of a Square Waveguide

12.3 The dominant mode of an empty square waveguide has a cutoff frequency of $f_0 = 1$ GHz.

(a) What is the width of the square?

(b) Find the fifth lowest distinguishable cutoff frequency and identify the mode, or modes, to which it pertains.

Coincident Cutoffs in a Rectangular Waveguide

12.4 **(a)** Give the dimensions a, b (in cm) of an empty rectangular waveguide for which the cutoff frequencies of the TE_{20} and TM_{11} modes are both equal to 10 GHz.

(b) Determine whether the TE_{10} and TE_{01} modes will propagate or evanesce in this waveguide at 7 GHz.

Range of Dominant-Mode Operation of a Rectangular Waveguide

12.5 The regime of dominant-mode operation of an empty rectangular waveguide extends between the free-space wavelengths $\lambda_0 = 4$ cm and $\lambda_0 = 6$ cm. What are the dimensions a, b of the waveguide?

Dielectric-Filled Circular Waveguide

12.6 The free-space wavelength at cutoff of the TE_{11} mode of a dielectric-filled circular waveguide is $\lambda_0 = 6$ cm. At double that frequency, the guide wavelength of the TM_{01} mode is found to equal the new free-space wavelength. What are the diameter of the waveguide and the relative permittivity of the dielectric?

Aspect Ratio for a Rectangular Waveguide

12.7 For a hollow, air-filled rectangular waveguide, it is observed that the guide wavelength for the TE_{10} mode at a certain frequency ω just equals the guide's width, a, while the guide wavelength for the TM_{11} mode at the second harmonic frequency 2ω just equals the guide's height, b. What is the ratio a/b?

Air-Filled Waveguide Joined to Dielectric-Filled Guide

12.8 A rectangular waveguide with dimensions 0.9 in. by 0.4 in. is empty for all $z < 0$ but has a dielectric filler with permittivity $\varepsilon = 2\varepsilon_0$ for all $z > 0$. Is it possible for this combined structure to allow only dominant-mode propagation along z? If so, over what frequency range?

Energy Storage in Waveguides Below Cutoff

12.9 By examining the imaginary part of the Poynting flux, show that a below-cutoff TE mode in any waveguide stores predominantly magnetic energy and that a below-cutoff TM mode stores mainly electric energy.

Lowest Modes of a Cylindrical Waveguide

12.10 An air-filled cylindrical waveguide has a dominant-mode cutoff frequency of 9 GHz.

(a) What is its inside diameter?

(b) Find the cutoff frequencies for the next three lowest-order modes.

TE Waveguide Modes of a Coaxial Line

12.11 A set of TE_{0m} waveguide modes, with no azimuthal variation, can propagate along a coaxial line (inner conductor radius a, outer conductor radius b, lossless, nonmagnetic dielectric with relative permittivity ε between them). Note that these are *not* the usual TEM transmission line modes. The fields are $H_z = \psi(r)$, $H_r = -(j\beta/p^2)\, d\psi/dr$, $E_\theta = (j\omega\mu_0/p^2)\, d\psi/dr$, where $\psi(r)$ satisfies Bessel's equation of order zero,

$$\frac{1}{r}\frac{d}{dr}\left[r\frac{\partial\psi}{dr}\right] + p^2\psi(r) = 0 .$$

Two independent solutions of this equation are $J_0(pr)$ and $Y_0(pr)$.

(a) By applying suitable boundary conditions, obtain the characteristic equation that determines the allowable value of p for each such mode.

Do not attempt to solve this characteristic equation, but suppose that $p = p_{0m}$ solves it and is known for the TE_{0m} mode.

(b) What is the cutoff frequency ω_c for the TE_{0m} mode?

(c) If the coaxial waveguide is operated at frequency $\omega = \frac{3}{2}\omega_c$, what is the phase constant β for the TE_{0m} mode?

(d) If the coaxial waveguide is operated at frequency $\omega = \frac{2}{3}\omega_c$, what is the attenuation constant α for the TE_{0m} mode?

TM Waveguide Modes of a Coaxial Line

12.12 A set of TM_{0m} waveguide modes, with no azimuthal variation, can propagate along a coaxial line (inner conductor radius a, outer conductor radius b, lossless, nonmagnetic dielectric with relative permittivity ε between them). Note that these are *not* the usual TEM transmission line modes. The fields are

$$E_z = \psi(r), \quad E_r = -(j\beta/p^2)\, d\psi/dr, \quad H_\theta = -(j\omega\varepsilon_0\, \varepsilon/p^2)\, d\psi/dr,$$

where $\psi(r)$ satisfies Bessel's equation of order zero,

$$\frac{1}{r}\frac{d}{dr}\left[r\frac{d\psi}{dr}\right] + p^2\psi(r) = 0\,;$$

two independent solutions of this equation are $J_0(pr)$ and $Y_0(pr)$.

By applying suitable boundary conditions, obtain the characteristic equation that determines the allowable value of p for each such mode.

Natural Frequency of a Rectangular Cavity

12.13 A cavity is a hollow space completely enclosed by a conducting wall. Harmonic fields can exist within a cavity if they oscillate at certain frequencies. A simple cavity is formed by a rectangular waveguide closed at both ends by transverse conducting walls, forming a box.

If the air-filled rectangular waveguide has dimensions 2.5 cm by 1.0 cm and the transverse walls that close the guide are 6.0 cm apart, what is the lowest frequency at which the cavity can sustain oscillations?

CHAPTER 13

Dielectric Slab Waveguides

Can we dispense with the metallic structures that form the boundaries of a waveguide? In a conducting pipe, the metal walls reflect the obliquely incident waves that would otherwise cross them; they thereby redirect, confine, and guide the waves along the pipe. Can a dielectric boundary similarly reflect fields that would otherwise escape and keep them confined to a dielectric region? Figure 13–1 compares the familiar mechanism of confinement by conducting boundaries with a hoped-for counterpart at dielectric boundaries.

We recall that waves that attempt to cross from an optically denser to a less dense medium at a sufficiently large (grazing) angle can be totally internally reflected. Can this process guide a wave? The answer is that for an appropriate thickness of a dielectric layer and for refractive indices in the proper relation, the wave *can* be guided along a layer, without conducting boundaries to confine the fields. Note, however, that the wave is then guided by the layer but not fully confined to it: total internal reflection (TIR) allows fields to cross the boundary, although those that appear on the other side merely decay exponentially away from the interface, propagating only parallel to the boundary. All real power is reflected back into the dielectric layer. Despite the penetration into the less dense medium, the layer does succeed in guiding the optical power and acts as a waveguide.

Dielectric Layers and Integrated Optics

Dielectric layers acting as waveguides are well suited for use in *integrated optics*. Glass or plastic films can be deposited on glass or plastic substrates, forming a wide and long layered structure. Different layer materials have different refractive indices; the index of a given material can be adjusted by ion implantation, for "fine tuning" of the layer's optical density. Such dielectric slab waveguides can be integrated with solid-state laser sources and with the electronics that can process the light signals they can confine and convey.

When we first analyzed oblique incidence of a wave onto a planar interface between two dielectrics, our interest was in how the wave would cross the boundary and be transmitted to the second medium, as well as reflected back

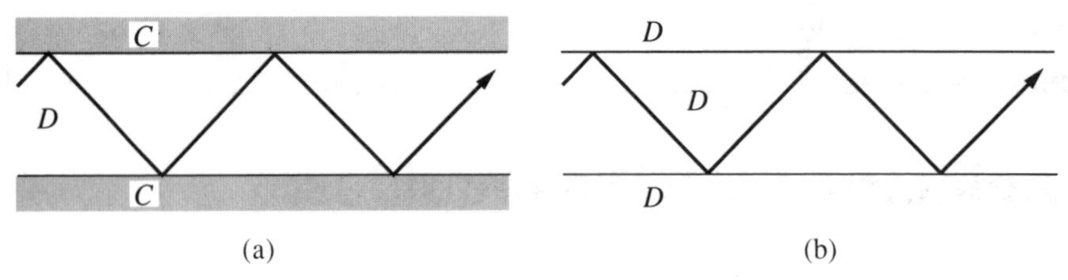

FIGURE 13–1 Waves guided by conductors (C) and dielectrics (D).

into the sourced one. Hence propagation in the direction *normal* to the interface was our prime concern. Now, our intent is to achieve confinement and guiding of the wave, so that we hope to design the dielectric layer to obtain propagation *parallel* to the interface, not away from it. Of course, the physics of the oblique encounter is unaltered by our change of attitude, but a corresponding reorientation of our notation is called for, so that propagation along the desired direction will continue to be designated by $e^{-j\beta z}$ and the nonuniformity transverse to that direction will still be denoted by the parameter p. That is, instead of decomposing the oblique propagation vector $\mathbf{k}$ into a component $\mathbf{p}$ parallel to the interface and a component $\boldsymbol{\beta}$ normal to it, as we did in deriving Snell's laws, we now interchange the roles of the two components: we still write $\mathbf{k} = \mathbf{p} + \boldsymbol{\beta}$ but now $\boldsymbol{\beta}$ is parallel to the interface and $\mathbf{p}$ is normal to it. As indicated in Figure 13–2, continuity of tangential fields now requires $\boldsymbol{\beta}$ to be identical for the incident, reflected, and refracted waves, instead of $\mathbf{p}$. We also change the notation for the imaginary propagation vector in the less dense medium, from $\boldsymbol{\alpha}$ to $\mathbf{q}$, to correspond to the interchange of $\boldsymbol{\beta}$ and $\mathbf{p}$ for the real vectors. Finally, we continue to use the notation k for ω/c, so that the

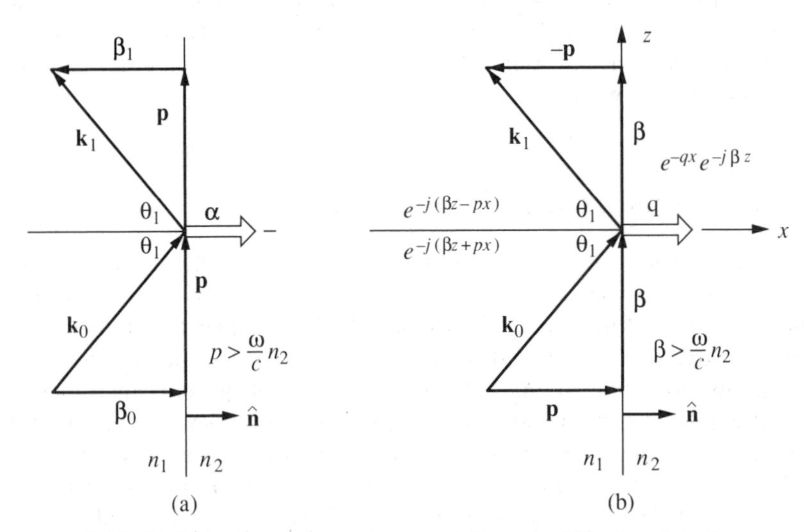

FIGURE 13–2 Previous and new notations for TIR at an interface.

magnitude of the propagation vector is written kn, the phase constant in the unbounded medium, as in

$$k^2n_1^2 = \beta^2 + p^2 \qquad k^2n_2^2 = \beta^2 - q^2. \tag{13.1}$$

Slab Waveguides

For total internal reflection not merely to reflect the incident wave back into the sourced medium but also keep it within a confined region, the wave must be re-reflected at another interface. We therefore consider a layer of finite thickness d, between two other media. For the TIR process to be operative, the index of refraction for the layer must exceed the index for each of the outer media. As shown in Figure 13–3, the inner layer is referred to as the *core*, of refractive index n_1, and one of the other media is then the *substrate*, of index n_2; the third dielectric, with index n_3, is the *cladding* or cover. The direction of desired propagation, parallel to the core, is denoted z; the coordinate normal to the layer is x. The structure is a *dielectric slab waveguide.*

We need $n_1 > n_2$ and $n_1 > n_3$; if the cladding and the substrate have the same index, $n_2 = n_3$, the structure is a *symmetric slab waveguide.* If they differ, it is an *asymmetric slab waveguide.* If, contrary to what we expect to need, n_1 were less than n_2 and n_3, it would be an *inverted slab guide.* These different cases exhibit different properties.

We expect a re-reflecting wave within the core, comprised of oppositely traveling waves that bounce between the interfaces; that is, we expect a standing wave in the core in the x-direction, but traveling (we hope) along z. We also expect exponentially decaying fields in the two outer media, decaying in the directions away from the layer, if we succeed in getting the TIR mechanism to operate at both interfaces.

That the core is dense translates mathematically into the fact that $\beta < kn_1$; that the substrate and outer medium are less dense and carry decaying fields is expressed by $\beta > kn_2$ and $\beta > kn_3$. The relationships among the components of the wave vectors are then expressed by

$$k^2n_1^2 = \beta^2 + p^2, \qquad k^2n_2^2 = \beta^2 - q_2^2, \qquad k^2n_3^2 = \beta^2 - q_3^2. \tag{13.2}$$

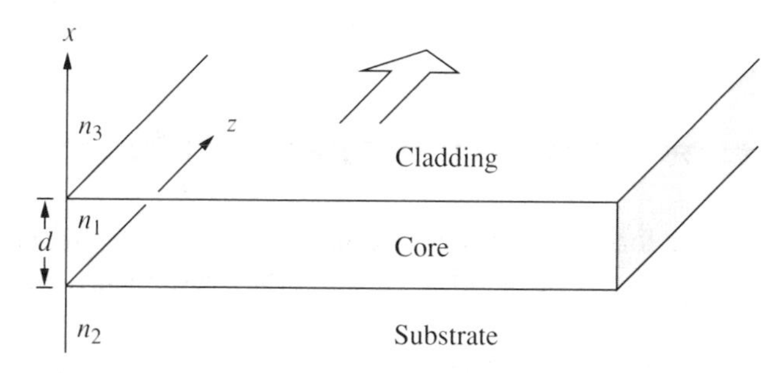

FIGURE 13–3 Dielectric slab waveguide.

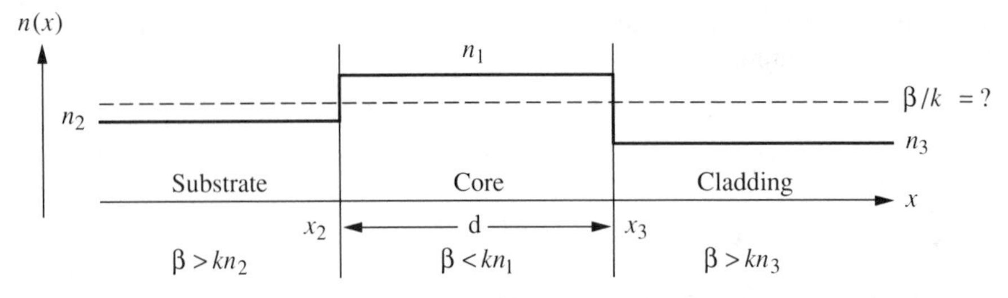

FIGURE 13–4 Refractive index variation in an asymmetric slab guide.

If the TIR process applies, we expect β and p, q_2, q_3 all to be real. We are given the refractive indices and ω, and hence $k = \omega/c$, and we ask what the phase constant β will be; that is, we seek the dispersion relation for this structure. Of course, β and ω will need to be the same for all the waves in all three regions, or else there is no hope of satisfying the continuity conditions at all points of the interfaces, at all times. We also seek the associated fields in all three media. The interfaces are at coordinates $x = x_2$ and $x = x_3$, with $x_3 - x_2 = d$, as indicated in Figure 13–4, which shows the stepwise constant variation of the refractive index $n(x)$. The level of the dotted line β/k is sought; we expect it to be "floating" between n_2 and n_1: $n_3 < n_2 < \beta/k < n_1$.

Derivation of Characteristic Equation

We are again seeking a nonuniform wave that propagates along z, as $\exp[j(\omega t - \beta z)]$. As before, such waves may be transverse electric (TE) or transverse magnetic (TM), derived from the axial field component alone: $\psi = H_z$ for TE or $\psi = E_z$ for TM, subject to

$$\nabla^2\psi + p^2\psi = 0, \qquad \text{with} \quad k^2 n^2 = \beta^2 + p^2. \tag{13.3}$$

For TE waves, as found earlier for waveguides,

$$\mathbf{H} = \hat{\mathbf{z}}\psi - \frac{j\beta}{p^2}\nabla\psi, \qquad \mathbf{E} = -\frac{\omega\mu}{\beta}\,\hat{\mathbf{z}} \times \mathbf{H} = \frac{j\omega\mu}{p^2}\,\hat{\mathbf{z}} \times \nabla\psi. \tag{13.4}$$

For TM waves,

$$\mathbf{E} = \hat{\mathbf{z}}\psi - \frac{j\beta}{p^2}\nabla\psi, \qquad \mathbf{H} = \frac{\omega\varepsilon}{\beta}\,\hat{\mathbf{z}} \times \mathbf{E} = -\frac{j\omega\varepsilon}{p^2}\,\hat{\mathbf{z}} \times \nabla\psi. \tag{13.5}$$

The slab is uniform in the y-direction, so that $\psi(x, y)$ reduces to just $\psi = \psi(x)$ and the Helmholtz equation becomes the one-dimensional version

$$\frac{d^2\psi}{dx^2} + p^2\psi = 0 \quad \text{(in core)}, \qquad \frac{d^2\psi}{dx^2} - q^2\psi = 0 \quad \text{(outside)}. \tag{13.6}$$

Consider the case of TE waves. Then

$$\mathbf{H} = \hat{\mathbf{z}}\psi - \frac{j\beta}{p^2}\frac{d\psi}{dx}\,\hat{\mathbf{x}}, \qquad \mathbf{E} = \frac{j\omega\mu}{p^2}\frac{d\psi}{dx}\,\hat{\mathbf{y}}, \tag{13.7}$$

in the core and p^2 changes to $-q^2$ when we consider the outer media:

$$\mathbf{H} = \hat{\mathbf{z}}\psi + \frac{j\beta}{q^2}\frac{d\psi}{dx}\,\hat{\mathbf{x}}, \qquad \mathbf{E} = -\frac{j\omega\mu}{q^2}\frac{d\psi}{dx}\,\hat{\mathbf{y}}; \tag{13.8}$$

in the substrate, q is q_2 and in the cladding, q is q_3.

We must ensure that the boundary conditions be satisfied at both interfaces: the tangential **E** and **H** fields must be continuous across them. For the TE wave, the tangential field components are H_z and E_y. In the core, these are $H_z = \psi$ and $E_y = (j\omega\mu/p^2)\,d\psi/dx$, subject to $d^2\psi/dx^2 + p^2\psi = 0$.

There are two independent solutions for ψ in the core: $e^{\pm jpx}$, so that

$$\psi = e^{-jpx}A + e^{jpx}B, \tag{13.9}$$

$$\frac{d\psi}{dx} = e^{-jpx}(-jpA) + e^{jpx}(jpB); \tag{13.10}$$

these are valid for $x_2 \le x \le x_3$ only. We need to determine the arbitrary constants A, B, by imposing continuity of tangential fields at the two interfaces.

The standard approach is to write the corresponding solutions to $d^2\psi/dx^2 - q^2\psi = 0$ outside, with its own unknown coefficients, and then to write the continuity conditions as simultaneous equations for all the coefficients. This leads to an elaborate calculation of the determinant of a 4×4 matrix; for nontrivial solutions for the coefficients, this determinant is set to zero, yielding the "characteristic equation" for the structure. We will use instead a powerful and more convenient approach, forming a two-component vector (matrix) of tangential field components, as

$$f(x) = \begin{bmatrix} H_z \\ E_y \end{bmatrix} = \begin{bmatrix} \psi \\ \dfrac{j\omega\mu}{p^2}\dfrac{d\psi}{dx} \end{bmatrix}. \tag{13.11}$$

What we have just found is the following, which defines the 2×2 matrix $R(x)$:

$$f(x) = \begin{bmatrix} \exp(-jpx) & \exp(jpx) \\ \dfrac{\omega\mu}{p}\exp(-jpx) & -\dfrac{\omega\mu}{p}\exp(jpx) \end{bmatrix} \begin{bmatrix} A \\ B \end{bmatrix} = R(x)\begin{bmatrix} A \\ B \end{bmatrix}. \tag{13.12}$$

We will need continuity of the matrix $f(x)$ at $x = x_2$ and at $x = x_3$. We can now eliminate the matrix of arbitrary coefficients A, B in favor of the equally unknown but physically more significant matrix $f(x_2)$:

$$f(x) = R(x)\begin{bmatrix} A \\ B \end{bmatrix}; \qquad f(x_2) = R(x_2)\begin{bmatrix} A \\ B \end{bmatrix}, \qquad \begin{bmatrix} A \\ B \end{bmatrix} = R^{-1}(x_2)f(x_2). \tag{13.13}$$

We note that the matrix $R(x)$ does have an inverse, because it is not singular: its determinant is det $R(x) = -2\omega\mu/p$, which is nonzero. This determinant is also independent of x, so that the inverse matrix exists for all x. That the determinant has these properties is no coincidence; the determinant of the matrix of solutions and their derivatives is called the Wronskian determinant of the differential equation and, by being nonzero, it indicates that the two solutions are indeed independent.

We can now write the solution matrix $f(x)$ everywhere in the core as

$$f(x) = R(x)R^{-1}(x_2)f(x_2) \qquad (x_2 \leq x \leq x_3) \tag{13.14}$$

and, in particular, we get the following relationship between the tangential component matrix at the two interfaces:

$$f(x_3) = R(x_3)R^{-1}(x_2)f(x_2). \tag{13.15}$$

The two column matrices $f(x_2)$ and $f(x_3)$ are to be matched to the solutions in the two outer media.

For the outside media, the Helmholtz equation is changed to the form $d^2\psi/dx^2 - q^2\psi = 0$, which allows e^{qx} and e^{-qx} as solutions. But the function $\psi = H_z$ must not be allowed to become infinitely strong in the outer regions, at large distances from the layer. This means that the exponentially increasing solution is disallowed for $x > x_3$ and the exponentially decreasing one is eliminated for $x < x_2$. This leaves $\psi = Ce^{-q_3x}$ for the cladding and $\psi = De^{q_2x}$ in the substrate. To find the coefficients C, D, we again form the two-component matrix of tangential fields, $f(x)$, as

$$f(x) = \begin{bmatrix} H_z \\ E_y \end{bmatrix} = \begin{bmatrix} \psi \\ -\dfrac{j\omega\mu}{q_3^2}\dfrac{d\psi}{dx} \end{bmatrix} = \begin{bmatrix} 1 \\ \dfrac{j\omega\mu}{q_3} \end{bmatrix} Ce^{-q_3x} \tag{13.16}$$

for the cladding and

$$f(x) = \begin{bmatrix} H_z \\ E_y \end{bmatrix} = \begin{bmatrix} \psi \\ -\dfrac{j\omega\mu}{q_2^2}\dfrac{d\psi}{dx} \end{bmatrix} = \begin{bmatrix} 1 \\ -\dfrac{j\omega\mu}{q_2} \end{bmatrix} De^{q_2x} \tag{13.17}$$

for the substrate. At the interfaces,

$$f(x_2) = \begin{bmatrix} 1 \\ -\dfrac{j\omega\mu}{q_2} \end{bmatrix} De^{q_2x_2} \qquad f(x_3) = \begin{bmatrix} 1 \\ \dfrac{j\omega\mu}{q_3} \end{bmatrix} Ce^{-q_3x_3} \tag{13.18}$$

and these must match the matrices already found from the core solution. The latter are related by $f(x_3) = R(x_3)R^{-1}(x_2)f(x_2)$. Substituting the forms that apply to the outer media gives

$$\begin{bmatrix} 1 \\ \dfrac{j\omega\mu}{q_3} \end{bmatrix} Ce^{-q_3x_3} = R(x_3)R^{-1}(x_2) \begin{bmatrix} 1 \\ -\dfrac{j\omega\mu}{q_2} \end{bmatrix} De^{q_2x_2}. \tag{13.19}$$

Regardless of the arbitrary amplitudes C, D, premultiplication by the row matrix $[1 \quad -q_3/j\omega\mu]$ yields zero, thereby eliminating both C and D. It follows that the boundary condition can be satisfied only if

$$\begin{bmatrix} 1 & -\dfrac{q_3}{j\omega\mu} \end{bmatrix} R(x_3)R^{-1}(x_2) \begin{bmatrix} 1 \\ -\dfrac{j\omega\mu}{q_2} \end{bmatrix} = 0. \tag{13.20}$$

There are no arbitrary constants left in this characteristic equation, which implicitly determines the unknown parameters p, q_2, q_3, as will be seen after simplification of the relation.

The matrix product $R(x_3)R^{-1}(x_2)$ is readily found as

$$R(x_3)R^{-1}(x_2) = \begin{bmatrix} e^{-jpx_3} & e^{jpx_3} \\ \dfrac{\omega\mu}{p} e^{-jpx_3} & -\dfrac{\omega\mu}{p} e^{jpx_3} \end{bmatrix} \begin{bmatrix} e^{jpx_2} & \dfrac{p}{\omega\mu} e^{jpx_2} \\ e^{-jpx_2} & -\dfrac{p}{\omega\mu} e^{-jpx_2} \end{bmatrix} \frac{1}{2}$$

$$= \begin{bmatrix} \cos pd & \dfrac{p}{j\omega\mu} \sin pd \\ -\dfrac{j\omega u}{p} \sin pd & \cos pd \end{bmatrix}, \tag{13.21}$$

where $x_3 - x_2 = d$ has been introduced. We may note as a check on the calculation that $\det\{R(x_3)R^{-1}(x_2)\} = 1$; this is a direct consequence of a property of determinants (that the determinant of a product is the product of determinants) and the fact we noted earlier that $\det R(x)$ is independent of x (the Wronskian is constant). The characteristic equation is now reduced to

$$\begin{bmatrix} 1 & -\dfrac{q_3}{j\omega\mu} \end{bmatrix} \begin{bmatrix} \cos pd & \dfrac{p}{j\omega\mu} \sin pd \\ -\dfrac{j\omega\mu}{p} \sin pd & \cos pd \end{bmatrix} \begin{bmatrix} 1 \\ -\dfrac{j\omega\mu}{q_2} \end{bmatrix} = 0 \tag{13.22}$$

or

$$\cos pd + \frac{q_3}{p} \sin pd - \frac{p}{q_2} \sin pd + \frac{q_3}{q_2} \cos pd = 0 \tag{13.23}$$

or

$$\left[\frac{p}{q_2} - \frac{q_3}{p}\right] \sin pd = \left[1 + \frac{q_3}{q_2}\right] \cos pd \tag{13.24}$$

or

$$\tan pd = \left[1 + \frac{q_3}{q_2}\right] \Big/ \left[\frac{p}{q_2} - \frac{q_3}{p}\right] \tag{13.25}$$

or, finally, in a slightly more convenient form (because it hides the spurious solution at $p = 0$),

$$\cot pd = \frac{p^2 - q_2 q_3}{p(q_2 + q_3)}. \tag{13.26}$$

Incidentally, this could be simplified to the form $\cot (pd) = -\cot (\theta_2 + \theta_3)$ or just $pd + \theta_2 + \theta_3 = l\pi$ by writing $\cot \theta_2 = q_2/p$, $\cot \theta_3 = q_3/p$, but this form requires more care in solving, as it risks spurious solutions with q_2 or q_3 not positive.

What has emerged from this blizzard of equations is a relation among the parameters p, q_2, q_3. But what are the unknowns of our problem? The given quantities were n_1, n_2, n_3, d, and ω (or k); the principal quantity sought is the phase constant β in $\exp [j(\omega t - \beta z)]$, which then yields the wavelength, phase and group velocities, impedance, fields. To get β, we need p or q_2 or q_3, because of the relations

$$k^2 n_1^2 = \beta^2 + p^2 \qquad k^2 n_2^2 = \beta^2 - q_2^2 \qquad k^2 n_3^2 = \beta^2 - q_3^2. \tag{13.27}$$

In particular, p alone would give β; by eliminating β^2 among these relations, we can express q_2 and q_3 in terms of p:

$$q_2^2 = k^2(n_1^2 - n_2^2) - p^2, \tag{13.28}$$

$$q_3^2 = k^2(n_1^2 - n_3^2) - p^2. \tag{13.29}$$

Substitution into the characteristic equation $\cot (pd) = [p^2 - q_2 q_3]/[p(q_2 + q_3)]$ leaves one equation for one unknown, p, which will then determine β. Finding p (and hence β) as a function of frequency ω (and of the parameters n_1, n_2, n_3, d) gives the dispersion relation and the full behavior of the slab waveguide as a transmission system.

To proceed with the solution of the characteristic equation for p, we first define new, dimensionless parameters V_2 and V_3 by

$$V_2^2 = k^2 d^2 (n_1^2 - n_2^2) \qquad V_3^2 = k^2 d^2 (n_1^2 - n_3^2). \tag{13.30}$$

These V's are real, because the slab is optically denser than the outer media. Note that they are *known* parameters and that they vary with frequency ω. We then have

$$q_2 d = \sqrt{V_2^2 - p^2 d^2} \qquad q_3 d = \sqrt{V_3^2 - p^2 d^2} \tag{13.31}$$

and the characteristic equation finally reduces to one equation for the one unknown pd as

$$\cot pd = \frac{p^2 d^2 - \sqrt{(V_2^2 - p^2 d^2)(V_3^2 - p^2 d^2)}}{pd\{\sqrt{V_2^2 - p^2 d^2} + \sqrt{V_3^2 - p^2 d^2}\}} \equiv F(pd). \tag{13.32}$$

We have named the function on the right side of the equation $F(pd)$ for convenience. This characteristic equation, which applies to the TE waves only, is to be solved for pd, given the V's. Thereafter, the phase constant β is obtainable from

$$\beta^2 d^2 = k^2 d^2 n_1^2 - p^2 d^2 . \tag{13.33}$$

Graphical Solutions

The characteristic equation $\cot pd = F(pd)$ is transcendental and may be solved numerically or graphically. The latter method is particularly instructive for purposes of discovering the effects of parameter variations; it involves plotting both $\cot pd$ and $F(pd)$ versus pd on the same graph and looking for the intersections.

As an aid to producing the needed graph, we note that the cot pd function is periodic, with period π, and attains all possible values within each period. The $F(pd)$ function begins (for $pd \to 0$) as $F \to -[V_2 V_3/(V_2 + V_3)]/pd$ and becomes zero at $pd = V_2 V_3/\sqrt{(V_2^2 + V_3^2)}$. The $F(pd)$ function ends (ceases to be real) when pd reaches the lesser of V_2 and V_3, at which point its value attains $F(V_2) = V_2/\sqrt{(V_3^2 - V_2^2)} = \sqrt{(n_1^2 - n_2^2)/(n_2^2 - n_3^2)}$ (assuming that $V_2 < V_3$). The level of this end point depends on the refractive indices, but not directly on the frequency. The intersections of the two curves provide the allowed values of p (the ones that satisfy the boundary conditions of continuity at the interfaces). Each intersection identifies a TE mode of propagation; the number of intersections depends on the operating frequency. For an allowed value of p, the corresponding phase constant β is found from $\beta = \sqrt{k^2 n_1^2 - p^2}$. Note that β can range only from kn_1 (at $pd = 0$) to kn_2 [at $pd = V_2 < V_3$, the end of the $F(pd)$ curve]. That is, the effective refractive index β/k can range from the value for the unbounded core material to that for the larger of the substrate and cladding indices.

Figure 13–5 illustrates the graphical solution of the characteristic equation,

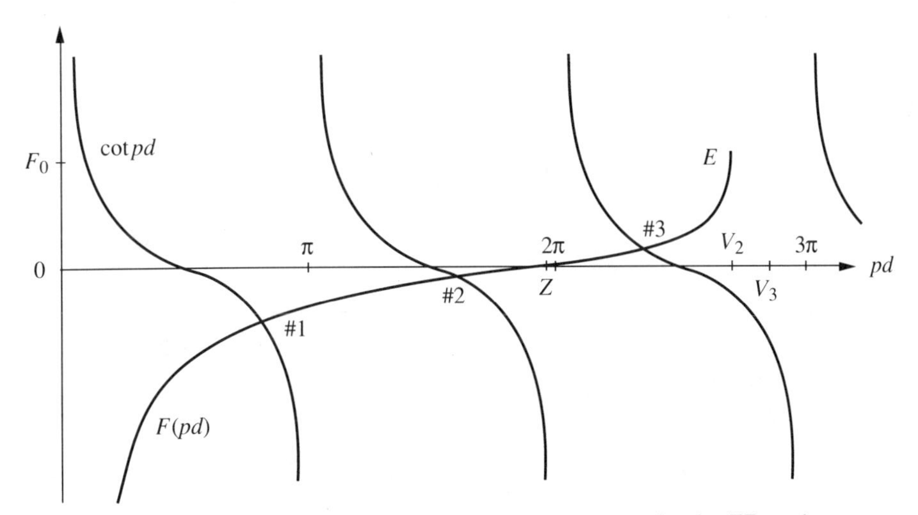

FIGURE 13–5 Graphical solution of characteristic equation for TE modes.

for $V_2 = 8.5$, $V_3 = 9.0$. For these values of the frequency-dependent parameters, there are just three intersections, three TE modes, one in each of the periods of the cot (pd) function, up to the end of the $F(pd)$ curve. The zero crossing of the $F(pd)$ curve, marked Z, is at $pd = V_2 V_3/\sqrt{V_2^2 + V_3^2} = 6.180$ for this example and the end point of the $F(pd)$ curve, marked E at $pd = V_2 = 8.5$, is at level $F_0 = V_2/\sqrt{(V_3^2 - V_2^2)} = 2.874$. The intersections are at $pd \approx 3$, $pd \approx 5$, and $pd \approx 7$, roughly, labeled by intersection numbers.

Cutoff Conditions

The variation of the propagation properties with frequency is of particular interest and is readily visualized from the graph. If the refractive indices are considered independent of frequency, then the V's are simply proportional to ω and the end point of the $F(pd)$ curve (point E in the example) moves to increasing values of pd, while maintaining its level F_0, as frequency increases.

If V_2 is too small, for example at too low an operating frequency, there may be no intersection at all and no real value of the phase constant β can be obtained. Figure 13–6 illustrates a case for which the $F(pd)$ curve ends, at point E, short of where it would cross the cot (pd) curve: the TE modes are then all below cutoff. The curve is drawn for $V_2 = 0.64$ and $V_3 = 1.00$. There is a minimum value of V_2, hence a minimum frequency, for which the end point of the $F(pd)$ curve moves (at level F_0) beyond the cot (pd) curve; this gives the least cutoff value. Note, however, that for a *symmetric* slab waveguide, with $n_2 = n_3$, we find that $V_2 = V_3$ and the level F_0 of the end of the $F(pd)$ curve becomes infinite. This guarantees that there must be an intersection with the cot (pd) curve, even as the frequency falls toward zero. A symmmetric slab waveguide can therefore be operated down to dc. For an asymmetric slab guide, there is a minimum operating frequency, at the first cutoff.

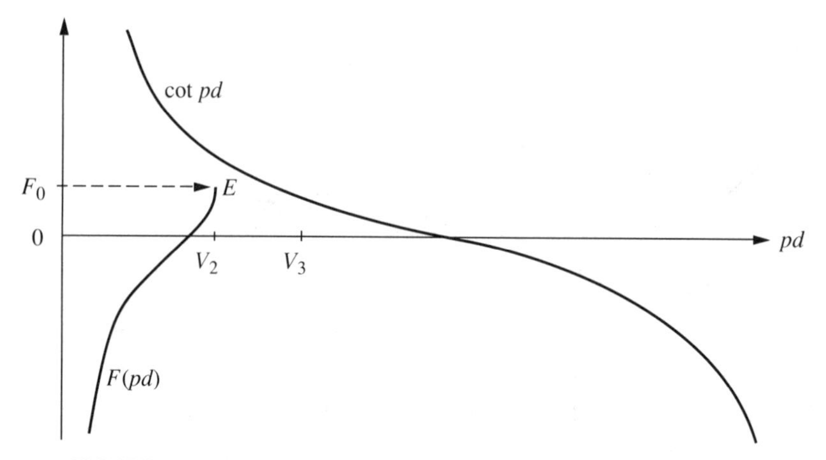

FIGURE 13–6 No intersections at frequencies below the minimum.

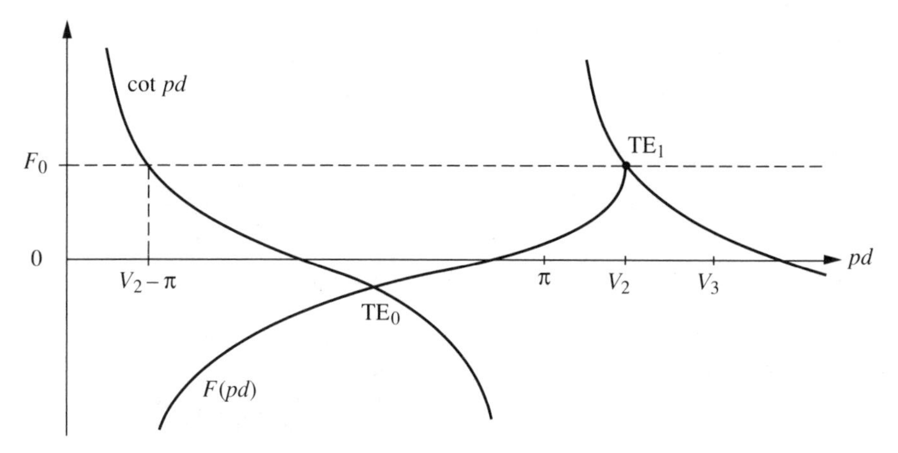

FIGURE 13–7 TE$_1$ mode just at cutoff; TE$_0$ mode above cutoff.

As frequency increases beyond the first cutoff, each new crossing of a branch of the periodic cot (*pd*) curve brings another TE mode above cutoff. Figure 13–7 shows the curves for the case that the TE$_0$ mode is above cutoff, but the TE$_1$ mode is just at cutoff; that is, the cot (*pd*) curve has just been reached by the tip of the *F*(*pd*) curve. The index *l* on the TE$_l$ mode designation can identify the period of the cot (*pd*) curve within which the intersection occurs: $l\pi < pd < (l + 1)\pi$.

Calculation of Cutoff Frequencies

From Figure 13–7 we can see that cutoff for a particular mode occurs at the points where the branch of the cot (*pd*) curve attains the cutoff level $F_0 = \sqrt{(n_1^2 - n_2^2)/(n_2^2 - n_3^2)}$, which does not depend directly on frequency. The cutoff values of *pd* for successive TE modes are spaced by π, the period of the cotangent function. Since $pd = V_2$ (if $V_2 < V_3$) at cutoff and V_2 is proportional to frequency, we can easily obtain the cutoff frequencies for each mode.

EXAMPLE 13.1

For a slab waveguide formed by a zinc sulfide core on a fused silica substrate, find the cutoff frequencies of the TE modes. The indices of refraction are $n_1 = 2.30$ for ZnS, $n_2 = 1.45$ for fused silica, and $n_3 = 1$ for air.

We have $\sqrt{n_1^2 - n_2^2} = 1.785$ and $\sqrt{n_1^2 - n_3^2} = 2.071$, so that $V_2 = (1.785)kd$ and $V_3 = (2.071)kd$. The cutoff level is $F_0 = V_2/\sqrt{V_3^2 - V_2^2} = 1.700 = \cot(0.5316) = \cot(0.5316 + l\pi)$, so that at cutoff, $pd = (0.5316 + l\pi)$ for the TE$_l$ mode. But at cutoff, $pd = V_2 = (1.785)kd$ and equating this to $pd = (0.5316 + l\pi)$ yields $(kd)_c = (0.2978 + l1.7596)$. Figure 13–7 was drawn at cutoff for the TE$_1$ mode for this structure, at $V_2 = 3.673$ or $kd = 2.057$.

It is important to note that unless the core is much thinner than a wavelength, many modes can propagate. In this example, since $kd = 2\pi(d/\lambda_0)$, we get for the cutoff condition of the TE_l mode $(d/\lambda_0)_c = (0.04739 + l0.2801)$, which indicates that to keep only one TE mode above cutoff, the TE_0 but not TE_1, the slab thickness d must be between $0.0474\lambda_0$ and $0.3275\lambda_0$. This means a layer considerably thinner than a wavelength, which is of the order of a micrometer at optical frequencies. ◆

Dispersion Relation and Group Velocity

The TE_l mode has $(l + 1)$ nulls of the $\psi(x)$ function within the core layer; the function is sinusoidal in the core and exponentially decaying in the outer media. Typical mode plots of $\psi = H_z$ are presented in Figure 13–8 for the TE_0 and TE_1 modes, with $pd = 2.5$ and $pd = 5.0$, respectively.

At cutoff, $q_2 \to 0$; this is the onset of exponential decay in the substrate (assuming the substrate is the denser of the outer media). The field is then constant in the substrate, not yet decaying; it extends far into the substrate. Above cutoff, the field decays in both outer media; its strength is significant only near the interfaces: the fields are more tightly bound to the core. Figure 13–9 shows typical profiles of the transverse electric field of the TE_0 mode, close to and far from cutoff. The ratio V_3/V_2 is 1.44 for both cases. Near cutoff, the field extends considerably into the substrate and cladding; far above cutoff, most of the field energy is found within the core. Note that the transverse field of the TE_l mode has l nulls within the core layer. Note also that the value and slope of the field are both continuous at the interfaces, which is what the characteristic equation ensures.

The dispersion relation, ω versus β or, if a dimensionless version is preferred, kd versus βd, can be plotted for particular refractive indices and core thickness. The relation is given by $\beta^2 = k^2n_1^2 - p^2$, with p found from the characteristic equation $\cot pd = F(pd)$. But the function $F(pd)$ depends on V_2 and V_3, which are proportional to k (if the indices are frequency independent; otherwise the V's are nonlinear functions of k), so that p is a complicated function of k: $\beta^2 = k^2n_1^2 - p^2(k)$. Assuming that the indices are independent of frequency, the resulting dispersion relation kd versus βd is plotted in Figure 13–10 for the asymmetric and for the symmetric slab waveguides. For

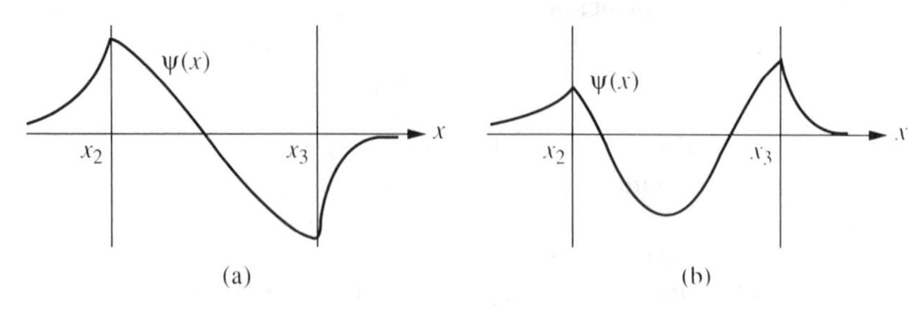

FIGURE 13–8 Axial field patterns of two modes of a slab waveguide.

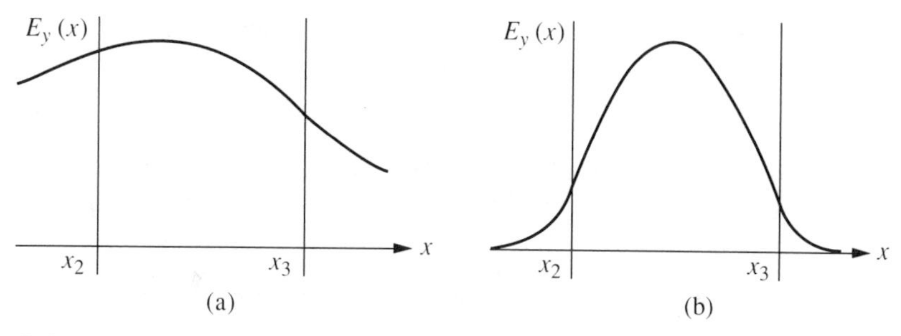

FIGURE 13–9 Electric field of TE_0 mode: (a) near and (b) far from cutoff.

the asymmetric one, the indices of the ZnS on fused silica case were used. Note that the slope of the dispersion curve, the group velocity, is asymptotic to the wave speed in the unbounded core medium, c/n_1, at high frequencies. In that limit, the exponential decay in the outer media is so strong that significant field strength occurs only in the core. Near cutoff, however, the slope becomes that for the unbounded substrate, c/n_2, because the fields then extend far into the substrate. The symmetric guide has no cutoff.

For TM modes of the slab waveguide, the equations are quite similar, but the factor $j\omega\mu$ is replaced by $j\omega\varepsilon = j\omega\varepsilon_0 n^2$ for nonmagnetic materials. The resulting characteristic equation turns out to be

$$\cot pd = \frac{p^2/n_1^4 - q_2 q_3/n_2^2 n_3^2}{[q_2/n_2^2 + q_3/n_3^2][p/n_1^2]}, \tag{13.34}$$

instead of Eq. (13.26) for the TE waves.

If a signal at frequency ω propagates along z as $\exp[j(\omega t - \beta z)]$, the phase velocity is $v_p = \omega/\beta$ and the group velocity is $v_g = d\omega/d\beta$; the latter is the speed at which a slowly varying modulating signal of the carrier at frequency ω propagates. In an unbounded medium of refractive index n, the phase constant and frequency are related by $\beta = kn$ and the normalized phase velocity is

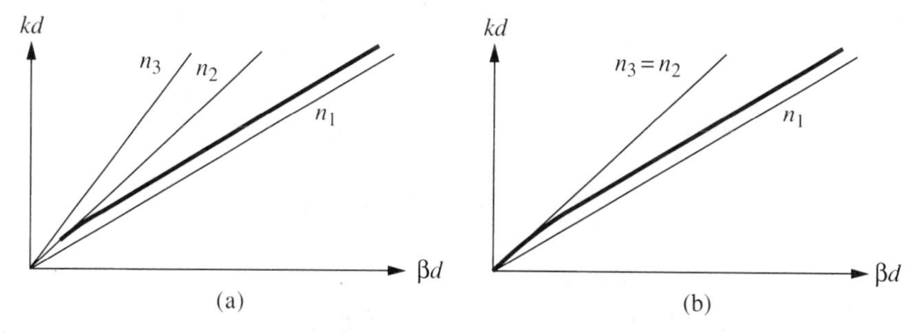

FIGURE 13–10 Slab waveguide dispersion relations.

$v_p/c = k/\beta = 1/n$. The *group index* is defined analogously by

$$\frac{v_g}{c} = \frac{1}{m} \qquad \text{so that} \qquad \frac{d\beta}{dk} = c\,\frac{d\beta}{d\omega} = \frac{c}{v_g} = m \tag{13.35}$$

If the refractive index n of a medium were independent of frequency, then $m = n$. For any material medium, however, n does depend on k. For $\beta = kn$,

$$m = \frac{d\beta}{dk} = \frac{d(kn)}{dk} = n + k\,\frac{dn}{dk} = n + \omega\,\frac{dn}{d\omega} = n - \lambda_0\,\frac{dn}{d\lambda_0}. \tag{13.36}$$

For an empty conducting waveguide, $k^2 = p^2 + \beta^2$ with p fixed by the geometry. Differentiating this dispersion relation yields $2k = 2\beta\, d\beta/dk$, so that

$$\frac{d\beta}{dk} = m = \frac{k}{\beta} = \left[1 - \frac{p^2}{k^2}\right]^{-1/2}. \tag{13.37}$$

Now, for a slab waveguide, the dispersion relation is $k^2 n_1^2 = p^2 + \beta^2$ and p is determined by $\cot(pd) = F(pd)$. But $F(pd)$ also involves V_2 and V_3 (and even n_1, n_2, n_3 as well for TM modes) and the V's are $V_l = kd\sqrt{n_1^2 - n_l^2}$. These depend on k and are also subject to material dispersion dn/dk. Hence, to obtain the group velocity v_g, or the group index m, all the relations that determine β for given k must be differentiated with respect to k, including $F(pd) \equiv F(pd, V_2, V_3, n_1, n_2, n_3)$. Thus, the first relation, $k^2 n_1^2 = p^2 + \beta^2$, differentiates to $2kn_1^2 + 2k^2 n_1\, dn_1/dk = 2p\, dp/dk + 2\beta\, d\beta/dk = 2kn_1[n_1 + k\, dn_1/dk] = 2kn_1 m_1$ or

$$n_1 m_1 = \frac{p}{k}\frac{dp}{dk} + \frac{\beta}{k}\frac{d\beta}{dk}, \tag{13.38}$$

with dp/dk to be found from the characteristic equation $\cot(pd) = F(pd)$. For example, for a TE mode of the symmetric slab, $F(pd)$ is really $F(pd, V)$, with $V = kd\sqrt{n_1^2 - n_2^2}$. Differentiating,

$$-\csc^2(pd)\,\frac{\partial(pd)}{\partial(kd)} = \frac{\partial F}{\partial(pd)}\frac{\partial(pd)}{\partial(kd)} + \frac{\partial F}{\partial V}\frac{\partial V}{\partial(kd)} \tag{13.39}$$

yields $\partial(pd)/\partial(kd)$ or dp/dk as

$$\frac{dp}{dk} = -\frac{[\partial F/\partial V][\partial V/\partial(kd)]}{\csc^2(pd) + \partial F/\partial(pd)}, \tag{13.40}$$

where $\partial V/\partial(kd)$ is obtainable from $V^2 = (kd)^2(n_1^2 - n_2^2)$ as

$$\begin{aligned} 2V\,\frac{\partial V}{\partial(kd)} &= 2kd(n_1^2 - n_2^2) + (kd)^2 2\left\{n_1\,\frac{\partial n_1}{\partial(kd)} - n_2\,\frac{\partial n_2}{\partial(kd)}\right\} \\ &= 2kd\left\{n_1\left(n_1 + k\,\frac{\partial n_1}{\partial k}\right) - n_2\left(n_2 + k\,\frac{\partial n_2}{\partial k}\right)\right\} \\ &= 2kd\{n_1 m_1 - n_2 m_2\}. \end{aligned} \tag{13.41}$$

Thus $\partial V/\partial(kd) = (kd/V)[n_1 m_1 - n_2 m_2]$ and, using the identity $\csc^2\theta = 1 + \cot^2\theta$, we obtain the required $(p/k)\, dp/dk$ in terms of the two partial derivatives of $F(pd, V)$ as

$$\frac{p}{k}\frac{dp}{dk} = -\frac{(pd/V)(\partial F/\partial V)[n_1 m_1 - n_2 m_2]}{1 + F^2 + \partial F/\partial(pd)}. \tag{13.42}$$

Finally, this can be used in Eq. (13.38), rewritten as $n_1 m_1 = (p/k)\, dp/dk + nm$, to obtain the group index for the TE wave on the symmetric slab as

$$m = \frac{n_1 m_1 - (p/k)\, dp/dk}{n} = \frac{n_1 m_1 - (p/k)\, dp/dk}{\sqrt{(n_1^2 - p^2/k^2)}}. \tag{13.43}$$

The required partial derivatives of $F(pd, V)$ are easily derived from

$$F(pd, V) = \frac{2(pd)^2 - V^2}{2(pd)\sqrt{V^2 - (pd)^2}}. \tag{13.44}$$

The group index m indicates how much slower than the speed of light c a narrow-band pulse travels. This information is often expressed as a *group delay*, $\tau_g = (L/c)m$, the time it takes the pulse to travel distance L. For long waveguides, this may be given more naturally as the delay per unit length, $\tau_g/L = m/c$, typically in μs/km. The group delay has contributions from the materials used, through $n = n(\omega)$, and from the waveguiding properties of the dielectric guide, through $\beta = \beta(k)$ even for constant n.

Tunneling

We wish to examine an alternate three-medium structure, one with two dense media separated by a less-dense gap; that is, the region intermediate between the two infinitely extended ones has a lower refractive index. This has already been alluded to as an "inverted slab guide" or as a means for tapping a portion of the light in one dense medium by bringing another dense one close to, but not touching, the first. We shall see that light may be able to cross the gap, even if it would be totally internally reflected in the absence of the second dense medium; this is an instance of "tunneling" across an otherwise "forbidden" gap, inside which only decaying fields would be observed if the other dense medium were not present. The process is analogous to quantum mechanical tunneling between nearby regions that are separated by a potential barrier.

The equations are similar to the ones we have already analyzed, except that we now have $k^2 n^2 = \beta^2 + p^2$ in the outer media and $k^2 n_1^2 = \beta^2 - q^2$ in the gap. We retain the $\exp[j(\omega t - \beta z)]$ form of propagating wave along z and ask whether the wave will be confined or able to cross the gap, along x. The slab is again uniform in the y-direction, so that $\psi(x, y)$ reduces to just $\psi = \psi(x)$ and the Helmholtz equation becomes again the one-dimensional version

$$\frac{d^2\psi}{dx^2} - q^2\psi = 0 \quad \text{(in gap)}, \qquad \frac{d^2\psi}{dx^2} + p^2\psi = 0 \quad \text{(outside)}. \tag{13.45}$$

We again consider the case of TE waves. Then

$$\mathbf{H} = \hat{\mathbf{z}}\psi + \frac{j\beta}{q^2}\frac{d\psi}{dx}\hat{\mathbf{x}} \qquad \mathbf{E} = -\frac{j\omega\mu}{q^2}\frac{d\psi}{dx}\hat{\mathbf{y}} \tag{13.46}$$

in the gap and q^2 changes to $-p^2$ when we consider the outer media:

$$\mathbf{H} = \hat{\mathbf{z}}\psi - \frac{j\beta}{p^2}\frac{d\psi}{dx}\hat{\mathbf{x}} \qquad \mathbf{E} = \frac{j\omega\mu}{p^2}\frac{d\psi}{dx}\hat{\mathbf{y}}; \tag{13.47}$$

in the substrate, p is p_2 and in the cladding, p is p_3.

We must ensure that the boundary conditions be satisfied at both interfaces: the tangential **E** and **H** fields must be continuous across them. For the TE wave, the tangential field components are H_z and E_y. In the gap, these are $H_z = \psi$ and $E_y = -(j\omega\mu/q^2)\, d\psi/dx$, subject to $d^2\psi/dx^2 - q^2\psi = 0$.

There are two independent solutions for ψ in the core, $e^{\pm qx}$, so that once again forming a two-component matrix of tangential field components, we get

$$f(x) = \begin{bmatrix} H_z \\ E_y \end{bmatrix} = \begin{bmatrix} \psi \\ -\dfrac{j\omega\mu}{q^2}\dfrac{d\psi}{dx} \end{bmatrix} \tag{13.48}$$

in the form

$$f(x) = \begin{bmatrix} \exp(-qx) & \exp(qx) \\ \dfrac{j\omega\mu}{q}\exp(-qx) & -\dfrac{j\omega\mu}{q}\exp(qx) \end{bmatrix} \begin{bmatrix} A \\ B \end{bmatrix} = Q(x)\begin{bmatrix} A \\ B \end{bmatrix}. \tag{13.49}$$

The matrix $Q(x)$ is similar to the $R(x)$ matrix we used earlier. To ensure continuity of the matrix $f(x)$ at $x = x_2$ and at $x = x_3$, we eliminate the matrix of arbitrary coefficients A, B in favor of $f(x_3)$ by use of

$$f(x) = Q(x)\begin{bmatrix} A \\ B \end{bmatrix}; \qquad f(x_3) = Q(x_3)\begin{bmatrix} A \\ B \end{bmatrix}, \qquad \begin{bmatrix} A \\ B \end{bmatrix} = Q^{-1}(x_3)f(x_3). \tag{13.50}$$

We note that the matrix $Q(x)$ does have an inverse, because it is not singular: its determinant is $\det Q(x) = -2j\omega\mu/q$, which is nonzero (and constant).

The solution matrix $f(x)$ everywhere in the gap is

$$f(x) = Q(x)Q^{-1}(x_3)f(x_3) \qquad (x_2 \le x \le x_3) \tag{13.51}$$

and the relationship between the tangential component matrix at the two interfaces is

$$f(x_2) = Q(x_2)Q^{-1}(x_3)f(x_3). \tag{13.52}$$

The two column matrices $f(x_2)$ and $f(x_3)$ are to be matched to the solutions in the two outer media.

For the outside media, the Helmholtz equation is changed to the form $d^2\psi/dx^2 + p^2\psi = 0$, which allows e^{jpx} and e^{-jpx} as solutions. Together with the $\exp[j(\omega t - \beta z)]$ factor, their interpretation is that of obliquely propagating waves. Since we are interested in the tunneling phenomenon, we can assume a given incident TE wave and its reflected counterpart in the substrate, and only a transmitted TE wave in the sourceless cladding; the reflection and transmission coefficients, Γ and T, are then the quantities of primary interest. Accordingly, the matrix of tangential field components $f(x)$ appears as

$$f(x) = R_2(x)\begin{bmatrix} 1 \\ \Gamma \end{bmatrix}\psi_0 \quad (x \leq x_2), \qquad f(x) = R_3(x)\begin{bmatrix} T \\ 0 \end{bmatrix}\psi_0 \quad (x \geq x_3), \tag{13.53}$$

where $R_2(x)$ and $R_3(x)$ are the $R(x)$ matrix that combines the $e^{\pm jpx}$ solutions and their derivatives, as used earlier, but with p_2 and p_3, respectively, for the substrate and cladding. The arbitrary amplitude factor ψ_0 allows us to normalize to unity and Γ in the substrate and to T in the cladding; the zero entry in the cladding ensures that the sourceless medium *not* have a wave that travels *toward* the interface, in accordance with the radiation condition. We note that the reflection and transmission coefficients are those for the magnetic field of this TE wave, not for its electric field, since ψ represents the transverse component of the magnetic field.

Since the boundary conditions make $f(x)$ unique at each interface, we need

$$\begin{aligned} f(x_2) = R_2(x_2)\begin{bmatrix} 1 \\ \Gamma \end{bmatrix}\psi_0 &= Q(x_2)Q^{-1}(x_3)f(x_3) \\ &= Q(x_2)Q^{-1}(x_3)R_3(x_3)\begin{bmatrix} T \\ 0 \end{bmatrix}\psi_0, \end{aligned} \tag{13.54}$$

so that the arbitrary amplitude ψ_0 cancels. To extract the desired reflection and transmission coefficients, we can premultiply by the inverse of $R_2(x_2)$, leaving

$$\begin{bmatrix} 1 \\ \Gamma \end{bmatrix} = R_2^{-1}(x_2)Q(x_2)Q^{-1}(x_3)R_3(x_3)\begin{bmatrix} T \\ 0 \end{bmatrix}, \tag{13.55}$$

and then premultiply by the row matrix $u_1' = [1 \quad 0]$ to eliminate Γ and extract T; thereafter, we can premultiply by the row matrix $u_2' = [0 \quad 1]$ instead, to extract Γ in terms of T. The results are

$$T = \frac{1}{u_1' R_2^{-1}(x_2)Q(x_2)Q^{-1}(x_3)R_3(x_3)u_1}, \tag{13.56}$$

$$\Gamma = \frac{u_2' R_2^{-1}(x_2)Q(x_2)Q^{-1}(x_3)R_3(x_3)u_1}{u_1' R_2^{-1}(x_2)Q(x_2)Q^{-1}(x_3)R_3(x_3)u_1}. \tag{13.57}$$

We use the notation u_1 for the transpose of u_1'; this is a column matrix.

The matrix product $Q(x_2)Q^{-1}(x_3)$ is readily found as

$$Q(x_2)Q^{-1}(x_3) = \begin{bmatrix} \cosh qd & \dfrac{q}{j\omega\mu}\sinh qd \\ \dfrac{j\omega\mu}{q}\sinh qd & \cosh qd \end{bmatrix}, \tag{13.58}$$

where $x_3 - x_2 = d$, the thickness of the gap, has been used. The explicit results are therefore

$$T = \frac{2e^{j(p_3x_3 - p_2x_2)}}{(1 + p_2/p_3)\cosh qd - j(q/p_3 - p_2/q)\sinh qd}, \tag{13.59}$$

$$\Gamma = \frac{(1 - p_2/p_3)\cosh qd - j(q/p_3 + p_2/q)\sinh qd}{(1 + p_2/p_3)\cosh qd - j(q/p_3 - p_2/q)\sinh qd} e^{-j2p_2x_2}. \tag{13.60}$$

We can readily verify the expected behavior of these coefficients in two limits. If the gap is closed, expressed by $d = 0$, these reduce to the usual expressions for transmission and reflection across a single interface: if $x_2 = x_3 = 0$, we find that $\Gamma = (p_3 - p_2)/(p_3 + p_2)$ and $T = 2p_3/(p_3 + p_2)$; we recall that the impedances of the two media are $\omega\mu/p$ and that Γ and T are Γ_h and T_h. If the cladding is remote, which we can express by an infinitely thick gap, $d \to \infty$, then the transmission coefficient approaches zero, corresponding to total internal reflection. For finite separation of the dense media, there is some power transmission across the gap and on to infinity in the cladding. However, the thickness of the gap must be sufficiently small for any significant transmission to occur; unless the product qd is small, the cosh qd and sinh qd factors make the transmission coefficient very small.

EXAMPLE 13.2

In Chapter 10 we considered an attempt of an oblique wave incident at $\theta_0 = 43°$ to cross from a nonmagnetic medium of index $n_2 = 3.9$ to one with index $n_1 = 2.5$ and we found that the wave was totally internally reflected. We now place a second dense medium, also with $n_3 = 3.9$, near and parallel to the first one, leaving the gap of index n_1 with a thickness d. For a TE wave, what are the reflection and transmission coefficients?

The incident wave defines both β and p in terms of kd as $\beta d = kdn_2 \sin\theta_0 = 2.6598kd$ and $pd = kdn_2\cos\theta_0 = 2.8523kd$. The attenuation constant in the less dense gap medium is therefore given by $qd = kd\sqrt{n_2^2 \sin^2\theta_0 - n_1^2} = 0.9080kd$. Hence $(q/p + p/q) = 3.4596$ and $(q/p - p/q) = -2.8229$ and the two coefficients are

$$T = \frac{2e^{jpd}}{2\cosh qd + j2.8229\sinh qd}, \tag{13.61}$$

$$\Gamma = -\frac{je^{-j2p_2x_2}3.4596\sinh qd}{2\cosh qd + j2.8229\sinh qd}. \tag{13.62}$$

If we have made the low-index gap quite small, say $kd = 1$ (or $d/\lambda_0 = 0.159$), then $qd = 0.9080$, cosh $qd = 1.4413$, sinh $qd = 1.0380$ and the magnitudes of the coefficients are $|T| = 0.4866$ and $|\Gamma| = 0.8737$; a substantial fraction of the incident wave is transmitted across the gap. If, however, the gap is not small, say $kd = 6$ (or $d/\lambda_0 = 0.955$), then $qd = 5.448$, cosh $qd = 116.15$, sinh $qd = 116.14$ and the magnitudes of the coefficients are then $|T| = 0.004977$ and $|\Gamma| = 0.99999$. This is almost total internal reflection!

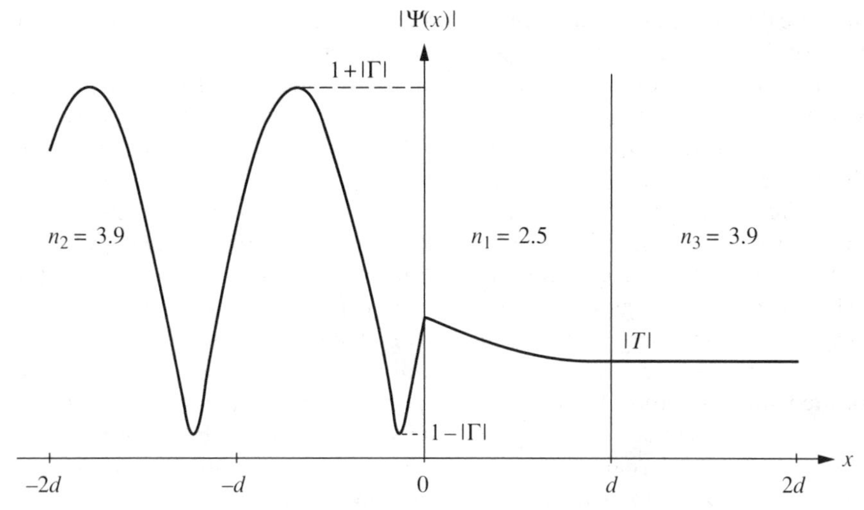

FIGURE 13–11 Tunneling of a TE wave across a gap.

Figure 13–11 is a plot of the magnitude of the axial magnetic field of the TE wave of this example, for $kd = 1$. For this case of frustrated total internal reflection, the incomplete reflection is evident in the standing wave in the medium on the left; the constant amplitude in the medium on the right corresponds to the single transmitted wave; the decaying amplitude in the middle represents tunneling across the gap. ◆

Summary

The dielectric slab waveguide is comprised of a dielectric layer, the core, sandwiched between two other dielectrics. We have analyzed its waveguiding properties by asking for propagation along the layer, with a transverse nonuniformity that conforms to total internal reflection at both interfaces. That is, we have sought to satisfy the requirements of continuity of tangential fields at the boundaries with a standing wave (sinusoid) in the core and decaying fields (exponentials) in the outer media. For given material refractive indices and core thickness and at a specified frequency, we found that only a finite number of such modes can propagate, with phase constant β less than kn_1 of the core but larger than kn_2 and kn_3 of the outer media, just as for total internal reflection.

By use of a matrix calculation that simply expresses the field continuity conditions, we readily found the characteristic equation that yields the phase constant of a propagating mode. This gives the dispersion relation, as well as the full mode pattern, for the asymmetric slab. A graphical solution yields insight into parameter variations, but the cutoff frequencies are obtainable analytically. We defined the group index and group delay as convenient means of describing the dispersive properties of the structure. Both the material dispersion (the variation of the material's refractive index with frequency) and the structure's waveguiding properties (the direct dependence of the phase constant, β, on k or frequency) contribute to the overall dispersion and group delay.

We also examined the transmission of a wave across a gap between two dense media, for a case that would otherwise represent total internal reflection at the first interface. We found a finite transmission coefficient, indicating tunneling across the region that, in the absence of the cladding, would not support an obliquely propagating wave. Thus, bringing a second dense medium in close proximity to the first, but with a small gap, allows a portion of the light that would be completely reflected to make its way across the gap to the second medium and propagate onward to infinity. This is referred to as frustrated total internal reflection; it confirms that decaying fields do exist in the less dense medium when total reflection does occur.

While dielectric slab guides are of interest in themselves, particularly in applications to integrated optics, many of their properties and the techniques used to analyze them will be seen to apply to optical fiber transmission systems as well.

PROBLEMS

Numerical Solution for Asymmetric Slab Characteristic Equation

13.1 **(a)** Obtain the three intersections of the cot pd and $F(pd)$ curves for the TE modes of an asymmetric slab guide, for $V_2 = 8.5$ and $V_3 = 9.0$, near $pd = 3$, 5, and 7, to four significant figures.

(b) For each value of pd found, obtain the corresponding values of $q_2 d$ and $q_3 d$.

(c) If the slab cladding is air and the operating frequency makes $d/\lambda_0 = 0.827$, find the value of d/λ_g for each value of pd found in part (a).

Simpler Form for Slab Waveguide TE Mode Characteristic Equation

13.2 **(a)** Transform the characteristic equation for TE_l slab guide modes,

$$\cot pd = \frac{p^2d^2 - \sqrt{V_2^2 - p^2d^2}\sqrt{V_3^2 - p^2d^2}}{pd(\sqrt{V_2^2 - p^2d^2} + \sqrt{V_3^2 - p^2d^2})}$$

into the simpler form

$$pd = \cos^{-1}\frac{pd}{V_2} + \cos^{-1}\frac{pd}{V_3} + l\pi .$$

(b) What restrictions on the ranges of allowable values of the multi-valued arccos functions must be imposed on the simpler form, to avoid spurious solutions?

Simpler Form for Slab Waveguide TE Mode Cutoff Equation

13.3 **(a)** Show that the cutoff condition for a TE_l mode of the slab waveguide can be reduced to

$$V_2 = l\pi + \cos^{-1}\frac{V_2}{V_3}.$$

Note that V_2/V_3 is independent of frequency (if the indices are).

(b) What restrictions on the multivalued arccos function must be imposed to avoid spurious solutions?

Characteristic Equation for Symmetric Slab Guide TE Modes

13.4 A symmetric slab dielectric waveguide has core width $2a$ and refractive indices n_1 for the core and n_2 for the two infinite claddings.

(a) Show that the characteristic equation for the TE_l mode can be written as

$$pa = \cos^{-1}\frac{pa}{V} + \frac{l\pi}{2}.$$

What is V?

(b) What restrictions on the multivalued arccos function must be imposed to avoid spurious solutions?

Number of TE Modes of a Symmetric Slab Waveguide

13.5 A symmetric slab dielectric waveguide has core width $2a$ and refractive indices n_1 for the core and n_2 for the two infinite claddings. The characteristic equation for TE_l modes can be expressed by

$$pa = \theta + \frac{l\pi}{2}, \quad \text{where} \quad pa = V\cos\theta, \quad qa = V\sin\theta, \quad \text{and}$$

$$V = ka\sqrt{n_1^2 - n_2^2}.$$

(a) In what frequency range is the TE_0 mode the only TE mode to propagate?

(b) If $n_1 = 1.5$, $n_2 = 1.4$, and the core is 50 vacuum-wavelengths thick, how many TE modes can propagate?

Characteristic Equation for Slab Waveguide TM Modes

13.6 Show that the characteristic equation for the TM modes of an asymmetric dielectric slab waveguide (core index n_1, thickness d; substrate index n_2, cladding index n_3) is

$$\cot pd = \frac{p^2/n_1^4 - q_2 q_3/n_2^2 n_3^2}{[q_2/n_2^2 + q_3/n_3^2][p/n_1^2]},$$

subject to

$$(pd)^2 + (q_2 d)^2 = V_2^2 \qquad (pd)^2 + (q_3 d)^2 = V_3^2,$$

where

$$V_2^2 = k^2 d^2 (n_1^2 - n_2^2) \qquad V_3^2 = k^2 d^2 (n_1^2 - n_3^2).$$

Cutoff for TM Modes of Asymmetric Slab Guide

13.7 An asymmetric slab waveguide has indices $n_1 = 2.3$, $n_2 = 1.45$, $n_3 = 1$. Find the cutoff value of d/λ_0 for the TM_l mode.

Simplified Characteristic Equation for TM Modes of Asymmetric Slab Guide

13.8 **(a)** By defining θ_2 and θ_3 through

$$\tan\theta_2 = \frac{q_2}{p}\frac{n_1^2}{n_2^2}, \qquad \tan\theta_3 = \frac{q_3}{p}\frac{n_1^2}{n_3^2},$$

show that the characteristic equation for the TM_l modes of a slab waveguide can be reduced to

$$pd = \theta_2 + \theta_3 + l\pi,$$

subject to the two simultaneous equations for the two unknowns θ_2, θ_3:

$$(\theta_2 + \theta_3 + l\pi)\sqrt{1 + \frac{n_2^4}{n_1^4}\tan^2\theta_2} = V_2,$$

$$(\theta_2 + \theta_3 + l\pi)\sqrt{1 + \frac{n_3^4}{n_1^4}\tan^2\theta_3} = V_3.$$

(b) Why does the restriction $0 \leq \theta_2 \leq \theta_3 \leq \pi/2$ need to be imposed?

Simpler Form for Slab Waveguide TM Mode Cutoff Equation

13.9 Show that the cutoff condition for a TM_l mode of the slab waveguide can be reduced to

$$V_2 = l\pi + \tan^{-1}\frac{n_1^2\sqrt{n_2^2 - n_3^2}}{n_3^2\sqrt{n_1^2 - n_2^2}}.$$

Characteristic Equation and Cutoff for Symmetric Slab Guide TM Modes

13.10 A symmetric slab dielectric waveguide has core width $2a$ and refractive indices n_1 for the core and n_2 for the two infinite claddings.

(a) Show that the characteristic equation for the TM_l mode can be written as

$$pa = \theta + \frac{l\pi}{2},$$

subject to

$$\left(\theta + \frac{l\pi}{2}\right)\sqrt{1 + \frac{n_2^4}{n_1^4}\tan^2\theta} = V.$$

What is V?

(b) What is the cutoff condition on V?

Wave Properties at Cutoff

13.11 In an asymmetric dielectric slab waveguide with $n_1 > n_2 > n_3$, the frequency is adjusted until a certain TM mode is exactly at cutoff. Without attempting to obtain or use the characteristic equation, what can you tell about the values of the parameters β, p, q_2, q_3, v_p, and v_g of the wave at the cutoff frequency ω_0?

Tunneling by a TE Wave

13.12 Two dielectrics, with $n = 1.45$, are separated by an air gap. In the absence of the second dielectric, a TE wave incident from within the first at 45° would be totally internally reflected. How close must the two dielectrics be to achieve 50% power transmission by tunneling across the gap?

Transmission and Reflection of a Tunneling TM Wave

13.13 Derive the transmission and reflection coefficients for a TM wave that tunnels from a substrate of index n_2, across a slab of index n_1 (with $n_1 < n_2 \sin\theta_0$) and thickness d, to a cladding of index n_3, as

$$T = \frac{2e^{j(p_3x_3 - p_2x_2)}}{A\cosh qd - jB\sinh qd}$$

$$\Gamma = \frac{e^{-j2p_2x_2}\{C\cosh qd - jD\sinh qd\}}{A\cosh qd - jB\sinh qd},$$

with

$$A = 1 + \frac{p_2n_3^2}{p_3n_2^2}, \qquad B = \frac{qn_3^2}{p_3n_1^2} - \frac{p_2n_1^2}{qn_2^2},$$

$$C = 1 - \frac{p_2n_3^2}{p_3n_2^2}, \qquad D = \frac{qn_3^2}{p_3n_1^2} + \frac{p_2n_1^2}{qn_2^2}.$$

Tunneling by a TM Wave

13.14 Two dielectrics, with $n = 1.45$, are separated by an air gap. In the absence of the second dielectric, a TM wave incident from within the first at 45° would be totally internally reflected. How close must the two dielectrics be to achieve 50% power transmission by tunneling across the gap?

CHAPTER 14

Dielectric Cylinders and Optical Fibers

We are now ready to analyze propagation of waves along a dielectric cylinder of radius a and refractive index n_1, surrounded by an unbounded medium of index n_2. We can treat this case in analogy with that of the dielectric slab waveguide and the hollow cylindrical conducting waveguide; it shares many features with those waveguides.

Step-Index Fiber

The case at hand is essentially, but not quite, that of the simple, step-index optical fiber. The true fiber has a core of radius a and index n_1 and a cladding of index n_2 but *finite* outer radius b, with another medium, air or some protective material, beyond the cladding. Figure 14–1 compares the geometries of the two-medium approximation with the three-medium stepped-index fiber. For practical fibers, the cladding is normally quite thick. As we may expect by analogy with the outer media of the slab waveguide, the fields should attenuate rapidly in the cladding as the distance from the interface increases (except at cutoff). The field strength that remains when the outermost cladding–air interface of the fiber is encountered should be negligible and it is a good approximation to consider the cladding unbounded. The three-medium geometry of the true fiber is not much more difficult to analyze than the core–cladding approximation; it merely leads to more complicated algebra while masking the insights we seek into the operation of the optical fiber.

Hybrid Modes

As was the case for the slab guide, the index of refraction of the core, n_1, should exceed that for the cladding, n_2, to get bound modes. The phase constant β should take some value between those for the unbounded media of indices n_1, n_2; that is, $kn_2 < \beta < kn_1$, so that radially decaying fields may be expected in the cladding but not in the core.

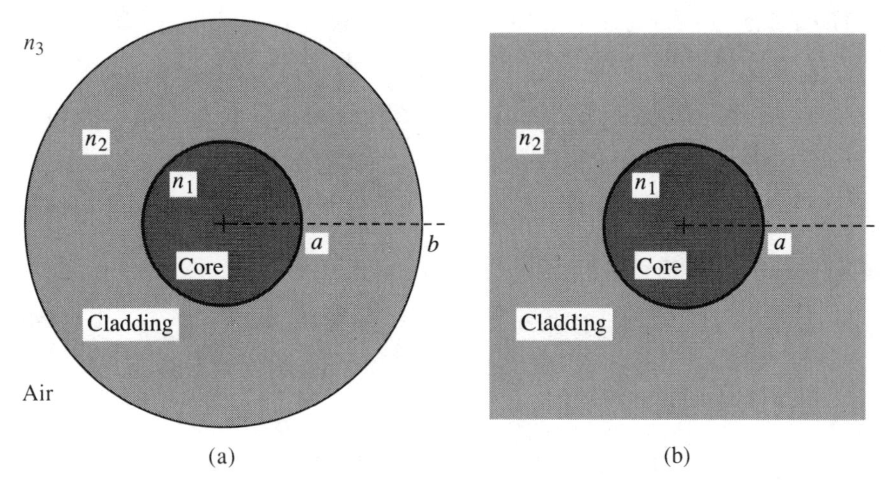

FIGURE 14–1 Step-index fiber and unbounded-cladding approximation.

We define p and q as we did before: since $\beta < kn_1$ in the core, we let the difference of the squares of these parameters be p^2 while, for the cladding, since $\beta > kn_2$, the difference is to be $-q^2$:

$$k^2 n_1^2 = \beta^2 + p^2 \qquad k^2 n_2^2 = \beta^2 - q^2, \tag{14.1}$$

with $k = \omega/c$; we seek a nonuniform wave that propagates along z: $e^{j(\omega t - \beta z)}$.

As before, such waves can be expressed entirely in terms of the axial fields E_z and H_z but now we will find that the waves do *not* separate completely into TM and TE modes, as they did for both the hollow pipe and the dielectric slab waveguides. Where have we lost this convenient, simplifying separation? It is due jointly to the nature of the boundary condition and to the curvature of the boundary. For a hollow conducting waveguide, the separation into independent TE and TM modes is always possible; the Helmholtz equation permits it and the boundary condition of zero tangential electric field allows it. For the cylindrical dielectric waveguide, however, the boundary condition does not assign a value at the interface, but only requires continuity of the tangential electric and magnetic fields. This was also the case for the dielectric slab waveguide, which did permit separation into TE and TM modes, but the interface was planar for that case. For the cylindrical fiber, we again have field continuity but we also have curvature of the interface. Curvature alone is not fatal: the hollow cylindrical pipe has the same geometry and allows separation into transverse modes. We will find that with the exception of one pair of special modes, the curvature of the interface, together with the field continuity condition, is too much for the equations to comply with, unless the TE and TM partial waves mix into what are referred to as *hybrid* modes; these have axial components of both the electric and the magnetic fields. The fields can still be obtained from just their axial components, but both axial fields are needed to satisfy all the conditions at the core–cladding interface.

The fields are expressed in terms of their axial components, as derived earlier from Maxwell's equations for a nonuniform wave, by

$$\mathbf{E} = \hat{\mathbf{z}}E_z - \frac{j\beta}{p^2}\nabla E_z + \frac{j\omega\mu_0}{p^2}\hat{\mathbf{z}} \times \nabla H_z, \tag{14.2}$$

$$\mathbf{H} = \hat{\mathbf{z}}H_z - \frac{j\beta}{p^2}\nabla H_z - \frac{j\omega\varepsilon_0 n_1^2}{p^2}\hat{\mathbf{z}} \times \nabla E_z \tag{14.3}$$

in the core ($r < a$); the axial fields must satisfy

$$\nabla^2 E_z + p^2 E_z = 0 \qquad \nabla^2 H_z + p^2 H_z = 0. \tag{14.4}$$

In the cladding ($r > a$), the same equations apply, but with p^2 replaced by $-q^2$ and with n_1 changed to n_2:

$$\mathbf{E} = \hat{\mathbf{z}}E_z + \frac{j\beta}{q^2}\nabla E_z - \frac{j\omega\mu_0}{q^2}\hat{\mathbf{z}} \times \nabla H_z, \tag{14.5}$$

$$\mathbf{H} = \hat{\mathbf{z}}H_z + \frac{j\beta}{q^2}\nabla H_z + \frac{j\omega\varepsilon_0 n_2^2}{q^2}\hat{\mathbf{z}} \times \nabla E_z \tag{14.6}$$

and the axial fields in the cladding must satisfy

$$\nabla^2 E_z - q^2 E_z = 0 \qquad \nabla^2 H_z - q^2 H_z = 0. \tag{14.7}$$

Of course, ω and β are the same in both the core and the cladding, or else it would not be possible to satisfy the boundary conditions for all time t and for all axial positions z.

The differential equations for $E_z(r, \theta)$ and $H_z(r, \theta)$ are two-dimensional Helmholtz equations. Both p and q are unknown and are to be found by applying the boundary conditions; they are needed to arrive at the value of β for a given operating frequency ω. But p and q are related: Eliminating β from Eq. (14.1) leaves

$$k^2(n_1^2 - n_2^2) = p^2 + q^2, \tag{14.8}$$

of which the left side is known. By applying the boundary conditions of continuity of the tangential electric and magnetic fields, we should arrive at a second equation that relates p and q. Upon solving the two equations for p and q, either of them yields the phase constant β (and hence the wavelength, phase velocity, group velocity, field pattern, power flow, impedance, and all else of interest) for the given frequency, from Eq. (14.1).

Derivation of Characteristic Equation

Separation of variables in the differential equation $\nabla^2\psi + p^2\psi = 0$ expresses ψ as $\psi(r, \theta) = R(r)T(\theta)$, with

$$T(\theta) = Ae^{-jl\theta} + Be^{jl\theta} \tag{14.9}$$

and with l an integer, as before, and with the separation equation for $R(r)$,

$$\frac{d^2R}{dr^2} + \frac{1}{r}\frac{dR}{dr} + \left(p^2 - \frac{l^2}{r^2}\right)R = 0, \tag{14.10}$$

recognized again as Bessel's equation. This is solved generally by

$$R(r) = CJ_l(pr) + DY_l(pr) \tag{14.11}$$

but with $D = 0$ here, to exclude $Y_l(pr)$ in the core, because $Y_l(x) \to \infty$ as $x \to 0$, which would give infinite field strength on axis. In the core, then, both E_z and H_z take the form

$$\psi(r, \theta) = J_l(pr)\{A \exp[j(\omega t - \beta z - l\theta)] + B \exp[j(\omega t - \beta z + l\theta)]\}, \tag{14.12}$$

with different pairs of constants A, B for E_z and H_z, of course. As for the hollow cylindrical conducting waveguide, this represents waves that spiral about the axis (unless $l = 0$) as they progress along it.

In the cladding, however, the equation for the axial fields takes the modified form $\nabla^2\psi - q^2\psi = 0$ and separation of variables leads to ψ as $\psi(r, \theta) = R(r)T(\theta)$ with $T(\theta) = A'e^{-jl\theta} + B'e^{jl\theta}$ again, but now with the new version of the radial separation equation

$$\frac{d^2R}{dr^2} + \frac{1}{r}\frac{dR}{dr} - \left(q^2 + \frac{l^2}{r^2}\right)R = 0, \tag{14.13}$$

as p^2 becomes $-q^2$. This is the modified Bessel equation and is solved by the *modified Bessel functions.* Two independent solutions are represented by

$$R(r) = C'I_l(qr) + D'K_l(qr) \tag{14.14}$$

and we now need to learn, or review, the most basic properties of these functions.

The modified Bessel functions $I_l(x)$ and $K_l(x)$ are related to the original ones $J_l(x)$ and $Y_l(x)$ in the same way that hyperbolic functions are related to the trigonometric ones: while $J_l(x)$ and $Y_l(x)$ are oscillatory and damped, $I_l(x)$ and $K_l(x)$ behave like growing and decaying exponentials, respectively. Near $x = 0$, however, they behave as x^l and x^{-l}, respectively (unless $l = 0$, whereupon they behave near $x = 0$ as a constant and as $\ln x$, respectively). For large argument ($x \to \infty$) and for any l, $I_l(x) \to \infty$ but $K_l(x) \to 0$. Figure 14–2 shows plots of the first few modified Bessel functions of both types.

For an unbounded cladding, we must exclude the $I_l(qr)$ solution, because it would cause the field strength to get stronger and stronger at large radii, far from the fiber, becoming infinitely strong at infinite radius. We therefore set $C' = 0$ in the radial solution, Eq. (14.14). We note, however, that for a more realistic model of a fiber, the cladding is of finite thickness and both $I_l(q_2 r)$ and $K_l(q_2 r)$ are needed in the cladding [and then only $K_l(q_3 r)$ in the outer-

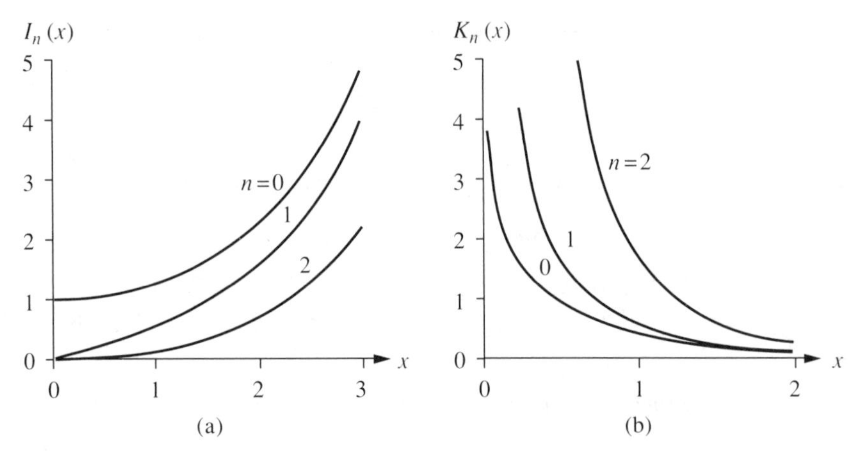

FIGURE 14–2 Modified Bessel functions.

most medium]. Still, if the cladding is thick, the coefficient C' will need to be quite small to suppress the otherwise enormous fields at the outermost interface; here, we are approximating C' by zero, corresponding to infinite cladding thickness.

In the cladding, then, both E_z and H_z take the form

$$\psi(r, \theta) = K_l(qr)\{A' \exp [j(\omega t - \beta z - l\theta)] + B' \exp [j(\omega t - \beta z + l\theta)]\}, \tag{14.15}$$

with different pairs of constants A', B' for E_z and H_z. Again, these are spiraling waves along the axis, but their transverse nonuniformity decays with radial distance away from the core–cladding interface.

There remains to apply the boundary conditions, that the tangential E and H field components must be continuous across the surface $r = a$. We note first that the $e^{-jl\theta}$ and $e^{jl\theta}$ solutions can be considered separately, as long as there is azimuthal symmetry. We also note that the azimuthal coefficient l must be the same integer for both the core and the cladding, to permit the continuity condition to apply at all angles θ. We can then deal with the radial nonuniformity alone and append the factor $\exp [j(\omega t - \beta z - l\theta)]$, representing spiral propagation, afterward.

We can eliminate the undetermined coefficients A and A' at once, in favor of the also undetermined but physically meaningful constant $E_z(a)$, by invoking the continuity of the axial component of the electric field:

$$E_z(r) = \begin{cases} E_z(a)\,\dfrac{J_l(pr)}{J_l(pa)} & r \le a, \\[2ex] E_z(a)\,\dfrac{K_l(qr)}{K_l(qa)} & r \ge a; \end{cases} \tag{14.16}$$

the same applies to the axial component of the magnetic field:

$$H_z(r) = \begin{cases} H_z(a)\,\dfrac{J_l(pr)}{J_l(pa)} & r \leq a\,, \\ H_z(a)\,\dfrac{K_l(qr)}{K_l(qa)} & r \geq a\,. \end{cases} \tag{14.17}$$

The same expressions eliminate the B and B' coefficients when waves that rotate the other way, as $\exp\,[j(\omega t - \beta z + l\theta)]$, are considered instead.

But continuity of the axial field components does not suffice. The azimuthal components E_θ and H_θ must also be continuous at $r = a$. These are expressible in terms of the axial components, as in Eqs. (14.2)–(14.3) and (14.5)–(14.6), by

$$E_\theta = -\frac{j\beta}{p^2}\,\hat{\boldsymbol{\theta}} \cdot \nabla E_z + \frac{j\omega\mu_0}{p^2}\,\hat{\boldsymbol{\theta}} \cdot \hat{\mathbf{z}} \times \nabla H_z \tag{14.18}$$

$$H_\theta = -\frac{j\beta}{p^2}\,\hat{\boldsymbol{\theta}} \cdot \nabla H_z - \frac{j\omega\varepsilon_0 n_1^2}{p^2}\,\hat{\boldsymbol{\theta}} \cdot \hat{\mathbf{z}} \times \nabla E_z \tag{14.19}$$

in the core, and by

$$E_\theta = \frac{j\beta}{q^2}\,\hat{\boldsymbol{\theta}} \cdot \nabla E_z - \frac{j\omega\mu_0}{q^2}\,\hat{\boldsymbol{\theta}} \cdot \hat{\mathbf{z}} \times \nabla H_z, \tag{14.20}$$

$$H_\theta = \frac{j\beta}{q^2}\,\hat{\boldsymbol{\theta}} \cdot \nabla H_z + \frac{j\omega\varepsilon_0 n_2^2}{q^2}\,\hat{\boldsymbol{\theta}} \cdot \hat{\mathbf{z}} \times \nabla E_z \tag{14.21}$$

in the cladding. Recalling that $\hat{\boldsymbol{\theta}} \cdot \nabla$ means $(1/r)\,\partial/\partial\theta$ and that this yields the factor $[-jl/r]$ when applied to the propagation factor $\exp\,[j(\omega t - \beta z - l\theta)]$, and noting also that $\hat{\boldsymbol{\theta}} \cdot \hat{\mathbf{z}} \times \nabla$ means $\hat{\boldsymbol{\theta}} \times \hat{\mathbf{z}} \cdot \nabla = \hat{\mathbf{r}} \cdot \nabla = \partial/\partial r$, we find that the azimuthal fields expressed in terms of the axial ones are

$$E_\theta(r) = -\frac{l\beta}{p^2 r}\,E_z + \frac{j\omega\mu_0}{p^2}\,\frac{\partial H_z}{\partial r}, \tag{14.22}$$

$$H_\theta(r) = -\frac{l\beta}{p^2 r}\,H_z - \frac{j\omega\varepsilon_0 n_1^2}{p^2}\,\frac{\partial E_z}{\partial r} \tag{14.23}$$

in the core and

$$E_\theta(r) = \frac{l\beta}{q^2 r}\,E_z - \frac{j\omega\mu_0}{q^2}\,\frac{\partial H_z}{\partial r}, \tag{14.24}$$

$$H_\theta(r) = \frac{l\beta}{q^2 r}\,H_z + \frac{j\omega\varepsilon_0 n_2^2}{q^2}\,\frac{\partial E_z}{\partial r} \tag{14.25}$$

in the cladding. But we have already expressed the core and cladding axial fields in terms of their values at the interface $E_z(a)$ and $H_z(a)$, so the matrix of azimuthal field components is related to the matrix of axial ones by

$$\begin{bmatrix} E_\theta(a) \\ H_\theta(a) \end{bmatrix} = \begin{bmatrix} -\dfrac{l\beta}{p^2 a} & \dfrac{j\omega\mu_0}{p}\dfrac{J_l'(pa)}{J_l(pa)} \\ -\dfrac{j\omega\varepsilon_0 n_1^2}{p}\dfrac{J_l'(pa)}{J_l(pa)} & -\dfrac{l\beta}{p^2 a} \end{bmatrix} \begin{bmatrix} E_z(a) \\ H_z(a) \end{bmatrix} \tag{14.26}$$

based on the core fields while, on the basis of the cladding fields, the relation is

$$\begin{bmatrix} E_\theta(a) \\ H_\theta(a) \end{bmatrix} = \begin{bmatrix} \dfrac{l\beta}{q^2 a} & -\dfrac{j\omega\mu_0}{q}\dfrac{K_l'(qa)}{K_l(qa)} \\ \dfrac{j\omega\varepsilon_0 n_2^2}{q}\dfrac{K_l'(qa)}{K_l(qa)} & \dfrac{l\beta}{q^2 a} \end{bmatrix} \begin{bmatrix} E_z(a) \\ H_z(a) \end{bmatrix} \tag{14.27}$$

instead. But these two expressions for the azimuthal fields must be the same, by continuity of the tangential fields. Subtracting the former from the latter gives the homogeneous matrix equation

$$\begin{bmatrix} \dfrac{l\beta}{a}\left(\dfrac{1}{q^2}+\dfrac{1}{p^2}\right) & -j\omega\mu_0 aF(q,p) \\ j\omega\varepsilon_0 aG(q,p) & \dfrac{l\beta}{a}\left(\dfrac{1}{q^2}+\dfrac{1}{p^2}\right) \end{bmatrix} \begin{bmatrix} E_z(a) \\ H_z(a) \end{bmatrix} = 0, \tag{14.28}$$

where we have used the abbreviations

$$F(q,p) = \frac{K_l'(qa)}{qaK_l(qa)} + \frac{J_l'(pa)}{paJ_l(pa)}, \tag{14.29}$$

$$G(q,p) = \frac{n_2^2 K_l'(qa)}{qaK_l(qa)} + \frac{n_1^2 J_l'(pa)}{paJ_l(pa)}. \tag{14.30}$$

For Eq. (14.28) to allow nonzero axial fields (from which the transverse components are derived), the determinant of the coefficient matrix must vanish, giving us the condition (using $\omega^2\mu_0\varepsilon_0 = k^2$)

$$l^2\frac{\beta^2}{k^2}\left[\frac{1}{p^2a^2}+\frac{1}{q^2a^2}\right]^2 - F(q,p)G(q,p) = 0. \tag{14.31}$$

This can be simplified somewhat by replacing β^2/k^2 with an equivalent expression that involves only p and q directly. The relations in Eq. (14.1) provide this sort of expression, in the form

$$\frac{\beta^2}{k^2p^2a^2} = \frac{n_1^2}{p^2a^2} - \frac{1}{k^2a^2} \qquad \frac{\beta^2}{k^2q^2a^2} = \frac{n_2^2}{q^2a^2} + \frac{1}{k^2a^2} \tag{14.32}$$

which add to

$$\frac{\beta^2}{k^2}\left[\frac{1}{p^2a^2}+\frac{1}{q^2a^2}\right] = \frac{n_1^2}{p^2a^2} + \frac{n_2^2}{q^2a^2} \tag{14.33}$$

and reduce the determinantal equation to the more symmetric form

$$l^2\left[\frac{1}{p^2a^2}+\frac{1}{q^2a^2}\right]\left[\frac{n_1^2}{p^2a^2}+\frac{n_2^2}{q^2a^2}\right]=F(q,p)G(q,p)$$

$$=\left[\frac{J_l'(pa)}{paJ_l(pa)}+\frac{K_l'(qa)}{qaK_l(qa)}\right]\left[\frac{n_1^2J_l'(pa)}{paJ_l(pa)}+\frac{n_2^2K_l'(qa)}{qaK_l(qa)}\right]. \quad (14.34)$$

This is the characteristic equation for the cylindrical dielectric waveguide. The unknowns are p and q, since the core radius a and the refractive indices n_1 and n_2 of the core and cladding are given and the azimuthal phase constant l has been preselected as the one of interest. This is only one relation between p and q; once we find either of these two unknowns, it will yield the axial phase constant β for given k (or frequency ω), for specified n_1, n_2, a, and l, from Eq. (14.1). But p and q are already known to be related also by Eq. (14.8), which we can rewrite as

$$p^2a^2+q^2a^2=V^2, \quad (14.35)$$

if we define the dimensionless parameter V by

$$V^2=k^2a^2(n_1^2-n_2^2). \quad (14.36)$$

This parameter involves only known quantities. The characteristic equation (14.34) and the constraint (14.35) are two equations for the two unknowns pa, qa. Upon solving these simultaneously, we can determine the phase constant β from

$$\beta^2a^2=k^2a^2n_1^2-p^2a^2 \quad \text{or} \quad \beta^2a^2=k^2a^2n_2^2+q^2a^2. \quad (14.37)$$

One approach to solving the two simultaneous equations for pa, qa is to plot each of the two relations on the same qa–pa plane and look for intersections of the two curves. The constraint (14.35) plots simply as a circle of radius V, which is proportional to the operating frequency (assuming that the refractive indices can be considered independent of frequency). The characteristic equation (14.34) plots as a curve with many branches, because the $J_l(pa)$ function is oscillatory. Each branch corresponds to a possible mode of propagation, attainable if the frequency is high enough for an intersection with the circle of radius V to occur.

For purposes of calculation or plotting, the presence of derivatives of the Bessel functions in the characteristic equation is an inconvenience. However, Bessel functions obey a number of *recursion relations* that relate the functions of order l, and their derivatives, to the Bessel functions with orders $l \pm 1$. Among the important relations are

$$J_{l-1}(x)+J_{l+1}(x)=\frac{2l}{x}J_l(x), \quad (14.38)$$

$$J_{l-1}(x)-J_{l+1}(x)=2J_l'(x). \quad (14.39)$$

The same relations apply also to the $Y_l(x)$ Bessel functions. For the modified functions, these appear as

$$I_{l-1}(x) - I_{l+1}(x) = \frac{2l}{x} I_l(x), \tag{14.40}$$

$$I_{l-1}(x) + I_{l+1}(x) = 2I_l'(x); \tag{14.41}$$

$$K_{l-1}(x) - K_{l+1}(x) = -\frac{2l}{x} K_l(x), \tag{14.42}$$

$$K_{l-1}(x) + K_{l+1}(x) = -2K_l'(x). \tag{14.43}$$

We can use these recursion relations to eliminate the derivatives of the Bessel functions from the characteristic equation and symmetrize it even further, by defining the abbreviations J^+, J^-, K^+, K^- as

$$J^{\pm} \equiv \frac{J_{l\pm 1}(pa)}{paJ_l(pa)}, \qquad K^{\pm} \equiv \frac{K_{l\pm 1}(qa)}{qaK_l(qa)}. \tag{14.44}$$

The characteristic equation (14.34) then transforms into

$$(J^+ + K^+)(n_1^2 J^- - n_2^2 K^-) + (J^- - K^-)(n_1^2 J^+ + n_2^2 K^+) = 0. \tag{14.45}$$

This form is easier to plot and to analyze for properties such as asymptotes and cutoff conditions.

Figure 14–3 shows the first three modes for $l = 1$ and a typical circle ($V = 3$) whose intersections with the several branches give the pairs of values

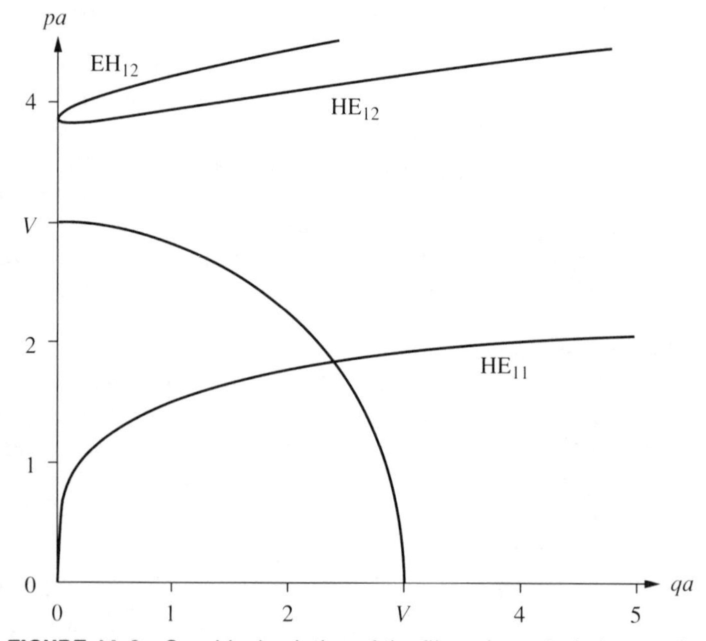

FIGURE 14–3 Graphical solution of the fiber characteristic equation.

of qa and pa that solve both equations simultaneously. The figure is plotted for $n_1 = 1.6$ and $n_2 = 1.4$.

HE and EH Modes

As the operating frequency increases, more and more intersections with branches of the characteristic curve are possible. Those branches that lie above the level $pa = V$ can have no intersection with the circle of radius V; they are cut off. For $l = 1$, there is one branch that reaches down to the origin of the qa–pa plane; there is then an intersection with the circle no matter how small its radius, so there is no cutoff frequency for that branch, which is designated the HE_{11} mode. All other modes have a cutoff frequency. Two branches emanate from each nonzero null of the $J_1(pa)$ Bessel function on the pa-axis; the corresponding modes are denoted HE_{1m} and EH_{1m}. For $l > 1$, the branches for the HE_{lm} and EH_{lm} modes emanate from separate cutoff points on the pa-axis (the axis for $qa = 0$, at cutoff).

We can determine the cutoff points (pa at $qa = 0$), and from these the cutoff frequency for each mode (since $pa = V$ at cutoff), by taking the limit of the characteristic equation as $qa \to 0$. From the behavior of the Bessel functions near zero argument, we find that $K^- \to 1/[2(l-1)]$ while K^+ becomes infinite as $K^+ \to 2l/(qa)^2$. For $l > 1$, we find that the cutoff points pa must satisfy either

$$J^- \equiv \frac{J_{l-1}(pa)}{paJ_l(pa)} = \frac{n_2^2}{(l-1)(n_1^2 + n_2^2)} \tag{14.46}$$

for the HE_{lm} modes, or else

$$J_l(pa) = 0 \quad (pa > 0) \qquad \text{that is,} \quad pa = j_{lm} \tag{14.47}$$

for the EH_{lm} modes. The case $l = 1$ is exceptional (because K^- is then not finite at $qa \to 0$); the cutoff condition is then just

$$pa = j_{1m} \qquad \text{for both } HE_{1(m+1)} \text{ and } EH_{1(m+1)}, \tag{14.48}$$

while $pa = 0$ (no cutoff) for the HE_{11} dominant mode.

TE and TM Modes

The mode designations remind us that the modes are hybrid, having an axial component of both the electric and the magnetic field. We can confirm this from Eq. (14.28), which is a homogeneous matrix equation that requires not only that the determinant of the coefficient matrix vanish for nontrivial fields, but also that the two axial components be properly related to each other when nonzero solutions do exist. Thus the first of the two equations comprising the matrix relation requires that $E_z(a)$ and $H_z(a)$ satisfy

$$l\frac{\beta}{k}\left[\frac{1}{p^2a^2} + \frac{1}{q^2a^2}\right]E_z(a) = [j\eta_0 H_z(a)]F(q, p) \tag{14.49}$$

and the second of the pair requires the axial fields to be related also by

$$l\frac{\beta}{k}\left[\frac{1}{p^2a^2}+\frac{1}{q^2a^2}\right]H_z(a)=\frac{E_z(a)}{j\eta_0}\,G(q,p). \tag{14.50}$$

Of course, it is the characteristic equation that permits both of these to be valid simultaneously, but they still require that *both* the axial field components be nonzero, since the coefficients on the left are not zero, with one pair of exceptions: one or the other of the two axial fields *can* be zero, but only for $l = 0$, the azimuthally symmetric modes that do not twist about the axis as they travel along it. We therefore can have an exceptional TM mode, for which $H_z(a) = 0$ but $E_z(a) \neq 0$, provided that $l = 0$ from Eq. (14.49) and $G(q, p) = 0$ from Eq. (14.50), and also an exceptional TE mode, for which $E_z(a) = 0$ but $H_z(a) \neq 0$, provided that $l = 0$ from Eq. (14.50) and $F(q, p) = 0$ from Eq. (14.49). More explicitly, the characteristic equations for these exceptional transverse modes are $F(q, p) = 0$ for the TE mode, or

$$\frac{J_0'(pa)}{paJ_0(pa)}=-\frac{K_0'(qa)}{qaK_0(qa)}\qquad\text{(TE)}, \tag{14.51}$$

and $G(q, p) = 0$ for the TM mode, or

$$\frac{n_1^2J_0'(pa)}{paJ_0(pa)}=-\frac{n_2^2K_0'(qa)}{qaK_0(qa)}\qquad\text{(TM)}, \tag{14.52}$$

both for $l = 0$ only. Since $J_0'(x) = -J_1(x)$ and $K_0'(x) = -K_1(x)$, these can also be written as

$$J^+ + K^+ = 0 \quad \text{for } \mathrm{TE}_{0m} \qquad \text{and} \qquad n_1^2J^+ + n_2^2K^+ = 0 \quad \text{for } \mathrm{TM}_{0m}. \tag{14.53}$$

We can easily see that these transverse modes do have a cutoff frequency. Since the $K_0(x)$ function is a decaying one, the ratio of slope to value must be negative and the right sides of Eqs. (14.51)–(14.52) must be positive. For these equations to be satisfied, the slope and value of the $J_0(pa)$ function must have the same sign; for this oscillatory function, this does occur, but only beyond a null and before a zero-slope point: for the *m*th branch of the transverse modes, TE_{0m} and TM_{0m}, the value of pa must be restricted to the range $j_{0m} < pa < j'_{0m}$. The lowest value of pa that permits transverse modes to propagate is $pa = j_{01} = 2.4048$ and V must exceed this value for these modes to be above cutoff.

Dominant Mode

For spiraling waves, $l \neq 0$, the modes are hybrid, with both axial field components E_z and H_z nonzero, designated HE_{lm} and EH_{lm}. The HE_{11} mode is dominant, having no cutoff frequency. Hence a single-mode fiber can be had by keeping $V < 2.4048$; beyond that point, the TE and TM modes begin to appear. This is a restriction on the core diameter or on the difference between the core and cladding refractive indices for a given operating frequency, since $V = 2\pi(a/\lambda_0)\sqrt{(n_1^2 - n_2^2)}$.

EXAMPLE 14.1

For a dielectric rod of permittivity $\varepsilon = 2.56$ and diameter $2a = 1$ cm in air, what is the frequency range for dominant-mode operation?

With $n_1^2 = \varepsilon = 2.56$ and $n_2^2 = 1$, the free-space wavelength must exceed $\lambda_0 = \pi(2a/V)\sqrt{1.56}$ with $V = 2.4048$, or $\lambda_0 > (1.6317)2a = 1.6317$ cm, which corresponds to a maximum frequency of $f_0 = 18.373$ GHz. ◆

Summary

The dielectric cylinder, which models the step-index optical fiber, can act as a waveguide. The mechanism is that of total internal reflection at the cylindrical boundary with the cladding, resulting in a standing wave across the core and a decaying field in the cladding; this entire field pattern propagates along the dielectric cylinder.

Because of the circular geometry, the standing wave in the core is not sinusoidal but has the form of an oscillatory Bessel function and the decaying fields in the cladding are not exponential but follow a modified Bessel function. The curvature of the boundary also has the effect of mixing the transverse modes of a dielectric slab or of a hollow conducting cylinder into a set of hybrid modes that have electric and magnetic fields that both have an axial component. The exceptions are the transverse modes for the azimuthally symmetric types; these do not twist about the axis as they progress along the dielectric. The dominant mode is the HE_{11} mode, which is hybrid and is the only one that can propagate in the range $0 < V < 2.4048$.

The dielectric cylinder can be used at microwave frequencies but has found glorious applications for lightwave propagation once it became possible to fabricate sufficiently pure and homogeneous glass fibers with sizes of the order of micrometers.

PROBLEMS

Polarization of Transverse Field of Dominant Mode

14.1 Determine the polarization of the transverse field $\nabla\psi(r, \theta)$, at the origin $r = 0$, if:

(a) $\psi(r, \theta) = J_1(pr)e^{-j\theta}$;
(b) $\psi(r, \theta) = J_1(pr)e^{j\theta}$;
(c) $\psi(r, \theta) = J_1(pr) \cos \theta$;
(d) $\psi(r, \theta) = J_1(pr) \sin \theta$.

These fields are relevant to the HE_{11} mode of dielectric cylinders. (*Note:* At $r = 0$, θ is undefined, as are the unit vectors $\hat{\mathbf{r}}$ and $\hat{\boldsymbol{\theta}}$; the rectangular coordinate unit vectors $\hat{\mathbf{x}}$ and $\hat{\mathbf{y}}$ are defined everywhere, however. Also note that $J_1(x) \to \frac{1}{2}x$ as $x \to 0$.)

Behavior of Bessel Function Ratios at Cutoff

14.2 **(a)** From the property that $K_l(x) \to C/x^l$ as $x \to 0$ (for some constant C and for any $l > 0$), determine the limit of the ratio $K_l'(x)/K_l(x)$ as $x \to 0$.

(b) From this result and the recursion relations for the modified Bessel functions, verify that the ratio $K^- = K_{l-1}(x)/[xK_l(x)] \to 1/[2(l-1)]$ as $x \to 0$ (for $l > 1$).

(c) Verify that the ratio $K^+ = K_{l+1}(x)/[xK_l(x)] \to 2l/x^2$ as $x \to 0$ (for $l > 0$).

(d) From the property that $K_0(x) \to C_0 \ln x$ as $x \to 0$ (for some constant C_0), determine the limit of the ratio $K_0'(x)/K_0(x)$ as $x \to 0$.

(e) Determine the limit of the ratio $K^- = K_{l-1}(x)/[xK_l(x)]$ as $x \to 0$, for $l = 1$.

(f) Determine the limit of the ratio $K^+ = K_{l+1}(x)/[xK_l(x)]$ as $x \to 0$, for $l = 0$.

Minimum Wavelength for Dominant-Mode Operation

14.3 For a fiber with core and cladding indices $n_1 = 1.45$ and $n_2 = 1.40$ and core diameter $2a = 50\,\mu\text{m}$, what is the minimum free-space operating wavelength for dominant-mode operation?

Maximum Core Diameter for Dominant-Mode Operation

14.4 For a fiber with core and cladding indices $n_1 = 1.45$ and $n_2 = 1.40$ and free-space operating wavelength $\lambda_0 = 0.6328\ \mu\text{m}$, what is the maximum core diameter for dominant-mode operation?

Transformation of Characteristic Equation to Simplified Form

14.5 With the abbreviations $x = pa$, $y = qa$, $f(x) = J_l'(x)/xJ_l(x)$, and $g(y) = K_l'(y)/yK_l(y)$, the characteristic equation for the cylindrical fiber, Eq. (14.34), reads

$$l^2\left[\frac{1}{x^2} + \frac{1}{y^2}\right]\left[\frac{n_1^2}{x^2} + \frac{n_2^2}{y^2}\right] = [f(x) + g(y)][n_1^2 f(x) + n_2^2 g(y)]\,.$$

Fill in the steps that transform this version of the equation, which has derivatives of the Bessel functions, into the simplified version, Eq. (14.45), which reads

$$(J^+ + K^+)(n_1^2 J^- - n_2^2 K^-) + (J^- - K^-)(n_1^2 J^+ + n_2^2 K^+) = 0\,,$$

where $J^\pm = J_{l\pm1}(x)/xJ_l(x)$ and $K^\pm(y) = K_{l\pm1}(y)/yK_l(y)$.

Steps Toward the Characteristic Equation for a Jacketed Fiber

14.6 The characteristic equation for a three-medium model of the cylindrical fiber (core, cladding, and jacket or air as the outermost medium) can be developed in close analogy with that for the two-medium version (core and infinitely extended cladding). For $n_1 > \beta/k > n_2 > n_3$, we expect bound waves to propagate, with $k^2n_1^2 = \beta^2 + p^2$, $k^2n_2^2 = \beta^2 - q_2^2$, $k^2n_3^2 = \beta^2 - q_3^2$ in the regions $r < a$, $a < r < b$, and $b < r$, respectively. In analogy with Eq. (14.16), we write $E_z(r) = [J_l(pr)/J_l(pa)]E_z(a)$ for $r \leq a$ and $E_z(r) = [K_l(q_3 r)/K_l(q_3 b)]E_z(b)$ for $b \leq r$. We seek an analogous expression suitable for the cladding, $a \leq r \leq b$. Verify that an appropriate expression is of the form

$$E_z(r) = [K_l(q_2 r) \quad I_l(q_2 r)]B^{-1}\eta \qquad \text{for } a \leq r \leq b,$$

where η is a two-component column vector with entries $E_z(a)$, $E_z(b)$; what is the 2×2 matrix B?

CHAPTER 15

Practical Versions of Optical Fibers

The properties of optical fibers are fundamentally those of the dielectric rod waveguide, but a number of practical considerations arise from the fact that optical wavelengths are so small. Furthermore, techniques have been developed that allow the shaping of the refractive index profile $n(r)$ to suit various purposes and optimize performance. We can now study some of the major consequences of these considerations.

Numerical Aperture

A key quantity in the analysis of the cylindrical dielectric waveguide is the parameter V, given for a step-index fiber of core radius a, core index n_1, and cladding index n_2 as

$$V = ka\sqrt{n_1^2 - n_2^2}, \tag{15.1}$$

where $k = \omega/c = 2\pi/\lambda_0$ makes this parameter proportional to the operating frequency (if the indices are not significantly frequency dependent). It is also proportional to the size of the core. The remaining factor, which measures the difference between the core and the cladding refractive indices, is termed the *numerical aperture* and abbreviated NA:

$$\text{NA} \equiv \sqrt{n_1^2 - n_2^2}. \tag{15.2}$$

Further physical significance of this important parameter, and the reason for its name, will become clearer later when we examine wave launching. For now, the key parameter V, which determines which modes can propagate and how tightly they are bound to the core, is just

$$V = \left(\frac{2\pi a}{\lambda_0}\right)\text{NA}. \tag{15.3}$$

The first practical point to keep in mind is that because optical wavelengths are so small, of the order of a micrometer, fibers of practical sizes will be many wavelengths in diameter. A typical fiber that does not demand extreme measures for its fabrication might have a core diameter of $2a = 50\ \mu\text{m}$; for an operating wavelength near $\lambda_0 = 0.8\ \mu\text{m}$, the ratio of diameter to wavelength is

$2a/\lambda_0 \approx 60$ and the parameter $V \approx 200(\text{NA})$. We saw when we formed a circle of radius V to superimpose on the plot of the characteristic equation that a reasonable number of modes can propagate if V is reasonably small; for example, dominant mode operation of the dielectric rod waveguide requires that $V < 2.4048$. It follows that to maintain V reasonably small, the numerical aperture NA must be very small, which requires that the core and cladding indices of refraction be quite close to each other. That is, the core and cladding glasses must be dissimilar, yet have nearly the same refractive indices n_1 and n_2. In practice, different concentrations of dopants for the same original type of glass can achieve the required difference in indices.

Since $n_1 \approx n_2$, it is convenient to define the relative difference

$$\Delta = \frac{n_1 - n_2}{n_2}. \tag{15.4}$$

Then the quantity that determines the numerical aperture can be approximated by

$$n_1^2 - n_2^2 = (n_1 + n_2)(n_1 - n_2) \approx (2n_2)(n_2 \Delta) = 2n_2^2 \Delta \tag{15.5}$$

and then

$$V \approx kan_2\sqrt{2\Delta}, \tag{15.6}$$

provided that Δ is small.

Even when the core index is only about 1% greater than the cladding index, so that $\Delta = 0.01$, V is fairly large. For example, for $n_2 = 1.5$ and $\Delta = 0.005$ (only $\frac{1}{2}$% difference in the indices), $V \approx 30$. To achieve single-mode operation, which requires that $V < 2.4$, the core diameter has to be made of the order of a few micrometers. Such fibers were developed much later than the thicker, multimode fibers.

When V exceeds 2.4048, more than one mode can propagate and share the available power. In practical cases, V is a large number, such as 30 in the example above, and quite a large number of modes can propagate. How many? We can arrive at a rough estimate of the number of modes that scramble along the multimode fiber and compete for the optical power by recalling a few facts about the modes of propagation along a dielectric cylinder. The modes that are above cutoff are those with $pa < V$; there is an HE_{lm} and an EH_{lm} mode, each with either $e^{jl\theta}$ or $e^{-jl\theta}$ azimuthal variation (or $\cos l\theta$ and $\sin l\theta$, if the real versions are preferred), with values of pa near j_{lm} (the mth zero of the Bessel function of order l). We can therefore expect two mode types with two forms of azimuthal variation for each root of the $J_l(x)$ Bessel function that is less than the value of V, making the number of propagating modes roughly four times the number of roots with values less than V. We can estimate the number of such roots from the behavior of the Bessel functions for large arguments. When x is large, $J_l(x)$ asymptotically approaches a damped sinusoid, as

$$J_l(x) \to \sqrt{\frac{2}{\pi x}} \cos\left(x - \frac{l\pi}{2} - \frac{\pi}{4}\right) \qquad \text{as } x \to \infty. \tag{15.7}$$

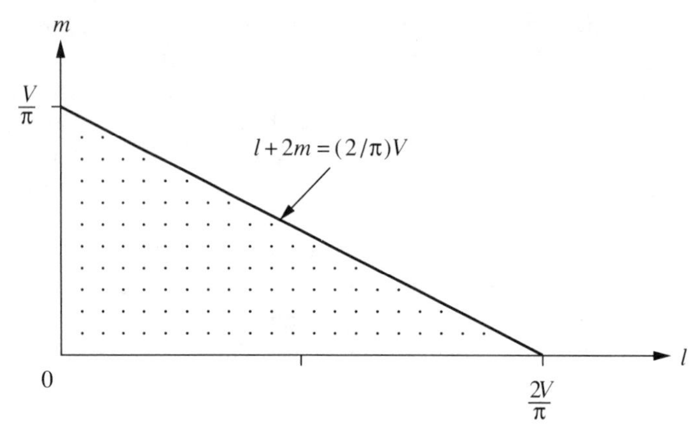

FIGURE 15–1 Number of mode-index pairs for given V.

Consequently, the zeros j_{lm} of the Bessel function approach values that are spaced more and more nearly π part:

$$j_{lm} \approx \frac{l\pi}{2} + \frac{\pi}{4} + \left(m - \frac{1}{2}\right)\pi \tag{15.8}$$

or, for large enough modal indices m,

$$j_{lm} \approx \frac{(l + 2m)\pi}{2}. \tag{15.9}$$

The question of how many modes can propagate therefore reduces (for large V only) to the question of how many integer pairs l, m there exist such that $(l + 2m)\pi/2 < V$; the number of modes will be four times that number, approximately. Figure 15–1 shows that the number of such integer pairs, indicated by dots in the lm-plane in the figure, is approximately the area of the triangle delimited by the axes and the line $(l + 2m)\pi/2 = V$, since the dots are spaced one unit apart. This area is just $\frac{1}{2}(2V/\pi)(V/\pi) = V^2/\pi^2$ and we conclude that, roughly, $(4/\pi^2)V^2$ modes can propagate when $V \gg 1$.

More precise counts of the number of modes that are above cutoff for a given value of V indicate that

$$N \approx 0.5V^2 \tag{15.10}$$

is an even closer estimate, still for large V. For example, for the typical case of $V = 30$ previously considered, about 450 modes can propagate along the fiber. In microwave parlance, multimode fibers are highly overmoded. Each mode has its own phase constant, guide wavelength, phase and group velocity, wave impedance, and field pattern; each captures its own share of the optical power that is carried by the multimode fiber. Under such circumstances, the fiber simply conveys optical energy and any attempts to take advantage of special features of one or another mode or of their coherence properties are not likely to be fruitful.

LP Modes

The fact that the core and cladding indices are very nearly equal in practical fibers allows considerable simplification of the characteristic equation that governs wave propagation along the fiber. With only minor loss of accuracy, we can set n_1 and n_2 equal to each other in the characteristic equation, but not of course in the relation $V = ka\sqrt{n_1^2 - n_2^2}$, which involves the difference between the indices directly. When the approximation $n_1 = n_2$ is applied to the characteristic equation in the form

$$(J^+ + K^+)(n_1^2 J^- - n_2^2 K^-) + (J^- - K^-)(n_1^2 J^+ + n_2^2 K^+) = 0, \quad (15.11)$$

where the superscripted symbols stand for

$$J^\pm \equiv \frac{J_{l\pm1}(pa)}{paJ_l(pa)} \qquad K^\pm \equiv \frac{K_{l\pm1}(qa)}{qaK_l(qa)}, \quad (15.12)$$

we see at once that the equation reduces to

$$(J^+ + K^+)(J^- - K^-) = 0, \quad (15.13)$$

with two sets of solutions, either $J^+ = -K^+$ or $J^- = K^-$; more explicitly,

$$\frac{J_{l\pm1}(pa)}{paJ_l(pa)} = \mp \frac{K_{l\pm1}(qa)}{qaK_l(qa)}. \quad (15.14)$$

Note that this is independent of the values of the approximately equal n_1, n_2 and hence provides a universal set of curves on which to superimpose the circle that expresses the constraint

$$p^2a^2 + q^2a^2 = V^2 = k^2a^2n_2^2\, 2\Delta, \quad (15.15)$$

where $\Delta = (n_1 - n_2)/n_2$ is the relative difference between the nearly equal indices. Figure 15–2 shows the first few intersections of the constraint circle for $V = 6$ with the branches of the characteristic curve for $l = 2$ in this limit of equal core and cladding refractive indices. The branches that satisfy $J^+ = -K^+$ and $J^- = K^-$ alternate; the former yield the EH modes and the latter give the HE modes.

With $n_1 \approx n_2$, the entire space is almost homogeneous, with a single index of refraction $n \approx n_1 \approx n_2$, and we should expect to find waves that are very nearly the same as the simple, transverse, uniform waves of a homogeneous medium. Such modes may be only approximately transverse and not quite uniform, however. D. Gloge arrived at approximate modes of propagation that are very nearly linearly polarized, called LP modes.

To obtain a set of such simple modes, we seek waves that vary in time and along the fiber as $e^{j(\omega t - \beta z)}$ and ask for *fixed* orientations of the transverse

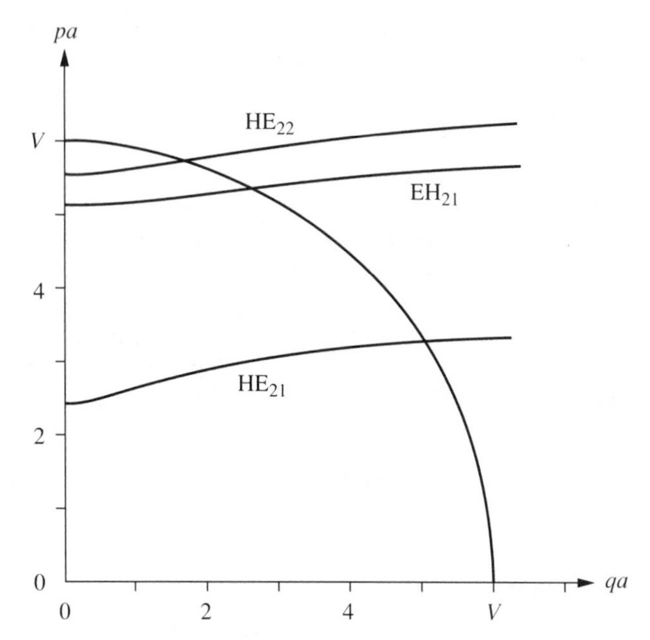

FIGURE 15–2 Fiber characteristic equation in limit $n_1 = n_2$, for $l = 2$.

fields, along fixed, perpendicular directions transverse to $\hat{\mathbf{z}}$, say

$$\mathbf{E} = [\hat{\mathbf{x}}E_0 + \hat{\mathbf{z}}E_z]e^{-j\beta z}, \qquad \mathbf{H} = [\hat{\mathbf{y}}H_0 + \hat{\mathbf{z}}H_z]e^{-j\beta z}. \tag{15.16}$$

If the medium were truly homogeneous ($n_1 = n_2 = n$), we would expect the axial components E_z and H_z to vanish and the transverse components to be related by the medium's impedance $\eta = \eta_0/n$ as $E_0 = (\eta_0/n)H_0$ and we would find that the phase constant would be $\beta = kn$, where $k = \omega/c$. The true result for the phase constant for a fiber is found from

$$k^2n_1^2 = \beta^2 + p^2, \qquad k^2n_2^2 = \beta^2 - q^2 \tag{15.17}$$

but for $n \approx n_1 \approx n_2$, these become

$$k^2n^2 \approx \beta^2 + p^2 \approx \beta^2 - q^2 \tag{15.18}$$

or, more simply,

$$kn \approx \beta \qquad \text{with} \quad kn \gg p \quad \text{and} \quad kn \gg q. \tag{15.19}$$

This is verified by the typical values we have encountered for practical fibers, $kan \approx 300$ while $pa \approx qa \approx 3$ or so. In the present case, we do not expect the axial components to be zero, but they should be weak.

Upon calculating $\nabla \times \mathbf{E}$ and $\nabla \times \mathbf{H}$ and letting the transverse fields be related by the impedance of the medium, as $E_0 = (\eta_0/n)H_0$, we find that we must indeed have axial components of the two fields and that if we neglect the derivatives of the weak axial fields compared to those of the strong transverse components, these satisfy

$$\frac{\partial E_0}{\partial x} = jknE_z, \qquad \frac{\partial H_0}{\partial y} = jknH_z. \tag{15.20}$$

But the transverse derivatives of the transverse fields are of the order of p or q times those fields and since $kn \gg p, q$, we conclude that the axial fields must indeed be much weaker than the transverse ones: $E_z \ll E_0$ and $H_z \ll H_0$. The transverse fields satisfy the Helmholtz equations

$$\nabla^2 E_0 + p^2 E_0 = 0 \qquad \text{in the core}, \tag{15.21}$$

$$\nabla^2 E_0 - q^2 E_0 = 0 \qquad \text{in the cladding}, \tag{15.22}$$

and these are satisfied by products of Bessel functions of the radius and trigonometric functions of the azimuth:

$$E_0(r, \theta) = E_0(a, 0)\,\frac{J_l(pr)}{J_l(pa)} \cos l\theta \qquad \text{in the core}, \tag{15.23}$$

$$E_0(r, \theta) = E_0(a, 0)\,\frac{K_l(qr)}{K_l(qa)} \cos l\theta \qquad \text{in the cladding}. \tag{15.24}$$

We could as well use $\sin l\theta$ instead of $\cos l\theta$; that would amount merely to a shift of the direction of zero azimuth. The normalizations in these expressions have ensured continuity of the transverse fields' tangential components across the interface at $r = a$. There remains to satisfy continuity of the axial components E_z and H_z, which are also tangential. But these are proportional to the two transverse derivatives of $E_0 = (\eta_0/n)H_0$, according to Eq. (15.20), so that both $\partial E_0/\partial x$ and $\partial H_0/\partial y$ (or $\partial E_0/\partial y$) must be made continuous at $r = a$.

By the chain rule of differentiation and the conversion from rectangular to polar coordinates,

$$\begin{aligned}\frac{\partial E_0}{\partial x} &= \left(\frac{\partial r}{\partial x}\right)\frac{\partial E_0}{\partial r} + \left(\frac{\partial \theta}{\partial x}\right)\frac{\partial E_0}{\partial \theta} \\ &= \cos\theta\,\frac{\partial E_0}{\partial r} - \frac{\sin\theta}{r}\frac{\partial E_0}{\partial \theta},\end{aligned} \tag{15.25}$$

$$\begin{aligned}\frac{\partial E_0}{\partial y} &= \left(\frac{\partial r}{\partial y}\right)\frac{\partial E_0}{\partial r} + \left(\frac{\partial \theta}{\partial y}\right)\frac{\partial E_0}{\partial \theta} \\ &= \sin\theta\,\frac{\partial E_0}{\partial r} + \frac{\cos\theta}{r}\frac{\partial E_0}{\partial \theta}.\end{aligned} \tag{15.26}$$

Hence, in the core, with the notation $E_{00} \equiv E_0(a, 0)$,

$$J_l(pa) jknE_z = E_{00}\,p\left\{J_l'(pr)\cos l\theta\cos\theta + \frac{lJ_l(pr)}{pr}\sin l\theta\sin\theta\right\}, \tag{15.27}$$

while as seen in the cladding,

$$K_l(qa) jknE_z = E_{00}\,q\left\{K_l'(qr)\cos l\theta\cos\theta + \frac{lK_l(qr)}{qr}\sin l\theta\sin\theta\right\}. \tag{15.28}$$

Analogous results apply to H_z from $\partial E_0/\partial y$, but the trigonometric factors are then $\cos l\theta \sin \theta$ and $-\sin l\theta \cos \theta$ instead.

For continuity of the axial fields at $r = a$, we therefore need

$$\frac{paJ_l'(pa)}{J_l(pa)} = \frac{qaK_l'(qa)}{K_l(qa)} \qquad \text{(LP modes)}. \tag{15.29}$$

For comparison with our previous results, we can make use of the recursion relations for Bessel functions, rewritten as

$$J_l'(x) = \pm J_{l\mp 1}(x) \mp \frac{l}{x} J_l(x) \qquad K_l'(y) = -K_{l\mp 1}(y) \mp \frac{l}{y} K_l(y), \tag{15.30}$$

to transform this continuity condition into the two equivalent forms, one for each choice of the upper or lower sign,

$$\frac{paJ_{l\mp 1}(pa)}{J_l(pa)} = \mp \frac{qaK_{l\mp 1}(qa)}{K_l(qa)} \qquad \text{(LP modes)}. \tag{15.31}$$

Now this does not agree at once with our previous characteristic equation, (15.14), for the hybrid modes in the limit of $n_1 = n_2$; that one came from the two alternative solutions $J^+ = -K^+$ or $J^- = K^-$ in that limit, or

$$\frac{J_{l\pm 1}(pa)}{paJ_l(pa)} = \mp \frac{K_{l\pm 1}(qa)}{qaK_l(qa)} \qquad \text{(hybrid modes)} \tag{15.32}$$

instead. However, all is not lost in confusion, because our condition for linearly polarized approximate modes, Eq. (15.31), can be viewed as the same as our previous result if we consider it to apply to the case of azimuthal variation as $e^{-j(l\mp 1)\theta}$ instead of $e^{-jl\theta}$, for then Eq. (15.31) is the same as

$$\frac{1}{J^+} = -\frac{1}{K^+} \quad \text{(upper sign)} \qquad \text{or} \qquad \frac{1}{J^-} = \frac{1}{K^-} \quad \text{(lower sign)}, \tag{15.33}$$

which clearly does agree with the limiting case of the hybrid modes. But is our LP-mode azimuthal variation described by l or by $(l \mp 1)$? We actually used $\cos l\theta$, which combines $e^{\pm jl\theta}$, so that the proper parameter appears to be l, not $(l \mp 1)$. The final reconciliation between the approximate LP modes and the more exact hybrid ones comes when we examine the axial fields of the LP modes, Eqs. (15.27)–(15.28), as these are the ones that define the azimuthal variation for the hybrid modes. From the recursion relations

$$J_{l-1}(x) + J_{l+1}(x) = \frac{2l}{x} J_l(x), \qquad J_{l-1}(x) - J_{l+1}(x) = 2J_l'(x) \tag{15.34}$$

for Bessel functions and the recursions for trigonometric functions

$$2 \cos l\theta \cos \theta = \cos (l-1)\theta + \cos (l+1)\theta, \tag{15.35}$$

$$2 \sin l\theta \sin \theta = \cos (l-1)\theta - \cos (l+1)\theta, \tag{15.36}$$

we find that Eq. (15.27) for E_z of the LP mode can be expressed in the core as

$$
\begin{aligned}
E_z &\propto J_l'(pr)\cos l\theta \cos\theta + \frac{lJ_l(pr)}{pr}\sin l\theta \sin\theta \\
&= \tfrac{1}{4}[J_{l-1}(pr) - J_{l+1}(pr)][\cos(l-1)\theta + \cos(l+1)\theta] \\
&\quad + \tfrac{1}{4}[J_{l-1}(pr) + J_{l+1}(pr)][\cos(l-1)\theta - \cos(l+1)\theta] \\
&= \tfrac{1}{2}\{J_{l-1}(pr)\cos(l-1)\theta - J_{l+1}(pr)\cos(l+1)\theta\}. \qquad (15.37)
\end{aligned}
$$

This is just a superposition of the axial fields of two hybrid modes, one with azimuthal variation given by $l-1$, the other by $l+1$. This confirms that the fields in Eq. (15.16) and the characteristic equation (15.29) or (15.31) for the simple LP modes are not only consistent with those for the more complicated hybrid modes in the limit of $n_1 = n_2$ but are actually constructed as a superposition of the hybrid modes.

Because of their relative simplicity and the accuracy of the approximations made when $n_1 \approx n_2$, the LP modes are in widespread use to characterize propagation along optical fibers, rather than the more correct, hybrid modes. Superpositions of the $HE_{(l+1)m}$ and $EH_{(l-1)m}$ modes form the approximately linearly polarized modes designated LP_{lm}. The LP_{01} mode corresponds to just the HE_{11} dominant mode. More generally:

HE_{1m} forms LP_{0m} modes ($l = 0$).
HE_{2m} and TM_{0m} and TE_{0m} modes form LP_{1m} modes ($l = 1$).
$HE_{(l+1)m}$ and $EH_{(l-1)m}$ modes form LP_{lm} modes ($l > 1$).

The cutoff condition ($q = 0$) for the LP_{lm} mode is given by

$$
J_{l-1}(pa) = 0 \qquad \text{or} \qquad pa = j_{(l-1)m} \quad \text{at cutoff}; \qquad (15.38)
$$

the dominant LP_{01} mode has no cutoff. Finally, we note that the LP_{lm} modes may have either of two orthogonal orientations of the linear polarization in the transverse plane and can have either $\cos l\theta$ or $\sin l\theta$ azimuthal variation of the transverse fields. Each therefore represents four distinguishable modes, as do the hybrid $HE_{(l+1)m}\cos(l+1)\theta$ and $EH_{(l-1)m}\cos(l-1)\theta$ modes or $HE_{(l+1)m}\sin(l+1)\theta$ and $EH_{(l-1)m}\sin(l-1)\theta$ modes of the axial fields, which comprise the LP modes.

Single-Mode Fiber

The dominant mode for a cylindrical fiber is the HE_{11} hybrid mode, called the LP_{01} linearly polarized mode when the core and cladding refractive indices are considered equal. It is the only mode that can propagate along the fiber when $V < 2.4048$, so that a single-mode fiber can be had if the core radius can be made small enough to maintain $V < 2.4$ even for reasonable differences of refractive indices of the core and cladding. For example, a single-mode fiber designed for operation at $\lambda_0 = 1.3\ \mu m$ may have a core diameter of only 8 μm, while the cladding diameter, which should be at least an order of magnitude thicker than the core, may be the standard 125 μm. It may have a numerical aperture of about NA = 0.115, so that it remains single-mode down to about $\lambda_0 = \pi(2a/V)\text{NA} = 1.2\ \mu$m.

The dominant LP_{01} mode has transverse fields that vary as

$$E_0(r, \theta) = \begin{cases} E_0(a) \dfrac{J_0(pr)}{J_0(pa)} & \text{in the core}, \quad (15.39) \\[2ex] E_0(a) \dfrac{K_0(qr)}{K_0(qa)} & \text{in the cladding}. \quad (15.40) \end{cases}$$

Its characteristic equation reduces to

$$\frac{paJ_1(pa)}{J_0(pa)} = \frac{qaK_1(qa)}{K_0(qa)} \tag{15.41}$$

when the core and cladding indices are considered equal. This equation has solutions down to $pa \to 0$ as $qa \to 0$, so that, technically, the dominant mode has no cutoff frequency. For small argument, the $K_0(y)$ function becomes

$$K_0(y) \to -\ln(0.89054y) \qquad \text{as } y \to 0, \tag{15.42}$$

while $yK_1(y) \to 1$; for small arguments, the ratio $xJ_1(x)/J_0(x) \to \frac{1}{2}x^2$ as $x \to 0$, so that near the origin of the qa–pa plane, the characteristic equation becomes

$$qa \approx 1.123 \exp\left[-\frac{2}{(pa)^2}\right]. \tag{15.43}$$

Since $V \approx pa$ when $qa \approx 0$, we find that if V is significantly less than 1,

$$qa \approx 1.123 \exp\left[-\frac{2}{V^2}\right] \tag{15.44}$$

is extremely small and the LP_{01} mode is practically not guided at all by the fiber. That is, the transverse field in the cladding, $E_0(a)[K_0(qr)/K_0(qa)]$, falls off exceedingly slowly with radius when qa is very small, approximately as

$$E_0(r) = E_0(a) \frac{K_0(qr)}{K_0(qa)} \approx E_0(a)\left[1 - \frac{1}{2} V^2 \ln \frac{r}{a}\right]. \tag{15.45}$$

This can easily reach the outer radius of the cladding without having died away. We conclude that although there is technically no cutoff frequency for the dominant mode, in practice the light is not really guided by the fiber if the parameter V is less than about unity.

Attenuation

The light that propagates along an optical fiber gradually weakens, attenuates, by absorption and scattering. Absorption occurs when impurities are encountered; the hydroxyl ion of water present in the glass as an impurity is particularly effective in absorbing light energy, and certain metal ions and oxides contribute to such losses as well. Control of impurities to keep them at levels of a few parts per billion has allowed these losses to contribute less than 1 dB/km to fiber attenuation.

Scattering of light arises from imperfections in the structure of the fiber, which cannot in practice be ideally uniform in density and perfectly straight in geometry. Only a tiny fraction of scattered light remains trapped as a propagating mode; most is lost from the primary beam. Thermal density fluctuations in the material, frozen into the glass in its manufacture, give rise to Rayleigh scattering. This contributes to losses at a rate that decreases with increasing wavelength as λ^{-4}; typically, the attenuation constant α due to Rayleigh scattering is given by

$$\frac{\alpha}{\alpha_0} = \left(\frac{\lambda_0}{\lambda}\right)^4 \qquad \text{with } \alpha_0 = 1.7 \text{ dB/km}, \quad \lambda_0 = 0.85\ \mu\text{m}. \tag{15.46}$$

This makes operation at longer wavelengths more attractive, as long as molecular absorption bands at wavelengths greater than about 1.8 μm are avoided. At wavelengths shorter than about 0.8 μm, Rayleigh scattering is excessive; between the two limits, a strong absorption peak near 1.39 μm, due to the hydroxyl ion, must be avoided. Three transmission "windows" have been used to advantage for fiber optic systems, in the ranges 0.8 to 0.9 μm, 1.2 to 1.3 μm, and 1.55 to 1.6 μm, in which absorption is not much worse than that imposed by the fundamental Rayleigh scattering limit. Figure 15–3 is a log-log plot of the wavelength variation of the attenuation rate due to Rayleigh scattering. Actual loss rates are always above this limit. The three transmission windows

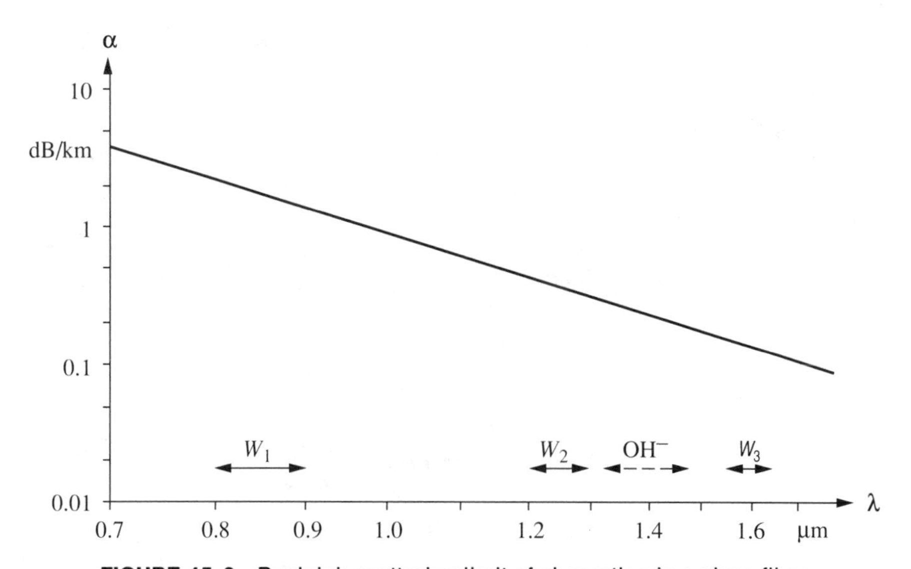

FIGURE 15–3 Rayleigh scattering limit of absorption in a glass fiber.

are indicated, as well as the region, marked OH^-, around the absorption peak caused by the hydroxyl ion.

Material and Multimode Dispersion

For a carrier signal at frequency ω propagating along z as $\exp[j(\omega t - \beta z)]$, the speed at which a slowly varying, information-bearing signal that modulates the carrier propagates is the group velocity $v_g = d\omega/d\beta = c/m$; the parameter m is the group index and the group delay in transmitting a narrow-band signal a distance L is $\tau_g = (L/c)m$. For a particular carrier frequency and a particular mode, there is a specific value of the group delay. The value of that delay is inconsequential, however, since it does not affect the signal information. What does cause concern is the distortion of the modulating signal that arises when more than a single value of the delay affects the components of a signal pulse. This can result from two factors.

First, a practical light source does not provide a pure, single carrier frequency; it is not precisely monochromatic. Instead, it exhibits a linewidth $d\lambda$ about its nominal wavelength λ. Since the group index m depends on frequency or wavelength, the different frequency components present in the carrier suffer different transmission delays.

Second, the propagating signal power is distributed among many modes, each of which has its own group delay. The net effect is that the differential delay spreads the signal pulse. Figure 15–4 shows a pulse whose envelope has the shape $g(t)$ as sent by the transmitter. If many modes carry replicas of this signal along the fiber, each with its own group index m_i, what is received at position z is a superposition of the delayed pulses of each mode:

$$g(t) \quad \text{sent} \qquad \sum_i a_i g\left(t - \frac{z}{c} m_i\right) \quad \text{received}. \tag{15.47}$$

As shown, this superposition results in an overall pulse that is spread in time from $(z/c)m_{\min}$ to $(z/c)m_{\max}$. This spreading of a pulse as it propagates limits the bit rate for signaling, to avoid having adjacent pulses overlap and produce intersymbol interference.

The pulse spreading that arises from the properties of the medium that make the group index a function of wavelength, and hence is operative even

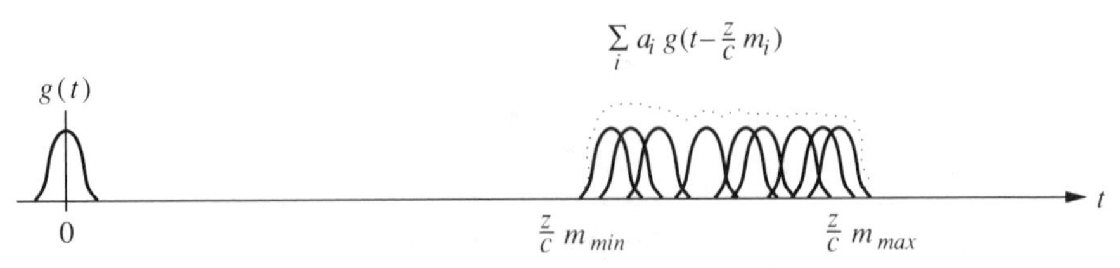

FIGURE 15–4 Pulse spreading by multimode dispersion.

when only a single mode propagates, is called *intramodal* or *material* or *chromatic* dispersion. The spreading that occurs because many modes carry the signal, each with a different group delay, is termed *intermodal* or *multimode* dispersion. The pulse $g(t)$ sent from $z = 0$ arrives at z at some average time $\langle t \rangle = (z/c)\langle m \rangle$, but it is spread to a received pulse width $\delta t = (z/c)\delta m$, where δm is the operative range of values of m.

For a single mode of propagation, there is only the material dispersion to contribute to the pulse spreading. In an unbounded medium of refractive index n, the phase constant and frequency are related by $\beta = kn$ and the group index is

$$m = \frac{d\beta}{dk} = \frac{d(kn)}{dk} = n + k\frac{dn}{dk} = n + \omega\frac{dn}{d\omega} = n - \lambda\frac{dn}{d\lambda}. \tag{15.48}$$

If the source has linewidth $\delta\lambda$, the pulse spreading is determined by $\delta m = (dm/d\lambda)\delta\lambda$ or $\delta m = (\lambda\, dm/d\lambda)(\delta\lambda/\lambda)$. Since

$$\frac{dm}{d\lambda} = \frac{d[n - \lambda\, dn/d\lambda]}{d\lambda} = -\lambda\frac{d^2n}{d\lambda^2}, \tag{15.49}$$

we get for the received pulse width

$$\delta t = \frac{z}{c}\left[-\lambda^2\frac{d^2n}{d\lambda^2}\right]\frac{\delta\lambda}{\lambda}; \tag{15.50}$$

the second derivative may be positive or negative, but only the absolute value of this expression has significance here. A typical value for $\lambda^2 d^2n/d\lambda^2$ for a glass fiber may be 0.03, and for an LED, the relative linewidth may be $\delta\lambda/\lambda \approx 0.02$; these yield a pulse spreading rate of $\delta t/z = 2$ ns/km. Note that a signaling rate of 100 Mbits/s, which is 1 bit per 10 ns, would not allow more than a few nanoseconds between pulses. A laser source has a much narrower linewidth, of the order of $\delta\lambda \approx 1$ nm, compared to $\delta\lambda \approx 20$ nm for an LED. Does that imply that an LED cannot be used for signaling over several kilometers? Actually, in silica glass, the chromatic dispersion $d^2n/d\lambda^2$ goes through a null at a wavelength of about 1.3 μm; operation at this special wavelength can eliminate the effects of this type of dispersion if no other consideration dictates the choice of an operating wavelength.

The other major contributor to the group delay is waveguide dispersion, which arises from the fact that each mode that carries part of the signal energy has its own group velocity. With many modes propagating, the operative value of δm in the expression $\delta t = (z/c)\delta m$ for the received pulse width δt at z becomes the difference between the arrival times of the slowest and the fastest of the modes that carry the power. The dispersion relation of the fiber provides the information about the group velocity of each propagating mode.

For the optical fiber, the dispersion relation is obtained by combining $k^2n_1^2 = \beta^2 + p^2$ and $k^2n_2^2 = \beta^2 - q^2$ and determining p and q from the characteristic equation. The group index for a mode is $m = \partial\beta/\partial k$; we can think of the ratio $\beta/k = n_0$ as an equivalent refractive index at the operating frequency.

Since $n_1^2 = n_0^2 + p^2/k^2$ and $n_2^2 = n_0^2 - q^2/k^2$ and n_1 and n_2 are so close to each other in a practical fiber, the equivalent index will be some compromise value between the core and cladding indices: $n_2 < n_0 < n_1$, with $n_0 \to n_2$ near cutoff but $n_0 \to n_1$ at high frequencies. With $n_1 \approx n_2$, n_0 can hardly vary, but it is precisely the variation of n_0 with frequency that we need in order to find the group index. A more convenient measure of the variation in the equivalent refractive index, or of the change from loose binding to the core near cutoff to tighter binding at high frequencies, is provided by the binding parameter

$$b = \frac{n_0 - n_2}{n_1 - n_2}, \qquad \text{where} \quad n_0 = \frac{\beta}{k}. \tag{15.51}$$

This parameter ranges from zero to unity: near cutoff, $n_0 \approx n_2$, the mode dwells mostly in the cladding and $b \approx 0$; at high frequencies, $n_0 \approx n_1$, the mode is tightly bound to the core and $b \approx 1$. Because $\Delta = (n_1 - n_2)/n_2$, we have

$$n_0 = n_2[1 + b\Delta] \qquad \text{or} \qquad \beta = kn_2[1 + b\Delta]. \tag{15.52}$$

Since β is obtained once the intersection point (qa, pa) of the characteristic equation and the circle $(pa)^2 + (qa)^2 = V^2$ has been found for a particular mode, we realize that b is a function of V.

To obtain the group index $m = \partial\beta/\partial k$ for a mode, we therefore need

$$m = \frac{\partial(kn_2)}{\partial k} + \frac{\partial[kn_2 b\Delta]}{\partial k}; \tag{15.53}$$

but $V \approx kan_2\sqrt{2\Delta}$ makes V and kn_2 proportional if we neglect the variation of the already small quantity Δ with k. This proportionality allows us to rewrite the last equation as

$$\begin{aligned} m &= \frac{\partial(kn_2)}{\partial k} + \frac{\partial[kn_2 b\Delta]}{\partial(kn_2)} \frac{\partial(kn_2)}{\partial k} \\ &= \frac{\partial(kn_2)}{\partial k} + \frac{\partial[Vb\Delta]}{\partial V} \frac{\partial(kn_2)}{\partial k} \\ &= \frac{\partial(kn_2)}{\partial k}\left[1 + \frac{\partial[bV]}{\partial V}\Delta\right], \end{aligned} \tag{15.54}$$

where we have consistently neglected $\partial\Delta/\partial k$. Now the first factor is

$$m_2 = \frac{\partial(kn_2)}{\partial k}, \tag{15.55}$$

the group index of the cladding material itself, so that the overall group index is expressed as

$$m = m_2\left[1 + \frac{\partial[bV]}{\partial V}\Delta\right]. \tag{15.56}$$

This displays the group index as having two contributions. The first term is the material dispersion m_2; it is the same for all modes of propagation and is usually small. The second term is the waveguiding contribution; it involves the mode-dependent term $\partial[bV]/\partial V$, which is large and can vary greatly from mode to mode.

Once again, it is the variation δm of the group index m from mode to mode that determines the spreading of the propagating pulse, so that the group delay ascribed to multimode dispersion becomes

$$\delta t = \frac{z}{c}\,\delta m = \frac{z}{c}\,m_2\,\delta\left\{\frac{\partial[bV]}{\partial V}\right\}\Delta. \tag{15.57}$$

To estimate this intermodal dispersion, we first find that the variation of $\partial[bV]/\partial V$ from the slowest to the fastest mode is of the order of unity for large V. Consequently, for $\Delta \approx 1\%$, the pulse spreading rate for multimode dispersion is roughly $\delta t/z \approx m_2\,\Delta/c \approx 50$ ns/km, an intolerably high rate for long-distance transmission (we found only $\delta t/z \approx 2$ ns/km from the material dispersion alone).

In practice, pulse spreading by multimode dispersion is not so disastrously high as just indicated by the rough calculation above, because different modes do not really propagate independently. There is mode mixing, as well as a greater attenuation for high-order modes, and these effects tend to reduce the differences in arrival times of the different modes that carry the signal. Nevertheless, intermodal dispersion dominates in multimode fibers and has to be dealt with. One approach to reducing the dispersive pulse spreading is to look beyond the step-index fiber structure.

Graded-Index Fibers

The variation in group velocity from mode to mode, which can result in excessively high pulse spreading and hence severe limitations on signaling rates, can be understood in terms of where the field energy is localized within the fiber, for each mode.

The Bessel function factor $J_l(pr)$ places the peak of the power carried by the mode at different radii within the core for different modes; for $l = 0$, the peak of the Bessel function occurs on axis, while for $l > 0$ the field peaks at some finite radius. The factor $\exp[\mp jl\theta]$, combined with $\exp[j(\omega t - \beta z)]$, causes the field power to twist around the axis as it travels along the fiber, in either azimuthal direction; for $l = 0$, propagation is only along the axis, with no spiraling around it. It follows that the energy in different modes effectively travels different overall distances while twisting around the axis, as it progresses axially along the fiber, as suggested schematically in Figure 15–5. The tightly twisted path is clearly longer than the straight one and the modal energy that travels at the speed of light in the glass along a corkscrew path near the periphery of the core must take longer to cover a given axial distance

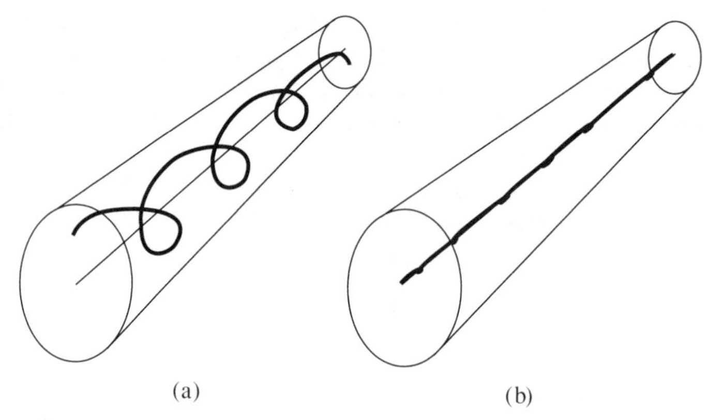

FIGURE 15–5 (a) Twisted versus (b) direct paths of field energy travel.

than does the energy in the $l = 0$ mode that travels straight along the core axis. This is a useful picture of the basis for modal differences in group delay.

This way of thinking about multimode dispersion suggests that if modes that corkscrew around the axis more than others could be made subject to a smaller refractive index, and hence speeded up, than are those modes that travel more nearly straight along the fiber, the different travel delays could possibly be equalized. Since the low-order modes reside closer to the axis while the energy in the higher-order ones is concentrated closer to the core–cladding interface and spirals about the axis, it should be beneficial to slow down the low-order modes by increasing the refractive index near the axis and to speed up the high-order modes by lowering the index near the edge of the core. This calls for a gradation $n = n(r)$ in refractive index with radius, with a maximum on axis and tapered down toward the cladding. The gradually varying profile of the desired refractive index makes this type of light guide a *graded-index* (GRIN) fiber.

To confirm that a GRIN fiber should have dispersive properties superior to those of a step-index fiber, the modes of a fiber with a core that has a radial refractive index variation must be studied. A variety of $n(r)$ profiles can be analyzed simultaneously by specifying an entire family of graded index variations, by use of a parameter α that describes the steepness of the index taper. For a GRIN fiber with a core of radius a, surrounded by a uniform cladding of fixed index n_2, the core index may be modeled by the family of index profiles given by

$$n^2(r) = \begin{cases} n_0^2\left[1 - 2\Delta\left(\dfrac{r}{a}\right)^{\alpha}\right] & r < a, \qquad (15.58) \\ n_0^2[1 - 2\Delta] = n_2^2 & r > a. \qquad (15.59) \end{cases}$$

For any member of this family of graded-index models, the peak index occurs on axis ($r = 0$) and is n_0, the minimum index is attained at (and within) the

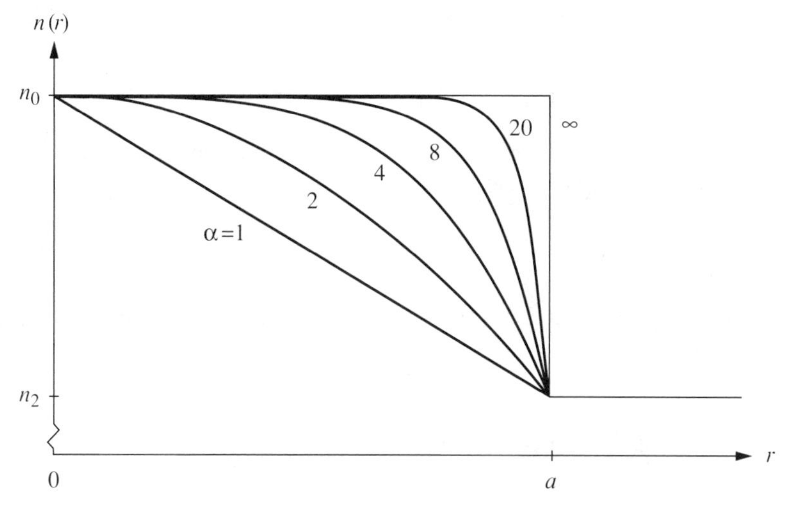

FIGURE 15–6 Family of GRIN index profiles.

cladding, with $n_2 = n_0[1 - \Delta]$ for small Δ, which is now defined as

$$\Delta = \frac{n_0 - n_2}{n_0}. \tag{15.60}$$

The rate of descent from the peak n_0 to the minimum n_2 is specified by α: the profile is linear if $\alpha = 1$, with $n(r) = n_0[1 - \Delta(r/a)]$; it is quadratic if we adopt $\alpha = 2$, whereupon $n(r) = n_0[1 - \Delta(r/a)^2]$; it has a steeper variation near the edge of the core for higher values of α. For $\alpha = \infty$, the step-index fiber model is recovered as a limiting case. Figure 15–6 illustrates several members of the family of graded-index profiles encompassed by this model.

Since $n(r)$ varies on a radial scale much wider than that of a wavelength, so that $dn/dr \ll kn$, it is permissible to neglect terms that involve derivatives of $n(r)$ when combining Maxwell's equations into a wave equation. The resulting equations for the fields in the core are then as they were for the step-index fiber, except that the parameter p becomes a function of radius: instead of the constant $p^2 = k^2n_1^2 - \beta^2$, we now have

$$p^2(r) = k^2n^2(r) - \beta^2. \tag{15.61}$$

For the cladding, we still have $q^2 = \beta^2 - k^2n_2^2$, however. We still seek propagation along the fiber axis, as $\exp[j(\omega t - \beta z)]$ and we expect β/k to take on some value between the cladding's $n_0(1 - \Delta)$ and the core's peak value n_0. Thus, near the axis, k^2n^2 exceeds β^2 and $p^2(r)$ should be positive but, near the cladding, $k^2n^2 \to k^2n_2^2$ becomes less than β^2 and $p^2(r)$ should turn negative.

Separation of variables in the wave equation again yields trigonometric functions for the azimuthal variation, or $Ae^{-jl\theta} + Be^{jl\theta}$ with l an integer, but now the differential equation for the radially varying factor $R(r)$ is

$$\frac{d^2R}{dr^2} + \frac{1}{r}\frac{dR}{dr} + \left[p^2(r) - \frac{l^2}{r^2}\right]R = 0 \tag{15.62}$$

in the core, but still the modified Bessel equation

$$\frac{d^2R}{dr^2}+\frac{1}{r}\frac{dR}{dr}+\left[-q^2-\frac{l^2}{r^2}\right]R=0 \tag{15.63}$$

in the cladding. For the model family of profiles under consideration, the function $p^2(r)$ in the core equation is

$$p^2(r)=k^2n^2(r)-\beta^2=k^2n_0^2\left[1-2\Delta\left(\frac{r}{a}\right)^{\alpha}\right]-\beta^2. \tag{15.64}$$

For general values of α, Eq. (15.62) is not solvable in terms of known functions of mathematical analysis. For the special value $\alpha = 2$, the equation has known solutions expressible in terms of Laguerre–Gauss functions. More generally, Eq. (15.62) is just the Schrödinger equation of quantum mechanics, after separation of variables in cylindrical coordinates:

$$\frac{d^2R}{dr^2}+\frac{1}{r}\frac{dR}{dr}+\left[k^2n^2(r)-\frac{l^2}{r^2}-\beta^2\right]R=0. \tag{15.65}$$

This can be interpreted as the Schrödinger wave equation for the "wave function" $R(r)$ and the "energy level" β^2 (more analogously, energy level $k^2n_0^2 - \beta^2$), for a particle in a "potential well" formed by the refractive index variation $n(r)$ and the cylindrical "angular momentum" $-l^2/r^2$ [more analogously, in an inverted potential well, since $-k^2n^2(r)$ plays the role of the potential energy]. The equivalent, inverted, potential energy well that makes the GRIN fiber equation the same as the Schrödinger equation is illustrated in Figure 15–7, which is plotted for $\alpha = 2$ and $l = 1$. (Because, with $\Delta = 0.01$, the peak level in the core and that in the cladding are only 1% apart, the $-l^2/r^2$ contribution to the potential well could not be seen on the same scale and has therefore been plotted with a constant offset to bring it into view.)

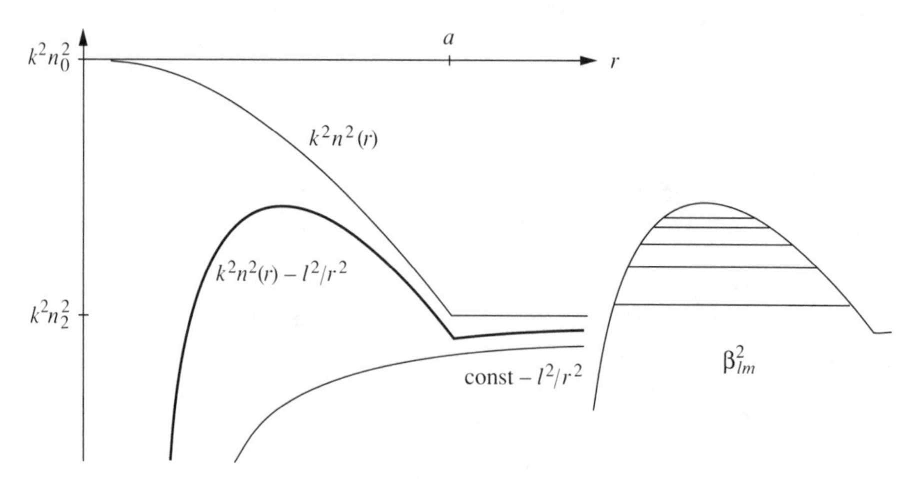

FIGURE 15–7 Equivalent potential well and energy levels for GRIN fiber.

What we expect from a Schrödinger equation is indeed what happens in a GRIN fiber: a discrete set of allowable "energy levels" β^2 is found as the eigenvalues of the equation, one for each "wave function" or mode of propagation. Calculating the "energy levels" in the given "potential well" is equivalent to finding the propagation constant β for each allowable mode. In the figure, next to the diagram of how the inverted potential well is formed, the effective well is redrawn, with a schematic set of quantized "energy levels" β^2. For each azimuthal number l, there is a separate set of these and the individual ones are labeled with a pair of subscripts, lm.

The "wave function" or mode pattern $R(r)$ is expected to be oscillatory wherever $k^2n^2(r) - l^2/r^2$ exceeds the eigenvalue β^2 [as was the $J_l(pr)$ solution in the core for the step-index fiber] and to become a decaying function beyond that point [as was the $K_l(qr)$ function for the step-index case]. A variety of numerical and approximate analytical techniques can be invoked to obtain the solution to the Schrödinger-type equation for the GRIN fiber mode patterns.

Does the gradation of the refractive index of the core indeed provide an improvement in the dispersive spreading of pulses as they propagate? The fact that the "potential well" has a shape and depth adjustable by changing the profile parameter α makes the resultant eigenvalues β dependent on α, besides being a function of k and of the indices l, m. Consequently, the group index $m = \partial\beta/\partial k$ is also a function of α, and so is δm, the difference between the group indices of the slowest and fastest propagating modes. While still retaining a contribution from material dispersion and a dependence on the source linewidth $\delta\lambda$, the group delay $\delta t/z = \delta m(\alpha)/c$ therefore becomes a function of α. The results of the elaborate calculations necessary to arrive at $\delta m(\alpha)$ do confirm the original expectation that speeding up the waves at the periphery of the core and slowing down the modes near the axis helps to reduce the dispersive pulse spreading. It is found that plots of group delay as a function of profile parameter α, for various source linewidths $\delta\lambda$, do exhibit a sharp minimum. This appears in the vicinity of the quadratic profile $\alpha = 2$; the precise value of α and the depth at the minimum are dependent on the linewidth.

Thus the GRIN fiber can overcome pulse spreading ascribable to waveguiding alone; the material dispersion $d^2n/d\lambda^2$ that remains can also be eliminated by choosing the operating wavelength to make this factor vanish. Fibers with a variety of refractive index profiles can be fabricated by carefully regulating the concentrations of dopants in the successive layers of glass as the fiber is formed.

Wave Launching

Getting light from a source into a fiber is not a trivial task. The end of a fiber constitutes an optical aperture that can accept only a limited amount of incident light, capture it, and send it along the fiber. We wish to estimate how much light can be captured by the end of a fiber.

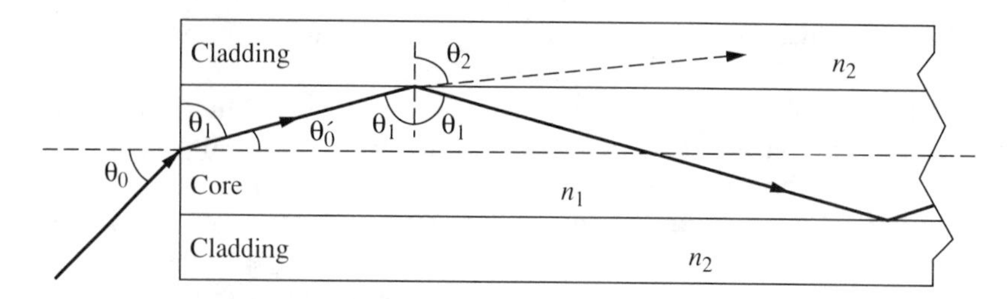

FIGURE 15–8 Capture of externally incident light ray by a fiber.

We can avoid the complications of dealing with the curvature of the cylindrical boundaries by applying the principles that govern the trapping of light in the slab geometry instead. This will be a reasonable approximation for a multimode fiber, for which the radius of the core is very large, compared to the wavelength of the light; it will avoid the use of Bessel functions in describing how total internal reflection traps light in the case of cylindrical geometry.

Figure 15–8 shows a ray of light in air, incident at angle θ_0 onto the end of a "slab" fiber, refracted as it enters the core, and then incident at angle θ_1 onto the boundary between the core and the cladding. If the angle θ_1 is too small, then transmission into the cladding at angle θ_2 can occur and the light can escape from the fiber; if the light is incident onto the core–cladding interface at a sufficiently large (grazing) angle θ_1, then total internal reflection can trap the light in the core and the ray can follow the fiber axis by reapeatedly reflecting at the two interfaces as it travels along the structure. Since θ_1 must be large enough to trap the light, the incident angle θ_0 must be small enough to avoid losing the light to the cladding.

We can work backward from the trapping condition to the maximum external incidence angle. If the light is not trapped in the core, refraction at the core–cladding boundary will be at angle θ_2 given by Snell's law:

$$n_1 \sin \theta_1 = n_2 \sin \theta_2 . \tag{15.66}$$

If, however, total internal reflection does occur at that boundary, θ_2 is replaced by $\pi/2$ and θ_1 must exceed the minimum θ_{10} given by

$$n_1 \sin \theta_{10} = n_2 . \tag{15.67}$$

When $\theta_1 > \theta_{10}$, we can get bound modes and the light is trapped. At the end of the fiber, the light incident at θ_0 in the outer medium of index n_0 ($n_0 = 1$ for air) is refracted at angle $\theta_0' = \pi/2 - \theta_1$, again by Snell's law. Thus

$$n_0 \sin \theta_0 = \sin \theta_0 = n_1 \sin \theta_0' = n_1 \sin\left(\frac{\pi}{2} - \theta_1\right) = n_1 \cos \theta_1 . \tag{15.68}$$

To find the maximum incidence angle θ_{00}, we set $\theta_1 = \theta_{10}$ and solve for $\theta_0 = \theta_{00}$. We have both

$$n_1 \sin \theta_1 = n_2 \qquad \text{and} \qquad n_1 \cos \theta_1 = \sin \theta_{00} . \tag{15.69}$$

Squaring and adding these two equations gives

$$n_1^2 \sin^2 \theta_1 + n_1^2 \cos^2 \theta_1 = n_1^2 = n_2^2 + \sin^2 \theta_{00} \tag{15.70}$$

or

$$\sin \theta_{00} = \sqrt{n_1^2 - n_2^2} \tag{15.71}$$

as the relation that determines the maximum external acceptance angle.

The quantity

$$\mathrm{NA} = n \sin \theta_{\max}, \tag{15.72}$$

which by Snell's law is the same on both sides of an interface between two media, is called the *numerical aperture* of an optical element; it tells how large a deviation from normal incidence will still allow transmission of the light into the element. For incidence from air to the fiber, this is just $\sin \theta_{00}$ and we have found that the fiber's numerical aperture is given by

$$\mathrm{NA} = \sqrt{n_1^2 - n_2^2} \approx n_2\sqrt{2\Delta}. \tag{15.73}$$

For example, with typical values like $n_2 \approx 1.45$ and $\Delta \approx 0.005$ for a glass fiber, we get $\mathrm{NA} \approx 0.145$, so that the maximum incidence angle is $\theta_{00} \approx 8°$. Only light incident within a cone of semiangle less than 8° from the axis can be accepted and trapped by the fiber. Rays incident at greater angles radiate into the cladding and get lost, instead of trapped.

If a relatively large, extended source shines upon the end of the fiber, with the light coming in equally from all the directions of the half-space in front of the fiber, only the fraction of the light that is directed within the above cone can be accepted and guided by the fiber. That fraction is the volume of the cone, as a ratio to the full hemisphere; this is $(1 - \cos \theta_{00})$ or, for small semiangles, $\frac{1}{2}\theta_{00}^2 \approx \frac{1}{2}(\mathrm{NA})^2$. For the example above, this is only about 1% of the incident light!

A more efficient transfer of light to the fiber can occur if a source smaller than the core's cross-sectional area is made to abut against the fiber. This requires a light source of very small size; integrated optics is the ideal structure for application of this technique.

Mode Coupling

We have treated the modes of propagation along a fiber as independent of one another, as if each is unaware of the existence of the others. This is mathematically correct for a fiber of perfect constitution and geometry. In real fibers, however, any imperfection can cause different modes to couple and exchange energy between them as they propagate. The fiber may be imperfect in geometry (not perfectly straight axially or round across), or it may exhibit deviations from the nominal refractive indices, or it may be bent, or its material properties may fluctuate, or its profile or boundary shape or curvature may not be ideal. Any such imperfection translates itself into a coupling between certain modes, such that some of the power in one mode gets fed to the other, and then back to the first, repeatedly.

Phenomenologically, the *coupled power equations* describe the variation with distance along the fiber of the power in each propagating mode, in terms of certain coupling coefficients. If $P_m(z)$ is the power in mode m at position z, the variation of this ideally conserved quantity is well described by

$$\frac{dP_m}{dz} = -\gamma_m P_m(z) + \sum_n h_{mn}[P_n(z) - P_m(z)], \tag{15.74}$$

in which γ_m is the loss constant for mode m and h_{mn} is the coupling coefficient for modes m and n; the sum is over all modes for which the coupling is significant. This equation shows strong modes to be feeding weaker ones, until the latter become the stronger ones. If $P_n > P_m$, the rate of change of P_m has a positive contribution from the coupling between the two modes, while the corresponding equation for dP_n/dz shows that it weakens as it feeds mode m.

What determines the coupling coefficients? A perturbation analysis of the effects of fluctuations $f(z)$ in some parameter that would be perfectly constant in the ideal fiber shows that the relevant quantity is the Fourier spectrum $F(k)$ of the random fluctuations $f(z)$:

$$F(k) = \int f(z) \exp[-jkz]\, dz. \tag{15.75}$$

The strength of the coupling between two modes is proportional to the *average power spectrum* of the fluctuations, evaluated at the *difference* between the two modes' propagation constants:

$$h_{mn} \propto \langle |F(\beta_m - \beta_n)|^2 \rangle. \tag{15.76}$$

The angular brackets denote averaging, over the statistics of the random fluctuations. This powerful result allows us to make predictions about which modes are likely to be affected by a given type of perturbation of the ideal fiber. For example, fluctuations on a large scale, such as gradual bending, have a spectrum that is significant only at low values of k; this implies that there will be strong coupling between modes m and n only if β_m and β_n are very close to each other, making $\beta_m - \beta_n$ small enough to be within the bandwidth of the fluctuation spectrum $F(k)$. Thus large-scale fluctuations couple only modes that are nearly degenerate (that have nearly equal β's). As another example, periodic fluctuations, such as striations, have a spectrum that is sharply peaked at a value $k = k_0$ that corresponds to their period $l = 2\pi/k_0$. The coupling coefficient will therefore be significant only for pairs of modes whose propagation constants differ by approximately k_0; that is, modes such that $|\beta_m - \beta_n| \approx k_0$ will be the ones to exchange energy between them in the presence of periodic fluctuations of period $2\pi/k_0$.

One effect of coupling among different modes is to increase losses along the fiber, as some of the energy gets transferred to modes that are not trapped within the core. However, another effect is to average the dispersion of many modes and thereby reduce the overall pulse spreading. When modes are strongly coupled to each other, the group delay may vary with distance as only $\sqrt{z}$, instead of as z; this is a significantly less serious variation.

Summary

We have examined a number of practical considerations relevant to the operation of optical fibers. Structurally, fibers are dielectric rod waveguides, but the smallness of optical wavelengths makes it very difficult to make the fibers' dimensions comparable to a wavelength. As waveguides, therefore, fibers allow propagation of a great many modes, even when the core and cladding are quite close to each other in refractive index. We have noted the simplification of the characteristic equation and of the modal description when the core and cladding are nearly identical optically.

The major technological problems attendant to making optical fiber transmission practical involved reducing attenuation to under 1 dB/km and overcoming the effects of material and multimode dispersion. The former was achieved by exceedingly careful fabrication and the latter by designing advantageous refractive index profiles in graded-index fibers to equalize multimode dispersion and by operating within the low-loss window near 1.3 μm, at which the material dispersion of glass fibers has a null.

We have now come to the end of our inquiry into the processes that govern the transmission of energy and information in the form of waves along various guiding structures, culminating in the application of the general theory to fiber optics. The optical fiber revolution in wave transmission demands a thorough understanding of the fundamentals of guided waves as a basis for effective system design and for more advanced study of fiber optics. The reader who has followed our discussion to this point should be prepared to appreciate and tackle the issues that arise in the design and utilization of fiber optic systems and to be part of that revolution.

PROBLEMS

Alternative Definition of Relative Index Difference

15.1 The relative index difference parameter is often defined as $\Delta' = (n_1 - n_2)/n_1$ instead of $\Delta = (n_1 - n_2)/n_2$. Verify that the difference between these two definitions is $\Delta - \Delta' = \Delta\Delta'$ and hence of second order in the small quantity Δ.

Estimate of Number of Propagating Modes

15.2 A step-index fiber has a core diameter of 200 μm and a numerical aperture NA = 0.27. If it is operated at 0.85 μm, how many modes can be expected to propagate?

Single-Mode Operation of Step-Index Fiber

15.3 A step-index fiber has a core of diameter = 20 μm and refractive index = 1.5. The fiber is to be operated at a free-space wavelength = 8 μm. If single-mode operation is desired:

(a) What is the maximum numerical aperture (NA) that the fiber can be allowed to have?

(b) What is the lowest value that the cladding's refractive index can be allowed to have?

Signaling Rate Along a Fiber

15.4 The group index of a certain optical fiber is found to range from 1.44 to 1.45 for the modes that can propagate at $\lambda_0 = 1.2$ μm. Neglecting material dispersion and source linewidth, estimate the maximum signaling rate (bits/s) that can be used for transmission over 5 km of the fiber.

Minimum Wavelength for Single-Mode Fiber

15.5 A step-index fiber has a core diameter of 16 μm and a numerical aperture NA = 0.16. If the fiber is to be used as a single-mode fiber, what must be the minimum free-space wavelength of the source?

Signaling Rate Limitation by Material Dispersion

15.6 A fiber is made of a glass for which the material dispersion is given by $\lambda^2(d^2n/d\lambda^2) = 0.25$ at $\lambda = 0.9$ μm. The source has a 3-nm linewidth at this wavelength. Pulses 20 ns wide are to be transmitted along a 10-km length of this fiber. (Note that the pulse width t_0 and pulse spread δt combine statistically into an overall pulse width $t = \sqrt{t_0^2 + \delta t^2}$.) What is the maximum signaling rate (bits/s) that can be used, as limited by material dispersion alone?

Estimates of Fiber Parameters

15.7 A step-index fiber has a core diameter of 50 μm and a numerical aperture NA = 0.16. The parameter V is 20 and the core and cladding have refractive indices of approximately 1.4.

(a) Obtain an estimate of Δ.

(b) Obtain an estimate of the number of propagating modes.

(c) Obtain an estimate of the free-space wavelength.

(d) If the light source is changed to one with a wavelength 10 times longer, how many propagating modes should be expected?

Estimates of Fiber Parameters from Specifications

15.8 A step-index fiber has a core diameter of 50 μm, a cladding diameter of 100 μm, a numerical aperture NA = 0.135, $\Delta = 0.004$, losses of 2 dB/km, and is operated at $\lambda_0 = 0.848$ μm.

(a) Estimate the refractive index of the core.
(b) Estimate the parameter V.
(c) Estimate the number of modes that can propagate.
(d) Estimate the guide wavelength λ of the LP_{21} mode.
(e) If the fiber is to be used for single-mode propagation experiments, estimate the minimum wavelength of a source that could be used.

Verification of Wave Launching Criterion

15.9 In estimating the fraction of incident light that could be captured by the end of a fiber, the ratio of the volume of a cone to that of a hemisphere was needed. Verify that the fraction of a hemisphere occupied by a cone of semiangle θ_{00} is $1 - \cos\theta_{00}$.

Significance of Numerical Aperture for Cylindrical Fiber

15.10 In estimating the fraction of incident light that could be captured by the end of a fiber, Snell's law was used with a slab model, rather than a cylindrical one, for the fiber. Verify that essentially the same result is obtained for incidence of a plane wave onto the end of a cylindrical fiber, as follows. The plane wave $e^{j[\omega t - k\sin\theta_0 y - k\cos\theta_0 z]}$ incident at angle θ_0 onto the end of the fiber at $z = 0$ can be expanded as a superposition of cylindrical fiber modes by use of the Fourier series identity

$$e^{-j\xi\sin\theta} = \sum J_l(\xi)e^{-jl\theta} \qquad \text{(sum over all integers } l).$$

Here, we apply this identity with $\xi = kr\sin\theta_0$, because $y = r\sin\theta$ in polar coordinates, so that $e^{-jk\sin\theta_0 y} = e^{-j(kr\sin\theta_0)\sin\theta}$. But the argument of the Bessel functions is pr in the fiber modes, so that $p = k\sin\theta_0$. Ignoring the required matching of polarizations, determine the largest permissible value of p for the modes to be bound to the fiber and translate this criterion into one for the maximum incidence angle θ_0 that can be captured by the fiber.

Estimates of Rayleigh Scattering Losses

15.11 Based on Eq. (15.46), Rayleigh scattering losses are typically expressed by $\alpha/\alpha_0 = (\lambda_0/\lambda)^4$, with $\alpha_0 = 1.7$ dB/km and $\lambda_0 = 0.85$ μm. Using this model, estimate the attenuation constant α due to Rayleigh scattering at:
(a) 0.8 μm;
(b) 1.25 μm;
(c) 1.6 μm.

Appendix: Mathematical Background

We collect in this appendix various mathematical formulas and relations for convenient reference. They include especially the mathematical identities, recursion relations, and vector and matrix manipulations that are used in the body of the text. Proving them can serve as valuable review exercises. This material is intended to remind the reader of matters that were once familiar already and to establish the notation we use. It is not intended to teach new material.

Complex Numbers

Our notation for complex numbers uses j as the imaginary unit. The rectangular and polar versions are related by

$$z = x + jy = re^{j\theta}, \tag{A.1}$$

where

$$r^2 = x^2 + y^2; \qquad \tan\theta = \frac{y}{x}. \tag{A.2}$$

Multiplication and division of complex numbers become

$$z_1 z_2 = (x_1 x_2 - y_1 y_2) + j(x_1 y_2 + x_2 y_1) = r_1 r_2 e^{j(\theta_1 + \theta_2)}, \tag{A.3}$$

$$\frac{z_1}{z_2} = \frac{(x_1 x_2 + y_1 y_2) + j(x_2 y_1 - x_1 y_2)}{(x_2^2 + y_2^2)} = \frac{r_1}{r_2} e^{j(\theta_1 - \theta_2)} \tag{A.4}$$

The real and imaginary parts are denoted

$$x = r\cos\theta = \operatorname{Re} z \qquad y = r\sin\theta = \operatorname{Im} z. \tag{A.5}$$

Euler's formula gives the exponential function of a complex argument:

$$e^z = e^{x+jy} = e^x(\cos y + j\sin y). \tag{A.6}$$

Special cases of this include

$$e^{\pm j\pi} = -1 \qquad e^{\pm j(\pi/2)} = \pm j. \tag{A.7}$$

Combinations of exponentials with equal and opposite imaginary exponents form trigonometric functions:

$$e^{j\theta} + e^{-j\theta} = 2 \cos \theta; \qquad e^{j\theta} - e^{-j\theta} = 2j \sin \theta. \tag{A.8}$$

Matrix Algebra

Our notation for the transpose and inverse of a matrix M is M' and M^{-1}, respectively.

Multiplication of a row matrix by a column matrix yields a single number, the sum of the products of corresponding components of the two matrices, which must have the same number of components. Matrix multiplication of two *conformable* matrices (number of columns of left factor equals number of rows of right one) forms the component in row i, column j of the product as the row-by-column product of the ith row of the left factor by the jth column of the right one:

$$\text{If} \quad C = AB \qquad \text{then} \quad C_{ij} = \sum_k A_{ik} B_{kj}. \tag{A.9}$$

The inverse of a square matrix M is another matrix, M^{-1}, such that

$$MM^{-1} = M^{-1}M = I, \tag{A.10}$$

where I is the unit matrix (1 on diagonal, 0 off-diagonal). The inverse exists if the *determinant* of M is nonzero; otherwise, the matrix is *singular*.

The inverse of a product is the product of the inverses, in reverse order:

$$(AB)^{-1} = B^{-1}A^{-1}. \tag{A.11}$$

The transpose of a product is the product of the transposes, in reverse order:

$$(AB)' = B'A'. \tag{A.12}$$

The determinant of a product is the product of the determinants:

$$\det (AB) = \det (BA) = (\det A)(\det B). \tag{A.13}$$

The determinant of a unit matrix (of any size) is unity.

The solution to the set of simultaneous linear equations

$$Mx = b \qquad \text{is} \qquad x = M^{-1}b, \tag{A.14}$$

if M is nonsingular.

$$\text{If} \quad Mx = 0 \qquad \text{then} \quad x = 0, \qquad \text{unless} \quad \det M = 0. \tag{A.15}$$

The product of a square matrix M and a column matrix (or vector) x is another column matrix y that generally bears no simple relation to x, but there are special column matrices z for any square matrix M such that the product is just proportional to (i.e., a scalar constant times) the column z itself: If $Mz = \lambda z$, then z is an *eigenvector* and the number λ is an *eigenvalue* of the matrix M. The eigenvalues and eigenvectors are found by solving the *homogeneous* equation

$$(M - \lambda I)z = 0, \qquad \text{which demands that} \quad \det(M - \lambda I) = 0. \tag{A.16}$$

The latter, the determinantal equation, yields the eigenvalues; thereafter, the former equation can provide the eigenvectors.

A *quadratic form* in a variable column matrix x is a single number $q = q(x)$ that is considered a function of the vector variable x and is formed from a (symmetric, square) matrix of coefficients M by the operation

$$q = x'Mx. \tag{A.17}$$

If x represents the position vector in a two-dimensional plane, the equation

$$(x - \xi)'M(x - \xi) = \alpha^2 \tag{A.18}$$

corresponds to a curve in the plane, a conic section, which can be an ellipse, a circle, a parabola, or a hyperbola, centered at the point ξ. The character of the curve is determined by the nature of the eigenvalues of the matrix M: If the eigenvalues are both positive, the curve is an ellipse (or a circle as a special case if the eigenvalues are also equal); if one eigenvalue is zero, the curve is a parabola; if the two eigenvalues have opposite signs, the curve is a hyperbola. The *discriminant* provides a short cut to determining the nature of the eigenvalues and hence of the conic section. If the matrix M has components

$$M = \begin{bmatrix} a & b \\ b & c \end{bmatrix}, \tag{A.19}$$

with $a > 0$, then the discriminant is given by

$$\Delta = ac - b^2 = \det M. \tag{A.20}$$

Then $\Delta > 0$ implies an ellipse; $\Delta = 0$ for a parabola; $\Delta < 0$ gives a hyperbola.

Coordinate Systems

Points in space are identified by giving their coordinates, as many as the dimensionality of the space. In two dimensions, the main coordinate systems are the rectangular (x, y) and the polar (r, θ). These are related by

$$x = r\cos\theta, \quad y = r\sin\theta; \qquad r^2 = x^2 + y^2, \quad \tan\theta = \frac{y}{x}. \tag{A.21}$$

In three dimensions, the primary coordinate systems are the rectangular (x, y, z), the cylindrical (ρ, φ, z) and the spherical (r, θ, φ) systems. They are related by the following transformations:

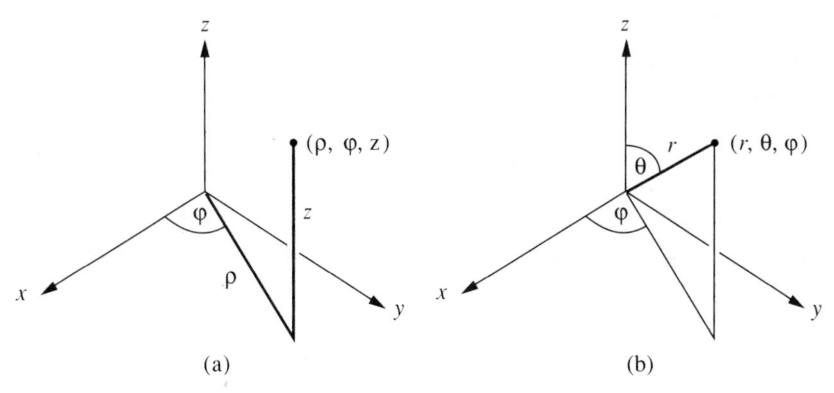

FIGURE A–1 Coordinates of a point, cylindrical and spherical.

Cylindrical:

$$x = \rho \cos \varphi, \quad y = \rho \sin \varphi; \qquad \rho^2 = x^2 + y^2, \quad \tan \varphi = \frac{y}{x}. \tag{A.22}$$

Spherical:

$$x = r \sin \theta \cos \varphi, \qquad y = r \sin \theta \sin \varphi, \qquad z = r \cos \theta; \tag{A.23}$$

$$r^2 = x^2 + y^2 + z^2, \qquad \cos \theta = \frac{z}{r}, \qquad \tan \varphi = \frac{y}{x}. \tag{A.24}$$

Figure A–1 aids in interpreting ρ as the distance between the point and the z-axis, r as the distance between the point and the origin, θ as the *elevation* angle between the position vector and the z-axis, and φ as the *azimuthal* angle between the xz-plane and the plane that contains the position vector and the z-axis.

The element of area in two dimensions is

$$dA = dx\, dy = r\, dr\, d\theta \tag{A.25}$$

and the volume element in three dimensions is given by

$$dV = dx\, dy\, dz = \rho\, d\rho\, d\varphi\, dz = r^2 \sin \theta\, dr\, d\theta\, d\varphi. \tag{A.26}$$

Vector Algebra

A vector has both a magnitude and a direction in space. The zero vector has zero magnitude (and hence no defined direction); a unit vector has magnitude unity and is fully specified by its direction. When we have wanted to emphasize that a vector is a unit vector, we have indicated this with a circumflex accent, as in $\hat{\mathbf{n}}$. Three mutually perpendicular unit vectors, such as those along the directions of the rectangular coordinate axes, $\hat{\mathbf{x}}$, $\hat{\mathbf{y}}$, $\hat{\mathbf{z}}$, form a *basis* and any vector **A** can then be expressed as a sum of multiples of these: $\mathbf{A} = a\hat{\mathbf{x}} + b\hat{\mathbf{y}} + c\hat{\mathbf{z}}$ has *components a, b, c* with respect to that basis.

Addition of vectors is performed by adding their individual components to get those of the sum and multiplication of a vector by a *scalar* (i.e., a number) gives a vector each of whose components is that scalar times the components of the original vector.

The *dot product* (or scalar product) of two vectors **A** and **B** is a *scalar*, given by the sum of the products of corresponding components of the two vectors, as in

$$\mathbf{A} \cdot \mathbf{B} = (a_1\hat{\mathbf{x}} + a_2\hat{\mathbf{y}} + a_3\hat{\mathbf{z}}) \cdot (b_1\hat{\mathbf{x}} + b_2\hat{\mathbf{y}} + b_3\hat{\mathbf{z}}) = a_1 b_1 + a_2 b_2 + a_3 b_3 . \tag{A.27}$$

The geometrical interpretation (when the vectors are real) is that this scalar is the product of the two magnitudes and of the cosine of the angle between the two vectors. Two vectors are perpendicular (or orthogonal) if their dot product is zero. The dot product of a vector with itself is the square of the magnitude of the vector: $\mathbf{A} \cdot \mathbf{A} = |\mathbf{A}|^2$.

The *cross product* (or vector product) of two vectors **A** and **B** (in three dimensions) is a *vector* whose components are given by the differences of the products of the noncorresponding components of the two vectors, as in

$$\begin{aligned} \mathbf{A} \times \mathbf{B} &= (a_1\hat{\mathbf{x}} + a_2\hat{\mathbf{y}} + a_3\hat{\mathbf{z}}) \times (b_1\hat{\mathbf{x}} + b_2\hat{\mathbf{y}} + b_3\hat{\mathbf{z}}) \\ &= (a_2 b_3 - a_3 b_2)\hat{\mathbf{x}} + (a_3 b_1 - a_1 b_3)\hat{\mathbf{y}} + (a_1 b_2 - a_2 b_1)\hat{\mathbf{z}} . \end{aligned} \tag{A.28}$$

The geometrical interpretation is that this vector has a magnitude that is the product of the two magnitudes and of the sine of the angle between the two vectors, and a direction that is perpendicular to the plane formed by the two vectors; the right-hand rule orients the cross product vector with respect to the original vectors: if the fingers of the right hand indicate the rotation of vector **A** toward vector **B**, the thumb points along the vector $\mathbf{A} \times \mathbf{B}$. It follows that the cross product is not commutative: $\mathbf{A} \times \mathbf{B} = -\mathbf{B} \times \mathbf{A}$. Two vectors are parallel (or collinear) if their cross product is zero. The cross product of a vector with itself is the zero vector.

The scalar triple product of three vectors is the dot product of one with the cross product of the other two; if the cyclic order of the three vectors is preserved, the order of the dot and cross is immaterial:

$$\mathbf{A} \cdot \mathbf{B} \times \mathbf{C} = \mathbf{A} \times \mathbf{B} \cdot \mathbf{C} . \tag{A.29}$$

The geometric interpretation is that this is the volume of the parallelepiped formed by the three vectors (or the negative of that volume). The vector triple product is the cross product of one with the cross product of the other two; the order does matter. The vector triple product can be simplified by use of the identity

$$\mathbf{A} \times (\mathbf{B} \times \mathbf{C}) = \mathbf{B}(\mathbf{A} \cdot \mathbf{C}) - \mathbf{C}(\mathbf{A} \cdot \mathbf{B}) . \tag{A.30}$$

The *dyadic product* (or outer product) of two vectors **A** and **B** is a *matrix* formed by the matrix product of the left factor as a column and the right factor as a row. If

$$\mathbf{A} = a_1\hat{\mathbf{x}} + a_2\hat{\mathbf{y}} + a_3\hat{\mathbf{z}} \quad \text{and} \quad \mathbf{B} = b_1\hat{\mathbf{x}} + b_2\hat{\mathbf{y}} + b_3\hat{\mathbf{z}},$$

then the dyadic **AB** is

$$\mathbf{AB} = \begin{bmatrix} a_1 b_1 & a_1 b_2 & a_1 b_3 \\ a_2 b_1 & a_2 b_2 & a_2 b_3 \\ a_3 b_1 & a_3 b_2 & a_3 b_3 \end{bmatrix}. \tag{A.31}$$

Vectors with components that are complex numbers are treated in the same way as real vectors but their geometric interpretation requires more care. While a real vector has a magnitude and a direction, a complex one can generally not be assigned a single direction, since the real and imaginary parts may not share one direction. There is also the peril of confusing the notion of the magnitude of a (real) vector and that of the magnitude of a complex number. Finally, we must abandon concepts like the angle between two complex vectors. The dot product of two complex vectors is a complex number. If that complex number is zero, we say that the two complex vectors are orthogonal. The dot product of a complex vector with itself need not be a positive number, but the dot product of the complex conjugate of a vector with the original vector is positive and can define the magnitude (squared) of the complex vector: $|\mathbf{A}|^2 = \mathbf{A}^* \cdot \mathbf{A}$. This is the sum of the squared magnitudes of the complex components of the vector.

Vector Differential Calculus

The gradient operator ∇ is defined by its effect in forming the differential df of any scalar function $f(\mathbf{r})$ of the position vector $\mathbf{r} = (x, y, z)$, when $\mathbf{r}$ is subjected to an infinitesimal change of position $d\mathbf{r}$:

$$df = f(\mathbf{r} + d\mathbf{r}) - f(\mathbf{r}) = d\mathbf{r} \cdot \nabla f(\mathbf{r}). \tag{A.32}$$

Consequently, in rectangular coordinates, the ∇ operator is given by

$$\nabla = \hat{\mathbf{x}}\left(\frac{\partial}{\partial x}\right) + \hat{\mathbf{y}}\left(\frac{\partial}{\partial y}\right) + \hat{\mathbf{z}}\left(\frac{\partial}{\partial z}\right). \tag{A.33}$$

The operator can be applied to a vector function of position, as a *divergence*, a *curl*, or as a dyadic operation. For the vector function of position

$$\mathbf{F}(\mathbf{r}) = F_1(\mathbf{r})\hat{\mathbf{x}} + F_2(\mathbf{r})\hat{\mathbf{y}} + F_3(\mathbf{r})\hat{\mathbf{z}},$$

the divergence of $\mathbf{F}(\mathbf{r})$ is the scalar

$$\nabla \cdot \mathbf{F} = \frac{\partial F_1}{\partial x} + \frac{\partial F_2}{\partial y} + \frac{\partial F_3}{\partial z}; \tag{A.34}$$

the curl of $\mathbf{F}(\mathbf{r})$ is the vector

$$\nabla \times \mathbf{F} = \hat{\mathbf{x}}\left(\frac{\partial F_3}{\partial y} - \frac{\partial F_2}{\partial z}\right) + \hat{\mathbf{y}}\left(\frac{\partial F_1}{\partial z} - \frac{\partial F_3}{\partial x}\right) + \hat{\mathbf{z}}\left(\frac{\partial F_2}{\partial x} - \frac{\partial F_1}{\partial y}\right); \tag{A.35}$$

and the dyadic gradient of $\mathbf{F}(\mathbf{r})$ is the matrix

$$\nabla\mathbf{F} = \begin{bmatrix} \frac{\partial F_1}{\partial x} & \frac{\partial F_2}{\partial x} & \frac{\partial F_3}{\partial x} \\ \frac{\partial F_1}{\partial y} & \frac{\partial F_2}{\partial y} & \frac{\partial F_3}{\partial y} \\ \frac{\partial F_1}{\partial z} & \frac{\partial F_2}{\partial z} & \frac{\partial F_3}{\partial z} \end{bmatrix}. \tag{A.36}$$

Second-order operators include the *Laplacian*, which is the divergence of the gradient when applied to a scalar $f(\mathbf{r})$,

$$\nabla^2 f = \nabla \cdot \nabla f = \frac{\partial^2 f}{\partial x^2} + \frac{\partial^2 f}{\partial y^2} + \frac{\partial^2 f}{\partial z^2}, \tag{A.37}$$

but is defined by the difference between the gradient of the divergence and the curl of the curl when applied to a vector:

$$\nabla^2 \mathbf{F} = \nabla\nabla \cdot \mathbf{F} - \nabla \times \nabla \times \mathbf{F}. \tag{A.38}$$

The reason for the use of the same notation for what are fundamentally different operations is that in rectangular coordinates (and only in rectangular coordinates), the operation has the same appearance when applied to scalars and to vectors:

$$\nabla^2 f = \frac{\partial^2 f}{\partial x^2} + \frac{\partial^2 f}{\partial y^2} + \frac{\partial^2 f}{\partial z^2},$$

$$\nabla^2 \mathbf{F} = \frac{\partial^2 \mathbf{F}}{\partial x^2} + \frac{\partial^2 \mathbf{F}}{\partial y^2} + \frac{\partial^2 \mathbf{F}}{\partial z^2},$$

where the latter means the vector

$$\nabla^2 \mathbf{F} = \hat{\mathbf{x}}\nabla^2 F_1 + \hat{\mathbf{y}}\nabla^2 F_2 + \hat{\mathbf{z}}\nabla^2 F_3.$$

Some second-order derivatives vanish identically: the divergence of a curl is identically zero and the curl of a gradient is identically the zero vector.

$$\nabla \cdot \nabla \times \mathbf{F} = 0, \qquad \nabla \times \nabla f = \mathbf{0}. \tag{A.39}$$

The gradient operator applied to a product yields results that combine the properties of vectors and of derivatives. The *divergence of a cross product* simplifies to

$$\nabla \cdot (\mathbf{F} \times \mathbf{G}) = \mathbf{G} \cdot \nabla \times \mathbf{F} - \mathbf{F} \cdot \nabla \times \mathbf{G}. \tag{A.40}$$

The *curl of a cross product* expands as

$$\nabla \times (\mathbf{F} \times \mathbf{G}) = \mathbf{F}\nabla \cdot \mathbf{G} - \mathbf{G}\nabla \cdot \mathbf{F} + \mathbf{G} \cdot \nabla\mathbf{F} - \mathbf{F} \cdot \nabla\mathbf{G}, \tag{A.41}$$

in which the expression $\mathbf{F}\nabla \cdot \mathbf{G}$ means $\mathbf{F}(\nabla \cdot \mathbf{G})$, which is the product of the scalar $\nabla \cdot \mathbf{G}$ by the vector $\mathbf{F}$, and the quantity $\mathbf{F} \cdot \nabla\mathbf{G}$ can be interpreted as either $(\mathbf{F} \cdot \nabla)\mathbf{G}$, which means the operator $(F_1\partial/\partial x + F_2\, \partial/\partial y\; + F_3\, \partial/\partial z)$ applied to each of the components of $\mathbf{G}$, or $\mathbf{F} \cdot (\nabla\mathbf{G})$, which means the product of the row matrix (vector) $\mathbf{F}$ with the dyadic gradient matrix $\nabla\mathbf{G}$; both yield the same result. The *gradient of a dot product* has the expansion

$$\nabla(\mathbf{F} \cdot \mathbf{G}) = \mathbf{F} \cdot \nabla\mathbf{G} + \mathbf{G} \cdot \nabla\mathbf{F} + \mathbf{F} \times \nabla \times \mathbf{G} + \mathbf{G} \times \nabla \times \mathbf{F}. \qquad \text{(A.42)}$$

The important vector differential operations in the main curvilinear coordinate systems appear different from the corresponding ones in rectangular coordinates because the basis vectors, which are unit vectors in the direction of increasing values of the coordinates, are then themselves functions of position.

In cylindrical coordinates:

Gradient: $$\nabla f(\rho, \varphi, z) = \hat{\boldsymbol{\rho}}\,\frac{\partial f}{\partial \rho} + \hat{\boldsymbol{\varphi}}\,\frac{1}{\rho}\frac{\partial f}{\partial \varphi} + \hat{\mathbf{z}}\,\frac{\partial f}{\partial z}; \qquad \text{(A.43)}$$

Divergence: $$\nabla \cdot \mathbf{F} = \frac{1}{\rho}\frac{\partial(\rho F_\rho)}{\partial \rho} + \frac{1}{\rho}\frac{\partial F_\varphi}{\partial \varphi} + \frac{\partial F_z}{\partial z}; \qquad \text{(A.44)}$$

Curl: $$\left.\begin{aligned} (\nabla \times \mathbf{F})_\rho &= \frac{1}{\rho}\frac{\partial F_z}{\partial \varphi} - \frac{\partial F_\varphi}{\partial z} \\ (\nabla \times \mathbf{F})_\varphi &= \frac{\partial F_\rho}{\partial z} - \frac{\partial F_z}{\partial \rho} \\ (\nabla \times \mathbf{F})_z &= \frac{1}{\rho}\frac{\partial(\rho F_\varphi)}{\partial \rho} - \frac{1}{\rho}\frac{\partial F_\rho}{\partial \varphi} \end{aligned}\right\}; \qquad \text{(A.45)}$$

Laplacian: $$\nabla^2 f(\rho, \varphi, z) = \frac{1}{\rho}\frac{\partial[\rho\, \partial f/\partial \rho]}{\partial \rho} + \frac{1}{\rho^2}\frac{\partial^2 f}{\partial \varphi^2} + \frac{\partial^2 f}{\partial z^2}. \qquad \text{(A.46)}$$

In spherical coordinates:

Gradient: $$\nabla f(r, \theta, \varphi) = \hat{\mathbf{r}}\,\frac{\partial f}{\partial r} + \hat{\boldsymbol{\theta}}\,\frac{1}{r}\frac{\partial f}{\partial \theta} + \hat{\boldsymbol{\varphi}}\,\frac{\partial f/\partial \varphi}{r \sin\theta}; \qquad \text{(A.47)}$$

Divergence: $$\nabla \cdot \mathbf{F} = \frac{1}{r^2}\frac{\partial(r^2 F_r)}{\partial r} + \frac{1}{r\sin\theta}\left\{\frac{\partial[\sin\theta F_\theta]}{\partial \theta} + \frac{\partial F_\varphi}{\partial \varphi}\right\}; \qquad \text{(A.48)}$$

Curl: $$\left.\begin{aligned} (\nabla \times \mathbf{F})_r &= \frac{1}{r\sin\theta}\left\{\frac{\partial[\sin\theta F_\varphi]}{\partial \theta} - \frac{\partial F_\theta}{\partial \varphi}\right\} \\ (\nabla \times \mathbf{F})_\theta &= \frac{1}{r\sin\theta}\frac{\partial F_r}{\partial \varphi} - \frac{1}{r}\frac{\partial[rF_\varphi]}{\partial r} \\ (\nabla \times \mathbf{F})_\varphi &= \frac{1}{r}\frac{\partial(rF_\theta)}{\partial r} - \frac{1}{r}\frac{\partial F_r}{\partial \theta} \end{aligned}\right\}; \qquad \text{(A.49)}$$

Laplacian: $$\nabla^2 f(r, \theta, \varphi) = \frac{1}{r^2} \frac{\partial[r^2\, \partial f/\partial r]}{\partial r}$$

$$+ \frac{1}{r^2 \sin\theta} \frac{\partial[\sin\theta\, \partial f/\partial\theta]}{\partial\theta} + \frac{1}{r^2 \sin^2\theta} \frac{\partial^2 f}{\partial\varphi^2}. \tag{A.50}$$

Vector Integral Calculus

Integrations of vectors are performed over lines, surfaces, and volumes in space. Both the vector field $\mathbf{F}(\mathbf{r})$ and the domain of integration C or S or V must be given. The integral is evaluated by converting it into an ordinary single, double, or triple integral over the parameters that describe the curve, surface, or volume of integration.

To specify a curve C, we give the position vector $\mathbf{r} = \mathbf{r}(u)$ as a function of a single parameter u that ranges from u_1 to u_2 as the curve is traversed. The vector field then becomes a function of u, as $\mathbf{F}(\mathbf{r}) = \mathbf{F}(\mathbf{r}(u))$, and the element of length along the curve, $d\boldsymbol{l}$, is expressed in terms of the differential du by $d\boldsymbol{l} = (d\mathbf{r}/du)\, du$, so that the line integral is evaluated as

$$\int \mathbf{F} \cdot d\boldsymbol{l} = \int \mathbf{F}(\mathbf{r}(u)) \cdot \frac{d\mathbf{r}}{du}\, du, \tag{A.51}$$

between the limits u_1 and u_2.

To specify a surface S, we give the position vector $\mathbf{r} = \mathbf{r}(u, v)$ as a function of two parameters u, v that range between appropriate limits as the surface is traversed. The vector field then becomes a function of u, v as $\mathbf{F}(\mathbf{r}) = \mathbf{F}(\mathbf{r}(u, v))$, and the element of area over the surface, $d\mathbf{S}$, is expressed in terms of the differentials du, dv by

$$d\mathbf{S} = \frac{\partial \mathbf{r}}{\partial u} \times \frac{\partial \mathbf{r}}{\partial v}\, du\, dv, \tag{A.52}$$

so that the surface integral is evaluated as the double integral

$$\int \mathbf{F} \cdot d\mathbf{S} = \iint \mathbf{F}(\mathbf{r}(u, v)) \cdot \left[\frac{\partial \mathbf{r}}{\partial u} \times \frac{\partial \mathbf{r}}{\partial v}\right] du\, dv. \tag{A.53}$$

To specify a volume V, we give the position vector $\mathbf{r} = \mathbf{r}(u, v, w)$ as a function of three parameters u, v, and w that range between appropriate limits as the volume is traversed. The scalar (or vector) field then becomes a function of u, v, and w as $f(\mathbf{r}) = f(\mathbf{r}(u, v, w))$, and the element of volume dV, is expressed in terms of the differentials du, dv, and dw by

$$dV = \frac{\partial \mathbf{r}}{\partial u} \times \frac{\partial \mathbf{r}}{\partial v} \cdot \frac{\partial \mathbf{r}}{\partial w}\, du\, dv\, dw, \tag{A.54}$$

so that the volume integral is evaluated as the triple integral

$$\int f\, dV = \iiint f(\mathbf{r}(u, v, w))\, \frac{\partial \mathbf{r}}{\partial u} \times \frac{\partial \mathbf{r}}{\partial v} \cdot \frac{\partial \mathbf{r}}{\partial w}\, du\, dv\, dw. \tag{A.55}$$

In each case, the sign of the element of integration must be made positive, by choosing the direction of traversal of the curve C along its orientation, or by ensuring that the parameters u and v give an element of area $d\mathbf{S}$ that conforms to the orientation of the surface S (or else we reverse the parameters' order), or by choosing the order of the three parameters u, v, and w to make the volume element dV positive (or else we interchange one pair of them).

If the integrand, and therefore the integral, is a vector, it may be dotted with each of the basis vectors of the rectangular coordinate system to yield the three components of the integral. Basis vectors of curvilinear coordinate systems cannot be moved from inside to outside of the integral, because they are not constant vectors.

Two theorems relate integrals of derivatives of fields over a region to integrals of the fields themselves over the boundary of the region. The *divergence theorem* is

$$\int_V \nabla \cdot \mathbf{F}\, dV = \oint_S \mathbf{F} \cdot d\mathbf{S}, \tag{A.56}$$

where S is the closed surface that bounds the volume V. For a closed surface, the convention is that the element of area $d\mathbf{S}$ is directed outward. *Stokes's theorem* is

$$\int_S \nabla \times \mathbf{F} \cdot d\mathbf{S} = \oint_C \mathbf{F} \cdot d\mathbf{l}, \tag{A.57}$$

where C is the closed curve that is the edge of the open surface S, with the curve and surface mutually oriented to conform with the right-hand rule: if the fingers of the right hand curl along the direction of the oriented curve C, the thumb points along the orientation of the surface S.

Fourier Transforms

The Fourier transform pair converts the description of a signal from and to the time and frequency domains. If $f(t)$ is a signal, its spectrum is given by $F(\omega)$, as in

$$F(\omega) = \int_{-\infty}^{\infty} f(t) \exp\,[-j\omega t]\, dt, \qquad f(t) = \int_{-\infty}^{\infty} F(\omega) \exp\,[j\omega t]\, \frac{d\omega}{2\pi}. \tag{A.58}$$

Bessel Functions

The solutions to the Bessel equation

$$\frac{d^2y}{dx^2} + \frac{1}{x}\frac{dy}{dx} + \left[1 - \frac{n^2}{x^2}\right] y = 0 \tag{A.59}$$

are linear combinations of the Bessel functions of order n and argument x, $J_n(x)$ and $Y_n(x)$. The latter is singular at $x = 0$. The mth zero of the Bessel functions of order n (not including $x = 0$) is denoted j_{nm} and y_{nm} for $J_n(x)$ and

$Y_n(x)$. The mth point at which either Bessel function has zero slope (not including $x = 0$) is called j'_{nm} or y'_{nm}. The Bessel functions satisfy the following *recursion relations.*

$$J_{n-1}(x) + J_{n+1}(x) = \frac{2n}{x} J_n(x), \tag{A.60}$$

$$J_{n-1}(x) - J_{n+1}(x) = 2 \frac{dJ_n(x)}{dx}; \tag{A.61}$$

$$Y_{n-1}(x) + Y_{n+1}(x) = \frac{2n}{x} Y_n(x), \tag{A.62}$$

$$Y_{n-1}(x) - Y_{n+1}(x) = 2 \frac{dY_n(x)}{dx}. \tag{A.63}$$

For large values of the argument x, the Bessel functions asymptotically approach slightly damped sinusoids, as

$$J_n(x) \to \sqrt{\frac{2}{\pi x}} \cos\left(x - \frac{n\pi}{2} - \frac{\pi}{4}\right) \quad \text{as } x \to \infty, \tag{A.64}$$

$$Y_n(x) \to \sqrt{\frac{2}{\pi x}} \sin\left(x - \frac{n\pi}{2} - \frac{\pi}{4}\right) \quad \text{as } x \to \infty. \tag{A.65}$$

The solutions to the modified Bessel equation

$$\frac{d^2y}{dx^2} + \frac{1}{x}\frac{dy}{dx} - \left[1 + \frac{n^2}{x^2}\right] y = 0 \tag{A.66}$$

are linear combinations of the modified Bessel functions of order n and argument x, $I_n(x)$ and $K_n(x)$. The latter is singular at $x = 0$; the former is singular at infinity. The modified Bessel functions satisfy the following *recursion relations.*

$$I_{n-1}(x) - I_{n+1}(x) = \frac{2n}{x} I_n(x), \tag{A.67}$$

$$I_{n-1}(x) + I_{n+1}(x) = 2 \frac{dI_n(x)}{dx}; \tag{A.68}$$

$$K_{n-1}(x) - K_{n+1}(x) = -\frac{2n}{x} K_n(x), \tag{A.69}$$

$$K_{n-1}(x) + K_{n+1}(x) = -2 \frac{dK_n(x)}{dx}. \tag{A.70}$$

The modified Bessel functions are related to the other kind in the same way that hyperbolic functions (cosh x, sinh x, etc.) are related to the trigonometric functions (cos x, sin x, etc.). The J and Y Bessel functions are oscillatory (and damped); the modified ones grow (I) or decay (K) like exponentials. For large values of the argument x, the modified Bessel functions asymptotically approach exponential behavior, as

$$I_n(x) \to \sqrt{\frac{1}{2\pi x}}\, e^x \qquad \text{as } x \to \infty\,, \tag{A.71}$$

$$K_n(x) \to \sqrt{\frac{\pi}{2x}}\, e^{-x} \qquad \text{as } x \to \infty\,. \tag{A.72}$$

For small values of the argument x, the modified Bessel functions become

$$I_n(x) \to \frac{(x/2)^n}{n!} \qquad \text{as } x \to 0\,, \tag{A.73}$$

$$K_n(x) \to \frac{(x/2)^{-n}}{(n-1)!} \quad (\text{only if } n > 0) \qquad \text{as } x \to 0\,, \tag{A.74}$$

while

$$K_0(x) \to -\ln\,(0.8905362x) \qquad \text{as } x \to 0\,. \tag{A.75}$$

PROBLEMS

Operations on Complex Numbers

A.1 Let $u = 3 + j2$ and $v = 5e^{j0.5}$. Find, in both rectangular and polar form:
(a) $u + v$ **(b)** $u - v$ **(c)** uv **(d)** u/v **(e)** $\sqrt{u}$ **(f)** u^*v

Properties of a Square Matrix

A.2 Let the matrix $M = M(x)$ be given by

$$M(x) = \begin{bmatrix} 1 & x & x^2 \\ x^2 & x & 1 \\ x^2 & 1 & x \end{bmatrix}$$

(a) For what values of x is this matrix singular?
(b) Find the eigenvalues of $M(-1)$.
(c) Find $M^2(1)$.
(d) Obtain $\{M(0)\}^{-1}$.

Identification of a Conic Section

A.3 Determine the type of conic section represented by the quadratic form $x^2 = y^2 + 4 + 6xy$.

Cylindrical and Spherical Coordinates of a Point

A.4 The rectangular coordinates of a point are (1, 2, 3).
(a) What are its cylindrical coordinates?
(b) What are its spherical coordinates?

Operations on Unit Vectors

A.5 Let the radius of the earth be one unit; let the unit vector $\hat{\mathbf{n}}_1$ point from the center of the earth to New York (40°45′06″N, 73°59′39″W) and $\hat{\mathbf{n}}_2$ to Paris (48°50′14″N, 2°20′14″E).

(a) What is the angle between $\hat{\mathbf{n}}_1$ and $\hat{\mathbf{n}}_2$?

(b) Where on earth (or in it) is $\hat{\mathbf{n}}_1 \times \hat{\mathbf{n}}_2$?

Vector Differential Calculus

A.6 **(a)** Find the gradient of the azimuthal coordinate φ, in cylindrical coordinates.

(b) Find the gradient of the azimuthal coordinate φ, in spherical coordinates.

(c) Find the divergence of the azimuthal unit vector $\hat{\boldsymbol{\varphi}}$, in cylindrical coordinates.

(d) Find the curl of the azimuthal unit vector $\hat{\boldsymbol{\varphi}}$, in spherical coordinates.

Line Integral

A.7 By direct integration, find the closed line integral of the vector field $\mathbf{F}(\mathbf{r}) = \mathbf{r} \cdot \hat{\mathbf{x}}\hat{\mathbf{y}}$ around the semicircle of radius a in the half-plane $y \geq 0$, centered at the origin of the xy-plane and closed by the diameter on the x-axis, oriented counterclockwise.

Line Integral by Stokes's Theorem

A.8 By using Stokes's theorem, find the closed line integral of the vector field $\mathbf{F}(\mathbf{r}) = \mathbf{r} \cdot \hat{\mathbf{x}}\hat{\mathbf{y}}$ around the semicircle of radius a in the half-plane $y \geq 0$, centered at the origin of the xy-plane and closed by the diameter on the x-axis, oriented counterclockwise.

Surface Integral

A.9 By direct integration, find the closed surface integral of the vector field $\mathbf{F}(\mathbf{r}) = \hat{\mathbf{z}} \cdot \mathbf{r}\mathbf{r}$ over the hemisphere $r = a$, $z > 0$ (closed by the disk $r < a$, $z = 0$).

Surface Integral by Divergence Theorem

A.10 By using the divergence theorem, find the closed surface integral of the vector field $\mathbf{F}(\mathbf{r}) = \hat{\mathbf{z}} \cdot \mathbf{r}\mathbf{r}$ over the hemisphere $r = a$, $z > 0$ (closed by the disk $r < a$, $z = 0$).

Fourier Transform

A.11 Find the Fourier transform $F(\omega)$ of the signal $f(t) = e^{-a|t|}$.

Bessel Functions

A.12 Show that $dJ_n(j_{nm})/dx = J_{n-1}(j_{nm})$.

Answers to Problems

Chapter 1

1.1 $(7.5)10^{14}$ to $(4.3)10^{14}$ Hz.

1.2 3.1 to 1.8 eV.

1.3 1.47 eV, 1.04 eV, 0.80 eV.

1.4 **(a)** 1 μs, 1 ns. **(b)** 1 nJ, 1 pJ.

1.5 89%.

1.6 $(1.999)10^8$ m/s.

Chapter 2

2.1 $v = 1/\sqrt{3}$, $\hat{\mathbf{n}} = (-1, -1, -1)/\sqrt{3}$.

2.2 $f(x, y, z, t) = 5 \exp[-9(3x + 4y - 12z - 26t)^2/169]$.

2.3 **(a)** 48 m. **(b)** 15.67 s.

2.4 $\pm 2vT$.

2.5 **(a)** $t = 4T$, $z = 0.4l$. **(b)** 0.90922.

2.6 (a, b, c) No. $f_0(u) = f(u) + C + \frac{1}{2}[D - E/v]u$, $g_0(u) = g(u) + \frac{1}{2}[D + E/v]u$.

2.7 (The answer is stated in the question.)

2.8

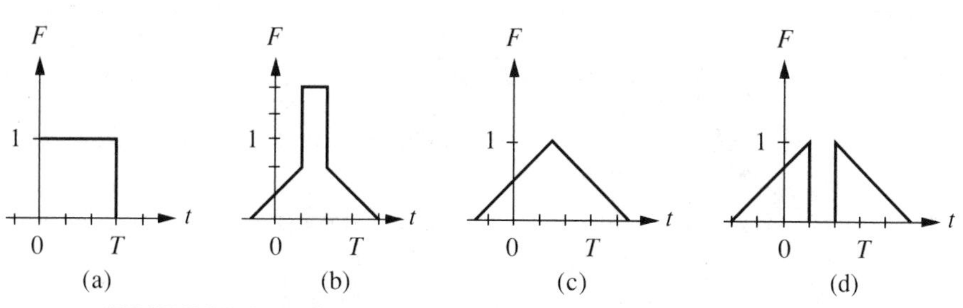

FIGURE P2–8 Sketches of superpositions of two pulse waves.

Chapter 3

3.1 No. $f_{01}(u) = f_1(u) + \frac{1}{2}(C_1 + C_2), f_{02}(u) = f_2(u) + \frac{1}{2}(C_1 - C_2)$.

3.2 On the surface of a sphere of radius $(\sqrt{3})a$, centered at the origin.

3.3 On a sphere of radius $a\sqrt{\gamma t}$.

3.4 $ds/dt = +c$.

3.5 **(a)** $\mathbf{E} = \hat{\mathbf{e}}F(t - [4x - 3y + 12z]/13c)$, $\mathbf{H} = \hat{\mathbf{h}}F(t - [4x - 3y + 12z]/13c)$.
(b) $\hat{\mathbf{e}} = (3\hat{\mathbf{x}} + 4\hat{\mathbf{y}})/5$, $\hat{\mathbf{h}} = (-48\hat{\mathbf{x}} + 36\hat{\mathbf{y}} + 25\hat{\mathbf{z}})/65$.

3.6 **(a)** $U(t) = \frac{1}{2}Qv\rho_0^2/[\rho_0^2 + (z_0 - vt)^2]^{3/2}$.
(b) $H_\varphi(\rho, z, t) = [Qv/4\pi]\rho/[\rho^2 + (z - vt)^2]^{3/2}$.

3.7 **(a)** $U(t) = -\frac{1}{2}Qgt\rho_0^2/[\rho_0^2 + (z_0 + \frac{1}{2}gt^2)^2]^{3/2}$.
(b) $H_\varphi(\rho, z, t) = -[Qg/4\pi]\rho t/[\rho^2 + (z + \frac{1}{2}gt^2)^2]^{3/2}$.

Chapter 4

4.1 **(a)** 1.40 kW/m^2. **(b)** 725 V/m. **(c)** 1.93 A/m. **(d)** (4.0) 10^{26} W.

4.2 **(a)** $T = \varepsilon/\sigma$. **(b)** $\frac{1}{2}[Q_0^2/4\pi\varepsilon][1/a - 1/b]$.

4.3 **(a)** $V(t) = [B_0 \pi R^2/T]e^{-t/T}$.
(b) $E_\varphi(\rho, \varphi, z, t) = [\frac{1}{2}B_0 R^2/T\rho]e^{-t/T}$, $J_\varphi = [\frac{1}{2}\sigma B_0 R^2/T\rho]e^{-t/T}$.
(c) $I_0 = [\frac{1}{2}\sigma h B_0 R^2/T]e^{-t/T} \ln (b/a)$.
(d) $p = [\sigma B_0^2 R^4/4T^2\rho^2]e^{-2t/T}$. **(e)** $P = [(\pi/4)\sigma h B_0^2 R^4/T] \ln (b/a)$.

4.4 **(a)** $V(t) = [B_0 \pi \rho_0^2/T]e^{-t/T}$.
(b) $E_\varphi(\rho, \varphi, z, t) = [\frac{1}{2}B_0 \rho/T]e^{-t/T}$, $J_\varphi = [\frac{1}{2}\sigma B_0 \rho/T]e^{-t/T}$.
(c) $I_0 = [\sigma h B_0/4T](b^2 - a^2)e^{-t/T}$.
(d) $p = [\sigma B_0^2 \rho^2/4T^2]e^{-2t/T}$. **(e)** $P = [(\pi/16)\sigma h B_0^2/T](b^4 - a^4)$.

4.5 **(a)** $V(t) = B(t)\pi\rho_0^2/T$ if $\rho_0 < R$, or $V(t) = B(t)\pi R^2/T$ if $\rho_0 > R$, for $t > 0$.
(b) $E_\varphi(\rho, \varphi, z, t) = \frac{1}{2}B(t)\rho/T$ if $\rho < R$, or $E_\varphi = \frac{1}{2}B(t)R^2/T\rho$ if $\rho > R$; $J_\varphi = \sigma E_\varphi$.
(c) $I_0 = [\sigma h B(t)/4T]\{(R^2 - a^2) + 2R^2 \ln (b/R)\}$.
(d) $p = [\sigma B^2(t)\rho^2/4T^2]$ for $\rho < R$, $p = [\sigma B^2(t)R^4/4T^2\rho^2]$ for $\rho > R$.
(e) $P = [(\pi/16)\sigma h B_0^2/T][(R^4 - a^4 + 4R^4 \ln (b/R)]$.

4.6 **(a)** $\mathbf{E} \times \mathbf{H} = -\hat{\boldsymbol{\theta}}[Q^2 v/16\pi^2\varepsilon_0]\rho/[\rho^2 + (z - vt)^2]^{5/2}$. **(b)** $[Q^2 v/32\pi\varepsilon_0(z_0 - vt)^2]$.

Chapter 5

5.1 **(a)** $E'(\omega) = E(\omega)e^{-j\omega T_1}$ for $|\omega| < \omega_0$, $E'(\omega) = E(\omega)e^{-j\omega T_2}$ for $|\omega| > \omega_0$.
(b) $E'(t) = [1 + \theta_1^2]^{-1}\{1 - e^{-\omega_0 T}[\cos (\omega_0 T\theta_1) - \theta_1 \sin (\omega_0 T\theta_1)]\}$
$+ [1 + \theta_2^2]^{-1}e^{-\omega_0 T}[\cos (\omega_0 T\theta_2) - \theta_2 \sin (\omega_0 T\theta_2)]$,
where $\theta_n = (t - T_n)/T$.

5.2 **(a)** $E_0 \sin (ky - \omega t)$, with $E_0 = 3$ V/m, $ky_0 = \pi/2 + l2\pi$ (l = integer), $y_0 = 8$ m, $\omega = kc$. **(b)** $\mathbf{E} = jE_0 \hat{\mathbf{x}}e^{-jky}$. **(c)** 9.37 MHz.

5.3 **(a)** $\sin (\omega' t - \omega l/c)$; $\omega' = \omega[1 - u/c]$.

(b) $\sin(\omega' t - \omega l/[c - v])$; $\omega' = \omega/[1 - v/c]$.
(c) $\sin(\omega' t - \omega l/[c - v])$; $\omega' = \omega[1 - u/c]/[1 - v/c]$.
(d) $\lambda' = 2\pi[c - v]/\omega$.

5.4 **(a)** $\mathbf{E} = E_1(2\hat{\mathbf{x}} - j\hat{\mathbf{y}})$. **(b)** $\mathscr{E} = E_1[\hat{\mathbf{x}}2\cos(\omega t - kz) + \hat{\mathbf{y}}\sin(\omega t - kz)]$.

5.5 Yes.

5.6 **(a)** RHEP. **(b)** RHEP. **(c)** LHEP. **(d)** LHEP.

5.7 **(a)** $X = -20/3$. **(b)** $X = -20/3$. **(c)** $X = 4$ and $Y = -3$.

5.8 **(a)** $dA/dt = \frac{1}{2}|\mathscr{E} \times d\mathscr{E}/dt|$. **(b)** $dA/dt = \frac{1}{2}\omega|\mathbf{E}_2 \times \mathbf{E}_1|$.

5.9 **(a)** $\theta = \tan^{-1} m$. **(b)** Lower sign. **(c)** $-\pi < \varphi < 0$ is RHEP; $0 < \varphi < \pi$ is LHEP.

5.10 **(a)** On the equator, at inclination ψ.
(b) RHCP at south pole; LHCP at north pole.
(c) Southern hemisphere is RHEP; northern hemisphere is LHEP.
(d) The polarization ellipses are orthogonal.

5.11 A is $(E_1, 0)$, B is $(0, E_2)$, C is $(E_1, E_2\cos\delta)$, D is $(E_1\cos\delta, E_2)$, with $\delta = |\delta_2 - \delta_1|$; E is $(E_1\sin\delta, 0)$, F is $(0, E_2\sin\delta)$. a^2 or b^2 is $E_1^2\cos^2(\delta_1 - \delta_0) + E_2^2\cos^2(\delta_2 - \delta_0)$ or $E_1^2\sin^2(\delta_1 - \delta_0) + E_2^2\sin^2(\delta_2 - \delta_0)$ and $\tan\theta = E_2\cos(\delta_2 - \delta_0)/E_1\cos(\delta_1 - \delta_0)$.

5.12 The polarization ellipse fits into the polarization pattern; the extrema of the pattern and the ellipse coincide.

5.13 **(a)** $l = (\lambda_0/4)/|n_1 - n_2|$. **(b)** Circular.

Chapter 6

6.1 $\Phi(z, t) = \Phi_0(z, t) - \kappa z$.

6.2 $\omega^2 = \omega_0^2 + k^2c^2$ or $k^2 = k_0^2 + \omega^2/c^2$.

6.3 **(a)** $f/f_0 = 2.2942$. **(b)** $f/f_0 = 1.1547$.

6.4 **(a)** $\lambda = 6.239$ m. **(b)** $v_p = 3.119$ m/s. **(c)** $v_g = 1.560$ m/s.

6.5 **(a)** $v_p/c = \sqrt{1 - (\omega/\omega_0)^2}$. **(b)** $v_g/c = [1 - (\omega/\omega_0)^2]^{3/2}$.

6.6 $v_p = a\omega/[1 + \ln(\omega/\omega_0)]$.

6.7 **(a)** $\langle a(t)b(t)\rangle = [\text{Re } A][\text{Re } B]$. **(b)** For real $a(t)$, $b(t)$, $\langle ab\rangle = \sum A_m B_m^*$.

6.8 (The answer is stated in the question.)

6.9 σ_i is $\omega\varepsilon$; σ_r is conductivity.

6.10 $-\omega\mu_i$ is a "magnetic" conductivity; μ_r is permeability.

6.11 **(a)** $I/w = (E_0/\eta_0)(1 - j\cot ks)$.
(b) $Z = [\eta_0 l/w][\sin^2 ks + j\sin ks\cos ks]$. **(c)** $s = \lambda_0/4$.

(d) $W_m = [\varepsilon_0 |E_0|^2 lws/8 \sin^2 ks][1 + \sin(2ks)/2ks]$,
$W_e = [\varepsilon_0 |E_0|^2 lws/8 \sin^2 ks][1 - \sin(2ks)/2ks]$.

6.12 **(a)** For $z > s$, $E = E_0[1 + e^{j(ks+\varphi)}]e^{-jkz}$; for $z < 0$, $E = E_0[1 + e^{-j(ks-\varphi)}]e^{jkz}$; for $0 < z < s$, $E = E_0[e^{-jkz} + e^{-j(ks-\varphi)}e^{jkz}]$.
(b) $\varphi = ks - \pi$, for example. **(c)** $s = \lambda_0/4$, for example.
(d) Over an area lw, $W_0 = lws\varepsilon_0 |E_0|^2$.

6.13 **(a)** $E = E_0\{[1 - e^{jN(ks+\varphi)}]/[1 - e^{j(ks+\varphi)}]\}e^{-jkz}$.
(b) $E = E_0\{[1 - e^{-jN(ks-\varphi)}]/[1 - e^{-j(ks-\varphi)}]\}e^{jkz}$.
(c) $s = \lambda_0/2N$ and $\varphi = -\pi/N$.

6.14 **(a)** $\mathbf{E} = E_1(2\hat{\mathbf{x}} - j\hat{\mathbf{y}})e^{-jkz}$, $\mathbf{H} = (E_1/\eta_0)(j\hat{\mathbf{x}} + 2\hat{\mathbf{y}})e^{-jkz}$;
$\mathscr{E} = E_1[\hat{\mathbf{x}}\, 2\cos(\omega t - kz) + \hat{\mathbf{y}} \sin(\omega t - kz)]$,
$\mathscr{H} = (E_1/\eta_0)[-\hat{\mathbf{x}} \sin(\omega t - kz) + \hat{\mathbf{y}}\, 2\cos(\omega t - kz)]$.
(b) The ratio of the superimposed energy density to that of the linearly polarized one is 5.

Chapter 7

7.1 **(a)** $\mathbf{E} = \mathbf{E}_0 e^{-\alpha z}e^{-j\beta z}$, $\mathbf{H} = (\hat{\mathbf{z}} \times \mathbf{E}_0/Z_0)e^{-\alpha z}e^{-j\beta z}$ for $z > 0$, with $Z_0 = j\omega\mu/(\alpha + j\beta)$; $\mathbf{E} = \mathbf{E}_0 e^{\alpha z}e^{j\beta z}$, $\mathbf{H} = (-\hat{\mathbf{z}} \times \mathbf{E}_0/Z_0)e^{\alpha z}e^{j\beta z}$ for $z < 0$. $E_0 = Z_0 I_0/2w$, opposite to the current.
(b) $Z = \frac{1}{2}(l/w)[\omega\mu/(\beta^2 + \alpha^2)][\beta + j\alpha]$.

7.2 Plot the relations $\alpha/\sigma\eta = [f/f_0]\{\frac{1}{2}[\sqrt{1 + [f_0/f]^2} - 1]\}^{1/2}$ and $\beta/\sigma\eta = [f/f_0]\{\frac{1}{2}[\sqrt{1 + [f_0/f]^2} + 1]\}^{1/2}$.

7.3 $l = 0.139$ m.

7.4 **(a)** $l = 0.216$ m. **(b)** $l = 152$ m.
(c) Only low frequencies have a chance of penetrating to significant depths.

7.5 $D = 1/\sigma\mu$.

7.6 22.5°.

7.7 $\beta^2 - \alpha^2 = \omega^2\mu\varepsilon$ and $2\boldsymbol{\alpha} \cdot \boldsymbol{\beta} = \omega\mu\sigma$. The components of $\boldsymbol{\alpha}$ and $\boldsymbol{\beta}$ tangential to the source plane are determined by the source.

Chapter 8

8.1 **(a)** $\mathbf{E}_1 = (2\hat{\mathbf{x}} + 5\hat{\mathbf{y}} - 18\hat{\mathbf{z}})E_0$.
(b) $\mathbf{D}_1 = (4\hat{\mathbf{x}} + 10\hat{\mathbf{y}} - 36\hat{\mathbf{z}})\varepsilon_0 E_0$, $\mathbf{D}_2 = (12\hat{\mathbf{x}} + 30\hat{\mathbf{y}} - 36\hat{\mathbf{z}})\varepsilon_0 E_0$.
(c) $w_{e1} = 353\varepsilon_0 E_0^2$, $w_{e2} = 195\varepsilon_0 E_0^2$.

8.2 **(a)** $\mathbf{H}_1 = (-\hat{\mathbf{x}} + 5\hat{\mathbf{y}} - 18\hat{\mathbf{z}})H_0$.
(b) $\mathbf{B}_1 = (-2\hat{\mathbf{x}} + 10\hat{\mathbf{y}} - 36\hat{\mathbf{z}})\mu_0 H_0$, $\mathbf{B}_2 = (12\hat{\mathbf{x}} + 30\hat{\mathbf{y}} - 36\hat{\mathbf{z}})\mu_0 H_0$.
(c) $w_{m1} = 350\mu_0 H_0^2$, $w_{m2} = 195\mu_0 H_0^2$.

8.3 **(a)** $\mathbf{E}_1 = (2\hat{\mathbf{x}} + 5\hat{\mathbf{y}} - [10.615 + j4.923]\hat{\mathbf{z}})E_0$.
(b) $\rho_S = [-14.770 + j9.846]\varepsilon_0 E_0$.

8.4 **(a)** $E_1 = \Gamma E_0$, $E_2 = \mathrm{T}E_0$, with $\Gamma = -\eta_0\sigma_S/(2 + \eta_0\sigma_S)$, $T = 2/(2 + \eta_0\sigma_S)$.

(b) $\mathbf{K} = 2\sigma_S \mathbf{E}_0/(2 + \eta_0 \sigma_S)$.

8.5 **(a)** $\sigma_S = 1/\eta_0$, $l = \lambda_0/4$.
(b) $E = E_0 \cos kz$ for $kl = \pi/2$, $H = -j(E_0/\eta_0) \sin kz$.
(c) $\mathbf{K} = \sigma_S \mathbf{E}_0$. **(d)** $\mathbf{K}_0 = -j(\mathbf{E}_0/\eta_0)$. **(e)** $\frac{1}{2}|E_0|^2/\eta_0$. **(f)** $W = \frac{1}{4}\varepsilon_0|E_0|^2 l$.

8.6 **(a)** $f_n = (2n+1)c/4l$ (n = integer). **(b)** $\Delta f = (c/l)0.13693$.

8.7 **(a)** $\sigma_S = 1/\eta_1 - 1/\eta_2$, provided that $\eta_2 > \eta_1$. **(b)** η_1/η_2.
If $\eta_2 < \eta_1$, then $|\Gamma| \geq |(\eta_2 - \eta_1)/(\eta_2 + \eta_1)|$.

8.8 **(a)** $\varepsilon_2/\varepsilon_1 = \mu_2/\mu_1 = \sigma_2/\sigma_1$. **(b)** No.

8.9 **(a)** $\Gamma_{21} + T_{12} = 1$; $E = 2E_0 \cos k_1 z$, $H = -2j(E_0/\eta_1) \sin k_1 z$ for $z < 0$,
$E = 2E_0 \cos k_2 z$, $H = -2j(E_0/\eta_2) \sin k_2 z$ for $z > 0$.
(b) $\frac{1}{2}\mathbf{E} \times \mathbf{H}^* = \hat{\mathbf{z}}j(|E_0|^2/\eta_1) \sin 2k_1 z$ for $z < 0$, $\frac{1}{2}\mathbf{E} \times \mathbf{H}^* = \hat{\mathbf{z}}j(|E_0|^2/\eta_2) \sin 2k_2 z$ for $z > 0$.

8.10 2.4838.

8.11 **(a)** $\Gamma = \{\Gamma_{21} + \Gamma_{32} e^{-j2kd}\}/[1 - \Gamma_{12}\Gamma_{32} e^{-j2kd}]$.
(b) $kd = (m + \frac{1}{2})\pi$, $\eta_2^2 = \eta_1 \eta_3$.

8.12 **(a)** $\frac{1}{9}$. **(b)** $\frac{1}{17}$.

8.13 **(a)** $a = \frac{21}{19}$, $b = \frac{2}{19}$.
(b) 0.89906. **(c)** Infinite bandwidth. **(d)** $0.6345 < r^2 < 1.5760$.

8.14 **(a)** $Z_0 = \eta_3[\eta_4 + j\eta_3 \tan \varphi_3]/[\eta_3 + j\eta_4 \tan \varphi_3]$.
(b) $Z(-d_2) = \eta_2[Z_0 + j\eta_2 \tan \varphi_2]/[\eta_2 + jZ_0 \tan \varphi_2]$.
(c) $\eta_2[\eta_1 - j\eta_2 \tan \varphi_2]/[\eta_2 - j\eta_1 \tan \varphi_2] =$
$\eta_3[\eta_4 + j\eta_3 \tan \varphi_3]/[\eta_3 + j\eta_4 \tan \varphi_3]$.
(d) $A = \eta_1 \eta_3^2 - \eta_4 \eta_2^2$.
(e) $\varphi_2 = 1.05901$, $\varphi_3 = 0.80994$.
(f) $d_2/\lambda_0 = 0.12641$, $d_3/\lambda_0 = 0.08250$.

8.15 **(a)** $f = c/2s$. **(b)** $f = c/s$.

8.16 **(a)** $H_2 = 17.77e^{-j0.032673}$ mA/m. **(b)** $P = 1.618$ W.

8.17 **(a)** Yes. **(b)** The transmitted wave has the same parity; the reflected wave changes parity. **(c)** The reflected wave is circularly polarized, of the opposite parity.

8.18 **(a)** $\Gamma = [-\sqrt{\varepsilon} + j \tan(\omega s\sqrt{\varepsilon}/c)]/[\sqrt{\varepsilon} + j \tan(\omega s\sqrt{\varepsilon}/c)]$. **(b)** 100%.

Chapter 9

9.1 $T_e = 1.21544$, $\Gamma_e = 0.21544$.

9.2 $T_h = 1.7941$, $\Gamma_h = 0.7941$.

9.3 36°.

9.4 No.

9.5 **(a)** $n = 1.732$. **(b)** $\theta_1 = 60°$.

9.6 $\frac{1}{8}$ W.

9.7 $\frac{1}{9}$.

9.8 **(a)** $T = 2/(2 + \eta_0 \sigma_S \sec \theta)$, $\Gamma = -\eta_0 \sigma_S \sec \theta/(2 + \eta_0 \sigma_S \sec \theta)$.
(b) $K = 2\sigma_S E_0/(2 + \eta_0 \sigma_S \sec \theta)$.
(c) $T = 2/(2 + \eta_0 \sigma_S \cos \theta)$, $\Gamma = \eta_0 \sigma_S \cos \theta/(2 + \eta_0 \sigma_S \cos \theta)$.
(d) $K = 2\eta_0 \sigma_S \cos \theta H_0/(2 + \eta_0 \sigma_S \cos \theta)$.

9.9 **(a)** $\sigma_S = \cos \theta/\eta_0$, $l = \lambda_0/(4 \cos \theta)$. **(b)** $\sigma_S = 1/(\eta_0 \cos \theta)$, $l = \lambda_0/(4 \cos \theta)$.

9.10 **(a)** $n_1 \sin \theta_1 = n_2 \sin \theta_2$. **(b)** (The answer is stated in the question.)
(c) $\Gamma_{21} + T_{12} = 1$; $\mathbf{E}_1 = \mathbf{E}_0 e^{-j\mathbf{p}\cdot\mathbf{r}} \cos \beta_1 z$, $\mathbf{E}_2 = \mathbf{E}_0 e^{-j\mathbf{p}\cdot\mathbf{r}} \cos \beta_2 z$.

9.11 **(a)** $n_1 \sin \theta_1 = n_2 \sin \theta_2$. **(b)** (The answer is stated in the question.)
(c) $\Gamma_{21} + T_{12} = 1$; $\mathbf{H}_1 = \mathbf{H}_0 e^{-j\mathbf{p}\cdot\mathbf{r}} \cos \beta_1 z$, $\mathbf{H}_2 = \mathbf{H}_0 e^{-j\mathbf{p}\cdot\mathbf{r}} \cos \beta_2 z$.

9.12 **(a)** $n_2/n_1 = \sqrt{2.48382 \cos^2 \theta + \sin^2 \theta}$.
(b) $n_2/n_1 = [1 + \sqrt{1 - 0.402605 \sin^2 2\theta}]^{1/2}/[0.897335 \cos \theta]$.
(c) 1.3198 for TE, 2.0985 for TM.

9.13 $\tan^{-1}\{n\sqrt{\xi^2 n^2 - 1}/[n^2 - 1]\}$ to $\tan^{-1}\{n\sqrt{n^2/\xi^2 - 1}/[n^2 - 1]\}$, with $\xi = 0.634512$. For $n = 2$, 42.06° to 73.84°.

9.14 $n_2 = [\sin^2 \theta + \cos \theta \sqrt{n^2 - \sin^2 \theta}]^{1/2}$, $d = \lambda_0/\{4[\cos \theta \sqrt{n^2 - \sin^2 \theta}]^{1/2}\}$.

9.15 $1/n_2 = \{[1 - \sqrt{1 - 4A \sin^2 \theta}]/2 \sin^2 \theta\}^{1/2}$, with
$A = (\cos \theta/n^2)\sqrt{n^2 - \sin^2 \theta}$; $d = \lambda_0/\{4[\cos \theta \sqrt{n^2 - \sin^2 \theta}]^{1/2}\}$.

9.16 **(a)** (The answer is stated in the question.) **(b)** $f = c/(2s \cos \theta)$.

9.17 **(a)** $\Gamma = [j \tan \beta_2 s/\sqrt{n^2 - \sin^2 \theta} - \sec \theta]/[j \tan \beta_2 s/\sqrt{n^2 - \sin^2 \theta} + \sec \theta]$.
(b) 100%.
(c) $\Gamma = [j \tan \beta_2 s\sqrt{n^2 - \sin^2 \theta} - n^2 \cos \theta]/[j \tan \beta_2 s\sqrt{n^2 - \sin^2 \theta} + n^2 \cos \theta]$.
(d) 100%.

Chapter 10

10.1 $\Gamma = e^{j1.42745}$. $T = 1.14286 + j0.98974$.

10.2 $\Gamma = e^{j1.98952}$. $T = 0.59341 + j0.91361$.

10.3 Yes.

10.4 No.

10.5 $n = 1.27202$.

10.6 **(a)** $|T_h|^2 = 2.499666$ for $n_2 = 2.5$, $n_1 = 3.9$, $\theta_0 = 43°$.
(b) (The answer is stated in the question.)
(c) $\langle w_m \rangle - \langle w_e \rangle = -[\frac{1}{4}\mu_0 |H_0|^2][0.6595]e^{-1.816(\omega z/c)}$.

10.7 **(a)** $\Gamma = e^{j0.92596}$. **(b)** Unaffected.

10.8 **(a)** $\Gamma = e^{j1.14015}$. **(b)** Unaffected.

10.9 **(a)** 1.4142. **(b)** 1.7534.

Chapter 11

11.1 (The answer is stated in the question.)

11.2 **(a)** $b \cosh \delta, b \sinh \delta$. **(b)** $b \cosh [\delta - \xi], b \sinh [\delta - \xi]$.
(c), (d) (The answer is stated in the question.) **(e)** $Z_0 = \eta\xi/2\pi$.
(f) (The answer is stated in the question.)

11.3 **(a)** $Z_2 = 49.1\ \Omega$. **(b)** $\Gamma = -0.100$.

11.4 **(a)** $V(z) = 2V_0 \cos kn(l - z), I(z) = 2j[V_0/Z_0] \sin kn(l - z)$.
(b) $P(z) = -j(|V_0|^2/Z_0) \sin 2kn(l - z)$.
(c) $V(z) = V_s[\cos kn(l - z)]/\cos knl, I(z) = j[V_s/Z_0][\sin kn(l - z)]/\cos knl$.
(d) $Z(z) = -jZ_0 \cot kn(l - z); Z_s = -jZ_0 \cot knl$.

11.5 **(a)** $\Gamma_l = 0.6 + j0.2$. **(b)** $\Gamma = -0.36785 - j0.51447$.

(c) $Z = [0.28094 - j0.48178]Z_0$.

11.6 **(a)** $|\Gamma| = 0.52381$. **(b)** $\varphi_l = \pi$. **(c)** $Z_l = 15.625\ \Omega$.

11.7 **(a)** $Z_l = (22 + j96)\ \Omega$; **(b)** VSWR = 11.

11.8 **(a)** VSWR = 1.2210. **(b)** 45.88 cm in front of the load.

11.9 **(a)** $c = r_0/(r_0 + 1); \rho = 1/(r_0 + 1)$. **(b)** $c = 1/x_0; \rho = 1/|x_0|$.
(c) 90° further, clockwise, along a circle centered at the origin.
(d) A circle centered at the origin.

11.10 $Z_0 = 50\ \Omega$. No.

11.11 **(a)** At $z = 0, V_1 = 0$; at $z = 2l, I_2 = 0$; at $z = l, V_2 = V_1 = V_0$ and $I_2 - I_1 = I_0$.
(b) $V_1(z) = V_0 \sin [\omega z/u_0]/\sin [\omega l/u_0], Z_0 I_1(z) = jV_0 \cos [\omega z/u_0]/\sin [\omega l/u_0]$
$V_2(z) = V_0 \cos [\omega z/u_0]/\cos [\omega l/u_0], Z_0 I_2(z) = -jV_0 \sin [\omega z/u_0]/\cos [\omega l/u_0]$.
(c) $I_0 = -j[V_0/Z_0]\{\tan [\omega l/u_0] + \cot [\omega l/u_0]\}$.
(d) VSWR = ∞ on both sides.

11.12 **(a)** $d/\lambda = 0.096116$. **(b)** $s/\lambda = 0.41255$.
(c) (The answer is stated in the question.)

Chapter 12

12.1 2.398 GHz.

12.2 **(a)** $f_0 = 8.049$ GHz. **(b)** $\varepsilon = 4.642$.

12.3 **(a)** 14.99 cm.
(b) 2.8284 GHz, for the TE_{22} or TM_{22} modes.

12.4 **(a)** $a = 2.998$ cm; $b = 1.731$ cm. **(b)** TE_{10} propagates, TE_{01} evanesces.

12.5 $a = 3$ cm; $b = 2$ cm or $b = 2.6833$ cm.

12.6 $2a = 2.663$ cm; $\varepsilon = 1.7436$.

12.7 $a/b = 1.9494$.

12.8 Yes; 6.557 to 9.273 GHz.

12.9 (The answer is stated in the question.)

12.10 **(a)** $2a = 1.952$ cm.
(b) 11.755 GHz (TM_{01}), 14.929 GHz (TE_{21}), 18.730 GHz (TM_{11} or TE_{01}).

12.11 **(a)** $J_0'(pa)Y_0'(pb) = Y_0'(pa)J_0'(pb)$. **(b)** $\omega_c = p_{0m}c/\sqrt{\varepsilon}$.
(c) $\beta = (\sqrt{5}/2)p_{0m}$. **(d)** $\alpha = (\sqrt{5}/3)p_{0m}$.

12.12 $J_0(pa)Y_0(pb) = Y_0(pa)J_0(pb)$.

12.13 6.4955 GHz.

Chapter 13

13.1 **(a)** $pd = 2.550, 5.051, 7.402$.
(b) $q_2 d = 8.109$, $q_3 d = 8.631$ for $pd = 2.550$; $q_2 d = 6.836$, $q_3 d = 7.449$ for $pd = 5.051$; $q_2 d = 4.178$, $q_3 d = 5.119$ for $pd = 7.402$.
(c) $d/\lambda_g = 1.603$ ($pd = 2.550$), $d/\lambda_g = 1.445$ ($pd = 5.051$), $d/\lambda_g = 1.161$ ($pd = 7.402$).

13.2 **(a)** (The answer is stated in the question.) **(b)** Range 0 to $\pi/2$.

13.3 **(a)** (The answer is stated in the question.) **(b)** Range 0 to $\pi/2$.

13.4 **(a)** $V = ka\sqrt{n_1^2 - n_2^2}$. **(b)** Range 0 to $\pi/2$.

13.5 **(a)** $0 < \omega < (\pi/2)(c/a)/\sqrt{n_1^2 - n_2^2}$. **(b)** 54.

13.6 (The answer is stated in the question.)

13.7 $d/\lambda_0 = 0.1123 + l(0.2801)$.

13.8 **(a)** (The answer is stated in the question.) **(b)** $q_2, q_3 > 0$.

13.9 (The answer is stated in the question.)

13.10 **(a)** $V = ka\sqrt{n_1^2 - n_2^2}$. **(b)** $V = l\pi/2$.

13.11 $\beta = kn_2$, $p = k\sqrt{n_1^2 - n_2^2}$, $q_2 = 0$, $q_3 = k\sqrt{n_2^2 - n_3^2}$, $v_p = c/n_2$, but v_g is unknown.

13.12 $d/\lambda_0 = 0.28791$.

13.13 (The answer is stated in the question.)

13.14 $d/\lambda_0 = 0.49506$.

Chapter 14

14.1 **(a)** RHCP wave (if the wave travels along $+\hat{\mathbf{z}}$). **(b)** LHCP wave. **(c)** linearly polarized wave. **(d)** linearly polarized wave.

14.2 **(a)** $-l/x \to \infty$. **(b), (c)** [The answer is stated in the question.] **(d)** $1/[x \ln x] \to \infty$. **(e)** $-\ln x \to \infty$. **(f)** $-1/[x^2 \ln x] \to \infty$.

14.3 49.3 μm.

14.4 1.283 μm.

14.5 [The answer is stated in the question.]

14.6 $B = \begin{bmatrix} K_l(q_2 a) & I_l(q_2 a) \\ K_l(q_2 b) & I_l(q_2 b) \end{bmatrix}.$

Chapter 15

15.1 (The answer is stated in the question.)

15.2 About 20,000.

15.3 **(a)** 0.306. **(b)** 1.468.

15.4 6 Mbits/s.

15.5 3.344 μm.

15.6 29.2 Mbits/s.

15.7 **(a)** 0.00653. **(b)** 200. **(c)** 1.257 μm. **(d)** Only the dominant mode.

15.8 **(a)** 1.51. **(b)** 25. **(c)** 310. **(d)** 0.562 μm. **(e)** 8.8 μm.

15.9 (The answer is stated in the question.)

15.10 $p < k\text{NA}$; $\sin \theta_0 < \text{NA}$.

15.11 **(a)** 2.17 dB/km. **(b)** 0.363 dB/km. **(c)** 0.135 dB/km.

Appendix

A.1 **(a)** $u + v = 7.388 + j4.397 = 8.597e^{j0.5369}$.
(b) $u - v = 1.388 + j0.397 = 1.444e^{j0.2787}$.
(c) $uv = 18.028e^{j1.088} = 8.369 + j15.967$.
(d) $u/v = 0.7211e^{j0.088} = 0.7183 + j0.0634$.
(e) $\sqrt{u} = \pm 1.8988e^{j0.294} = \pm(1.8174 + j0.5503)$.
(f) $u^*v = 18.028e^{-j0.088} = 17.958 - j1.584$.

A.2 **(a)** $x = \pm 1$ and $x = -0.5 \pm j0.8660$. **(b)** $\lambda = 0$ and $\lambda = -1$. **(c)** $M^2(1) = 3M(1)$. **(d)** $M^{-1}(0) = M(0)$.

A.3 Hyperbola.

A.4 **(a)** $\rho = 2.236$, $\varphi = 1.107$, $z = 3$.

(b) $r = 3.742$, $\theta = 0.6405$, $\varphi = 1.107$.

A.5 **(a)** $52.464°$.

(b) $37.66°$N, $154.32°$E, about 0.2 unit deep under the Pacific, east of Japan.

A.6 **(a)** $\hat{\boldsymbol{\varphi}}/\rho$. **(b)** $\hat{\boldsymbol{\varphi}}/r \sin\theta$. **(c)** 0. **(d)** $\hat{\mathbf{r}} \cot\theta/r - \hat{\boldsymbol{\theta}}/r$.

A.7 $\frac{1}{2}\pi a^2$.

A.8 $\frac{1}{2}\pi a^2$.

A.9 πa^4.

A.10 πa^4.

A.11 $2a/(a^2 + \omega^2)$.

A.12 (The answer is stated in the question.)

Index